# Dictionary of Gemmology

*To Doreen for her invaluable help and encouragement*

# Dictionary of Gemmology

*Second Edition*

P. G. Read

Butterworth-Heinemann Ltd
Linacre House, Jordan Hill, Oxford OX2 8DP

A member of the Reed Elsevier plc group

OXFORD LONDON BOSTON
MUNICH NEW DELHI SINGAPORE SYDNEY
TOKYO TORONTO WELLINGTON

First published 1982
Second edition 1988
Paperback edition 1994
Reprinted 1995



**British Library Cataloguing in Publication Data**
Read, Peter G. (Peter George)
Dictionary of Gemmology – 2nd ed.
1. Gemmology–encyclopaedias
I. Title
549

ISBN 0 7506 1675 X

**Library of Congress Cataloguing in Publication Data**
Read, Peter G.
Dictionary of Gemmology/P.G. Read – 2nd ed.
p. cm.
ISBN 0 7506 1675 X
1. Precious stones – Dictionaries. I. Title
QE392.R39 1988
553.8'03'21–dc19

Printed and bound in Great Britain by the University Press, Cambridge

# Preface

The *Dictionary of Gemmology* represents an attempt to bring together in one volume concise descriptions of the principal gem materials, as well as definitions of associated scientific terms and brief working explanations of the many types of gemmological instruments. The subject matter has been selected with both the professional gemmologist and the student in mind, and includes not only the most recently introduced technology and materials, but also concepts of a more fundamental or historic nature.

For completeness, the dictionary contains trade names of both natural and man-made materials, together with names which are either now in disuse, or are considered undesirable or misleading. In each case these entries are cross-referenced to the currently accepted name for the material, or, where appropriate, the gem species or variety. Information on gem occurrence is restricted to the commercially important sources of gem-quality material (except in the case of rare or collectors' stones), gem-producing countries being given their new names where applicable (e.g. Thailand for Siam, the Malagasy Republic for Madagascar, Namibia for South West Africa, Sri Lanka for Ceylon, Tanzania for Tanganyika, Zaire for the Congo and Zimbabwe for Rhodesia).

To assist the user, rare stones and those 'near-gem' minerals which are cut mainly for collectors are described as such in the preamble to the relevant entry. For reasons of space, many self-explanatory terms have been excluded, and with words which have two or more meanings, only the gemmological definitions are given. Wherever possible, measurement details are quoted in international SI units, conversion factors being included for any less familiar scientific units of measurement such as electron volt and wave number.

Abbreviations used in the dictionary are as follows:

R.I. Refractive Index
D.R. Double Refraction (the prefix + or – indicating the optic sign)
S.G. Specific Gravity
H Hardness on the Mohs scale
UV Ultra Violet
IR Infra Red
LW Long Wave
SW Short Wave

Errors and omissions are a particular hazard in a book which draws its information from a multitude of sources, and the author wishes to thank colleagues whose contributions have helped to increase the scope of this second edition. He would welcome any corrections and additional entries for future editions.

The author's grateful thanks are due to the late Mr H. Wheeler, former Secretary of the Gemmological Association of Great Britain, for his help with general information, and for making the Sir James Walton Memorial library available for research, to the late Mr B. W. Anderson and to Dr E. Gübelin for their advice and information, to Mr E. A. Thomson, President of the CIBJO Coloured Stone Commission, who provided details on gemstone nomenclature, to Mr R. V. Huddlestone, formerly Managing Director of Diamond Grading Laboratories Ltd., who advised on diamond grading terms, to Mr J. G. Green, Director of the Rayner Optical Company for his help with metallurgical and optical data, and to Mr M. J. O'Donoghue for his up-to-date information on gem materials.

P.G.R.

# A

**abalone** An edible univalve mollusc (genus *Haliotis*) which has an ear-shaped shell prized for its multi-coloured lining of mother-of-pearl. The mollusc produces coloured baroque pearls having the same iridescent surface as the shell lining. Occurrence: American, Australian and Japanese and Korean waters.

**Abbé refractometer** A specialized refractometer designed for the measurement of the refractive indices of liquids.

**Abbé-Pulfrich refractometer** An instrument for determining a specimen's refractive index by the precise measurement of its critical angle.

**aberration** When applied to an optical component, such as a hand lens, this describes the failure of the lens to bring all the light rays from one point to the same focus. *Chromatic aberration* is caused by the dispersion of the lens glass, and results in colour fringes round the image. It is corrected by making the lens in two sections, one biconvex and the other biconcave, each one having a different dispersion. *Spherical aberration,* which occurs in strongly curved lenses, is caused by the focal point of rays passing through the edge of the lens lying closer to the lens than that of the rays passing through its centre. The resulting image has an out-of-focus circumference. To avoid this, the single lens is replaced by two or more lenses of differing radii. Alternatively, the outer circumference of the lens is blanked off.

**abrasion tester** In one version, this consists of a small cone-shaped grinding wheel, treated with diamond powder, which is used to measure the depth of abrasion produced in a specimen over a preset time. The relationship between abrasion hardness and hardness as measured on the Mohs scale can be seen from the fact that sapphire (H. 9) wears away 5000 times faster than diamond (H. 10) when both are tested in the direction of maximum hardness.

**abrasive** A substance which is used for grinding or polishing purposes. In the polishing of gemstones, the method employed is a combination of rough grinding using a coarse abrasive (e.g. diamond dust, emery powder or carborundum particles) followed by a final polishing operation using a finer abrasive (e.g. cerium oxide, putty powder — tin oxide, jeweller's rouge — powdered haematite, or green rouge — chromium oxide). For diamond polishing both operations use diamond dust of the appropriate grade or particle size.

**absolute temperature scale** The scale is graduated in kelvins (K), (which have the same temperature interval span as degrees Celsius

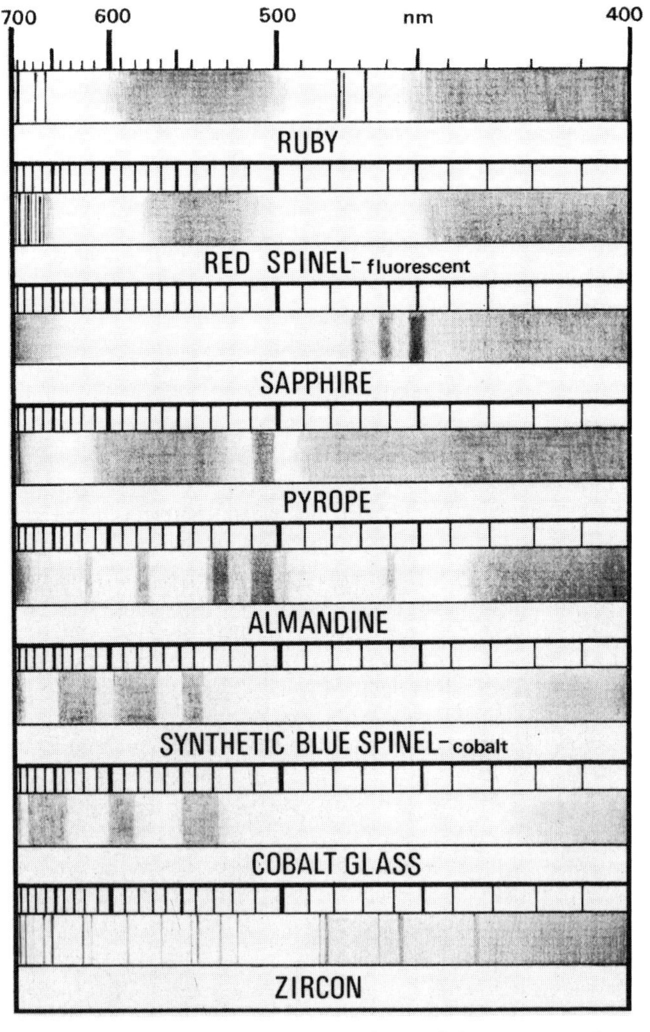


*Figure A.1* A selection of the more prominent of the gemstone absorption spectra.

or Centigrade). The absolute temperature scale is used mainly for thermodynamic work or colour temperature measurement. 0°C = 273.16 K; zero kelvin, or absolute zero = −273.16°C. See ***absolute zero.***

**absolute zero** The temperature (−273.16°C) at which no more energy can be extracted from an object, and the volume of a gas is theoretically zero.

**absorbance** The effect of absorption in a medium taking into account the ray path length.

**absorption spectrum** The pattern of dark bands or lines which become visible when the light passing through a gemstone (or reflected off its surface) is dispersed into its spectral components by an instrument such as a spectroscope. See ***spectroscope*** and *Figure A.1.*

**accabar** A black variety of coral.

**acetone** A colourless and volatile organic liquid ($CH_3COCH_3$) which is useful as a solvent of organic compounds. As a test liquid it can be used to identify cellulose-based plastics, which it softens. See ***amyl acetate.***

**acetylene tetrabromide** A 'heavy' liquid ($C_2H_2Br_4$) which can be used for specific gravity determinations (S.G. 2.95). It can also be used for the immersion estimation of refractive index (R.I. 1.63). See ***Becke line method.***

**achrite** See **diopside.**

**achroite** The colourless variety of tourmaline.

**achromatic lens** A lens which has been corrected for chromatic

*Figure A.2* Acicular rutile inclusions in quartz.

aberration. See ***aberration.***

**acicular** A term describing a crystal having a slender needle-like habit (e.g. rutile needles in quartz). *Figure A.2.*

**acidizing** The cleaning of rough diamonds in a solution containing hydrofluoric acid.

**acid rock** A type of igneous rock containing a high proportion of silica.

**acrylic resin** A transparent plastic used in the production of gemstone simulants and for the cores of solid-bead type imitation pearls. R.I. 1.50; S.G. 1.18. (Trade name is Perspex.)

**actinolated quartz** Colourless quartz containing crystals of actinolite.

**actinolite** A constituent of some nephrites and a member of the amphibole group of minerals. $Ca_2(Mg,Fe)_5(Si_4O_{11})_2(OH)_2$. Monoclinic. R.I. 1.620, 1.642; D.R. −0.022; S.G. 3.0-3.1; H. 5½-6. Transparent, green. Pleochroism (green, yellow). Occurrence: Tanzania.

**adamant** Ancient name for diamond derived from the Greek 'adamas' meaning 'untameable'. See ***adamantine.***

**adamantine** The high surface lustre or reflectivity associated with diamond, high zircons, demantoid garnet and some diamond simulants. See ***lustre.***

**adamantine spar** A silky brown sapphire.

**adamite** A collector's gemstone comprising the mineral zinc arsenate hydroxide, with some copper and cobalt. Orthorhombic. R.I. 1.76, 1.77; D.R. 0.01; S.G. 4.3; H. 3½. Transparent, green. Occurrence: Greece. Adamite is also the trade name for a synthetic corundum polishing powder.

**adductor muscle** A muscle connecting the two halves of a bivalve mollusc. It is used for closing the shell.

**Adelaide ruby** A misleading name given to almandine garnet found near Adelaide, Australia.

**adularescence** An effect, also known as *Schiller*, caused by the interference between light rays reflected from thin laminated plates or layers within the gemstone (e.g. the bluish sheen seen in moonstone). See ***sheen.***

**adularia** A variety of orthoclase feldspar.

**aeroides** A pale sky-blue aquamarine.

**African emerald** A misleading name for green fluorite found in Namibia.

**African jade** A misleading name for green grossular garnet.

**agalmatolite** A dense variety of the mineral pyrophyllite. A hydrous aluminium silicate, it belongs to the same family as ***steatite*** and is used as a carving material. H. 1-1½. Occurrence: China.

**agaphite** A vitreous variety of Iranian turquoise.
**agate** A cryptocrystalline quartz variety. See ***chalcedony.***
**agatized coral** See ***fossil coral.***
**agatized wood** See ***fossil wood.***
**agglomerate** A mass of fused volcanic fragments.
**aggregate** A mass of particles or irregularly intergrown crystals.
**AGS** See ***American Gem Society.***
**agstein** See ***jet.***
**aigrette** A hair ornament in the form of a spray of gems.
**akabar** A black variety of coral.
**akori** A blue variety of coral.
**alabandine ruby** A misleading name for almandine garnet.
**alabaster** A fine-grained massive gem variety of gypsum (hydrated calcium sulphate) $CaSO_4.2H_2O$. Monoclinic R.I. 1.52–1.53; D.R. +0.01; S.G. 2.3–2.33; H. 2. Translucent to opaque, white, pink and light brown. Occurrence: England, Italy.
**alabaster glass** A special opalescent type of glass used in the manufacture of imitation pearls.
**alabaster onyx** A misleading name for a banded travertine or stalagmitic calcite.
**alalite** See ***diopside.***
**Alaska black diamond** A misleading name for haematite.
**Alaska diamond** A misleading name for the rock crystal variety of quartz.
**Alaska jade** A misleading name for pectolite.
**alasmodon pearls** Freshwater pearls found in the *Alasmodon margaritifera* mollusc in Nova Scotia, Canada.
**albertite** A mineral asphalt with a glistening pitch-like lustre. Used for carvings and as a jet simulant. R.I. around 1.55; S.G. 1.097; H. 2½.
**albite** Moonstone variety of plagioclase feldspar with ***chatoyancy.***
**alencon diamond** A misleading name for the rock crystal variety of quartz.
**alexandrine** A misleading name for a colour-change synthetic corundum or spinel.
**alexandrite** A rare colour-change variety of chrysoberyl which appears red in tungsten lighting and green in daylight.
**alexandrite garnet** A misleading name for a natural colour-change garnet.
**alexandrium** A man-made lithium aluminium silicate. R.I. 1.58; H. 6-7. It is made in many colours, depending on the dopant (e.g., pink and pale lavender — neodymium). Colour change is introduced by a trace of cerium. The vivid blue variety, 'Laserblue', is produced with copper dopant (no colour change).
**allepo stone** See ***eye agate.***

**allochromatic gems** Gem minerals which owe their colour to impurities rather than to their basic chemical constituents (the term 'allochromatic' means 'other coloured'). When in their pure state, such minerals are colourless. The allochromatic gem ruby, for example, is a variety of corundum which owes its colour to a trace of chromic oxide, pure corundum being colourless. See ***idiochromatic gems.***

**allotrope** A form of an element which can exist in different forms of the same state (i.e. solid, liquid or gaseous). Carbon, for example, can exist as the solid allotropes graphite, diamond and amorphous carbon. See ***polymorphism.***

**alluvial deposits** Minerals carried by rivers and tidal currents from their primary source and deposited in river beds, dried up river courses and marine terraces to form secondary deposits.

**almandine** A purplish-red species of the garnet group.

**almandine spinel** A misleading name for a natural purple spinel.

**almandite** A misleading name for a synthetic spinel.

**almaschite** A Romanian variety of amber.

**alomite** See ***sodalite.***

**alpha particles** Helium nuclei (once thought to be rays) emitted by some radioactive substances. See ***beta particles*** and ***gamma radiation.***

**alpha rays** See ***alpha particles.***

**alpine diamond** A misleading name for pyrites.

**alshedite** See ***sphene.***

**altered diamond** See ***treated diamond.***

**alumag** Trade name for a synthetic spinel.

**alumina** See ***aluminium oxide.***

**aluminium oxide** A white or pink powder made from crushed natural or synthetic corundum, and used for polishing gemstones. Also called alumina, diamontine, Linde A and sapphire/ruby powder.

**alveolar** Having pits over the surface which resemble a honeycomb.

**ama** A Japanese diving girl who fishes for oysters.

**amalgam** A mixture of a metal with mercury (e.g. gold amalgam).

**amarillo stone** A figured variety of chalcedony from Texas.

**amaryl** Trade name for a light green synthetic corundum.

**amatista** The amethyst variety of quartz.

**amatrice** See ***amatrix.***

**amatrix** *'American matrix'* is a rock comprising variscite intergrown with quartz or chalcedony (also called variscite quartz). S.G. 2.6; H. 5–6. See also ***variscite.***

**amazonite** An opaque green variety of microcline feldspar (also called amazon stone).

**amazon jade** A misleading name for amazonite. See ***feldspar.***

**amazon stone** See ***feldspar.***

**amber** A fossilized pine-tree resin, consisting of a mixture of hydrocarbons plus succinic acid. Amorphous. R.I. 1.54; S.G. 1.07; H. 2½. Transparent to opaque, yellow, reddish-brown, greenish, bluish-violet, black. Occurrence: Sea amber — Baltic coast, the Black Sea, Sicily. Pit amber — Burma, Germany, Romania, USSR (near Kaliningrad, formerly Königsberg). See ***ambroid*** and ***black amber.***

**amber boron nitride** Trade name for a synthetic cubic boron nitride manufactured as an industrial abrasive by De Beers Industrial Diamond Division. Using the criterion of indentation hardness, it has just over half the hardness of diamond (i.e. 9½ + on the Mohs scale). See ***borazon.***

**ambergris** A grey waxy substance which is obtained from the sperm whale and used as a fixer for perfumes.

**amberine** A misleading name for a yellowish-green moss agate.

**amblygonite** A collector's stone comprising the mineral lithium aluminium phosphate. $LiAl(PO_4)(F, OH)$. Triclinic. R.I. 1.611, 1.637; D.R. +0.026; S.G. 3.015–3.033; H. 6. Transparent, yellow to colourless and pale purple. Occurrence: Brazil, USA. Pale purple variety from Namibia.

**ambroid** 'Reconstructed' or 'pressed' amber made by heating small pieces of amber to 180 °C and welding them together under pressure to form larger pieces.

**American brilliant cut** See ***Tolkowsky brilliant cut.***

**American Gemological Institute** See ***Gemological Institute of America.***

**American Gem Society** (AGS) Founded by Robert M. Shipley in 1934 as a professional society of leading jewellers with the object of promoting high standards of business ethics and encouraging gemmological education among its members. The Society awards the titles of Registered Jeweler and Certified Gemologist to qualified members and member firms. Headquarters: 2960 Wilshire Boulevard, Los Angeles, California 90010, USA.

**American jade** See ***californite.***

**American ruby** A misleading name for almandine garnet and rose quartz.

**amethyst** The purple variety of quartz.

**amethyst-citrine** A quartz containing both amethyst- and citrine-coloured varieties.

**ametrine** A mixture of amethyst and citrine.

**Amici prism** A double prism element (used in prism spectroscopes) consisting of two glasses of differing refractive indices, arranged to give dispersion with mininium deviation of the yellow wavelengths. In the prism spectroscope two Amici prisms are usually combined together, the abutting centre sections being formed as a single prism element. *Figure A.3*.

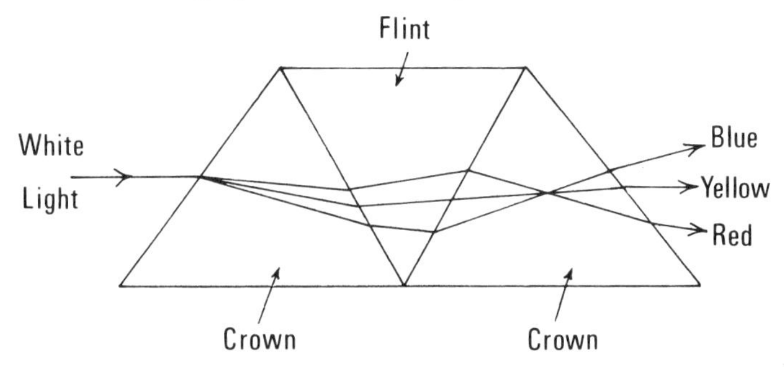


*Figure A.3* An Amici compound prism designed to give zero deviation in the yellow section of the spectrum.

**amino plastic** A variant of bakelite, in which urea replaces phenol. Translucent; dyed as a gemstone simulant (e.g. amber). R.I. 1.55–1.62; S.G. 1.50; H. 2.

**ammolite** An aragonite-based gem material derived from the nacreous layer of ammonite fossils. The polished surface of this material consists of closely-connected patches having a play of colour similar to that of black opal. Occurrence: Alberta, Canada.

**ammonite** A fossil cephalopod with a flat spiral shell. Ammonites whose shells have been replaced by pyrite are sometimes used in jewellery. See ***ammolite.***

**amorphous** A substance in which the atoms and molecules are positioned randomly (the word 'amorphous' means 'without shape'). Because of its lack of internal order at the atomic level, an amorphous substance never has a naturally-occurring characteristic external shape (e.g. glass, amber and jet). See ***crystalline.***

**amourant** Trade name for a diamond simulant composite gem having a colourless synthetic corundum crown and a strontium titanate pavilion.

**amphibole** A collective name for a particular group of silicate minerals having similar physical and chemical characteristics. Members of the amphibole group include nephrite, tremolite, actinolite, smaragdite, asbestos and hornblende.

**amygdaloidal** A rock, such as basalt, which contains almond-shaped nodules.

**amyl acetate** An organic liquid which can be used as a test liquid to identify cellulose-based plastics, which it softens. See ***acetone.***

**anacona ruby** A misleading name for rose quartz.

**analcime** See ***analcite.***

**analcite** A collector's stone consisting of a hydrated aluminium silicate, which is a member of the zeolite group of minerals. $NaAlSi_2O_6.H_2O$. Cubic. R.I. 1.487; S.G. 2.22-2.29; H. 5-5½. Transparent, colourless. Occurrence: World-wide. Also called analcime.

**anatase** A collector's stone, which, together with rutile and brookite, is a polymorph of titanium oxide (also called octahedrite). $TiO_2$. Tetragonal. R.I. 2.493, 2.554; D.R.–0.061; S.G. 3.82-3.95; H. 5½-6. Transparent to translucent, brown or blue. Occurrence: Brazil, France, Switzerland, USSR.

**andalusite** A rare aluminium silicate gem (polymorphous with kyanite and sillimanite). $Al_2SiO_5$. Orthorhombic. R.I. 1.633, 1.643; D.R. –0.01; S.G. 3.12-3.18; H. 7½. Transparent brownish-green and green with strong pleochroism (green, yellow, red). Occurrence: Brazil, Canada, Sri Lanka, USA, USSR. An impure variety, chiastolite, is an opaque yellow-white material containing carbonaceous inclusions in the form of a black cross (*Figure A.4*) (H. 5½). Occurrence: Australia, Bolivia, Burma, Chile, France, Sri Lanka, USA, USSR. See ***Viridine andalusite.***

*Figure A.4* The chiastolite variety of andalusite.

**Andamooka opal** A large piece of rough opal weighing in the region of 900 carats which was found in the Andamooka field, Australia, in 1949. After being cut into a 203-carat cabochon, it was set in a necklet and presented to Queen Elizabeth II.

**Anderson Medal** A silver medal awarded to the top candidate in the Preliminary Examination of the Gemmological Association of Great Britain, whose papers also meet the required standard set for the award. See ***Tully Medal.***

**andesine** A variety of plagioclase feldspar.

**andesine jade** A misleading name for andesine.

**andradite** A species of the garnet group which includes the varieties green demantoid and golden-yellow topazolite.

**angelo pearl** An imitation pearl comprising a mother-of-pearl nucleus covered with layers of applied nacre.

**angel skin** See ***coral.***

**angle of incidence** The angle between a ray of light meeting a surface and an imaginary line (called the *normal*) drawn perpendicular to that surface at the point of incidence.

**angle of minimum deviation** An angle measured using a table spectrometer or goniometer when determining the refractive index of a transparent faceted material such as a gemstone or a prism. It is the smallest angle which can be obtained between the line of the incident ray, and the line of the ray emerging (after refraction) from the material. The refractive index is then calculated from the formula:

$$\text{R.I.} = \frac{\sin \tfrac{1}{2}\,(A+B)}{\sin \tfrac{1}{2}\,A}$$

where $A$ = the angle between the two gem or prism faces transmitting the light ray and $B$ = the angle of minimum deviation.

**angle of reflection** The angle between a ray of light reflected from a surface and an imaginary line (called the *normal*) drawn perpendicular to that surface at the point of reflection.

**angle of refraction** The angle made between a ray of light after it enters a denser medium and an imaginary line (called the *normal*) passing through the medium and drawn perpendicular to its surface at the point of entry of the ray.

**anglesite** A collector's stone comprising the mineral lead sulphate. $PbSO_4$. Orthorhombic. R.I. 1.877, 1.894; D.R. +0.017; S.G. 6.30–6.39; H. 3. Transparent to translucent, colourless or with a yellow, green or bluish tint. Occurrence: World-wide.

**ångström unit** A unit formerly used as the standard to quantify the wavelength of light rays and X-rays. One ångström unit is equal to one ten-millionth of a millimetre (1 Å = $10^{-7}$ mm). The standard international (SI) unit now used for the measurement of these very short wavelengths is the nanometre (nm). 1 nm = 10 Å.

**anhedral** A term used to describe crystals having a badly-formed or abnormal external shape.

**anhydrite** Anhydrous calcium sulphate. $CaSo_4$. Orthorhombic. R.I. 1.57, 1.61; D.R. +0.04; S.G. 2.9; H. 3½. Transparent, colourless, bluish and mauve. Occurrence: Italy.

**anhydrous** A material containing neither free water, nor water of crystallization.

**aniline** An organic oily liquid with a refractive index of 1.58. Can be used as an immersion liquid for the approximation of R.I. See ***Becke line method.***

**anions** Negatively charged ions. See ***cations.***

**anisotropic** An anisotropic crystal is one which splits up light entering it into two rays which are polarized at right-angles to each other and which travel at different velocities in the gem. As a result anisotropic gems have two refractive indices. See ***isotropic, ordinary ray*** and ***extraordinary ray.***

**annealing** A heat treatment process for softening work-hardened metals (i.e. metals that have been hammered, beaten, rolled or drawn). Silver is annealed to a more malleable state by heating it to a dull red temperature and then quenching it in water, or allowing it to cool more slowly in air.

**anomalous birefringence** Internal stresses in a singly-refracting material may result in the production of dark bands when it is rotated between the crossed filters of a polariscope. The resulting extinction of light through the material is never as distinct as that produced by a doubly-refracting material, which causes the polarized light viewed through the top filter to be transmitted and extinguished four times during a 360° rotation of the gem.

**anorthite** A calcium aluminium silicate ($CaAl_2Si_2O_8$) which is a constituent of the plagioclase feldspars.

**anthosiderite** A pseudomorph of quartz and goethite after cummingtonite.

**anthracite** A compact dense brittle substance consisting of 99% carbon. It is used as a jet simulant.

**antigorite** A leafy-green serpentine.

**antilles pearl** An imitation pearl formed from the shell of a sea snail.

**antique cut** A square or rectangular gemstone cut with rounded corners and sides (also called the cushion cut). *Figure A.5.*

**Antwerp rose cut** Also called the Brabant, this cut is similar to the ***Dutch rose cut,*** but the step angles are shallower. See also ***rose cut.***

**anyolite** A green zoisite containing black hornblende inclusions and large opaque ruby crystals. Because of its colour contrast it is used mainly as an ornamental rock. Occurrence: Tanzania.

**apache tears** A variety of obsidian.

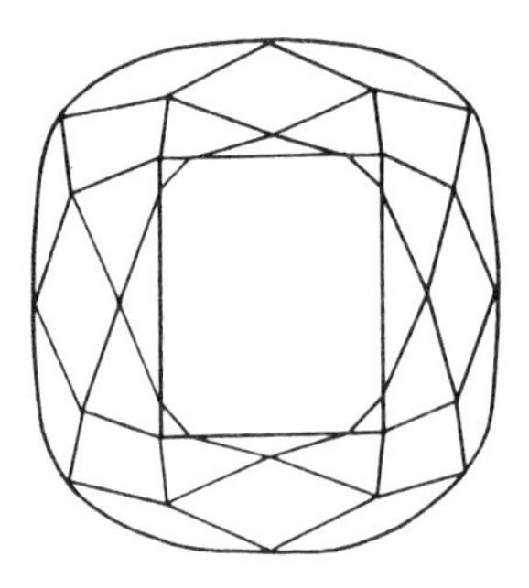

*Figure A.5* The antique or cushion cut.

**apatite** A calcium phosphate gem also containing fluorine or chlorine. $Ca_5$ (F, C1, OH) $(PO_2)_3$. Hexagonal. R.I. 1.636, 1.639; D.R.−0.003; S.G. 3.2; H. 5. Transparent, blue, yellow (with rare-earth spectrum due to didymium), pink, green, violet. Pleochroism, strong in blue (blue, pale yellow). Occurrence: Brazil, Burma, Canada, Mexico, Sri Lanka, USA.

**aphrizite** A black tourmaline.

**aplanatic lens** A lens which has been corrected for spherical aberration. See ***aberration.***

**apochromatic** Term applied to a lens which has been corrected for both spherical and chromatic aberration.

**apophyllite** A collector's gemstone comprising the mineral hydrated potassium calcium silicate. Tetragonal. $KCa_4(Si_8O_{20})(OH,F).8H_2O$. R.I. 1.535, 1.537; D.R. ±0.002; S.G. 2.3-2.5; H. 4½-5. Transparent, colourless or with red, blue, yellow or green tint. Occurrence: Germany, India, Mexico, Switzerland, USA.

**appraisal** (of gemstones) An estimation of the value of gemstones or jewellery. An appraisal is often carried out for insurance purposes or estate valuation. It depends upon the correct identification of the gemstones, and their detailed market assessment in terms of colour, clarity, cut and weight. An insurance appraisal is based on the retail replacement value. An estate valuation is based on an estimate of their realizeable market value.

**apparent depth** The distance of an inclusion beneath the surface of a gem as measured optically (e.g. by means of a dial gauge on a microscope) is a measure of the *apparent depth* of that inclusion. To obtain the *real depth,* the figure for the apparent depth must be multiplied by the refractive index of the gem. See ***direct method (of R.I. measurement).***

**apricotine** Trade name for apricot-coloured garnets or quartz from New Jersey, USA.

**apyrite** A peach-coloured tourmaline.

**aqua fortis** Nitric acid.

**aqua gem** A misleading name for a light blue synthetic spinel.

**aqualite** A misleading name for blue tourmaline.

**aquamarine** A pale blue or pale blue-green variety of beryl.

**aqua regia** A mixture of nitric acid and hydrochloric acid capable of dissolving gold and platinum.

**arabian diamond** A misleading name for the rock crystal variety of quartz.

**arabian magic diamond** A misleading name for a synthetic colourless or yellow corundum.

**aragonite** A dimorphous form of calcium carbonate used as a carving and ornamental material (also a major constituent in pearls). $CaCO_3$. Orthorhombic. R.I. 1.53, 1.685; D.R. −0.155; S.G. 2.93-2.95; H. $3\frac{1}{2}$-4. Translucent to opaque, white with grey, brown, green or blue tints. Transparent material (colourless or in various colours) is occasionally faceted for collectors. Occurrence: England, Germany, Hungary, Spain, USA. A yellow stalagmitic calcite from Namibia is also marketed as 'aragonite'.

**arandisite** A rare collector's stone consisting mainly of a tin silicate together with the surrounding brown limonite. R.I. 1.70; S.G. 4; H. 5.

**Archaean** The earlier part of the Precambrian era. See ***Precambrian.***

**Archimedes' Principle** This states that a body totally immersed in a fluid experiences an upward force equal to the weight of the fluid it displaces. This principle is the basis of specific gravity measurements made by the hydrostatic weighing method, and with the aid of heavy liquids. See ***hydrostatic weighing*** and ***heavy liquids.***

**Argentinian Gemmological Institute** See ***Primer Instituto Gemologico Latin Americano.***

**Arizona ruby** A misleading name for pyrope garnet found in Arizona, USA. See ***garnet.***

**Arizona spinel** A misleading name for garnet.

**Arkansas diamond** A misleading name for the rock crystal variety of quartz found in Arkansas, USA.

**arkansite** A transparent brookite.

**Armenian stone** See ***lapis lazuli.***

**artificial coloration** The improvement or inducement of colour in gemstones by staining, heat/chemical treatment or irradiation. Heat treatment is used, for example, to change yellow and brown topaz to pink, and to turn some brown zircons blue. Staining is used to change or improve the colour of gems having a porous surface (chalcedony varieties and jades). Heating and X-ray irradiation is used to improve the colour of sapphires. A surface colour can be induced into some gems (such as sapphire) by coating them with a chemical paste containing, for example, titanium and iron oxides, and heating them to around 1600 °C. Yellow cape series diamonds can be transformed to fancy coloured stones by nuclear irradiation followed by heat treatment. Only those processes which are permanent and irreversible are considered to be legitimate practices. High value gems such as rubies, sapphires and diamonds whose colour has been improved or changed in this way should be declared as 'treated'. See ***heat treated stones*** and ***treated diamonds.***

**aschentrekker** A Dutch word meaning 'ash puller' applied to tourmaline. Because of tourmaline's pyro-electricity, the Dutch, who first imported the gem material into Europe, used a heated piece of the rough stone to attract and remove ash particles from their meerschaum pipes.

**Ashover spar** A yellow fluorspar from Derbyshire, England.

**asparagus stone** See ***apatite.***

**assay** The determination of the constituents or purity of a substance by chemical analysis and other means. The testing of the gold, silver or platinum content of articles (in an Assay Office) before hallmarking. See ***carat*** and ***hallmarks.***

**assembled stones** See ***composite stones.***

**Associacào Brasileira de Gemologia** Headquarters: Caixa Postal 18154, Sao Paulo, S.P., Brazil.

**Association Españia de Gemologia** Headquarters: Paseo de Gracia, 64 Ent. 02A, Barcelona 7, Spain.

**Association Frànçaise de Gemmologie** Headquarters: 17 Rue Cadet, 75009, Paris 9, France.

**asterism** An effect due to reflections from crystals, fibres or channels within a gemstone which produces a 'star' on the surface of the gem. See ***sheen.***

**asterated stones** Stones displaying a 'star' effect. They are usually cut as cabochons to show the star to best advantage. See ***asterism.***

**astridite** A dark green chrome-rich jadeite with lighter coloured veins and intergrown with picotite, quartz, opal and limonite. S.G. 3.35. Occurrence: New Guinea.

**astrilite** Trade name for the man-made diamond simulant lithium niobate.

**astryl** Trade name for a synthetic rutile diamond simulant.

**atlas pearls** A misleading trade name for beads made from the white satin spar variety of calcite.

**atmospheric pressure** The pressure (due to the atmosphere) which exists at the surface of the Earth. One atmosphere is the pressure exerted by a 760 mm column of mercury, and is equal to 1.05

kilograms per square centimetre.

**atom** The smallest part of an element which can take part in a chemical reaction. See also ***element, compound*** and ***molecule.***

**atomic number** Used in the periodic classification of the elements, this represents the number of unit positive charges on the nucleus of the atom of each element (the charge on the nucleus is normally neutralized by an equal number of orbiting electrons). See ***Table of Elements*** in Appendix H.

**atomic weight** The atomic weight of an element is its mass compared with that of an atom of oxygen (which is assigned a value of 16.0), e.g. the atomic weight of hydrogen is 1.0078 and that of carbon is 12.0. See ***Table of Elements*** in Appendix H.

**augelite** A rare collector's stone comprising the mineral hydrated aluminium phosphate. $2Al_2O_3.P_2O_5.\ 3H_2O$. Monoclinic. R.I. 1.574, 1.588; D.R. +0.014; S.G. 2.7; H. 5. Transparent, colourless. Occurrence: Bolivia, USA.

**Aurora Borealis stone** A rhinestone whose colour is produced by a thin interference coating on its facets.

**Australian Gemmological Association** See ***Gemmological Association of Australia.***

**Australian jade/turquoise** Misleading names for a material found in Australia and thought to be variscite.

**Australian ruby** A misleading name for garnet.

**australite** A variety of tektite found in Australia.

**Austrian Gemmological Association** See ***Erste Österreichische Gemmologische Gesellschaft.***

**autoclave** A thick-walled metal vessel which can be sealed and heated to produce high internal pressures. It is used in the hydrothermal production of synthetic stones. *Figure A.6.* See also ***hydrothermal process.***

**autoradiography** A technique for checking the radioactivity of a specimen in which the specimen is placed on a sheet of light-excluded photographic paper (or on a photographic plate). If the specimen is radioactive, a 'picture' of the field of radiation will appear on the photographic paper or plate when it is developed. The exposure time required to produce an *autoradiogram* of this nature is usually in terms of hours rather than minutes, and depends on the speed of the photographic material and the strength of the radioactivity.

**aventurine feldspar** Also called sunstone, this is a variety of plagioclase feldspar.

**aventurine glass** Made to simulate green and golden aventurine quartz and aventurine feldspar (or sunstone).

**aventurine quartz** An opaque green or golden-brown quartz with spangles of mica (colour caused by green mica or iron impurities).

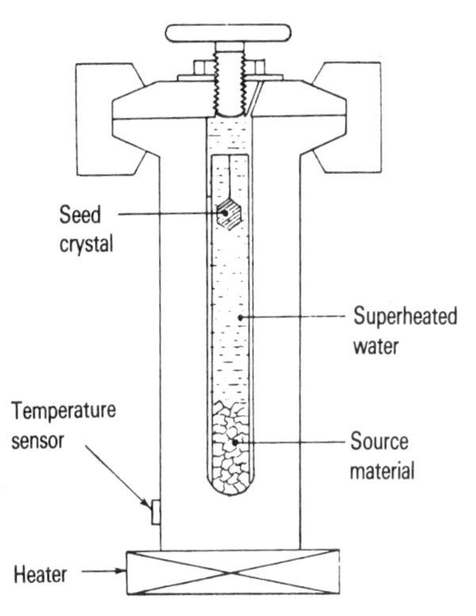


*Figure A.6* An autoclave as used in the hydrothermal synthesis of quartz and emerald. Source material is dissolved in superheated water and deposited onto a seed crystal.

**avory** Trade name for a microcrystalline cellulose polymer made from wood pulp and used as an ivory simulant.

**awabi** The Japanese name for vividly coloured green/yellow/blue abalone pearls found in the Haliotidae univalve mollusc. These molluscs occur in the Gulf of California, along the Florida coast of the USA, along the Queensland coast of Australia and in Japanese and Korean waters.

**axestone** New Zealand nephrite.

**axinite** This collector's gemstone is a complex borate silicate. $Ca_2(Fe, Mg, Mn(Al_2(BO_3.OH.Si_4O_{12})$. Triclinic. R.I. 1.675-1.685; D.R. −0.01; S.G. 3.27-3.29; H. 6½-7. Transparent to translucent, reddish-brown, violet and blue. Occurrence: England, France, Mexico, USA.

**axis of symmetry** An imaginary line positioned so that when a crystal is turned round on it, the characteristic profile of the crystal appears two, three, four or six times during each complete revolution. There are usually several possible axes of symmetry in a crystal, and these are described as two-, three-, four-, or six-fold axes, depending on the number of times the crystal profile appears during a single rotation. *Figure A.7.*

**Aztec stone** See ***smithsonite.***

**azules opal** A water opal with a bluish haze and red and green flecks.

**azure quartz** A blue variety of quartz also called siderite (which

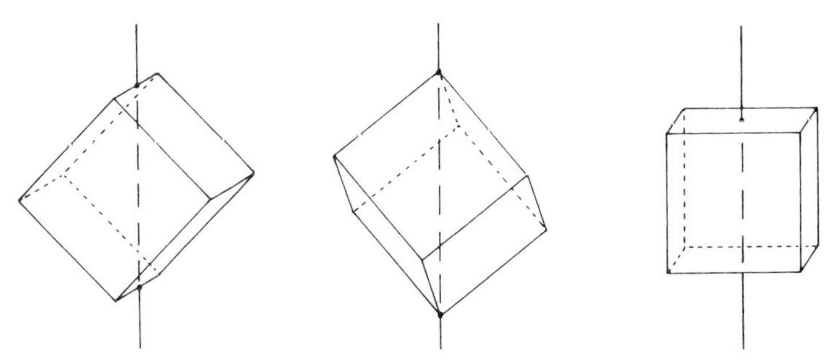

*Figure A.7* From left to right, examples of two-fold, three-fold and four-told axes of symmetry in a cubic crystal.

should not be confused with the mineral chalybite, also called siderite).

**azurite** A copper carbonate (also called chessylite). $Cu_3(OH)_2(CO_3)_2$. Monoclinic. R.I. 1.73, 1.84; D.R. +0.11; S.G. 3.7-3.9; H. 3½-4. Transparent to opaque, deep blue. Pleochroism, medium (dark blue, light blue). Occurrence: Australia, Chile, France, USA, USSR.

**azurite** A misleading name for synthetic blue spinel; also a trade name for blue smithsonite.

**bacalite** A variety of amber from California, USA.
**baffa diamond** A misleading name for the rock crystal variety of quartz.
**baguette** An elongated rectangular gemstone cut, mainly used for small diamonds (sometimes called a *baton*). *Figure B.1.*
**baikalite** A name given to diopside found in Baikal in the USSR.
**bakelite** Trade name for a phenolic resin (patented in 1906)

*Figure B.1* The baguette or baton cut.

sometimes used as an amber simulant, particularly in Edwardian times. Amorphous. R.I. 1.61-1.66; S.G. 1.25-1.30; H. 2.
**balance** Types of balances used for weighing gem materials range from the relatively insensitive spring balance to the substitutional beam balance and the electronic force balance. A brief description of each type is given under ***Balance Systems*** in Appendix A. See also ***hydrostatic weighing.***
**balas ruby** A misleading name for red spinel (dating back to the Middle Ages).
**bal de feu** Trade name for the man-made diamond simulant strontium titanate.
**bali** A Burmese weight equal to 58.32 carats. See also ***lathi, rati, tickal*** and ***viss.***
**ballas** See ***boart.***
**ballerina setting** A setting in which a central stone is surrounded by radially mounted baguette diamonds which give the effect of the skirt of a ballerina.
**Bannister's graph** A graph which enables the composition of glass imitation gems to be determined by relating their specific gravity to their refractive index. *Figure B.2.*
**barion cut** A mixed cut for diamond, comprising an emerald-cut crown and a modified brilliant-cut pavilion. The barion cut, which has 61 facets (plus a culet), was introduced in 1971 to improve the brilliance and fire of the emerald cut when used for diamond.
**barite** Also called barytes and heavy spar, this collector's stone comprises the mineral barium sulphate. $BaSO_4$. Orthorhombic. R.I. 1.636, 1.648; D.R. +0.012; S.G. 4.47; H. 3. Transparent to

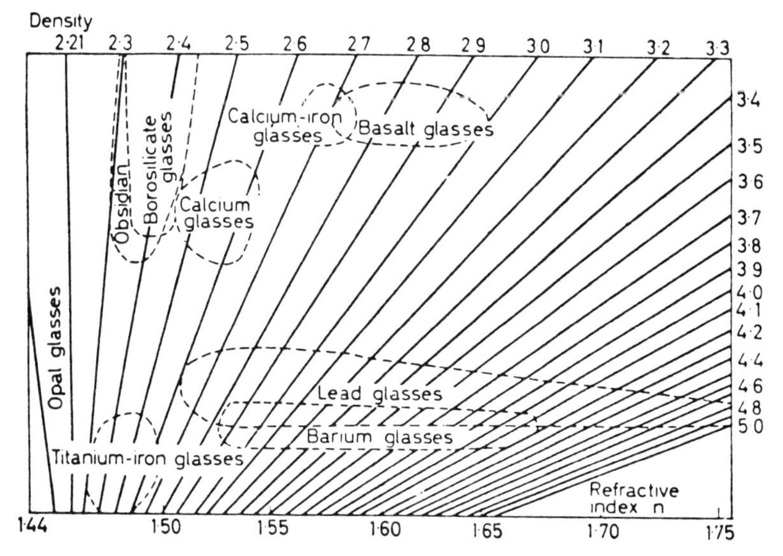


*Figure B.2* Bannister's graph which helps to identify the composition of a glass from its refractive index and specific gravity or density. A vertical line is drawn from the bottom edge of the graph to correspond with the R.I. of the specimen. The appropriate glass group to which the specimen belongs is then indicated by the point where the vertical R.I. line crosses the appropriate radial line representing specific gravity.

opaque, colourless, yellow, green, red, blue, brown. Occurrence: world-wide.

**barium titanate** A man-made crystal with potential as a diamond simulant. $BaTiO_3$. Cubic (also tetragonal and hexagonal forms). R.I. 2.40; S.G. 5.90; H. 6-6½. Crystals are grown by the ***Czochralski process.***

**baroda gem** A trade name for a diamond simulant formed by faceted glass backed by metallic foil.

**baroque pearls** Pearls, both natural and cultured, which have an irregular shape.

**barytes** See ***barite.***

**basal cleavage** A cleavage plane parallel to a prism's lateral axes (e.g. a prismatic topaz crystal has perfect basal cleavage at right-angles to its length). See also ***cleavage.***

**basal pinacoid** The faces of a basal pinacoid are parallel to the crystal's lateral axes, and often form the terminating faces of a prism. See also ***pinacoid.***

**basalt** A dark igneous rock, low in silica, often occurring in columnar formations.

**basalt glass** A natural glass containing 50% silica. Amorphous.

R.I. 1.58-1.65; S.G. 2.7-3.0; H. 6. Semi-transparent to opaque, black, grey-brown, dark blue and bluish-green. Also called tachylyte.

**basanite** A matt black variety of jasper, sometimes used as a streak plate for testing precious metals (called the Lydian stone in ancient times). See ***quartz.***

**basic rock** An igneous rock having a low silica content.

**bastard amber** A term used to describe amber whose cloudy appearance is due to bubble inclusions.

**bastard emerald** A misleading name for peridot, quartz coloured to resemble emerald or any green stone resembling emerald.

**bastard ivory** An intermediate type of ivory whose hardness is between that of the hard and soft varieties. Ivory from Thailand, although generally soft, is sometimes of this type.

**bastite** An altered enstatite (also called schiller spar). Hydrated magnesium silicate. S.G. 2.6; H. 3½-4. Opaque, leek-green with a silky sheen. Occurrence: Germany.

**baton** See ***baguette.***

**bayldonite** A complex hydrated arsenate of lead and copper. Monoclinic. R.I. 1.95, 1.99; D.R. +0.04; S.G. 4.35; H. 4½. Translucent to opaque, greenish. Occurrence: England (Cornwall), Namibia.

**bearded girdle** A term applied to the series of fine fractures produced round the edge of a diamond's girdle when this has been polished (i.e. bruted or rondisted) too rapidly.

**beccarite** A green zircon.

**Becke line method** A method of approximating the refractive index of faceted transparent gemstones by immersing them in a series of liquids of known refractive indices. If, when viewed through a microscope, the facet edges of the gemstone change from light to dark when focusing down from the liquid into the stone, then the R.I. of the gemstone is *greater* than that of the liquid. If the opposite occurs, and the facet edges change from dark to light, then the R.I. of the stone is *less* than that of the liquid.

**beekite** See ***fossil coral.***

**Beilby layer** After polishing a specimen of calcite, Sir G. T. Beilby discovered that by lightly etching away its top surface, the underlying scratches caused by the initial stages of polishing were uncovered. He developed the theory that the final high polish on a gemstone (diamond excepted) is produced not by abrasive action, but by the high lapping temperature which causes the surface layer of the gem to flow in a liquid-like manner. The resulting highly reflective skin was called the *Beilby layer.*

Because of diamond's high melting point, the polish achieved on its facets is not due to the formation of a Beilby layer but is entirely the product of fine abrasive action.

In 1937 Professor G. I. Finch at Imperial College, London, substantiated and extended Beilby's findings using electron diffraction techniques at grazing incidence to the polished surface. At Diamond Grading Laboratories Ltd., London, R. V. Huddlestone confirmed the existence of the Beilby layer by the use of Nomarski interference contrast techniques. Results of this continuing investigation suggest that production of the layer is influenced by the lap speed and the difference between the hardness of the material and the abrasive.

With gemstones like corundum and quartz, the Beilby layer produced in this way immediately recrystallizes to conform to the gem's crystal structure. In other stones, such as calcite and kyanite, the Beilby layer tends to solidify as a molecular layer of amorphous material, which only recrystallizes if it is parallel to a principal crystal plane. With stones such as spinel and zircon, the Beilby layer solidifies on all surfaces as an amorphous skin, but because of its extreme thinness, it has no effect on the optical indices of doubly-refracting stones when these are measured on a refractometer. Despite the evidence, however, strong doubt has been expressed over the existence of the Beilby layer and the validity of the theory.

**Belgian Gemmological Society** See ***Société Belge de Gemmologie.***

**belonite** A rod-shaped variety of natural glass. See ***obsidian.***

**Bengal amethyst** A misleading name for purple sapphire. See ***corundum.***

**benitoite** A rare gemstone of barium titanium silicate. $BaTi(Si_3O_9)$. Trigonal (with maximum symmetry). R.I. 1.757, 1.804; D.R. +0.047; S.G. 3.65-3.68; H. 6½. Transparent to translucent, light and dark blue. Pleochroism, very strong (two shades of blue and colourless). Occurrence: San Benito County, California, USA.

**benzene** A liquid hydrocarbon. $C_6H_6$. Used as a dilutant for organic-based heavy liquids and for the approximation of R.I. by immersion. R.I. 1.50; S.G. 0.88. Note: care should be taken when using benzene because it is a suspect carcinogenic liquid.

**benzine** A mixture of liquid hydrocarbons derived from petrol.

**berigem** Trade name for green apatite.

**berilo** A misleading name for green apatite.

**bernat** A German amber simulant consisting of amber-coloured plastic having an R.I. close to 1.54, and an S.G. of 1.23. Specimens have been manufactured which contain plant and insect inclusions.

**bernstein** The German name for amber.

**Bertrand refractometer** The first direct-reading critical-angle refractometer for gemstone use was designed by Professor Bertrand in 1885. *Figure B.3.*

**beryl** A beryllium aluminium silicate. $Be_3Al_2(SiO_3)_6$. Hexagonal. Transparent to opaque. H. 7½.

Varieties:

*aquamarine* — light sea-green to sea-blue. R.I. 1.570, 1.575;

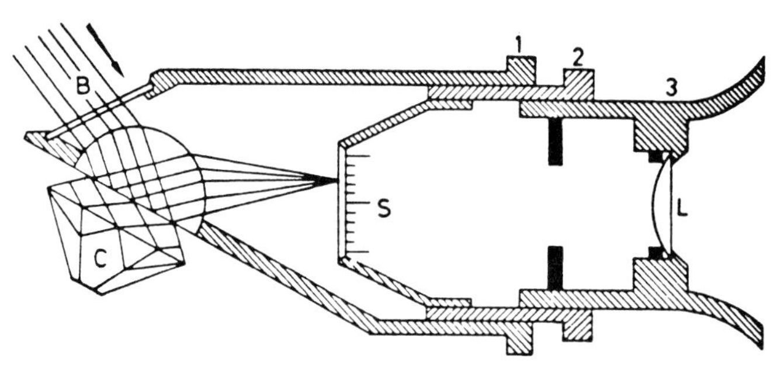


*Figure B.3* Sketch showing the optical system in the Bertrand refractometer. Focusing is achieved by the sliding sections 2 and 3.

D.R. −0.005; S.G. 2.69. Pleochroism, medium (blue, colourless). Occurrence: Brazil, Burma, the Malagasy Republic, Namibia, USA, USSR.

*bixbite* — red. R.I. and S.G. constants as for morganite. Occurrence (rare): USA.

*emerald* — R.I. 1.579, 1.585; D.R. −0.006; S.G. 2.71. Pleochroism, medium (yellowish-green, bluish-green). Occurrence: Afghanistan, Brazil, Colombia, India, Pakistan, South Africa, USSR, Zambia, Zimbabwe.

*goshenite* — colourless. R.I. and S.G. constants as for aquamarine. Occurrence (rare): USA.

*heliodor* — yellow. R.I. 1.568, 1.573; D.R. −0.005; S.G. 2.68. Pleochroism, weak (pale yellow, pale bluish-green). Occurrence: Brazil, the Malagasy Republic, Namibia.

*maxixe* — dark blue. R.I. 1.584, 1.592; D.R. −0.008; S.G. 2.80. Pleochroism, strong. Susceptible to fading in daylight. In maxixe beryl, the colour is due to $NO_3$ impurity ions. See also ***maxixe-type beryl.*** Occurrence (rare): Brazil.

*morganite* — pink. R.I. 1.586, 1.594; D.R. −0.008; S.G. 2.80. Pleochroism, medium (pink, bluish-pink). Occurrence: Brazil, the Malagasy Republic, Namibia, USA, Zimbabwe.

**beryl glass** A fused amorphous beryl. $Be_3Al_2(SiO_3)_6$. R.I. 1.50-1.52; S.G. 2.41-2.49; H. 7. Transparent, green, blue, pink. (Man-made; coloured by additives).

**beryllonite** A rare gem composed of sodium beryllium phosphate. $NaBe(PO_4)$. Monoclinic (pseudo orthorhombic). R.I. 1.553, 1.562; D.R. −0.009; S.G. 2.80-2.85; H. 5. Transparent, colourless or pale yellow. Occurrence: Finland, USA, Zimbabwe.

**beta rays** See ***beta particles.***

**beta particles** Fast moving electrons (once thought to be rays) emitted from a radioactive material such as a beta-emitting isotope. See ***alpha particles*** and ***gamma radiation.***

**Bethersden marble** A blue-grey to reddish-brown marble containing the fossilized shells of freshwater snails. The marble is similar to paludina limestone, or Purbeck marble, but contains larger shells. Occurrence: England.

**bevel cut** A simple step-cut crown used for portrait stones in which a large table facet has its edges bevelled in one or two steps to meet the girdle. See ***lasque diamond.***

**bezel** Also called the *crown,* that portion of a polished stone above the girdle.

**bezel facets** The eight four-sided facets surrounding the table facet of a brilliant-cut stone (also called kite facets and top main facets). See ***brilliant cut.***

**biaxial** The term used to describe a doubly-refracting crystal having two optical axes or directions along which it is singly refractive. In the seven crystal systems, orthorhombic, monoclinic and triclinic crystals all have biaxial optical characters. See ***uniaxial.***

**Biggs jasper** A silicified volcanic ash found near Biggs on the Columbia River, USA.

**billitonite** A variety of tektite found in Belitung Island (formerly Billiton Island) in Indonesia.

**binocular microscope** A microscope fitted with twin oculars. Less expensive versions have a single objective lens system whose image is shared between the oculars. A stereo binocular microscope uses two objectives, each coupled to its respective ocular. See ***Greenough microscope*** and ***magnifiers.***

**binghamite** A chatoyant quartz with goethite inclusions.

**bioluminescence** The luminous glow produced by fireflies, glow worms and decaying organic matter. It is the result of the oxidation of certain chemical constituents of the substance.

**biotite** A black, dark brown or greenish-black mica. $K(Mg,Fe)_3AlSi_3O_{10}(OH,F)_2$. Monoclinic. Transparent to translucent. S.G. 2.7-3.3; H. 2-3. Biotite is widely distributed in granites, schists, gneisses and contact metamorphic rocks.

**bipyramid** A crystal habit comprising two pyramids joined at the common base (e.g. an octahedron).

**bird's-eye marble** An encrinital Derbyshire marble from Ashford, England.

**birefringence** See ***double refraction.***

**biron synthetic emerald** This is produced by the hydrothermal method. In early productions the stones were coloured by vanadium. Now they are coloured by both vanadium and chromium. R.I. 1.567, 1.572; D.R. +0.005; S.G. 2.67.

**bishop's stone** A traditional name for amethyst. See ***quartz.***

**bivalve** A mollusc with a hinged double shell (e.g. oyster, mussel and clam).

**Biwa pearls** Non-nucleated cultured pearls (often oval or baroque in shape) farmed round the shores of Lake Biwa in Japan. The pearls are grown in large freshwater mussels *(Hyriopsis schlegeli)* by inserting small fragments of mantle into the body of the mussel. S.G. 2.67–2.70.

**bixbite** See ***beryl.***

**black amber** A misleading name for jet.

**black coral** A variety of coral which grows in the waters off the northern coast of Australia, around Malaysia and in the Red Sea.

**black diamond** A gem quality diamond whose colour is due to numerous microscopic black inclusions (e.g. the Amsterdam diamond, weighing 33.74 carats). Industrial quality black diamond is called carbonado. See ***boart.***

**black diamond** A misleading name for haematite.

**black moonstone** A misleading name for a dark variety of transparent labradorite having blue iridescence and some chatoyancy. See ***feldspar*** (plagioclase).

**blackmorite** A reddish-yellow potch opal from Montana, USA.

**black opal** An iridescent opal having a dark background caused by the iron-rich matrix in which it is found.

**black pearls** Greyish, greenish or brownish-black pearls found in the Gulf of California, Mexico. The colour is said to be caused by the content of the sea water. R.I. 1.53–1.69; S.G. 2.61–2.69.

**Black Prince's Ruby** This stone, set in the front of the British Imperial State Crown, is a red spinel in a virtually uncut condition.

**bleeding of colour** Deeply coloured areas around open pits, fissures and factures on surfaced diffused corundums. See ***diffusion technique.***

**blende** See ***sphalerite.***

**blende refractometer** See ***refractometer.***

**blister pearls** Pearls (also called chicot pearls) which have grown in contact with the shell of the mollusc. When they are extracted, the area which was in contact with the shell is bare of nacre. Because of this it is usually smoothed off and hidden by the setting.

**block amber** Pieces of amber (usually pit amber) which are large enough for fashioning into gems or ornaments.

**block caving** An underground mining technique used in most South African diamond mines. Concrete-lined 'scraper drift' tunnels are driven through the pipe. Cone-shaped draw points are cut upwards from openings in the roof of the scraper drifts into the overhanging 'blue ground'. The blue ground is then undercut and breaks up, falling via the draw points into the scraper drifts where it is pulled out by mechanical drag-line scrapers.

**blocker** See ***blocking.***

**blocking** A term used to describe the first stage of the diamond faceting operation in which the table facet and the first eight crown and eight pavilion facets are cut by the *blocker* or *cross cutter.*

**blonde shell** The yellow unmottled material obtained from the under-shell of the hawksbill sea turtle. See ***tortoiseshell.***

**bloodshot iolite** A reddish variety of iolite from Sri Lanka. The colour is caused by thin hexagonal platelets of either haematite or goethite. Because of the parallel orientation of these platelets, the depth of colour varies with the angle of viewing. See ***cordierite.***

**bloodstone** A dark green variety of cryptocrystalline quartz containing spots or streaks of red/brown jasper (also called heliotrope). It should not be confused with blutstein, the German word for haematite. See ***chalcedony.***

**blue alexandrite** A misleading name for a colour-change sapphire.

**blue earth** A greeny-blue sand consisting of grains of glauconite (a hydrous potassium-iron silicate) from which pit amber is mined.

**blue ground** See ***kimberlite.***

**blue john** See ***fluorspar.***

**blue malachite** A misleading name for azurite.

**blue moonstone** A misleading name for blue-stained chalcedony.

**blue opal** A misleading name for lazulite.

**blue pearls** Pearls having a leaden-grey colour which is caused by a central dark core rich in conchiolin.

**blue quartz** A coarse-grained quartz aggregate. The dull blue colour is produced by crocidolite fibres. Occurrence: Austria, Brazil, Namibia, Scandinavia.

**bluestone** See ***sodalite.***

**blue-white** A colour grading term applied to top white (i.e. colourless) diamonds. Its use is now strongly discouraged because of ambiguity and misuse. See also ***overblue.***

**boakite** A brecciated green and red jasper.

**boart** A term applied to a group of industrial-quality natural diamonds (e.g. microcrystalline diamonds of non-gem colour and quality). Because of its microcrystalline structure, boart is usually crushed for use as an abrasive powder. Varieties:

*hailstone boart* — consisting of alternate layers of diamond and other material.

*carbonado* — a mixture of microcrystalline diamond and amorphous carbon.

*framesite* — similar to carbonado, but more granular and containing less diamond.

*stewartite* — similar to carbonado, but containing some magnetite.

*ballas* or *shot boart* — microcrystalline diamond in which the cystals are orientated radially to form a sphere, usually free of inclusions.

Occurrence: In most diamond areas as a proportion of the 'run-of-mine' production. See ***diamond.***

**bobrowka garnet** A demantoid garnet.

**bog oak** A black oak (preserved in peat) which was used in Victorian mourning jewellery.

**Bohemian chrysolite** A misleading name for moldavite.

**Bohemian diamond** A misleading name for the rock crystal variety of quartz.

**Bohemian emerald** A misleading name for green fluorspar.

**Bohemian garnets** Pyrope garnets found in Czechoslovakia (formerly Bohemia) and used as rose-cut gems in Victorian jewellery.

**Bohemian ruby** A misleading name for red varieties of garnet.

**Bohemian topaz** A misleading name for citrine. See ***quartz.***

**boke** Rose-coloured Japanese coral.

**boleite** A collector's gemstone. $Pb_9Ag_3Cu_8Cl_{21}(OH)_{16}.H_2O$. Tetragonal (pseudo cubic). R.I. 2.03, 2.05; D.R. 0.02; S.G. 5.05; H. 3–3½. Transparent, blue. Occurrence: USA (California), Mexico.

**bolster crystals** Rough diamond crystals having a rounded elongated form like a long pillow. See also ***cushion crystals.***

**Bombay bunch** See ***grading of pearls.***

**bonamite** See ***smithsonite.***

**bone** An organic skeletal material sometimes used to simulate ivory. It has a greater specific gravity than ivory and, under the microscope, bone peelings show a multitude of cracks. Ivory contains waxy parallel surface contours. See ***lines of Retzius.***

**bone turquoise** See ***odontolite.***

**boort** See ***boart.***

**boracite** A collector's gemstone comprising the mineral magnesium chloro-borate. $Mg_6Cl_2B_{14}O_{26}$. Cubic (pseudo isometric) or orthorhombic. R.I. 1.661-1.671; S.G. 2.96; H. 7. Transparent, pale green. Occurrence: Germany, USA.

**borazon** Trade name for a synthetic cubic boron nitride manufactured as an industrial abrasive by General Electric of America. Using the criterion of indentation hardness, it has just over half the hardness of diamond (i.e. 9½ + on the Mohs scale). See also ***amber boron nitride.***

**bornholm diamond** A misleading name for the rock crystal variety of quartz.

**bornite** A collector's stone comprising a sulphide of copper and iron, also known as 'peacock ore' because of the iridescence produced by surface tarnish. S.G. 4.9-5.4; H. 3. Opaque, copper-red.

**boron** The element which is responsible for the semi-conductor properties and blue colour in Type IIb diamonds.

**boron carbide** A synthetically produced industrial abrasive with a hardness superior to that of carborundum (silicon carbide).

**bort** See ***boart.***

**bortz** See ***boart.***

**botryoidal** An external mineral shape or habit resembling a bunch of grapes (e.g. malachite)

**bottlestone** A misleading name for gems cut from moldavite.

**boule** A cylindrical or pear-shaped synthetic crystal grown by the Verneuil flame-fusion process. *Figure B.4.*

**bourguignon pearls** Wax-filled glass pearl simulants.

**bourse** A business exchange, association or club, whose members deal in diamonds or gemstones.

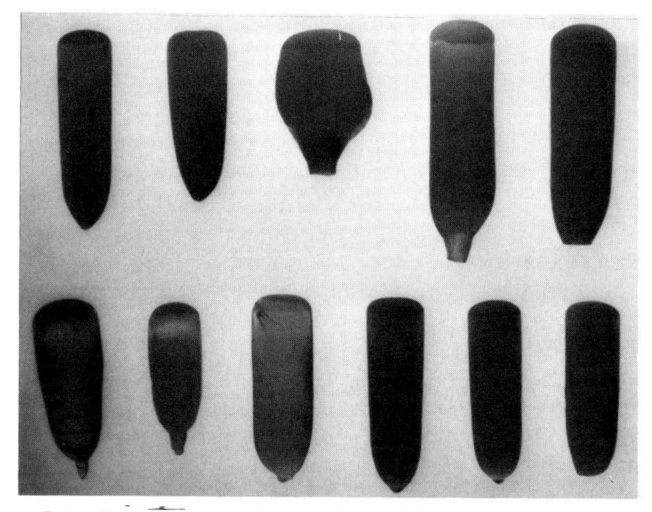

*Figure B.4* Synthetic corundum and spinel boules grown in a Verneuil furnace.

**bouteillenstein** See ***moldavite.***

**bowenite** A hydrated magnesium silicate comprising a hard variety of serpentine (used to simulate jade). Monoclinic (cryptocrystalline). R.I. 1.56; S.G. 2.58-2.59; H. 4-5. Translucent, yellow-green to blue-green (often containing whitish patches). Occurrence: Afghanistan, China, New Zealand.

**bowesite** An opaque green rock containing diopside, epidote, grossularite, plagioclase, quartz, sphene, iron oxide and calcite. It has a surface pattern similar to nephrite. R.I. 1.57; S.G. 2.78-3.10. Occurrence, Australia.

**bowr** See ***boart.***

**Brabant** See ***Antwerp rose cut.***

**brachy axis** The shorter of the two unequal-length lateral axes in an orthorhombic or triclinic crystal. The longer of these two axes is called the *macro* axis.

**brachy pinacoid** The faces of a brachy pinacoid are cut by the shorter (brachy) axis in an orthorhombic or triclinic crystal. See ***pinacoid*** and ***macro pinacoid.***

**Bragg's Law** A law first enunciated by W. L. Bragg which states that the reflection of a beam of X-rays by a family of parallel atomic planes when passing through a crystal can only take place when

$$n\lambda = 2d\sin\theta$$

Where $n$ is an integer, $\lambda$ the wavelength of the rays, $d$ the spacing between the planes and $\theta$ the angle of incidence and reflection of the beam. $\theta$ is sometimes referred to as the 'Bragg angle'. This equation lies at the root of all X-ray crystal analysis.

**brass** An alloy of copper and zinc; or bronze, copper and tin.

**Brazilian Gemmological Association** See ***Associacào Brasileira de Gemologia.***

**brazilianite** A hydrous sodium aluminium phosphate discovered as a new gem mineral in Brazil in 1944. $Al_3Na(PO_4)_2(OH)_4$. Monoclinic. R.I. 1.603, 1.623; D.R. +0.02; S.G. 2.980-2.995; H. 5½. Transparent, yellow. Occurrence: Brazil, USA.

**Brazilian aquamarine** A misleading name for blue topaz.

**Brazilian diamond** A misleading name for the rock crystal variety of quartz.

**Brazilian emerald** A misleading name for green tourmaline or synthetic yellowish-green spinel.

**Brazilian onyx** A misleading name for banded calcite.

**Brazilian peridot** A misleading name for light green tourmaline.

**Brazilian ruby** A misleading name for pink topaz or pink tourmaline.

**Brazilian sapphire** A misleading name for blue topaz or blue tourmaline.

**Brazilian topaz** A yellow variety of topaz.
**Brazil twinning** Twinning in which the individual crystals are related by reflection over the form and are of opposite hand. Amethyst, for example, has, in some cases, been found to be composed of regular polysynthetic Brazil twins as thin lamellae parallel to the terminal faces.
**brazing** High-temperature soldering using an alloy of brass and zinc and a gas-operated brazing torch.
**breccia** The description given to angular fragments of mineral which are cemented together into a rock by secondary mineralization (e.g. brecciated agate, jasper, marble and serpentine). Breccia is distinguished from conglomerate by the angular nature of the fragments.
**break facets** The triangular facets which are adjacent to the girdle on a brilliant-cut stone. There are 16 break facets on the crown and 16 break facets on the pavilion (also called upper and lower break facets respectively, and cross, skew or skill facets). See ***brilliant cut*** and *Figure B.6.*
**breath test** A simple test for diamond. If the surface of a diamond is breathed on, the resulting moisture film will evaporate much more rapidly that it will from the surface of a simulant. The effect is due to diamond's much larger thermal conductivity. It is valid only as a comparative test, and then both the test stone and a diamond sample must be at the same temperature.
**breithauptite** A collector's stone comprising the mineral nickel antimonide. S.G. 7.54. Copper-red.
**Brewster angle** The angle of reflection at which light rays undergo maximum plane polarization at a flat surface (also called the polarizing angle).
**Brewster's law** A law that states that complete polarization of a monochromatic ray reflected from the surface of a denser medium occurs when it is normal (i.e. at right-angles) to its associated refracted ray in that medium (Brewster angle = arc tan of R.I. of reflecting medium; R.I. of reflecting medium = tan of its Brewster angle). *Figure B.5.*
**briancon diamond** A misleading name for the rock crystal variety of quartz.
**Bridgeman-Stockbarger process** A method of growing synthetic crystals in which the source material is first placed in a crucible in the upper part of a vertical furnace. Then the crucible is slowly lowered to the cooler part of the furnace, and crystals begin to grow as the melt temperature falls. The process is used to manufacture laser crystals and gemstone materials such as synthetic scheelite.
**bright-line spectrum** A spectrum which contains emission rather

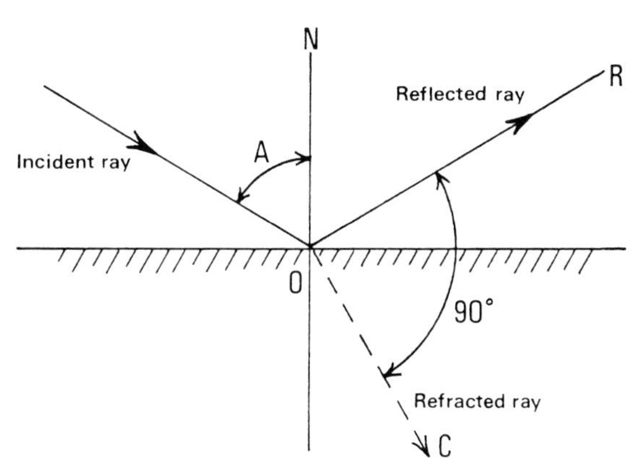


*Figure B.5* A light ray OR, reflected from the surface of a denser medium becomes completely polarized when it is at 90° to its refracted ray OC. Angle A is called the Brewster or polarizing angle.

than absorption lines. These bright emission lines are caused by electronic disturbances within the atoms of a specimen when it is vaporized (e.g. in a flame, an electric arc or a laser beam). Bright-line spectra are used principally in the analysis of materials, the pattern of the lines making possible the identification of constituent elements.

**Brighton diamond** A misleading name for the rock crystal variety of quartz.

**Brighton emerald** A misleading name for a glass emerald simulant or a green glass bead pebble found on the south coast beaches of England.

**brilliance** The term applied to a polished gemstone to describe the effect of the light reflected from its surface and (by means of total internal reflection) from within the stone. See also ***fire*** and ***scintillation.***

**brilliant** The term used for a diamond cut in the round brilliant profile.

**brilliant cut** The most often used cut for diamonds, this consists of 57 facets (plus a culet, or collet, polished on the pointed end of the pavilion to safeguard it from damage). There are 33 crown facets (including the central table facet) and 24 pavilion facets. Variants of the round brilliant cut are the marquise (or navette), the oval and the pear-shape, all of which have 57 facets. *Figure B.6.*

**brilliante** Trade name for a synthetic rutile diamond simulant.

**brillianteerer** A name, derived from the Dutch word *briljanteerder,* given to the diamond cutter who polishes the final sequence of 24 crown and 16 pavilion facets, and gives all the facets their finishing polish.

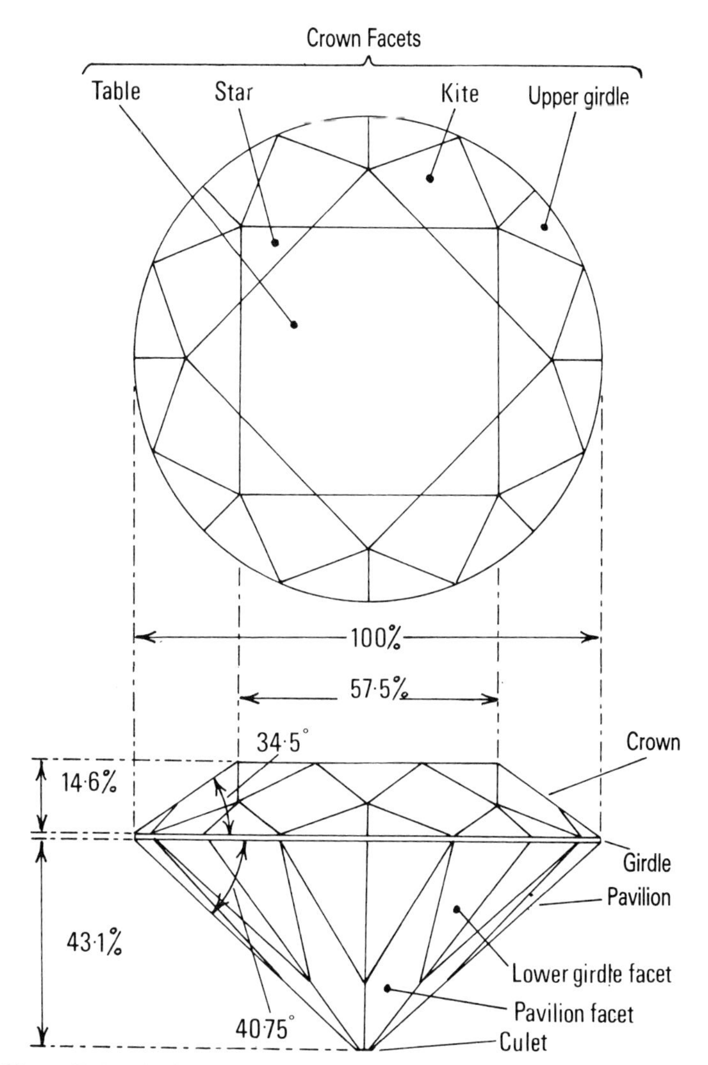


*Figure B.6* The ideal Scan DN proportions and angles for a brilliant-cut diamond. The Tolkowsky ideal cut has a slightly smaller table (53%) and a deeper crown (16.2%).

**briolette** An elongated pear-shaped stone having a circular cross-section, whose surface consists entirely of triangular facets.

**Bristol diamond** A misleading name for the rock crystal variety of quartz.

**britannia metal** An alloy of tin, copper and antimony. See also ***pewter.***

**britannia silver** An alloy having a higher silver content (and a softer working character) than sterling silver.

**brittleness** A weakness in a gemstone which, despite its hardness, makes it susceptible to fracture damage. Zircon, with a hardness of 7-7½ on the Mohs scale, is particularly brittle, and its facet edges are susceptible to chipping.

**bromoform** A volatile 'heavy' liquid used in the approximation of specific gravity and as an immersion fluid for the estimation of refractive index. $CHBr_3$. R.I. 1.59; S.G. 2.89.

**bronze** An alloy of mainly copper and tin.

**bronzite** An iron-rich enstatite having a chatoyant bronze-like lustre.

**brookite** A collector's stone which together with anatase and rutile is a polymorph of titanium oxide. $TiO_2$. Orthorhombic. R.I. 2.583-2.741; D.R. +0.122 to +0.158; S.G. 3.87-4.08; H. 5½-6. Translucent, yellowish, brown, reddish-brown. Occurrence: France, Switzerland, USA.

**brown diamonds** Next in frequency of occurrence to the yellow cape series diamonds. The brown tints in diamond are thought to be due to the presence of both nitrogen and amorphous carbon. See ***brown series.***

**brown quartz** Faceted brown quartz gems are known as cairngorms, a name derived from a now much-depleted source in the Cairngorm Mountains, Scotland. Occurrence: Switzerland, USA. Brown quartz with a greyish tinge is known as smoky quartz. Occurrence: Australia, Japan, Spain, USA.

**brown series** A diamond category containing the range of brown to brownish-yellow and greenish stones which show the characteristic 504 nm absorption spectrum (brown grades include finest light brown, fine light brown, light brown and dark brown).

**bruting** Also called rondisting and girdling, this is the production of the basic girdle profile of a brilliant-cut diamond. The sawn or cleaved rough diamond is rotated on a power-driven spindle, and another diamond is brought into contact with it as a cutting tool.

**bruter** The craftsman who specializes in producing the girdle profile of a polished diamond.

**buddstone** A bright green chlorite-rich crypto-crystalline quartz from Southern Africa. See ***chalcedony.***

**buergerite** An iron-rich tourmaline.

**buoyancy error** A weighing error which becomes noticeable when weighing bulky objects whose volume is significantly different from that of the counterweights (or the calibration weights). This error is due to the difference between the 'buoyancy' or air displacement of the object being weighed and that of the counterweights (owing to differences in their specific gravities. See

*Archimedes Principle*). As a cubic metre of air weighs only 1.29 grams (compared with 3520 kilograms for the same volume of diamond), this error is very small. By mutual agreement (and the use of standard materials for balance counterweights) buoyancy error is ignored in normal commerce. This error does become important, however, when a high degree of accuracy is required (e.g. in research work where it may be essential to determine the absolute mass of a substance). One laboratory method of eliminating buoyancy error is to carry out weighings in a vacuum. For precision weighing in air, manufacturers of analytical balances supply a correction formula which compensates for differences in specific gravity (i.e. air displacement) between the object being weighed and the counterweights.

**Burma sapphire** A misleading name for a synthetic blue corundum.

**Burmese shell** Pearl shell from the Mergui Archipelago, Burma.

**burmite** A reddish variety of amber found in Burma.

**burnt amethyst** Amethyst which has been heat treated to produce yellow quartz. See also ***heat-treated stones.***

**button pearls** Also called *boutons,* these pearls have a rounded top and a flattened base.

**buxton diamond** A misleading name for the rock crystal variety of quartz.

**bye** A term used at the mines for colour grading rough yellow diamonds (i.e. first bye, second bye, etc.). An alternative term is by-water. Stones of top white colour and top quality are described as 'first water'.

**by-water** See ***bye.***

**byon** The native name given to the gem-bearing alluvial gravel of Upper Burma.

**byssolite** This is a form of hair-like fibrous actinolite found in alpine fissures and as a 'horsetail' inclusion in adradite garnet.

**bytownite** A reddish or pale yellow plagioclase feldspar. See ***feldspar.***

**Byzantine mosaic** See ***Roman mosaic.***

# C

**cabochon** A gemstone cut having a curved or domed top surface and a hollow flat or convex base (the latter being called a double cabochon). Used mainly for opaque stones and stones exhibiting chatoyancy or asterism. *Figure C.1.*

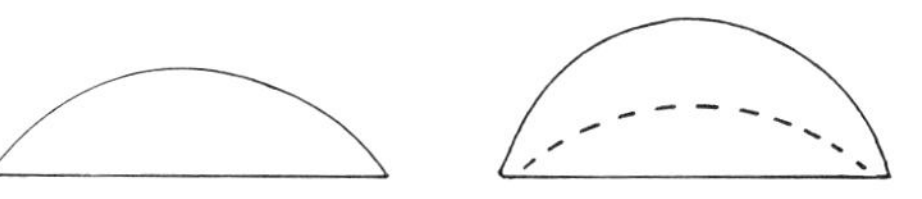

*Figure C.1* Profile of the cabochon cut. Stones are sometimes hollow-cut, as shown on the right, to lighten their colour.

**cacholong** A variety of common opal having a mother-of-pearl lustre (also called mother-of-pearl opal). Translucent to opaque, white or yellowish-white, highly porous.

**cacoxenite** A hydrous iron phosphate, $Fe_4(OH)_3(PO_4)_3.12H_2O$, sometimes found as a sheaf-like inclusion in quartz.

**cairngorm** See ***brown quartz.***

**calaite** See ***turquoise.***

**calamine** Name used for both hydrous zinc silicate and zinc carbonate. See ***hemimorphite*** and ***smithsonite.***

**calbenite** See ***myrickite.***

**calcentine** Trade name for a treated Canadian aragonite. Opaque with patches and bands of red, blue and yellow.

**calcite** A calcium carbonate which is a component in many rocks. It is also the basis of all true marbles and limestones. In its orthorhombic aragonite form it is a major constituent of pearls, and is also used for carving . $CaCO_3$. Trigonal. R.I. 1.486, 1.658; D.R. −0.172; S.G. 2.71; H. 3. Transparent to opaque, colourless, white, black and shades of yellow, brown, grey. Optical quality calcite is called Iceland spar, and is used in instruments such as the dichroscope. Satin spar is a fibrous form of calcite, and a banded stalagmitic variety (sometimes sold as aragonite) is used for carving. Occurrence: World-wide.

**calibré stones** A term used to described small square trap cut stones which are polished to standard sizes to fit channelled settings in jewellery.

**Californian iris** The kunzite variety of spodumene.

**Californian jade** A misleading name for californite.

**Californian moonstone** A misleading name for chalcedony.

**Californian onyx** A misleading name for a banded stalagmitic calcite and aragonite.

**Californian ruby** A misleading name for garnet.

**Californian tiger's eye** A chatoyant bastite.

**Californian turquoise** A misleading name for variscite.
**californite** A massive green variety of idocrase used to simulate jade. Occurrence: Pakistan, USA (California).
**caliper gauge** (for gemstones) A specialized gauge for estimating the weight of gemstones, and in particular diamonds. The gauge is used to measure the distance between the culet and table facets, and the diameter of the girdle. The weight of the gemstone is arrived at by referring these measurements to a table supplied with the gauge. A more refined version of the caliper gauge is the Leveridge dial gauge. *Figure C.2.* See also ***Moe diamond gauge.***

*Figure C.2* The Leveridge dial gauge for estimating the weight of mounted gemstones.

**callais** An ancient name for turquoise.
**cambay stone** An Indian cornelian.
**Cambrian** A rock system on the Earth's surface comprising the rocks laid down during the Cambrian period, 570-500 million years ago. The Cambrian period is the first part of the Palaeozoic era. See ***Palaeozoic.***
**cameo** A relief carving in which the differently coloured layers of a gem material such as agate, shell or coral are used to produce a contrasting background to the main figure or design.
**Canada balsam** A resin from the balsam fir tree which is used as a cement between glass components in optical instruments, and as a mounting medium for microscope specimens. Because of its refractive index (1.53) it is also used in nicol polarizing prisms

(made from Iceland spar) to reject the 'ordinary' ray (R.I. 1.658) while allowing the 'extraordinary' ray (R.I. 1.486) to pass through. See ***nicol prism.***

**Canada moonstone** A name for the peristerite variety of albite feldspar.

**Canadian blue stone** See ***sodalite.***

**Canadian Gemmological Association** Headquarters: Box 1106, Station Q, Toronto, Ontario, M4T 2P2, Canada.

**Canadian jade** A nephrite from British Columbia, Canada.

**canary diamond** A strongly coloured yellow diamond (termed a *fancy*).

**canary glass** Glass coloured yellow by uranium.

**canary stone** A yellow variety of cornelian.

**cancrinite** A rare semi-opaque yellow or orange gemstone having a complex hydrous silicate composition containing carbon, sodium, calcium and aluminium. Hexagonal. R.I. 1.491, 1.513 to 1.502, 1.524; D.R. −0.022; S.G. 2.42-2.50; H. 5-6. Occurrence: Canada, Norway, USA, USSR.

**candite** A blue variety of spinel.

**candle** The ceramic or fireclay pedestal on which boules are grown in a Verneuil furnace.

**candling** (of pearls) A technique for revealing the difference between cultured and natural pearls. To make the test, the pearl is rotated slowly in front of a strong light which is completely masked except for a 1 mm square test aperture. If the pearl is a cultured one, the structure of the mother-of-pearl bead will be projected onto its surface as parallel lines. If the pearls are in a necklace, they can be tested by stretching the necklace taut between its two ends and rotating it under a strong light. If any of the pearls are cultured, the internal bead will reflect the light through the nacreous covering, producing two gleams or flashes of light for each complete rotation of the pearl.

**cannel coal** A bituminous coal from Scotland and the north of England (the name means candle, as this coal was a source of wax for candle making). Occasionally used as a simulant for jet (distinguished by its brittleness).

**cape** A colour grade for polished diamonds. See ***Colour Grading Standards*** in Appendix B.

**cape cut** A term used to describe a polished gemstone whose facets are irregularly or haphazardly cut.

**cape emerald** A misleading name for prehnite.

**cape chrysolite** A misleading name for prehnite.

**cape ruby** A misleading name for pyrope garnet.

**cape series** See ***cape stones.***

**cape stones** A diamond category which includes all stones having a discernible trace of yellow (e.g. in the CIBJO grading system, White, Slightly Tinted White, Tinted White, Tinted Colour). The term *cape series* is applied to diamonds which show the characteristic 415.5 nm absorption spectrum. These range from top white to deep yellow stones. See also ***brown series,*** and ***Colour Grading Standards*** in Appendix B.

**capra gem** Trade name for a synthetic rutile diamond simulant.

**carat** A measure of the purity of gold used in jewellery. It is based on a scale of twentyfourths, 24 carat gold being pure gold, and 9 carat gold, for example, containing 9 parts of pure gold to 15 parts of alloy (also expressed as 0.375, i.e. 9/24). The usual metals alloyed with gold are silver, nickel, platinum and palladium (all of these being used to produce 'white' gold), zinc (green gold in combination with silver) and copper (red gold).

**carat weight** A unit of weight for gemstones. Originally derived from the seed of the middle-eastern Carob tree, the carat weight was standardized world-wide in 1914 as the metric carat. There are five metric carats to the gram; 141.747 carats to the ounce Avoir, and 155.517 carats to the ounce Troy. One carat is also equal to 4 grains (a measure for pearls and small rough diamonds) and 100 points (a measure for small polished diamonds).

**carbonado** See ***boart.***

**carbon disulphide** A liquid used for the immersion approximation of refractive index. R.I. 1.63. See ***Becke line method.***

**Carboniferous** A rock system on the Earth's surface comprising the rocks laid down during the Carboniferous period, 345-280 million years ago. The Carboniferous period is part of the Palaeozoic era. See ***Palaeozoic.***

**carbonyl** Trade name for carbon tetrachloride in the USA.

**carbon tetrachloride** A volatile liquid used as a grease solvent and a cleaning agent. $CCl_4$. As with other volatile liquids used in gemmology, inhalation of its vapour should be avoided. R.I. 1.44; S.G. 1.59.

**carborundum** Trade name for silicon carbide. SiC. Used as a polishing and industrial abrasive, it is made by fusing together sand and coke (i.e. silica and carbon). Some crystals of the material have been grown and faceted. Hexagonal. R.I. 2.65, 2.69; D. R. +0.043; S.G. 3.17; H. 9-9½. Transparent, colourless to bluish-green and brownish.

**carbuncle** Name given to a cabochon-cut almandine garnet popular in Victorian times.

**carnegie gem** Trade name for a composite diamond simulant consisting of a synthetic spinel crown section and a strontium titanate pavilion.

**carnelian** A common alternative spelling for cornelian.

**carneol** Trade name for a pink-dyed chalcedony.

**carob** See ***carat.***

**carré** Name given to a square trap-cut stone.

**cascalho** Name given to diamond-bearing gravel in Brazil.

**casein** A synthetic material made from the protein of milk, and used as a simulant for amber, ivory and tortoiseshell. R.I. 1.55-1.56; S.G. 1.32-1.34; H. 2-2½.

**cassiterite** A collector's stone comprising the mineral tin oxide. $SnO_2$. Tetragonal. R.I. 1.997, 2.093; D.R. +0.096; S.G. 6.8-7.1; H. 6-7. Transparent to translucent, colourless and shades of yellow, brown and brownish-red. Occurrence: Australia, Bolivia, England, Malaysia, Namibia, Spain, Tasmania.

**castor oil** A vegetable oil sometimes mixed with diamond dust to produce the abrasive paste which is applied to the polishing surface of a scaife when faceting diamonds. See also ***olive oil.***

**catalin** Trade name for a phenolic resin sometimes used as an amber simulant.

**catalinate** A jasper from Santa Catalina Island, Gulf of California, Mexico.

**catalyst** A substance which accelerates a chemical reaction but is unchanged by the reaction.

**cathay cat's eye** An imitation chrysoberyl cat's eye made from fused mosaics of parallel coloured glass fibres which are either clad or embedded in a glass of lower refractive index. R.I. 1.8; S.G. 4.58; H. 6.

**cathay stone** See ***cathay cat's eye.***

**cathodoluminescence** The fluorescent effect displayed by some materials when they are bombarded with a beam of electrons. Television pictures are generated by the cathodoluminescence of the phosphors on the screen of the cathode ray tube. For minerals, this type of luminescence was discovered as a side effect when viewing samples in an electron microscope. It has been developed into a useful research tool for detecting the presence of rare earths and specific minerals in agglomerates.

**cathode rays** Electrons emitted from the cathode of a high-vacuum tube under the influence of an electric field.

**cations** Positively charged ions. See also ***anions.***

**cat's eye** See ***operculum***.

**cat's eye opal** An opal with harlequin iridescence and a chatoyant streak.

**cat's eyes** Stones possessing the property of chatoyancy (e.g. chrysoberyl, quartz, tourmaline, tiger's eye). See ***chatoyancy.***

**catsteyte** See ***cathay cat's eye.***

**catty** A Thai weight equal to approximately 3015 carats.

**Cave Creek jasper** A bright red jasper found in Maricopa County,

Arizona, USA.

**cave pearls** Concretions of calcium carbonate (having a pearly lustre) which form in limestone caves.

**cedarite** A variety of amber from Manitoba, Canada.

**celestial stone** See ***turquoise.***

**celestine** A collector's stone (also called celestite) comprising the mineral strontium sulphate. $SrSO_4$. Orthorhombic. R.I. 1.623, 1.633; D.R. +0.01; S.G. 3.97-4.00; H. 3½. Transparent, colourless and pale blue. Occurrence: Namibia, USA.

**celestite** See ***celestine.***

**cellon** Trade name for a non-flammable variety of celluloid.

**cellosolve** See ***oxitol.***

**celluloid** A plastics material made from camphor and cellulose nitrate or cellulose acetate (safety celluloid). Sometimes used as an amber simulant. R.I. 1.49–1.51; S.G. 1.36–1.42 (nitrate) or 1.29–1.40 (acetate); H. 2½–3. See ***rhodoid.***

**Celsius temperature scale** Also known as Centigrade. The degree Celsius has been adopted as the international standard for temperature measurement. On this scale, the freezing point of water is 0°C, and its boiling point 100°C. To convert from the Celsius scale to the Fahrenheit scale, multiply by nine and divide by five then add 32.

$$°F = \frac{9}{5}°C + 32$$

**Cenozoic** The latest of the four eras into which geological time and rock sequences can be divided. It stretched from 65 million years ago to the present day and comprises the ***Quaternary*** and ***Tertiary*** periods. See also ***Mesozoic, Palaeozoic*** and ***Precambrian.***

**centre of symmetry** A crystal has a centre of symmetry when identical faces and edges occur on exactly opposite sides of a central point.

**Central Selling Organization** (CSO) The De Beers group which receives, sorts and markets 80% of the world's rough diamonds. Within this group, gem diamonds are handled by the Diamond Trading Company, and industrial diamonds by Industrial Distributors Ltd.

**cephalopod** A mollusc with a distinct tentacled head. See ***ammonite.***

**cerachat** Chalcedony.

**ceragate** A waxy yellow-coloured chalcedony.

**ceric oxide** See ***cerium oxide.***

**cerium** A rare-earth used in oxide forms ($CeO_2$ and $Ce_2O_3$) as a colour dopant in cubic zirconium oxide to produce orange and red varieties.

**cerium oxide** A yellowish-pink abrasive powder used in the polishing of gemstones (also called ceric oxide and cerium).

**cerkonier** An ancient name for zircon.

**certificate** A document recording all the details (e.g. constants, weight, dimensions, grading for colour, clarity and cut, etc.) of a polished gemstone. Usually issued by grading laboratories, and mainly used for diamonds.

**Certified Gemologist** (CG) A title awarded by the American Gem Society to members of the Society who have passed the qualifying examinations. See ***American Gem Society.***

**ceruleite** A hydrated copper aluminium arsenate. $CuAl_2(OH)_2AsO_4.7H_2O$. Cryptocrystalline. R.I. 1.60; S.G. 2.7. Opaque, sky-blue (similar in appearance to turquoise).

**cerulene** See ***ceruline.***

**ceruline** Calcite coloured with malachite and azurite.

**cerussite** A collector's stone comprising the mineral lead carbonate. $PbCO_3$. Orthorhombic. R.I. 1.804, 2.078; D.R. −0.274; S.G. 6.46-6.57; H. 3½. Transparent, colourless, greyish, brown, green, black. Occurrence: Austria, Czechoslovakia, Namibia, USA.

**Ceylon chrysolite** A misleading name for yellowish-green tourmaline.

**Ceylon cut** A mixed cut, usually consisting of a brilliant-cut crown, a step-cut pavilion and an oval girdle. To obtain maximum yield, the cut is often lacking in symmetry.

**Ceylon diamond** A misleading name for colourless zircon.

**Ceylon Gem Society** See ***Gem Society of Ceylon*** (now Sri Lanka).

**Ceylon opal** A misleading name for moonstone.

**Ceylon peridot** A misleading name for yellowish-green tourmaline.

**ceylonite** A dark green spinel found in Sri Lanka. R.I. values of 1.77-1.80, and S.G. values of 3.63-3.90, are higher than for the normal range of spinels.

**CG** See ***Certified Gemologist.***

**chalcedony** A cryptocrystalline form of quartz. $SiO_2$. R.I. 1.53, 1.54; S.G. 2.58-2.64; H. 6½. Trigonal. Translucent to opaque. Varieties:

*agate* — all colours with curved wavy concentric bands.

*bloodstone* — opaque, dark green with spots of red jasper. Also called heliotrope.

*chalcedony* — translucent, unbanded greys and blues.

*chrysoprase* — translucent, apple-green.

*cornelian* — translucent, reddish-orange.

*fire agate* — reddish iridescent botryoidal stone overlaid with translucent chalcedony.

*moss agate* — colourless translucent chalcedony with dendritic

green inclusions of hornblende.
*onyx* — black and white with straight or even banding.
*plasma* — dark green containing chlorite.
*sard* — translucent, brownish-red.
*sardonyx* — brownish-red and white with straight banding.

Occurrence: World-wide.

**chalcopyrite** Also known as copper pyrite. $CuFeS_2$. Tetragonal. S.G. 4.1-4.3; H. 3½-4. Opaque, brass-yellow. Occurrence: World-wide.

**chalumeau** The inverted oxy-hydrogen burner used in the Verneuil furnace.

**chalybite** See ***siderite.***

**chambersite** A rare collector's stone comprising the mineral manganese borate. $Mn_3B_7O_{13}Cl$. Orthorhombic. R.I. 1.732, 1.744; D.R. 0.012; S.G. 7.0; H. 7. Transparent, brownish-lilac or purple. Occurrence: Switzerland.

**chameleon diamond** A diamond which reversibly changes its colour on heating and/or exposure to light.

**chamelionite** A colour-change tourmaline.

**champagne diamond** A brownish-yellow diamond whose colour is not deep enough for it to be classified as a fancy.

**champlain marble.** A misleading name for a massive dolomite from Vermont, USA.

**charoite** An ornamental fibrous rock, consisting mainly of a calcium or sodium potassium silicate. $(Ca,Na,K,Sr,Ba)Si_4O_{10}(OH,F).H_2O$. Cryptocrystalline. R.I. 1.55; S.G. 2.6-2.78; H. 5½-6. Opaque, purple with swirls of greenish-black and orange. Occurrence: USSR (bank of the Chara river, Yakutia).

**chasing** A method of decorating metal surfaces by hammering a hardened steel punch along the lines of a design to produce grooves. See ***embossing.***

**Chatham synthetic emeralds** Marketed as Chatham Created Emeralds, these are synthetic emeralds grown by a flux-melt process developed in 1940 by C. F. Chatham of the USA. A 1014-carat Chatham synthetic emerald is displayed in the Smithsonian Institution, and another, weighing 1275 carats, is in the Harvard Museum. Probably because of an absence of iron in the synthetic product, its constants are slightly lower than those of the natural gemstone. (More recent productions may contain iron and have higher constants.) R.I. 1.560, 1.563; D.R. −0.003; S.G. 2.65; H. 7½.

**Chatham synthetic rubies** Marketed as Chatham Created Rubies, these are synthetic rubies grown by a flux-melt process. They have constants substantially the same as the natural gemstone, but unlike natural rubies lack any trace of iron (normally detected with an X-ray spectrometer or by SW UV transparency).

**chaton** A glass gem whose pavilions are treated with a mercury amalgam to produce a reflecting mirror surface.

**chatoyancy** An effect caused by groups of parallel crystals, fibres or channels within a gemstone which create a 'cat's eye' line of light across the surface of the stone. Chatoyant gems are usually cut as cabochons to show the effect to best advantage. See ***sheen.***

**checky** A Turkish weight equal to 1600 carats.

**Chelsea filter** Also called an emerald filter, this consists of a combination of two carefully chosen filters, whose combined transmission response is intended to match the red transmission and yellow-green absorption of emerald. Emeralds (natural and synthetic) appear pink or red when viewed through the filter, but most emerald simulants appear green. The filter can also be used to detect cobalt coloured synthetics (e.g. light and dark blue spinels) which, unlike the gems they simulate, appear red through the filter. The filter was developed in 1934 by B. W. Anderson and C. J. Payne in collaboration with the gemmology class at the Chelsea College of Science and Technology, London (hence the name Chelsea filter).

**chemawinite** A variety of amber found in Canada and the USA.

**chemiluminescence** The glow given off by a substance such as phosphorus when it oxidizes (not be be confused with phosphorescence, which is now exclusively applied to an 'after-glow' effect occurring after the source of excitation is removed).

**cherry opal** A North American name for fire opal. Also the name for a cherry-red and a yellow non-iridescent opal found in Mexico.

**chert** A flint-like cryptocrystalline variety of quartz.

**chessylite** See ***azurite.***

**chevvü** A Sri Lankan weight equal to 21.86 carats. Also called a chow. See also ***manchandi.***

**chiastolite** A variety of andalusite.

**chicken bone jade** A yellowish burned or buried (tomb) jade.

**chicot pearls** See ***blister pearls.***

**Chihuahua geodes** Geodes from the Sierra Gallego area of Chihuahua, Mexico, which have a rind of chalcedony grading inwards to megacrystalline amethyst or smoky quartz.

**Chinese cat's eye** See ***operculum.***

**Chinese jade** See ***nephrite.***

**Chinese turquoise** A misleading name for a mixture of calcite, quartz and blue-dyed soapstone.

**chips** Cleavages or broken rough diamonds under 2.0 carats. See also ***macles, melée, shapes*** and ***stones.***

**chlorastrolite** A fibrous rock (also misleadingly called green stone) consisting mainly of pumpellyite (a complex hydrated calcium aluminium silicate). Orthorhombic. R.I. 1.70; S.G. 3.1-3.5; H. 5-6. Opaque, chatoyant green with circular white and green markings. Occurrence: USA (Lake Superior).

**chloromelanite** A black-speckled green variety of jadeite. S.G. 3.4; H. 6½-7.

**chlorospinel** A grass-green variety of spinel.

**chlor-utahlite** See ***variscite.***

**chondrodite** A collector's stone comprising the mineral magnesium silicate (with fluorine and hydroxyl). $2Mg_2SiO_4.Mg(F,OH)_2$. Monoclinic. R.I. 1.59, 1.62 to 1.60, 1.63; D.R. +0.03; S.G. 3.1-3.2; H. 6½. Translucent, yellow, red, brown. Occurrence: Sweden, USA.

**chow** See ***chevvü.***

**chromatic aberration** See ***aberration.***

**chrome chalcedony** A green variety of chalcedony (also called mtorodite) which owes its colour to chromium. It should not be confused with the chrysoprase variety of chalcedony which is coloured by nickel. The two green chalcedonies can be distinguished by means of a strong chromium doublet in the deep red, or by a narrow nickel absorption band at 632 nm. Chrome chalcedony appears red under the Chelsea filter, while chrysoprase appears green. Occurrence: Zimbabwe.

**chrome diopside** A bright green variety of diopside. Occurrence: Republic of South Africa.

**chrome epidote** A deep green variety of epidote (also called tawmawite) having strong pleochroism (green, bright yellow). Occurrence: Upper Burma, Zimbabwe.

**chrome idocrase** An emerald-green idocrase.

**chrome tourmaline** A variety of tourmaline which owes its green colour to chromium. Occurrence: Tanzania.

**chromium** One of the eight transition metals which are mainly responsible for colour in gemstones. Cr. Stones coloured by chromium include ruby, emerald, red spinel, pyrope garnet, demantoid garnet, jadeite and pink topaz. Atomic number 24; atomic weight 52.01; melting point 1900°C; S.G. 7.1.

**chromium oxide** A dark green abrasive powder used for polishing gemstones (also called green rouge and green chrome).

**chromosphere** The gaseous envelope of the sun which is the main cause of the fine-line absorption spectra seen in daylight. See ***Fraunhofer lines,*** also ***Table of Principal Fraunhofer Lines*** in Appendix J.

**chrysoberyl** A beryllium aluminium oxide. $BeAl_2O_4$. Orthorhombic. R.I. 1.744, 1.753 to 1.749, 1.759; D.R. +0.009 to +0.01; S.G. 3.68-3.78; H. 8½.

Varieties:

*alexandrite* — transparent, green in daylight, red in tungsten light.

*chrysoberyl* — transparent, green, yellow, brown.

*chrysoberyl cat's eye* — translucent, yellowish, also called cymophane.

Pleochroism, strong in alexandrite (green, yellowish, pink in daylight; red, yellowish-red, green in tungsten light). Occurrence: Alexandrite originally in USSR, now in Brazil, Burma, Sri Lanka, Zimbabwe. Other varieties from Brazil, Burma, the Malagasy Republic, Sri Lanka, Zimbabwe.

**chrysoberyllus** A misleading name for greenish-yellow beryl.

**chrysocolla** A cryptocrystalline gem usually cut as a cabochon. $CuSiO_32H_2O$. R.I. 1.50; S.G. 2.00-2.45; H. 2-4 (may be as high as 6 if quartz content is significant). Semi-translucent to opaque, green, blue. Occurrence: Chile, USA, USSR, Zaire.

**chrysolite** A now discarded gemmological name for yellow, yellow-green and greenish gems (e.g. chrysoberyl, peridot, tourmaline). See ***Ceylon chrysolite*** and ***peridot.***

**chrysolithus** A yellow beryl.

**chrysopal** A green common opal.

**chrysoprase** A misleading name for a green-dyed chalcedony.

**chrysoprase** A bright green cryptocrystalline quartz. See ***chalcedony.***

**chrysoquartz** Green aventurine quartz.

**chrysotile** A fibrous serpentine which forms a valuable scource of asbestos. $Mg_3Si_2O_5(OH)_4$. Monoclinic. S.G. 2.5-2.6; H. 2½-4. Translucent to opaque, greenish, brownish, grey, yellow, white. Occurrence: World-wide.

**CIBJO** Confédération Internationale des Bijoutiers, Joaillers et Orfèvres. An international confederation of jewellery and silverware trades.

**CIE** Commission Internationale de l'Eclairage. An international body which specifies standards of illumination, colour measurements and colour description.

**CIE chromaticity chart** A colour chart plotted in chromaticity co-ordinates $(x,y)$ derived from red/green/violet tristimulus values $(X, Y, Z)$. The chart enables colour hue and colour saturation to be specified in terms of $x,y$ coordinates.

**cinnabar matrix** A quartz containing red cinnabar inclusions.

**cinnamon stone** An orange-brown hessonite garnet.

**cipollino marble** A marble having alternating bands of white and green, quarried on the Greek island of Euboea.

**cire perdue** See ***lost wax casting.***

**cirolite** Trade name for the man-made diamond simulant yttrium aluminium garnet.

**ciro pearl** Trade name for an imitation pearl.

**citrine** A yellow variety of quartz.

**clarified amber** Cloudy amber which has been clarified by heating it in oil. See ***rape seed oil.***

**clarity** A classification term in the grading of polished gemstones (particularly diamond) which denotes the degree of freedom from those features such as inclusions which would inhibit the passage of light through the stone. The term *quality* is similarly used in the sorting of rough diamonds. See ***Clarity Grading Standards*** in Appendix C.

**claw setting** A setting in which the gemstone is secured by claws just above the line of the girdle.

**cleavage** A property possessed by some crystalline materials which enables them to be divided or cleaved along a plane of weak molecular bonding. Cleavage planes exist in many gem materials, and these stones are said to have *imperfect, easy* or *perfect* cleavage (e.g. beryl, diamond and topaz, respectively). See ***basal cleavage, prismatic cleavage*** and ***octahedral cleavage.***

**cleavages** A shape category for rough diamonds over 2.0 carats consisting of broken crystal fragments or crystals damaged by cleavage of fracture. *Figure C.3.* See also ***chips, macles, melée, shapes*** and ***stones.***

**cleaving** A method of dividing a diamond crystal in two along one of its four cleavage planes (parallel to the octahedral faces). Cleaving is performed by first scratching a notch or 'kerf' along the surface of the diamond. A cleaver's blade is then inserted into

*Figure C.3* Rough diamond crystals showing, left to right, a triangular twinned 'macle', a 'shape' (distorted unbroken octahedron) a 'stone' (octahedron) and a 'cleavage' (broken crystal). (De Beers).

the notch, and when tapped acts as a wedge to part the stone in two. *Figure C.4.*

**cleiophane** See ***zinc blende.***

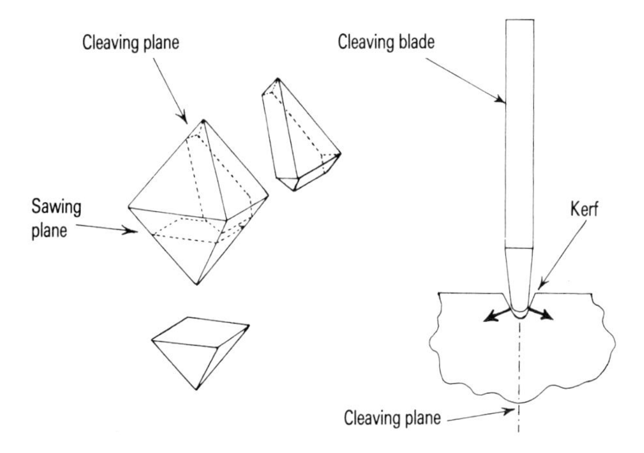


*Figure C.4* Sketch showing one of the four cleavage planes in a diamond together with the cleaving technique. The tip of the cleaver's blade functions as a wedge to part the crystal.

**Clerici's solution** A water-based 'heavy' liquid used in the approximation of specific gravity. It contains thallium malonate and thallium formate, and should be used with care because of its poisonous and corrosive nature. S.G. 4.15.

**clino axis** The lateral axis in the monoclinic crystal system which is inclined to the vertical axis. See ***ortho axis.***

**clinohumite** A rare collector's stone. Yellow, orange. $Mg(OH,F)_2.4\ Mg_2\ (SiO_4)$. R.I. 1.631, 1.668; D.R. +0.037; S.G. 3.15-3.21; H. 6. Occurrence: USSR.

**clinozoisite** A light green to greenish-brown or red variety of epidote, having little iron content. Monoclinic. Light green to greenish-brown variety R.I. 1.724, 1.734; D.R. +0.01; S.G. 3.37; H. 6-7. Red variety R.I. 1.715, 1.731; D.R. −0.016; S.G. 3.30; H. 6-7. Occurrence: (light green, greenish-brown) Burma, Zimbabwe; (red) Norway.

**closed form** A crystal form which is made up entirely of similar and interchangeable flat crystal surfaces or faces. See ***form.***

**close set** A gemstone mounted so that only its top surfaces are visible.

**closed setting** A gemstone setting consisting of a metal rim or collet fitted with a closed base.

**close goods** A sorting classification used at diamond mines for good quality crystals.

**cloud agate** An agate which has cloud-like markings.

**coated beryl** See ***Lechleitner emerald simulants.***

**coated diamonds** Diamonds which are covered with a thin translucent to opaque skin of low quality green, grey or black diamondiferous material. Under the coating the diamond may be of a good colour and quality. Coated diamonds are 'opened' for appraisal purposes by polishing two 'windows' on opposite sides of the stone. Occurrence: Mainly Sierra Leone and Zaire.

**cobalt** One of the eight transition metals which are mainly responsible for colour in gemstones. Co. Mainly seen in synthetic blue spinels and cobalt glass, it is also the cause of colour in pink smithsonite and some pink non-gem materials. Atomic number 27; atomic weight 58.94; melting point 1492°C; S.G. 8.6.

**cobalt glass** A blue glass coloured by cobalt which is used in the manufacture of gem simulants.

**cobaltite** A collector's stone comprising a sulphide of arsenic and cobalt. CoAsS. Cubic. S.G. 6.0-6.3; H. 5½. Opaque, silver-white tinged with pink (metallic lustre). Occurrence: Canada, England, Norway, Sweden.

**coesite** A rare form of silica which crystallizes under high temperatures and pressures and is sometimes found as an inclusion in diamond.

**coin silver** An alloy consisting of 9 parts fine silver and 1 part copper. Formerly used for USA silver coins.

**colemanite** A collector's stone comprising the mineral hydrous calcium borate. $Ca_2B_6O_{11}.5H_2O$. Monoclinic. R.I. 1.586, 1.614; D.R. +0.028; S.G. 2.42; H. 4½. Translucent, colourless to milk white. Occurrence: USA.

**collet** See ***culet.***

**collet** The metal rim (on a ring shank or on a piece of jewellery) in which a gemstone is set.

**collimate** To make divergent or convergent rays parallel.

**collimator** A lens system used to align divergent rays (from a point source) into a parallel path. A collimating lens is included in the design of the hand spectroscope, and exists as a separate unit in the table spectrometer or goniometer.

**colloid** A finely divided substance dispersed in another. Also a viscous solution or semi-solid jelly.

**Colorado diamond** A misleading name for a transparent smoky quartz.

**Colorado goldstone** Aventurine quartz.

**Colorado jade** A misleading name for green microcline feldspar.

**Colorado ruby** A misleading name for pyrope garnet.

**Colorado topaz** A misleading name for the citrine variety of quartz.

**colorimeter** An instrument for measuring the colour of a specimen. This is usually done by measuring the intensity of the red, green and violet light transmitted by (or reflected from) the specimen via colour filters (the results approximating the CIE tristimulus values). Tristimulus values are generally converted into the *x, y* coordinates of the CIE system. See ***diamond colorimeter*** and ***visual colorimeter.***

**colour blindness** See ***defective colour vision.***

**colour centres** Most of the irradiation-induced artificial colour changes in gems involve the production of *colour centres* which produce colour by the selective absorption of light. Heating the gem produces the reverse change, although exposure to light or dark conditions may result in a loss of colour with some particularly unstable colour centres. The production of a colour centre involves the 'loss' of one electron from a normally occupied position in the crystal lattice. This results in a hole colour centre. The presence of an extra electron causes an electron colour centre. Colour in some gemstones is caused by defects in the crystal produced either by natural irradiation (e.g. diamond and zircon) or by the presence of impurity atoms within the lattice structure (e.g. dispersed nitrogen in yellow cape series diamonds). These lattice defects are also known as colour centres.

**coloured diamonds** See ***diamond.***

**colour grading** The criterion used for the colour grading of cape and brown series polished diamonds is the degree of freedom from colour when viewed under specified conditions. See ***Colour Grading Standards*** in Appendix B.

For coloured gemstones, the criteria are hue, colour saturation, brightness and colour purity (i.e. freedom from contaminating colours). See ***diamond colorimeter, spectrophotometer*** and ***visual colorimeter.***

**colour temperature** The effective temperature of a light source (compared with an incandescent source) which determines its emission spectrum. A light source having a colour temperature of 4000 K will have its maximum output towards the red end of the spectrum and will be deficient in violet. Sources with colour temperatures of 5000 K and 6000 K will have a more balanced visible emission spectrum.

**colour zoning** The distribution of colour in a gemstone. Colour zoning forms an important identification feature with natural and flame-fusion sapphires. The zones of colour in natural sapphires are straight and parallel. In synthetic flame-fusion sapphires the zones are curved and concentric.

**columbite** A tantalate and niobate (niobium is also called columbium) of iron, related to samarskite. S.G. 5.2-8.0; H. 6. Opaque, black with a semi-metallic lustre.

**columnar** A crystalline structure composed of a series of slender prisms. When these are very slender the material is called fibrous.

**coluvial** A deposit formed by heterogeneous gravity-transported aggregates from cliff falls and avalanches.

**colza oil** See ***rape seed oil.***

**commercial white** A UK colour grade for polished diamonds. See *Colour Grading Standards* in Appendix B.

**common opal** An opal without iridescence (potch opal).

**complementary colour** Gemstone colours are the result of the gem absorbing part of the spectrum of the white light passing through it (or reflected off its surface). If yellow is absorbed, the stone will appear to be coloured with the complementary colour violet. Conversely, if violet is absorbed the stone will appear yellow. If blue/green is absorbed the complementary colour red will result.

**compound microscope** The standard modern microscope in which magnification is carried out in two stages, first by the objective lens and then by the eyepiece lens or ocular. See ***magnifiers.***

**composite stones** Except for opal doublets and triplets, these stones are made for the purpose of deception. Common forms are doublets in which the crown can be of the gem mineral being faked, and the pavilion of a cheaper material such as quartz or coloured glass. Many doublets were produced in Victorian times in which a thin crown section of garnet was fused to a coloured glass pavilion (known as a garnet-topped doublet or GTD). Triplets, such as *soudé emerald,* consist of a crown of quartz, synthetic white spinel or colourless beryl, with a quartz or synthetic spinel pavilion. The colouring element completing the triplet consists of a thin layer of gelatine or sintered glass (or, in the case of an alexandrite simulant, a colour filter), which is fused or cemented between the crown and pavilion sections. Opal doublets are formed from a thin top layer of precious opal and backed by common opal or plastic, the latter being hidden by the mount. Opal triplets are formed by cementing a dome of clear quartz to the thin top layer of the opal doublet. *Figure C.5.*

**compound** A chemical combination of two or more elements. Unlike a simple mixture of elements, a chemical combination is accompanied by the absorption or emission of heat, and the properties of the resulting compound may be quite different to those of the constituent elements (e.g. the chemical combination of hydrogen and oxygen to form water).

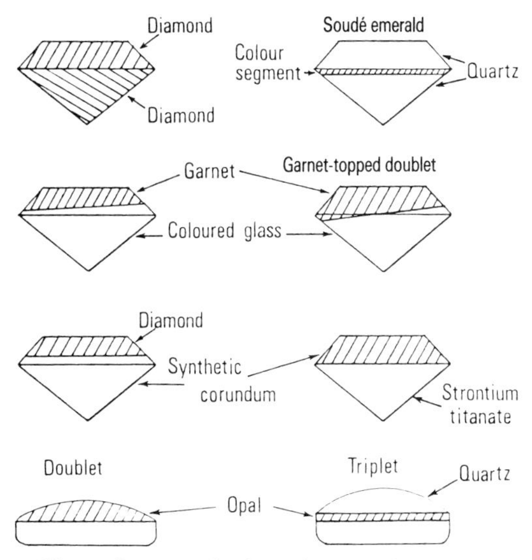


*Figure C.5* A selection of composite stones.

**comptonite** See ***thomsonite.***

**conchiolin** The dark brown organic substance secreted by molluscs and forming the outer coating of their shells. Pearls consist of approximately 12% of conchiolin.

**conchoidal fracture** See ***fracture.***

**conchology** The study of shells and shellfish.

**conch pearls** Non-nacreous pearls, usually pink and ovoid in shape. They are obtained from the univalve mollusc *Strombas gigas.*

**conglomerate** Water-worn fragments of rock cemented into a sedimentary mass (e.g. pudding stone).

**Congo emerald** A misleading name for dioptase.

**Congo ivory** A misleading name for an ivory simulant manufactured in South Africa.

**Connemara marble** A serpentine variety of marble (also known as verde-antique). See ***ophicalcite.***

**contact angle** See ***water contact angle.***

**contact liquid** The liquid used to make a good optical contact between the test surface of the critical angle refractometer prism and the facet of the gemstone under test by excluding any air interface. To maintain the full measuring range of the refractometer, the R.I. of the contact liquid must not be lower than the maximum scale reading. The standard liquid (devised by B. W. Anderson and C. J. Payne) is a solution of sulphur and tetraiodoethylene in methylene iodide (R.I. 1.81). With extended range refractometers (i.e. blende and diamond prism versions), West's solution is used. This has an R.I. of 2.05, and consists of an 8:1:1 mixture of yellow phosphorus and sulphur in methylene iodide. Because of the presence of phosphorus in the mixture, the dried residue is spontaneously combustible, and the liquid must therefore be handled with care. An alternative, which, while easier to prepare, is still dangerous, consists of selenium bromide in methylene iodide.

**contact metamorphism** The metamorphic alteration of pre-existing rock induced by thermal contact with intrusive molten rock magma. A feature of contact metamorphism is the development of successive zones round the intrusion.

**contact twin** A crystal whose two halves have grown with one half rotated through 180° to the other. In diamonds a contact twin is called a *macle.* Repeated twinning produces a *lamellar* structure. See ***interpenetrant twins, parallel growth*** and ***polysynthetic twinning.***

**contemporary inclusion** See ***inclusions.***

**contra luz** A rare variety of opal from Brazil which resembles a water opal with a slightly bluish milkiness. Its play of colour is visible both by transmitted and reflected light.

**co-ox** A green cubic zirconium oxide.

**copal** A 'young' tree resin, sometimes used as a simulant for the fossil resin, amber. Although copal resin has constants similar to those of amber, unlike amber it is softened by ether, and crumbles easily under a knife blade. Also called kauri gum.

**copper** One of the eight transition metals which are mainly responsible for colour in gemstones. Cu. Stones coloured by copper include malachite, turquoise, dioptase and synthetic green sapphire. Atomic number 29; atomic weight 63.57; melting point 1083°C; S.G. 8.93.

**copper emerald** A misleading name for dioptase.

**copper lapis** A misleading name for azurite.

**copper pyrite** See ***chalcopyrite.***

**coque de perle** An imitation pearl (resembling a blister pearl) which is cut from the central whorl of the nautilus shell. Because of the thinness of the shell, it is usually filled with wax or a cement to strengthen it.

**coral** A branching plant-like structure formed by the skeletal remains of various types of marine polyp, and consisting mainly of fibrous calcite. $CaCO_3$. R.I. 1.486, 1.658; D.R. −0.172; S.G. 2.6-2.7 for white and pink varieties; 1.34 for the black variety; H. 3½. Occurrence: In shallow sub-tropical waters around the coastlines of the Mediterranean, Australia, Japan, Malaysia, the Persian Gulf. Varieties: white, pink ('angel skin'), red, black.

**coral agate** An agate with coral-like markings.
**coralline** Trade name for a red-dyed chalcedony.
**coralline marble.** A fossil marble containing various corals. See ***red ogwell marble*** and ***petoskey stone.***
**cordierite** A complex silicate of magnesium and aluminium, also called iolite and dichroite. $Mg_2Al_4Si_5O_{18}$. Orthorhombic. R.I. 1.53, 1.54 to 1.54, 1.55; D.R. −0.008 to −0.012; S.G. 2.57-2.61; H. 7-7½. Transparent to translucent, blue. Pleochroism, strong (light blue, dark blue and yellow). Occurrence: Brazil, Burma, India, the Malagasy Republic, Namibia, Sri Lanka, Tanzania.
**cornelian** See ***chalcedony.***
**cornish diamond** A misleading name for the rock crystal variety of quartz.
**coro pearl** Trade name for an imitation pearl.
**corozo nut** The fruit grown by the Ivory palm. As the nut matures it develops a hard white kernel which provides a source of vegetable ivory. R.I. 1.54; S.G. 1.40-1.43; H. 2½. Occurrence: Colombia, Peru.
**corundolite** Trade name for a synthetic spinel diamond simulant.
**corundum** An aluminium oxide. $Al_2O_3$. Trigonal. R.I. 1.764, 1.772; D.R. −0.008; S.G. 3.96-4.01; H. 9. Varieties: *Ruby* (red); *Sapphire* (colourless, blue, pink, orange, yellow, green, purple). Also star rubies and sapphires (asterism caused by rutile needles). Pleochroism: ruby, strong (deep red, yellowish-pink); blue sapphire, medium (blue, pale greenish-blue); none in yellow sapphire, in other colours second ray has a yellowish tint. Occurrence: Ruby from Burma, Sri Lanka, Tanzania, Thailand. Sapphire from Australia, Burma, Cambodia, Kashmir, Sri Lanka, Thailand, USA.
**Cotham marble** A light grey marble with dark brown dendritic markings resembling trees. Also known as landscape marble. Occurrence: Cotham, England.
**cotterite** Quartz with white clay inclusions.
**counterfeit amber** See ***surface colour-treated amber.***
**craquelées** A cracked rock crystal.
**crater glass** A natural glass, associated with meteor craters, consisting of approximately 90% silica. R.I. 1.46-1.54; S.G. 2.10-2.31. Slaggy, white, greenish-yellow or black. See also ***queenstownite.***
**creedite** A rare collector's stone comprising a complex hydrated aluminium fluorine calcium sulphide. Monoclinic. R.I. 1.460-1.485; D.R. −0.025; S.G. 2.71; H. 3½. Transparent to opaque, white, purple. Occurrence: USA.
**creolin** A variety of brecciated jasper.
**creolite** A red and white banded jasper from California, USA.

**crepe stone** French jet (black glass) treated to produce a dull crepe appearance for mourning jewellery.

**crescent vert** Trade name for a synthetic emerald produced by the flux-melt process. R.I. 1.564, 1.568; D.R. −0.004; S.G. 2.66.

**Cretaceous** A rock system on the Earth's surface comprising the rocks laid down during the Cretaceous period, 135-65 million years ago. The Cretaceous period is the last part of the Mesozoic era. See ***Mesozoic.***

**crispite** A quartz or agate with green hair-like inclusions.

**cristobalite** A form of silica found as sub-microscopic spheres in precious opal. See ***opal*** and ***sheen*** (iridescence).

**critical angle** (of total reflection) The incident angle at which a ray of light, travelling from a denser medium into a rarer one, is refracted at 90° to the normal and travels along the interface between the two media. *Figure C.6.* At angles greater than the

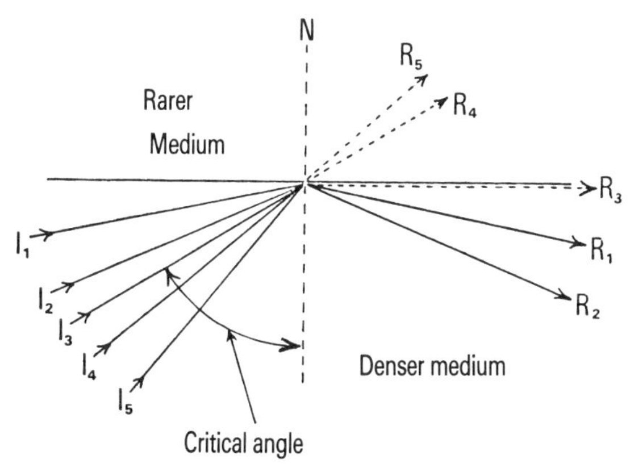


*Figure C.6* Light rays meeting a rarer medium at angles greater than the critical angle are totally reflected ($I_1$, $R_1$, and $I_2$, $R_2$). At the critical angle, the ray $I_3$ is refracted along the interface of the media. At angles less than the critical angle, the rays are refracted into the rarer medium ($I_4$, $R_4$ and $I_5$, $R_5$).

critical angle the ray is reflected (see ***law of reflection***) from the interface; at angles less than the critical angle the ray is refracted into the rarer medium (see ***law of refraction***). The phenomenon of critical angle is made use of in the *critical-angle refractometer,* and is an important factor in the optics of many gemstone cuts (e.g. the brilliant cut).

$$\text{Critical angle} = \arcsin \frac{\text{R.I. of rarer medium}}{\text{R.I. of denser medium}}$$

See ***refractometer.***

**crocidolite** A quartz pseudomorph of blue asbestos, better known as tiger's eye. As this is also the name given to the blue variety of the original asbestos mineral, the quartz pseudomorph is more correctly called pseudocrocidolite. See ***quartz.***

**crocidolite opal** A chatoyant opal with included crocidolite.

**crocoite** A collector's stone comprising the mineral lead chromate. $PbCrO_4$. Monoclinic. R.I. 2.31, 2.66; D.R. +0.35; S.G. 5.9-6.1; H. 2½-3. Transparent to translucent, red, orange. Occurrence: Brazil, Romania, Tasmania, USA, USSR.

**crocus** An iron oxide polishing powder.

**cross cut** See ***scissors cut.***

**cross cutter** The name given to the diamond cutter who grinds the table facet, the sixteen main crown and pavilion facets and the culet. Also called a blocker.

**cross facets** See ***break facets.***

**crossed filters** Chromium-rich gemstones often fluoresce red when irradiated with blue light. B. W. Anderson adapted the technique of crossed filters to make use of this phenomenon for gem identification purposes. Crossed filter equipment (*Figure C.7*)

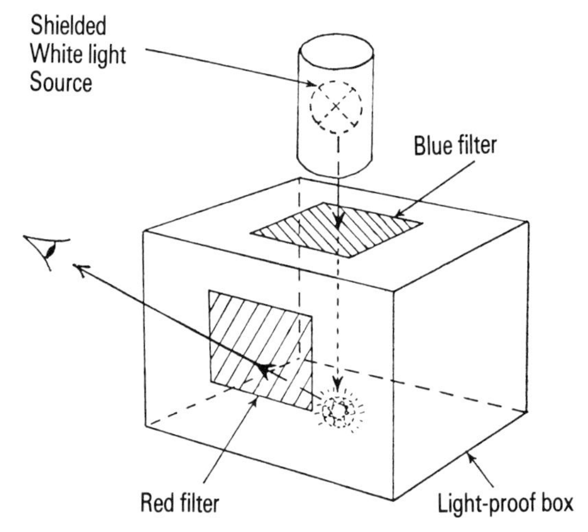


*Figure C.7* Sketch illustrating the use of crossed filters to verify luminescence.

consists of a strong source of white light, a blue filter (which can be a flask of copper sulphate solution) and a red filter. If, when viewed through the red filter, the specimen is seen to glow red, then it must be fluorescing. The effects are commonly far brighter than those seen under ultra-violet light.

**cross work** See ***blocking.***

**cross stone** The name given to twinned crystals of staurolite (also called 'fairy stone') and the chiastolite variety of andalusite.

**crown** The section of a polished gemstone above the girdle. Also called the bezel.

**crown angle** The angle between the plane of the girdle and the crown facets. See ***brilliant cut.***

**crown glass** A group of glasses which have no lead oxide in their composition. See also ***flint glass*** and ***Bannister's graph.***

**crown height** The perpendicular distance between the plane of the girdle and the plane of the table facet, measured as a percentage of the girdle diameter. See ***brilliant cut.***

**crown jewels** Trade name for a synthetic corundum diamond simulant.

**crusite** See ***andalusite*** (chiastolite).

**cryolite** A sodium aluminium compound, $Na_3(AlF_6)$, sometimes found as a crystal in three-phase inclusions in topaz.

**cryptocrystalline** A crystalline material composed of an aggregate of microscopic crystals or crystalline fibres. Such materials are always massive in habit, and are generally semi-translucent or opaque.

**crystal axes** Imaginary lines of reference which pass through the centres of crystal faces (or edges) to meet at a point inside the crystal called the *origin.*

**crystal lattice** Structure formed by the regular three-dimensional arrangement of atoms and molecules in a crystal.

**crystalline** A term used to describe a substance in which the atoms and molecules are aligned in a regular and symmetrical three-dimensional pattern. In most instances, this underlying symmetrical structure makes itself visible in the external shape of the rough specimen. The most important feature possessed by a crystalline substance (and absent from an amorphous one) is that many of its physical properties vary with the orientation of the crystal.

**crystallography** The science of crystal structures.

**crystallus** A rock crystal variety of quartz.

**crystal systems** Crystals can be grouped into seven basic crystal systems: *Cubic, tetragonal, hexagonal, trigonal, orthorhombic, monoclinic* and *triclinic.* These crystal systems are defined in terms of imaginary lines of reference called crystal axes, and by their elements of symmetry. See ***axis of symmetry, elements of symmetry,*** and the seven crystal systems under their respective names.

**CSO** See ***Central Selling Organization.***

**cubaite** A rock crystal variety of quartz.

**cubic system** A crystal system (also called isometric) having the highest order of symmetry of all the seven systems. The cubic

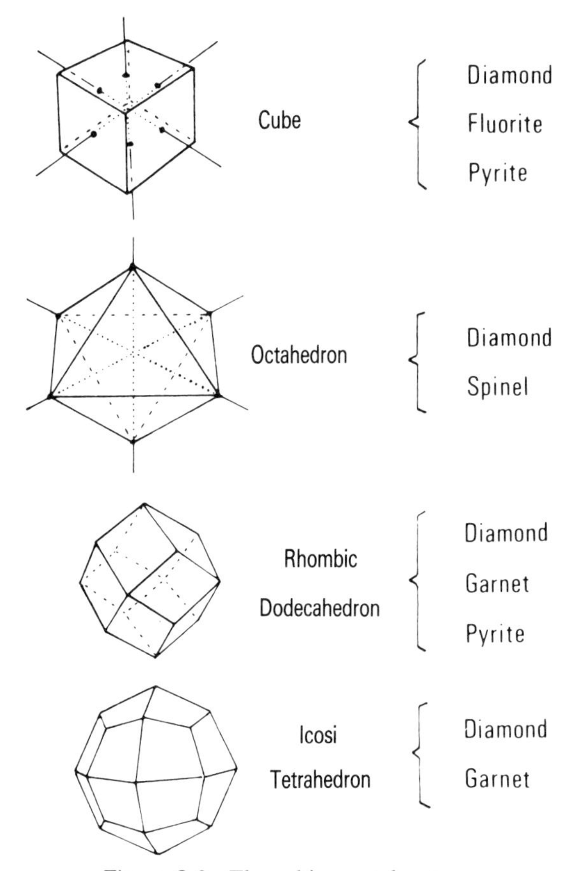


*Figure C.8* The cubic crystal system.

system has three axes, all of which are of equal lengths and intersect each other at right-angles. There are thirteen axes of symmetry (six two-fold, four three-fold and three four-fold), nine planes of symmetry and a centre of symmetry. *Figure C.8.*

**cubic boron nitride** See ***amber boron nitride*** and ***borazon.***

**cubic zirconium oxide** A man-made diamond simulant introduced in 1976. $ZrO_2$. Cubic. R.I. 2.09-2.18; S.G. 5.54-6.0; H. 8 (constants vary with proportion of stabilizer). Colourless and various colours (pink, orange, red, yellow, green, purple) produced by the addition of rare-earth and transition metal oxides. Crystals are grown by the 'skull crucible' process and stabilized in the cubic crystal system by the addition of calcium oxide or yttrium oxide.

**culet** A small facet cut at the pointed junction of the pavilion facets to prevent damage to the otherwise vulnerable tip.

**Cullinan** The largest rough diamond ever found was discovered in a side wall of the Premier mine near Pretoria in South Africa. Weighing 3106 carats the Cullinan (also known as the Star of Africa) was cut into nine major stones and 96 smaller ones. Of the major stones, the 530.2-carat Cullinan I is a pear-cut stone and is mounted in the Royal Sceptre of the British Crown Jewels (it is the largest cut diamond in the world). The 317.4-carat Cullinan II is a cushion-cut stone which is set in the British Imperial State Crown.

**cultured pearl** A pearl which was initiated by the manual insertion into the pearl mollusc of an artificial nucleus, usually in the form of a mother-of-pearl bead. S.G. 2.72-2.78. See ***Biwa pearls*** and ***mabe pearls.***

**cuneate** Wedge-shaped.

**cuprite** A collector's stone comprising the mineral red copper oxide. $Cu_2O$. Cubic. R.I. 2.85; S.G. 5.85-6.15; H. 4. Transparent to opaque, carmine red. Occurrence: World-wide. Gem quality crystals from Namibia and New Mexico, USA.

**cupellation** A method of refining (or assaying) gold and silver. The metal is heated with lead on a porous block. The lead melts and carries with it into the block all the base metal impurities.

**cushion cut** See ***antique cut.***

**cushion crystals** Rough diamond crystals having a flattened cushion shape. See ***bolster crystals.***

**cut** The criteria by which a polished diamond is graded for its proportions, facet angles and overall symmetry as compared with those of the ideal cut (e.g. Scan DN or Tolkowsky proportions). Also called the diamond's *make.*

**cuts of gemstones** See ***antique cut*** (cushion), ***brilliant cut*** (round, marquise/navette, oval, pear-shape), ***baguette*** (baton), ***cabochon, emerald cut*** (trap), ***rose cut*** (Antwerp rose/Brabant) and ***scissors cut*** (cross).

**cuvette** Small glass or plastic container, sometimes used as an immersion cell.

**cyanite** See ***kyanite.***

**cyclotron** As used in gemstone colour enhancement techniques a cyclotron is an apparatus designed to accelerate electrons as well as positively charged particles. It consists of two flat D-shaped metal cylinders, called *dees,* which are placed in a magnetic field. Particles emitted from a source at the centre follow a spiral path and are accelerated each time they cross from one dee to the other. This is effected by means of a radio-frequency alternating potential which is applied across the dees and synchronized with particle rotations. *Figure C.9.*

**cyclotroned diamonds** See ***treated diamonds.***

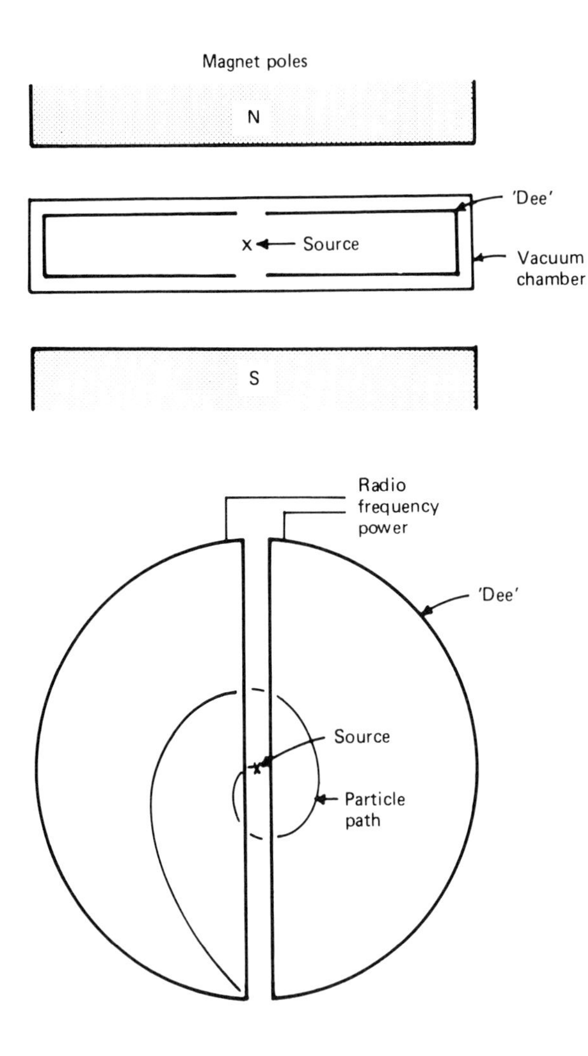


*Figure C.9* Diagram showing the components of the cyclotron. Top; side view showing the magnet assembly. Bottom; plan view.

**cymophane** See ***chrysoberyl.***

**cyprine** A blue variety of idocrase.

**cyst pearl** A pearl which has formed within the body of the pearl mollusc and is spheroid in shape. See ***blister pearl.***

**Czochralski process** A method of growing synthetic crystals in which a seed crystal is dipped into a heated crucible containing the molten source material, and is then very slowly raised out of the melt at a carefully controlled rate. The molten source material crystallizes on the seed and grows downwards as it is 'pulled' out of the crucible. Used to grow rare-earth garnets, synthetic alexandrite, lithium niobate and synthetic scheelite.

**dallasite** A green and white variety of jasper from Vancouver Island, Canada.

**damburite** Trade name for synthetic pink corundum.

**damonite** Trade name for the diamond simulant synthetic rutile.

**damsonite** The trade name for a light violet to grey-purple variety of chalcedony. It is mainly obtained from a quartz mine in Arizona, USA.

**danburite** A misleading name for synthetic yellow corundum.

**danburite** A calcium boro-silicate. $CaB_2(SiO_4)_2$. Orthorhombic. R.I. 1.630, 1.636; D.R. −0.006; S.G. 3.0; H. 7. Transparent, colourless, pale yellow, pink. Occurrence: Burma, Japan, the Malagasy Republic, Mexico, USA.

**daourite** A red tourmaline.

**dark brown** A colour grade for polished diamonds. See ***Colour Grading Standards*** in Appendix B.

**dark cape** A colour grade for polished diamonds. See ***Colour Grading Standards*** in Appendix B.

**dark-field illumination** Illumination in which the light is directed sideways into the specimen, and there is no direct light path between the source of illumination and the eye. For both hand lens and microscope inspection of gemstones, this is the preferred method of illumination when viewing internal features such as inclusions, and enables these features to be seen clearly against the dark background of the gem. See also ***incident illumination*** and ***light-field illumination.***

**darlingtonite** Jasper.

**Darwin glass** Also called Queenstownite, this is a natural glass. Amorphous. R.I. 1.47-1.50; S.G. 2.27-2.29. Transparent to opaque, colourless, yellowish-green, olive-green, black. Occurrence: Tasmania.

**datolite** A collector's stone comprising the mineral calcium boro-silicate. $Ca(B,OH)SiO_4$. Monoclinic. R.I. 1.625, 1.669; D.R. −0.044; S.G. 2.90-3.00; H. 5-5½. Transparent to opaque, colourless, pale yellow or green, milk white (cut as cabochon). Occurrence: Austria, Canada, England, USA.

**dauphine diamond** A misleading name for the rock crystal variety of quartz.

**dauphine twinning** Twinning with parallel axes in which the individual crystals are related by a rotation of 180° about the c-axis and are of the same hand. *Figure D.1.*

**davidsonite** A greenish-yellow beryl from the vicinity of Aberdeen, Scotland, UK.

**De Chaulnes' method** (of R.I. measurement) See ***direct method.***

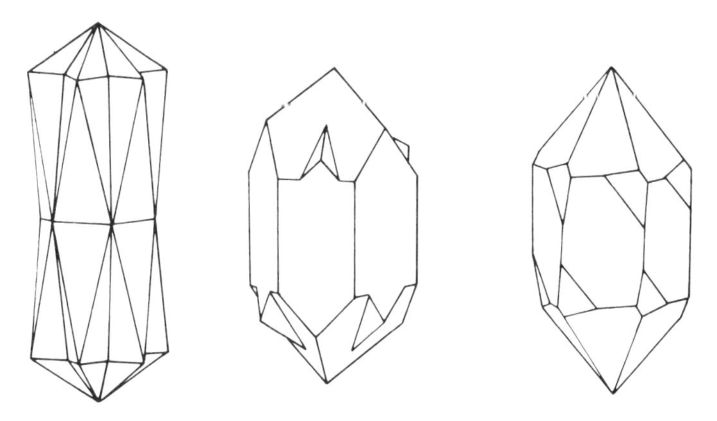

*Figure D.1* Examples of Dauphiné twinning.

**decraqueler** A method of 'healing' cracks in the surface of pearls by soaking them in warm olive oil (warning — pearls tend to turn brown when heated to around 150°C).

**defective colour vision** Known as colour blindness, one common form is an insensitivity to those wavelengths in the red longer than 680 nm (normal vision extends to 750 nm). In another type of deficiency, red and green produce the same sensation as yellow. Under poor lighting conditions these effects become more marked.

**De la Mar pearl** Trade name for an imitation pearl.

**delatynite** A Romanian variety of amber.

**delawarite** An aventurine feldspar found in Delaware, USA.

**delta pearls** Trade name for an imitation pearl.

**demantoid** A green variety of andradite garnet.

**demi-parure** See ***parure.***

**demion** The cornelian variety of chalcedony.

**dendritic** A term used to describe the 'branching' or fern-like type of inclusion as seen in moss agate. Also used to describe the branching habit of some minerals.

**density** The density of a substance is defined in terms of its mass per unit volume (it should not be confused with specific gravity, which is the ratio of a substance's mass compared with the mass of an equal volume of pure water at 4°C). The international SI units chosen for density measurement are the kilogram per cubic metre ($kg/m^3$). Using these units, the density of diamond is 3520 $kg/m^3$ (S.G. of diamond is 3.52). See ***specific gravity*** and ***relative density.***

**density bottle** Also called a specific gravity bottle, this provides a means of accurately determining the specific gravity of a gemstone by using heavy liquids. The heavy liquids are first blended until the gemstone becomes freely suspended within the mixture. The S.G. of the liquid (and hence that of the gemstone) is determined by pouring the resulting mixture into the density bottle (the capillary channel in its stopper ensuring a complete fill) and then weighing the bottle. The weight of the liquid is found by subtracting the weight of the empty bottle. The S.G. of the gemstone is calculated by dividing the weight of the liquid (in grams) by the internal volume of the bottle (in millilitres). This latter figure is usually engraved on the side of the bottle. *Figure D.2.*

*Figure D.2* Density bottle. (Baird and Tatlock).

**dentine ivory** Ivory derived from elephant tusks, the tusks of the walrus and the hippopotamus, the front teeth of the narwhal (a dolphin-like arctic whale) and, more rarely, the tusks of fossilized mammoths. Dentine ivory consists almost entirely of dentine, although enamel and other organic substances are associated with the complete tusk or tooth. R.I. 1.54; S.G. 1.7-2.0; H. 2-3.

**derbyshire spar** A variety of fluorspar.

**desert amethyst** A misleading name for solarized glass.

**detritus** Debris produced from rocks by wearing action, i.e. gravel, sand and silt.

**deuterium** A heavy isotope of hydrogen having a neutron as well as a proton in its nucleus, which doubles its atomic weight to 2.

**Deutsche Gemmologische Gesellschaft** Headquarters: 6580 Idar-Oberstein 2, Gewerbehalle, Postfach 2260, West Germany.

**Devonian** A rock system on the Earth's surface comprising the rocks laid down during the Devonian period, 395-345 million years ago. The Devonian period is part of the Palaeozoic era. See ***Palaeozoic.***

**dewpoint** The temperature at which the water vapour present is just sufficient to saturate the air fully. At temperatures below the dewpoint, condensation occurs.

**DGemG** See ***Deutsche Gemmologische Gesellschaft.***

**diadem** A plain or gem-set headband or crown.

**diagem** Trade name for the man-made diamond simulant strontium titanate.

**diakon** Trade name for a transparent acrylic resin plastic sometimes used for imitation gems.

**dialite** Trade name for a diamond simulant doublet comprising a synthetic spinel crown and a strontium titanate pavilion.

**diamagnetism** See ***magnetism.***

**diamanite** Trade name for the man-made diamond simulant yttrium aluminium garnet.

**diamanté** Colourless glass gems used to decorate fabrics. Also a term for jewellery set with glass imitation stones.

**diamantiferous** Diamond-containing material.

**diamite** Trade name for the man-made diamond simulant yttrium aluminium garnet.

**diamogem** Trade name for the man-made diamond simulant yttrium aluminium garnet.

**diamonair** Trade name for the man-made diamond simulant yttrium aluminium garnet.

**diamonaura** Trade name for the man-made diamond simulant yttrium aluminate.

**diamon-brite** Trade name for the man-made diamond simulant yttrium aluminium garnet.

**diamond** Crystalline carbon. C. Cubic. R.I. 2.417; S.G. 3.52; H. 10. Transparent, colourless and shades of yellow (cape series), brown and green; also rare 'fancy' shades of pink, orange, yellow, brown, blue, green. Industrial diamonds are of poor colour and quality, and are often micro-crystalline (See ***boart***). Occurrence: Australia, Brazil, China, India, Southern Africa (including Namibia), USSR. See ***type I diamond, type II diamond*** and ***lonsdaleite.***

**diamond bourse** See ***bourse.***

**diamond colorimeter** An instrument for colour grading polished diamonds. The American Gem Society *Shipley colorimeter* (no longer manufactured) and the Eickhorst *Diamond-Photometer* both assess the yellowness of a diamond by measuring the ratio of its light transmission in the yellow and in the blue. The Okuda DC-530A measures a diamond's absorption in the blue and red by means of an integrating sphere. All of these instruments are more correctly described as filter-photometers. Before testing, diamonds are checked for fluorescence, because blue fluorescing stones (which appear whiter under normal lighting) will give incorrect readings. *Figure D.3.*

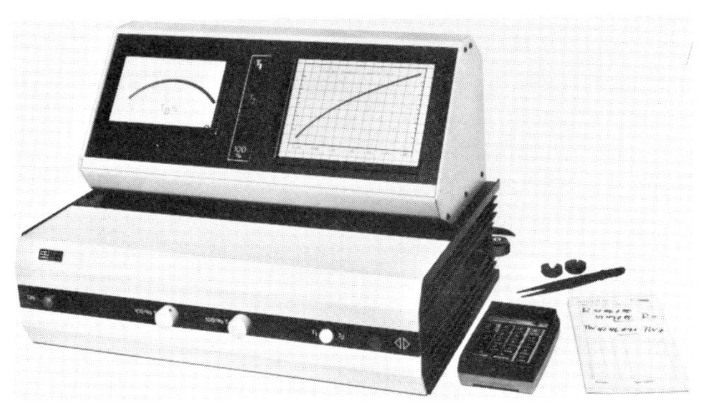

*Figure D.3* The Diamond-Photometer uses the ratio of yellow and blue light transmission to measure the depth of colour in cape series polished diamonds. (Eickhorst and Co.)

**diamond-cut** Term used by lapidaries to describe brilliant-cut gemstones other than diamond.

**diamond cutter** Any craftsman employed in the sawing, bruting and polishing of diamonds.

**diamond gauge** A stencil gauge consisting of a thin sheet of metal or plastic containing a series of holes marked in carat weights. The weight of a diamond is estimated by finding the hole which just fits over the girdle of the brilliant-cut stone. A more sophisticated version, designed by Dr E. Gübelin in 1946, enabled the cut of a diamond to be assessed by providing the means for measuring the angles and proportions between the girdle, the pavilion and the crown. This was later superseded by the GIA Proportionscope. See also ***caliper gauge.***

**diamond grading** The classification of polished diamonds by *colour, clarity, cut* and *carat* weight (i.e. the four Cs of diamond grading). See ***grading standards*** in Appendices B, C and D.

**diamond grading lamp** A lamp designed to provide a diffused illumination matching that of north daylight. The colour temperature of these lamps is usually in the region of 5000-6200 K. Some lamps are fitted with a LW UV tube so that any fluorescence in the diamond can be detected. See also ***grading lamp*** and *Figure 7* in Appendix B.

**diamond identification tests** See ***breath test, dot-ring test, fingerprinting, light spill test, reflectivity meter, thermal conductivity diamond tester, water contact angle*** and ***X-ray diamond tester.***

**diamondiferous** Diamond-containing material.

**diamondite** Trade name for colourless synthetic corundum used as a diamond simulant.

**diamond mine** Usually associated with a diamond pipe, this initially takes the form of an open-cast operation with a spiral roadway cut down into the surrounding rock to provide access to the diamond-bearing kimberlite. When a certain depth is reached it becomes more economic to sink a shaft and to extract the kimberlite by driving shafts horizontally through the pipe. A completely different type of diamond mine exists along the desert coastline of southern Namibia, where diamonds are extracted from the gravels which lie up to thirty feet beneath the sand on ancient marine terraces. See ***kimberlite.***

**diamond paper** A folded paper container for diamonds, usually with an inner liner. See ***Stone Papers*** in Appendix E.

**diamond powder** Crushed diamond which is carefully graded for particle size (from one micron upwards) and used for sawing, grinding and polishing diamonds and other hard gemstones such as corundum. Also used as an industrial abrasive.

**diamond proportions** See ***brilliant cut*** and *Figure B.6.*

**diamond proportion scope** An optical instrument containing a graticule which enables the proportions and angles of a brilliant cut diamond to be checked. The graticule can either be printed on the face of a shadowgraph screen (*Figure D.4*), or can be part of a special microscope eyepiece.

**diamond refractometer** See ***refractometer.***

**diamond simulant** A transparent colourless product having a superficial resemblance to diamond. Diamond simulants range from naturally-occurring colourless gemstones (e.g. white sapphire, zircon, topaz, quartz) to man-made materials (including glass), and composite stones. See ***cubic zirconium oxide, gadolinium gallium garnet, lithium niobate, strontium titanate, synthetic rutile, yttrium aluminium garnet, composite stones.***

**diamond sorting** The classification of rough (uncut) diamonds for colour, quality (freedom from inclusions), shape and carat weight. See ***Sorting Standards*** in Appendix D.

**Diamond Trading Company** See ***Central Selling Organization.***

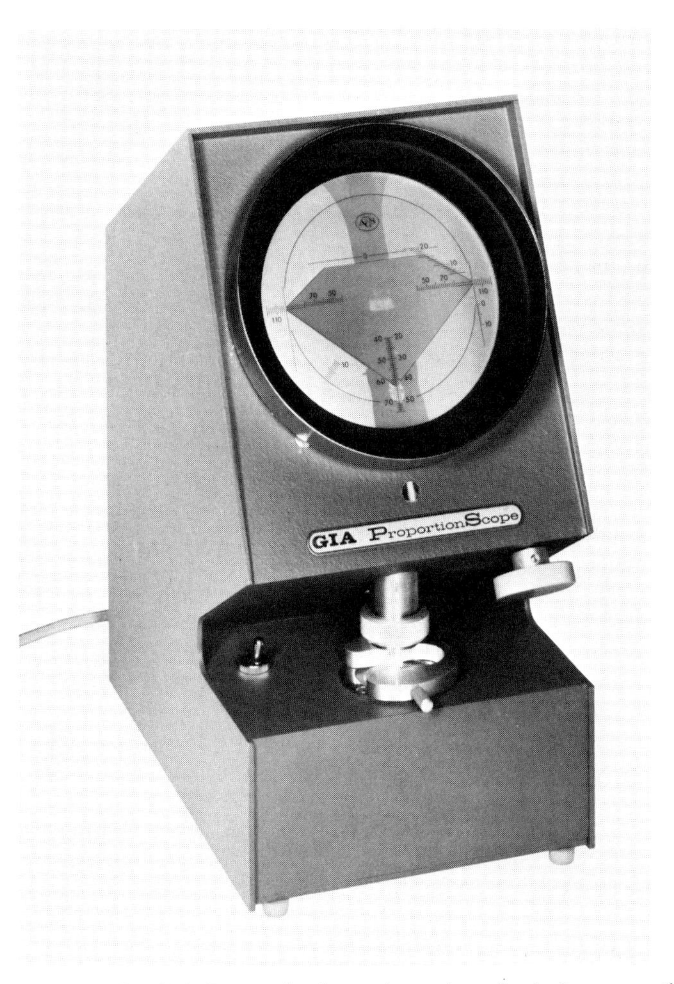


*Figure D.4* The GIA ProportionScope is used to check the proportions and angles of a brilliant-cut diamond's crown and pavilion.

**diamone** Trade name for the man-made diamond simulant yttrium aluminium garnet.

**diamonesque** Trade name for the diamond simulant cubic zirconium oxide manufactured by the Ceres Corporation of Waltham, Massachusetts, USA.

**diamonette** Trade name for colourless synthetic corundum used as a diamond simulant.

**diamonflame** Trade name for colourless synthetic corundum used as a diamond simulant.

**diamonique I** Trade name for the man-made diamond simulant yttrium aluminium garnet.

**diamonique II** Trade name for the man-made diamond simulant gadolinium gallium garnet.

**diamonique III** Trade name for the man-made diamond simulant cubic zirconium oxide.

**diamonite** Trade name for the diamond simulant synthetic rutile.

**diamonte** Trade name for the man-made diamond simulant yttrium aluminium garnet.

**diamontina** Trade name for the man-made diamond simulant strontium titanate.

**diamontine** See ***aluminium oxide.***

**diamothyst** Trade name for the diamond simulant synthetic rutile.

**diarita** Trade name for a colourless doublet comprising a synthetic spinel crown and a strontium titanate pavilion.

**diaspore** A collector's stone, comprising the mineral aluminium hydroxide, which has a distinct colour change (greenish-brown in daylight to pinkish-brown under tungsten light). AlO(OH). Orthorhombic. R.I. 1.702, 1.750; D.R. +0.048; S.G. 3.35-3.40; H. 6½-7. Pleochroism, medium (pinkish-brown, green). Occurrence: Czechoslovakia.

**diasterism** A star effect produced by light passing *through* a gemstone rather than by being reflected from its surface. Rose quartz contains microscopic needles of rutile which produce the effect of diasterism when the gem is viewed against a light source in the correct direction.

**diatomic** See ***molecule.***

**diatomite** Also called 'fossil tripoli', this is a polishing powder made from the soft silica remains of diatoms (i.e. microscopic unicellular algae which form fossil deposits).

**dichroism** An optical property possessed by some coloured doubly-refracting gemstones in which the two refracted rays undergo differential selective absorption and emerge differing in colour or in depth of colour. In uniaxial stones two colours or shades can occur, and in biaxial stones three colours or shades may be seen (trichroism). The general term covering all such effects is pleochroism. See ***differential selective absorption.***

**dichroite** See ***cordierite.***

**dichroscope** An instrument for detecting the presence of pleochroism in coloured doubly-refracting gemstones. The two polarized rays passing through the gemstone are separated (either by using a crystal of Iceland spar, or by using polarizing filters) and presented side-by-side in the eyepiece to facilitate the detection of colour or shade differences. *Figure D.5.*

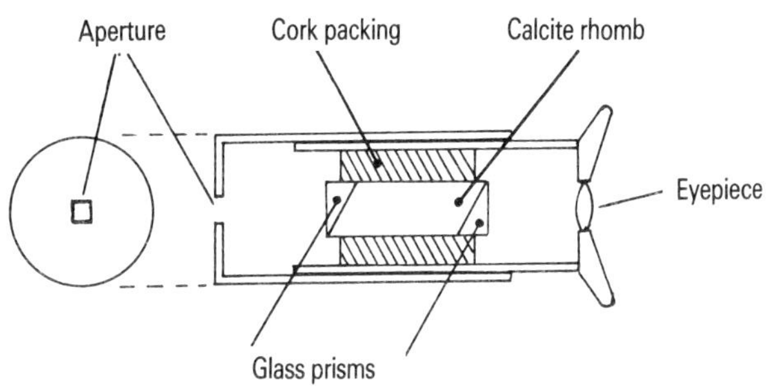


*Figure D.5* Diagram showing the construction of the prism-type dichroscope.

**didymium** Collective name for two rare-earths neodymium and praseodymium which are inseparable in nature. Didymium is present in yellow apatite. Neodymium oxide ($Nd_2O_3$) and praseodymium oxide ($Pr_2O_3$) are used as colour dopants to produce lilac and amber-coloured varieties of cubic zirconium oxide.

**differential selective absorption** In some coloured doubly-refracting gems, the light passing through the gem in the form of two polarized rays may emerge differing in shade or colour. When this happens the two rays are said to have experienced differential selective absorption (i.e. a different portion of the visible spectrum has been absorbed from each ray). The resulting effect is called pleochroism. See ***dichroism.***

**diffraction** The bending or fanning out of light rays when they pass through a narrow aperture. With a diffraction grating, the subsequent path-length-difference interference between the rays results in the production of a colour spectrum. See ***diffraction grating.***

**diffraction grating** An optical grating consisting of a series of fine parallel lines printed or engraved on the surface of a glass plate. Collimated light rays passing through (or reflected from) the grating are dispersed into a spectrum by the mutual interference between the emerging rays. The pitch of the lines is in the order of 15000-30000 per inch. Diffraction gratings are used in some spectroscopes, and produce a spectrum which is evenly spaced out from red to violet (unlike the prism spectroscope where the spectrum, although brighter, is bunched at the red end and spread out at the violet end). *Figure D.6.* See ***spectroscope.***

**diffusion column** A glass column containing a diffused mixture of heavy liquids in which the specific gravity decreases progressively from the bottom to the top. Gemstones having specific gravities within the top and bottom limits of the column will settle at the

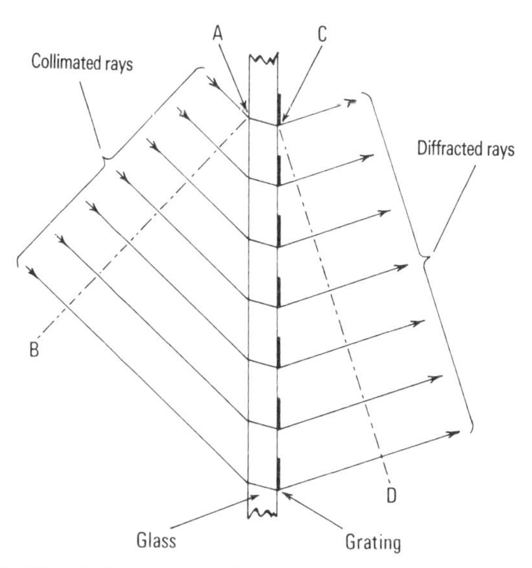


*Figure D.6* Sketch showing the diffraction of rays as they emerge from a diffraction grating. The resulting differences in path lengths (AB to CD) produce a spectrum by means of interference effects between the rays.

appropriate level. This affords a bulk means of measuring the S.G. of individual stones in a mixed group.

**diffusion technique** A method in which colourless or weakly coloured corundums are colour-enhanced by diffusing colour into the surface of pre-formed gemstones. This is done by coating the stone in paste containing the appropriate transition element oxides (chromium for ruby, iron and titanium for sapphire) and heating it to around 1800°C for 24 hours. The resulting colour layer is around 0.01–0.25 mm thick.

**di-iodomethane** See ***methylene iodide.***

**dike** See ***dyke.***

**dimorphism** Term describing the ability of a substance to crystallize in two different crystal systems (e.g. carbon crystallizes in the hexagonal system as graphite, and in the cubic system as diamond).

**dinny bone** A fossilized dinosaur bone used as a carving material. Occurrence: USA.

**diopside** A calcium magnesium silicate. $CaMgSi_2O_6$. Monoclinic. R.I. 1.670, 1.700; D.R. +0.03; S.G. 3.29; H. 5½. Transparent to translucent, bottle-green; colourless, violet/blue, yellow and brownish stones are sometimes found. Occurrence: Austria, Brazil, Burma, the Malagasy Republic, South Africa, Sri Lanka, USA.

**dioptase** An emerald-green hydrous copper silicate. $CuSiO_3.H_2O$. Trigonal. R.I. 1.644, 1.697 to 1.658, 1.709; D.R. +0.053; S.G. 3.28-3.35; H. 5. Transparent to translucent, green. Occurrence: Chile, Namibia, USA, USSR, Zaire.

**dioptre** The power of a lens or mirror system which is expressed as the reciprocal of the focal length in metres.

$$\text{Power in dioptres} = \frac{1}{\text{focal length in metres}}$$

The power is positive for a converging lens and concave mirrors, and negative for a diverging lens and convex mirrors.

**diorite** Also called orbicular diorite, a decorative rock composed of feldspar, hornblende, biotite and quartz. Whitish-grey with circular black patterns. Also a greenish-black granular plutonic rock whose composition lies between that of acid rocks such as granite, and basic rocks such as gabbro.

**directional hardness** In some crystalline materials, hardness varies with the orientation of the crystal. Kyanite, for example, has a hardness of 4 in one direction, and a hardness of 7 at right-angles to this. With diamond, the hardest directions are parallel to the octahedral faces, and the softest direction is parallel to the axis of the crystal (i.e. the plane of the dodecahedral face).

**direct method** (of R.I. measurement) A method of approximating the refractive index of a transparent gemstone by measuring its apparent depth and dividing this into its real depth. These measurements can be made with a microscope fitted with a vernier focus scale (or a dial gauge attachment). The gemstone is mounted, table facet up, on a glass slide and focus readings are taken on the table (A) and the culet (B). The microscope is then focused onto the surface of the glass, and a third reading is taken (C).

$$\text{Refractive index} = \frac{C-A}{B-A}$$

*Figure D.7.*

**dirhem** An Iranian unit of weight equal to 72.88 carats. See also *miscal.*

**dirigem** Trade name for synthetic green spinel.

**dispersion** Dispersion of white light occurs when it enters an optically denser or rarer medium (at an angle other than normal). The white light is split into its spectral colours, each of which is refracted by a different amount (red is refracted least, and violet most). Dispersion is the cause of the coloured 'fire' exhibited by diamond *(Figure D.8).* The dispersion of a gem is measured as the difference in its refractive index when this is measured at two selected wavelengths, one in the red and one in the violet. These

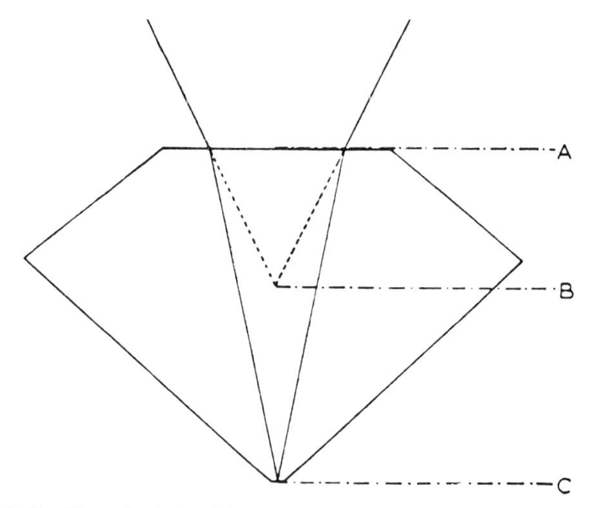


*Figure D.7* The principle of determining the refractive index of a gemstone by the 'direct method'.

two wavelengths are chosen as the B and G Fraunhofer lines. The B line is in the red at 687 nm, and the G line is in the violet at 430.8 nm. See ***Dispersion*** in Appendix F.

**distant vision method** (of R.I. measurement) Also known as the 'spot method' and the 'Lester Benson method' after its inventor. This enables refractive index measurements to be made on the curved surfaces of cabochons. A drop of contact fluid is first placed on a flat surface. The smallest possible spot of contact fluid is then transferred to the centre of the curved cabochon surface by

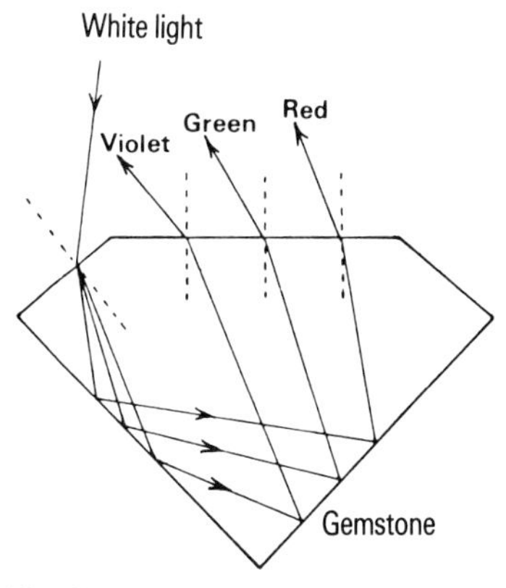


*Figure D.8* The white light entering a brilliant-cut diamond is dispersed into its spectral colours, and totally internally reflected as 'fire'.

lightly touching the drop of contact fluid with the surface of the cabochon. Next, the cabochon is placed on the refractometer glass with its spot of liquid acting as an optical coupler. Finally, the refractometer scale is viewed with the eye positioned about 18 inches from the eyepiece. By careful movement of the line of sight it is possible to see the small contact liquid spot as a 'bubble'. If the line of sight is moved in line with the scale, this bubble will change from dark to light. When the bubble is exactly half light and half dark this will coincide on the scale with the R.I. reading for the cabochon. The Rayner Dialdex refractometer was designed to facilitate distant vision readings by removing the problem of focusing the eye on an internal scale. This problem can also be resolved by viewing 2½ inches from the eyepiece via a 0.8 mm pinhole aperture. See ***refractometer.***

**disthene** See ***kyanite.***

**distrene** Trade name for a glass-like polystyrene synthetic resin.

**ditroite** See ***sodalite.***

**di' Yag** Trade name for the man-made diamond simulant yttrium aluminium garnet.

**djevalite** Trade name for the diamond simulant cubic zirconium oxide manufactured by Hrand Djevahirdjian SA of Monthey, Switzerland.

**dobo pearls** Pearls fished from the Aru islands north-west of Darwin, Australia.

**dodecahedron** A twelve-sided crystal in the cubic system. The rhombic dodecahedron has twelve rhomb- or lozenge-shaped faces.

**dolomite** A collector's stone comprising the mineral calcium magnesium carbonate. Also called pearl spar. $CaMg(CO_3)_2$. Trigonal. R.I. 1.502, 1.681; D.R. −0.179; S.G. 2.85-2.95; H. 3½-4½. Transparent, colourless, pastel colours. Occurrence: Australia, Brazil, Spain, USA.

**domeykite** A collector's stone comprising the mineral copper arsenite. S.G. 7.2-7.9; H. 3½-4. Opaque, tin-white to steel-grey (quickly tarnishes in air). Occurrence: Michigan, USA.

**dome** A form whose faces intersect the vertical axis and one horizontal axis, but are parallel to the third axis (e.g. the termination on a topaz prism).

**doom palm nut** The kernel of fruit from the doom palm providing a source of vegetable ivory. R.I. 1.54; S.G. 1.38-1.40; H. 2. Occurrence: Central and North Africa.

**dop** A device for holding a gemstone during sawing or faceting. It may be as simple as a metal cup (on the end of a rod) in which the stone is cemented or soldered, or it may be a mechanical claw-type clamp which grips the gem in the area of the girdle. See *Figure T.1.*

**dot-ring test** A simple test which makes use of the total internal reflection characteristic of an unmounted brilliant-cut diamond (of ideal proportions) to distinguish it from its simulants. A small black pencil or ink dot is made on a sheet of white paper, and the suspect stone is laid table facet down so that the dot is positioned symmetrically under its culet. If the stone is a simulant having a significantly lower R.I. than diamond, the dot will appear as a black ring round the culet. If the stone is a diamond, a strontium titanate or a rutile, no ring will be visible (strontium titanate and rutile can be distinguished from diamond by their excessive dispersion or fire).

**double refraction** When a light ray enters a gem belonging to any crystal system but the cubic one, it is split into two rays which are plane polarized at right-angles to each other. These two rays travel through the gem at different velocities and are therefore refracted by different amounts. Gems which cause light to split into two polarized rays are called doubly-refracting, birefringent or anisotropic. See also ***ordinary ray, extraordinary ray*** and ***isotropic.***

**doublets** See ***composite stones.***

**dravite** A brown variety of tourmaline.

**drilling** An industrial diamond classification which includes stones below the quality of 'near gem' diamonds. These stones are mainly used for mounting in the heads of rock drills.

**druse** A rock cavity lined with crystals whose chemical composition is derived from the surrounding rock. See also ***geode*** and ***vug.***

**dry diggings** A diamond deposit based on a pipe source rather than an alluvial source. See ***wet diggings.***

**ductility** The pliability of a metal which allows it to be reduced in cross-section by being drawn or stretched under tension.

**dugong pearls** Imitation pearls made from the teeth of the sea cow.

**dullam** The concentrated Sri Lankan gem gravels which result from the initial washing operation.

**duluth agate.** An agate variety from Lake Superior, Canada.

**dumortierite** An ornamental stone consisting of a complex aluminium borate silicate, often found in gem quality impregnating quartz. $(Al,Fe)_7BSi_3O_{18}$. Orthorhombic. R.I. 1.686, 1.723; D.R. –0.037; S.G. 3.41; H. 8 (in quartz, R.I. 1.54-1.55; S.G. 2.8-2.9). Opaque, dark blue, violet-blue and red-brown. Pleochroism, medium (black, deep red-brown, brown). Occurrence: Brazil (transparent bluish-green variety, R.I. 1.668, 1.688; D.R. —0.02; S.G. 3.35; H. 7½–8), Canada, France, USA.

**durangite** A collector's stone comprising the mineral sodium aluminium fluo-arsenate. $Na(Al,F)\,AsSO_4$. Monoclinic. R.I. 1.66,

1.712; D.R. −0.05; S.G. 3.97-4.07; H. 5. Transparent, orange-red. Pleochroism, strong (colourless, orange-yellow). Occurrence: Durango, Mexico.

**dust pearls** Very small seed pearls.

**Dutch rose cut** A flat-based cut with a pyramid crown consisting of triangular facets. Similar to the ***Antwerp rose,*** or Brabant, but with a higher pyramid. See also ***rose cut.***

**dyed gemstones** Many stones, such as turquoise, serpentine, opal, jadeite, nephrite and the chalcedony varieties have porous surfaces which are easily stained or dyed to enhance their appearance. As this treatment is not always permanent, such stones, if identified, should be described as dyed or treated.

**dyke** (US *dike*) A geological formation comprising a fissure in ancient rock strata which has been filled by the intrusion of igneous rock.

**dynagem** Trade name for the man-made diamond simulant strontium titanate.

# E

**ear shell** See *abalone.*

**earth stone** Ancient name for amber.

**ebonite** Vulcanized rubber, used in Victorian times as a simulant for jet.

**eclogite** A pyroxene garnet rock found in South African diamond mines.

**edenite** See *smaragdite.*

**edinite** See *prase.*

**egeran** A Hungarian variety of idocrase.

**Egyptian alabaster** A banded stalagmitic marble found in Egypt.

**Egyptian pebbles** Jasper pebbles of variegated yellow and brown.

**Eickhorst diamond photometer** See *diamond colorimeter.*

**eight cut** A simplified version of the 57-facet brilliant cut used for very small diamonds (below 2 mm girdle diameter). The table facet is surrounded by eight 4-sided crown facets, and the pavilion consists of eight triangular facets. Also called old English cut and single cut.

**eilat stone** A blue/green mottled stone consisting of the mineral chrysocolla intergrown with turquoise and malachite. Also known as elath stone. S.G. 2.8-3.2. Occurrence: Israel.

**ekanite** A metamict radioactive calcium thorium silicate. $K(Ca,Na)_2ThSi_8O_{20}$. Amorphous. R.I. 1.597; S.G. 3.28; H. 6-6½. Translucent, green, occasionally with asterism (4-rayed star). Occurrence: Sri Lanka.

**elath stone** See *eilat stone.*

**elbaite** Pink lithium tourmaline from Elba and the USA (zoned 'watermelon' elbaite from Newry, Maine). Elbaite tourmalines may also contain potassium and sodium. They are predominantly pink, red or pale green, and include the majority of gem tourmalines.

**Elbe brilliant cut** A diamond cut developed by Dr M. G. Elbe which achieved extra brilliance by means of a deep faceted girdle.

**elco pearls** Trade name for an imitation pearl.

**el doradoite** A yellowish quartz from California, USA.

**eldoradoite** A blue chalcedony.

**electric emerald** A misleading name for a green glass emerald simulant.

**electro-conductivity** A property possessed by a few gemstones which are capable of passing an electric current if a voltage is applied across them (e.g. natural type IIb blue diamonds whose semiconductor characteristic is due to boron impurities; artificially-coloured blue diamonds do not possess electro-conductivity).

**electroforming** The building up of a metal form by electrolytically depositing metal onto a conductive matrix or template. See ***electroplating***.

**electroluminescence** A type of luminescence produced in some gemstones when an electric current is passed through them (e.g. natural blue diamonds).

**electromagnetic spectrum** This covers the broad range of radiated electromagnetic energy from very long-wave radio transmissions through the visible spectrum to the ultra-short wavelengths of X-ray, gamma and cosmic rays. *Figure E.1.*

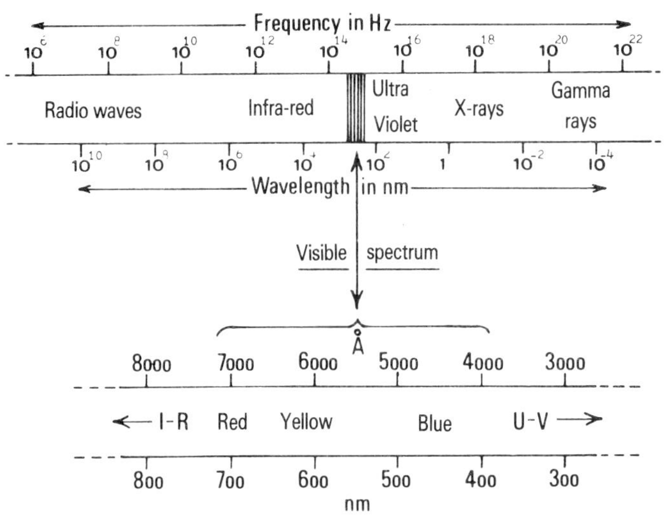


*Figure E.1* The electromagnetic spectrum, showing the wavelengths and relative position of the visible spectrum.

**electron** A negatively charged stable particle of elementary matter which orbits the electrically positive nucleus of an atom, and also acts as a carrier of electricity.

**electron accelerator** As used in gemstone colour enhancement techniques, an electron accelerator is an apparatus in which electrons, produced by heating a filament in a vacuum, are accelerated by an electric field. The field is generated by applying a high voltage, typically in the range of one million volts, to the electrode system. *Figure E.2.*

**electron microprobe** An instrument used in gemmological research for the non-destructive analysis of gemstone constituents and inclusions. It consists of a vacuum chamber for the specimen, an electron gun, X-ray spectrometers and an inspection microscope.

*Figure E.2* A voltage-multiplier electron accelerator with the capability of producing 1.5 MeV electrons. Photograph courtesy of Bell Laboratories.

The gem to be analysed is positioned under the focused beam of electrons using the microscope. As the electrons hit the surface of the gem, X-rays are emitted, each constituent element in the bombarded area emitting X-rays at a characteristic wavelength. This X-radiation is detected and its wavelengths measured by the spectrometers. Tables of emission spectra are used to identify the elements responsible for the recorded X-radiation wavelengths.

**electron microscope** A microscope which uses electrons instead of light rays to scan or penetrate a specimen. The electrons are generated by a heated cathode and focused on the specimen in a vacuum chamber. In a scanning electron microscope (SEM), the electrons scattered by the specimen are refocused onto a fluorescent screen to produce an image of 25 × to 250 000 × magnification.

**electron spin resonance spectrometer** An instrument used in gemmological research for the non-destructive analysis of crystalline impurities. It consists of a powerful magnet assembly

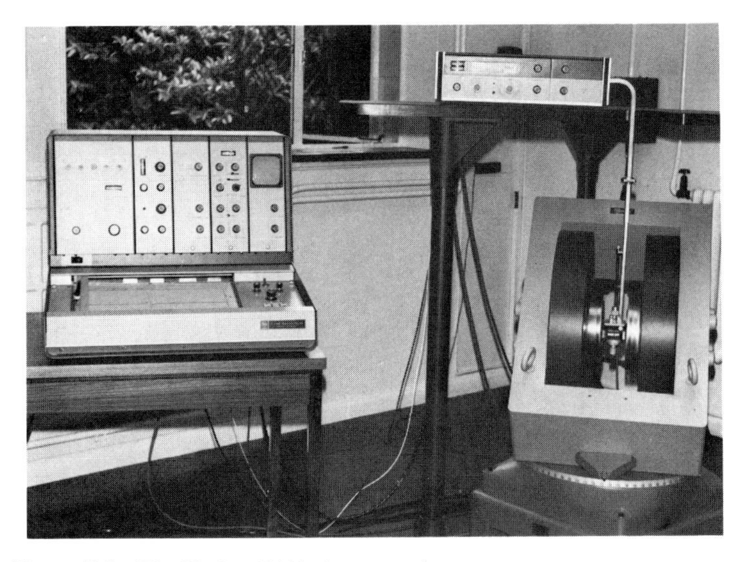

*Figure E.3* The Varian E109 electron spin resonance spectometer (ESR). The magnet assembly is on the right-hand side with a microwave-guide leading up from the specimen cavity between the magnet's pole pieces to the microwave generator above it. (De Beers).

(containing the specimen holder), a microwave generator and detector, and a control unit. The spectrometer measures the magnetic resonance of defect elements in the specimen's crystal lattice by detecting the microwave energy absorbed by the elements at characteristic magnetic field strengths. The ESR spectrometer was used in De Beers Diamond Research Laboratory, Johannesburg to correlate the yellowness of diamonds with the amount of dispersed nitrogen in the crystal lattice. *Figure E.3.*

**electron-treated diamond** See ***treated diamond.***

**electron volt (eV)** The kinetic energy gained by an electron as it passes through a potential difference of 1 volt in a vacuum ($1\text{eV} = 1.6 \times 10^{-19}$ joules). This unit of photon energy is often used by physicists to specify wavelength. In this context, the visible spectral range of 400 nm-700 nm is equivalent to 3.10eV-1.77eV, i.e.

$$\text{wavelength in nm} = \frac{10\,000}{\text{eV} \times 8.006}$$

$$\text{eV} = \frac{10\,000}{\text{nm} \times 8.006}$$

See also ***wave number.***

**electroplating** The deposition of one metal on another by means of an electric current in a solution of a salt of the metal being deposited. The article to be plated, and an anode of the plating metal, are suspended in the solution, and a voltage applied across them. Silver is normally plated on copper or nickel, and gold is plated on silver. See ***electroforming.***

**electrum** Name given by the ancient Greeks to amber, from which the word electricity is derived. Also a natural alloy of gold and silver.

**element** A substance that cannot be changed by chemical means into a simpler substance. Stable elements which occur in nature range from hydrogen (the lightest) to uranium (the heaviest). Elements normally exist in chemical combination with other elements. See ***compound*** and ***molecule.***

**elements of symmetry** See ***axis of symmetry, centre of symmetry*** and ***plane of symmetry.***

**elephant ivory** See ***dentine ivory.***

**elie ruby** A misleading name for pyrope garnet.

**elite pearl** Trade name for an imitation pearl.

**elixirite** A banded rhyolite from New Mexico, USA.

**ellandra pearls** Trade name for an imitation pearl.

**eluvial deposits** Deposits which are intermediate between residual or 'primary' deposits and alluvial or 'secondary' deposits. These deposits are usually of heavier minerals (diamond, gold, platinum) which have been weathered from their original rock outcrop, and carried a short distance downhill.

**embossing** The raising of a decorative design on the surface of a metal by means of a metal punch and a hammer. See ***chasing.***

**emeralda** Trade name for a synthetic yellow-green spinel.

**emerald** See ***beryl.***

**emerald-coated beryl** See ***Lechleitner emerald simulants.***

**emerald cut** A cut originally developed for emeralds. The cut was designed both to enhance the colour of emerald and to allow for its shock sensitivity by removing the otherwise vulnerable corners. The cut is also known as the step or trap cut, and is used additionally for diamonds and other gems. *Figure E.4.*

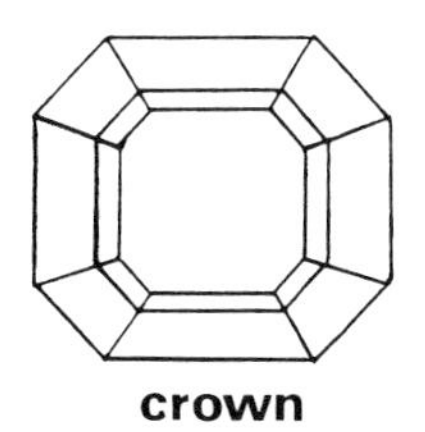


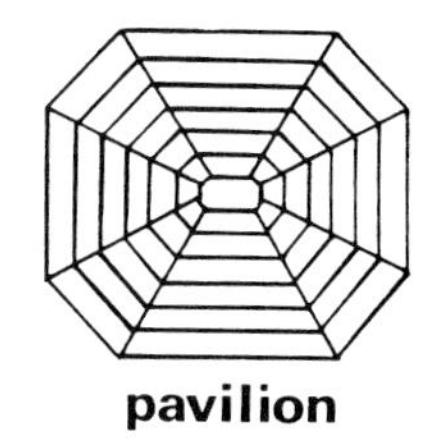


*Figure E.4* The emerald, trap or step cut.

**emerald filter** See ***Chelsea filter.***
**emeraldine** Trade name for dyed green chalcedony.
**emeraldite** A misleading name for green tourmaline.
**emerald malachite** A misleading name for dioptase.
**emerald matrix** A misleading name for green fluorspar.
**emeralite** A misleading name for pale green tourmaline.
**emerauldine** A misleading name for dioptase.
**emerita** Trade name for coated Lechleitner emerald simulants.
**emery** A coarse carborundum powder used for polishing.
**emildine** A South African spessartine garnet
**emilite** A South African spessartine garnet
**emission spectrum** A spectrum containing bright emission lines (as seen with a spectroscope). The bright lines are either characteristic of elements in an incandescent radiation source, or may be due to fluorescent effects (e.g. the emission lines seen in the spectrum of a fluorescent lamp or in chrome-rich red spinel). See also ***bright line spectrum.***
**enantiomorph** A crystal which has mirror image habits and optical characteristics, occurring in both right- and left-handed formations. *Figure E.5.*

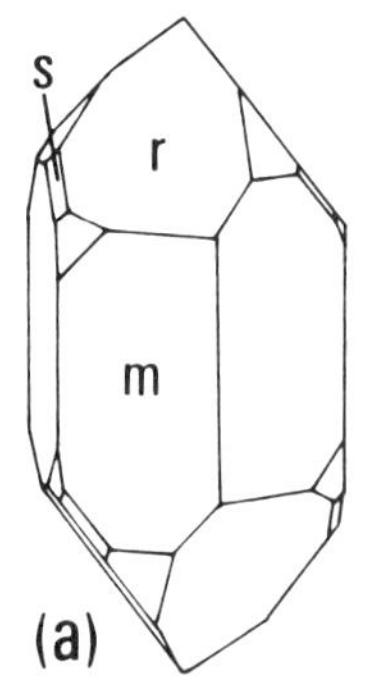


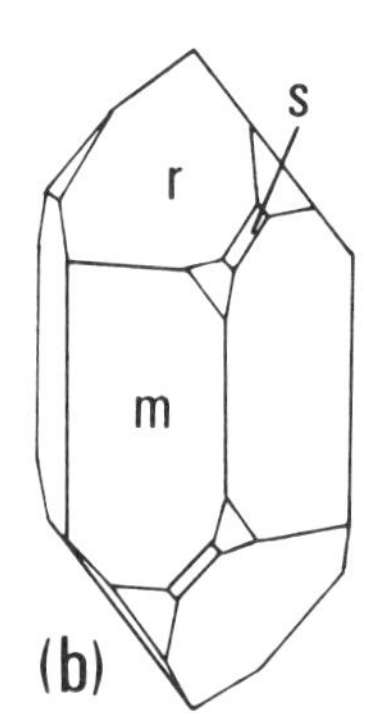


*Figure E.5* The property of enantiomorphism in quartz crytals. In the left-handed crystal (a) the trigonal pyramid 's' is situated in the upper left-hand corner of the prism face 'm' beneath the positive rhombohedron 'r'. In the right-handed crystal (b) the opposite occurs.

**encrinital marble** A marble with attractive mosaic-like markings produced by the fossilized remains of the stalks of crinoids (sea lilies). Occurrence: Derbyshire, England.
**endogenetic** A term applied to inclusions which were formed by or resulted from internal causes. See ***exogenetic.***
**endoscope** An optical instrument, now no longer available, designed for the identification of natural and cultured drilled

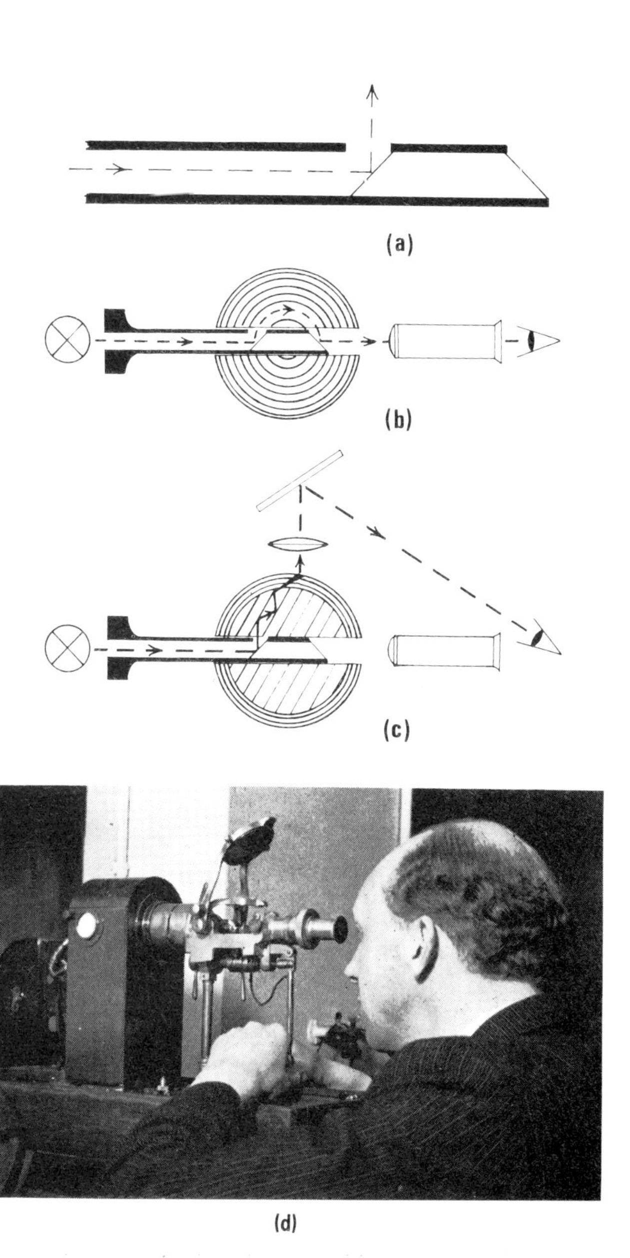


*Figure E.6* (a) The construction of the needle section of the endoscope. (b) A natural pearl is identified by its concentric layers, which channel light rays into the viewing telescope. (c) Light escapes through the mother-of-pearl bead in a cultured nucleated pearl and can be seen as a line of light on the pearl's surface. (d) The endoscope in use.

pearls (medical versions are used to view internal organs). An explanatory sketch, showing the main components of the pearl endoscope, can be seen in *Figure E.6.*

**endura emerald** A misleading name for a green glass simulant of emerald.

**enhydros** Also known as water agate, this is a cloudy-white chalcedony pebble containing sealed-in water. When an enhydros is shaken this water can be heard splashing in the cavity. Occurrence: Brazil, USA.

**enstatite** A magnesium-iron silicate. $(Mg,Fe)SiO_3$. Orthorhombic. R.I. 1.663, 1.673; D.R. +0.01; S.G. 3.26–3.28; H. 5½. Transparent to opaque, brownish-green, green, grey, bronze (called bronzite), grey-green cat's eye. Occurrence: Austria (bronzite), Burma, India (star enstatite), Norway, South Africa, Sri Lanka (cat's eye), USA.

**Eocene** A division of the Tertiary period of the Cenozoic era of geological time, 54–38 million years ago. See ***Cenozoic.***

**eosite** A close-grained carving quartzite of bluish-white colour with veins or splotches of brownish red. Occurrence: USSR.

**eosphorite** A collector's stone comprising a hydrated aluminium phosphate. $(Mn,Fe)AlPO_4(OH)_2.H_2O$. Monoclinic. R.I. 1.638, 1.667 to 1.639, 1.671; D.R. −0.029 to −0.032; S.G. 3.05; H. 5. Transparent, pale pink, yellow, yellowish-brown, brownish-pink. Pleochroism, strong in pink (yellowish, pale pink, colourless). Occurrence: Brazil.

**epiasterism** A star effect seen in reflected rather than transmitted light (e.g. in star rubies and sapphires). See also ***diasterism*** and ***sheen.***

**epidosite** See ***epidote.***

**epidote** A calcium aluminium silicate with some iron, also called pistacite. $Ca_2(Fe,Al,OH)Al_2(SiO_4)_3$. Monoclinic. R.I. 1.736, 1.770; D.R. −0.034; S.G. 3.4; H. 6½. Transparent to translucent, green, brownish-green, black-brown. Pleochroism, strong (green, brown, yellow). Occurrence: Austria, Mexico, Mozambique, Norway, USA.

**epigenetic inclusions** See ***inclusions*** (post-contemporary).

**Eppler brilliant cut** One of several 'ideal' cuts for diamond, mainly favoured in Europe. It has table facet width, crown depth and pavilion depth of 56%, 14.4% and 43.2% respectively compared with the girdle diameter. The crown angle is 33.17°, and the pavilion angle is 40.83°. See ***Johnson and Rösch brilliant cut, Parker brilliant cut, Scan DN brilliant cut*** and ***Tolkowsky brilliant cut.***

**Erb and Gray refractometer** The first gem refractometer to be designed and manufactured in the USA, this model had an eyepiece which pivoted to cover the scale range, and in its first version was fitted with a rotateable glass hemisphere.

**erinide** Trade name for a sythetic yellow-green spinel.

**erinite** Trade name for a synthetic yellow-green spinel.

**erinoid** Trade name for a casein-based plastic sometimes used as an amber simulant.

**Erste Österreichische Gemmologische Gesellschaft** Headquarters: Graben 12, 1010 Vienna, Austria.

**essence d'orient** Paste once made from the scales of a fish called a *bleak*. Imitation pearls made of glass or mother-of-pearl are dipped in the paste to give them a lustrous outer coating.

**essonite** A hessonite garnet.

**etching** The decoration of metal surfaces by means of controlled erosion achieved through the use of acids and alkalies. The metal surface is first coated with an etch-resistant layer (e.g. a resin or bituminous compound), and the decorative pattern is scratched through this layer prior to etching.

**etch pits** Pits or etch marks exhibited on the faces of crystals. These may be either raised or sunken features. They are due to solvent action on the crystal and are related in orientation to the underlying lattice structure (e.g. trigons on diamond crystals whose apices point to the edge of the octahedral face).

**ether** A colourless volatile liquid. $C_2H_5$-O-$C_2H_5$. Used as a test liquid to distinguish copal from amber. Copal is softened by ether, but amber is unaffected.

**ethylene dibromide** Liquid having a low surface tension which is sometimes used in place of water for specific gravity determinations by the hydrostatic weighing method. $C_2H_4Br_2$. (S.G. 2.1998 at 10°C; 2.1798 at 20°C). *Note: Care should be taken when using ethylene dibromide as it is a suspect carcinogenic liquid.*

**euban** Rock crystal variety of quartz.

**euclase** A collector's stone comprising the mineral beryllium aluminium silicate. $BeAl(SiO_4)OH$. Monoclinic. R.I. 1.652, 1.672; D.R. +0.02; S.G. 3.1; H. 7½. Transparent, colourless, pale green, pale blue, sapphire blue (rare). Occurrence: Brazil, Tanzania (colourless), USSR, Zimbabwe.

**euhedral** Term used to describe crystals having a well-formed characteristic shape.

**eureka can** A metal container, fitted with an overflow pipe, which is used to determine the specific gravity of solid specimens (method invented by Archimedes to assess the purity of gold). The container is first completely filled with water, and then the specimen is gently lowered into the can until it is fully immersed. The water displaced by the specimen through the overflow pipe is weighed and the S.G. of the specimen is calculated by dividing its weight by the weight of the water displaced.

**evening emerald** A misleading name for peridot.

**exceptional white** A CIBJO colour grade for polished diamonds. See ***Colour Grading Standards*** in Appendix B.

**exogenetic** A term applied to inclusions, which were formed by or resulted from external causes. See ***endogenetic.***

**extraordinary ray** Of the two polarized rays passing through a uniaxial crystal (i.e. one belonging to the tetragonal, hexagonal or trigonal crystal system), the extraordinary ray is the one whose velocity and associated R.I. ($\varepsilon$) varies according to its orientation in the crystal. When this ray produces a higher-value R.I. reading than the ordinary ray the gemstone is optically positive, when it produces a lower reading the stone is optically negative. See also ***ordinary ray*** and ***optic sign.***

**extrusive rock** An igneous rock formed by the rapid cooling of molten rock magma on the surface of the Earth (e.g. volcanic rock).

**eye agate** A variety of agate having bands in the form of concentric circles or as ovals.

**eye stone** See ***thomsonite.***

# F

**fabricated gemstones** See ***composite stones.***

**fabulite** Trade name for the man-made diamond simulant strontium titanate.

**facet** A flat surface polished on a gemstone.

**faceting head** A device for holding a gemstone while polishing it on a rotary lap or scaife. A faceting head may also include index stops for pre-setting the facet angles, and may form part of a semi- or fully-automatic faceting machine. See ***dop.***

**Fahrenheit temperature scale** A temperature scale used mainly for domestic purposes. The freezing point of water on this scale is 32 °F and its boiling point is 212 °F. To convert from the Fahrenheit to the Celsius (Centigrade) scale, subtract 32; then divide by 9 and multiply by 5.

$$C = (F - 32) \times \frac{5}{9}$$

**faience** A glazed siliceous material (originating from ancient Egypt) used for beads, pendants and rings, and in decorated earthenware and porcelain. It consists of a gritty inner core, probably of powdered quartz or steatite, and an outer coating of coloured glaze.

**fairburnite** See ***fortification agate.***

**fairy stone** See ***staurolite.***

**falcon's eye** See ***quartz.***

**fales** Any gemstone containing differently coloured layers.

**false amethyst** A misleading name for purple fluorspar.

**false chrysolite** A misleading name for moldavite.

**false cleavage** Also called pseudo-cleavage or parting, this occurs in gem minerals which, although they do not possess cleavage planes, have a direction of weakness called a parting plane. Parting is usually caused by secondary or lamellar twinning of the crystal, and occurs in ruby and labradorite.

**false diamond** A misleading name for the rock crystal variety of quartz.

**false doublet** A composite stone in which the gem material being imitated is totally absent.

**false emerald** Green fluorspar.

**false lapis** A misleading name for lazulite or dyed jasper.

**false topaz** A misleading name for citrine or yellow fluorspar.

**falun brilliants** Trade name for lead glass or paste imitation stones.

**fancy coloured diamonds** See ***diamond.***

**fancy cut** Any style of diamond cut other than the round brilliant or eight cut (e.g. emerald cut, marquise, oval, pear shape, heart shape, etc.)

**fancy pearls** Naturally coloured oriental pearls.

**fashoda garnet** A pyrope garnet.

**fatty amber** A type of amber which resembles goose fat owing to a cloudy appearance caused by included bubbles.

**fayalite** An iron silicate forming an end member of an isomorphous series containing peridot. $Fe_2SiO_4$. See ***peridot.***

**feather** See ***inclusions.***

**feather gypsum** Satin spar. See ***calcite.***

**feldspar** A group of gem mineral species comprising orthoclase and microcline, $KAlSi_3O_8$ (monoclinic), and plagioclase $(Ca,Na)Al_2Si_2O_8$ (triclinic).

Varieties:

*orthoclase* — adularia (transparent, colourless), moonstone (translucent, yellow and colourless with opalescence), orthoclase (transparent yellow). R.I. 1.520, 1.525; D.R. −0.005; S.G. 2.56-2.59; H. 6. Occurrence: Burma, India, the Malagasy Republic, Sri Lanka, USA.

*microcline* — amazonite (opaque green). R.I. 1.522, 1.530; D.R. −0.008; S.G. 2.56-2.58; H. 6½. Occurrence: Brazil, Canada, India.

*plagioclase* — andesine (opaque, jade-green), bytownite (reddish and pale yellow), labradorite (opaque, multi-coloured sheen and transparent yellow), albite moonstone (white, cream, fawn or brownish-pink with blue iridescence), oligoclase (transparent yellow), sunstone or aventurine feldspar (opaque to translucent, bronze or green spangled). R.I. 1.54, 1.55 to 1.56, 1.57; D.R. −0.01 (labradorite +0.008); S.G. 2.62-2.65; H. 6. Occurrence: Canada, USA, USSR.

**feldspar-apyre** A misleading name for andalusite.

**Fellow of the Gemmological Association** (FGA) A title awarded by the Gemmological Association of Great Britain to candidates who have passed the qualifying examinations. See ***Gemmological Association of Great Britain.***

**ferrer's emerald** A misleading trade name for a glass simulant of emerald. Also known as ferros emerald.

**ferric oxide** See ***jeweller's rouge.***

**ferrolite** Trade name for a black iron slag.

**ferros emerald** See ***ferrer's emerald.***

**FGA** A suffix used by qualified gemmologists who are Fellows of the Gemmological Association of Great Britain.

**FGAA** A suffix used by qualified gemmologists who are Fellows of the Gemmological Association of Australia.

**fibre optics** A technique for transmitting light by means of flexible glass or acrylic fibres which act as light guides. The light is channelled down the length of the guide by means of total internal reflection from the walls of the guide. When a large bundle of fibres is used to transmit, for example, a coherent image from one end to the other, light leakage or 'cross-talk' between the fibres is minimized by coating each one with a material of lower refractive index. In gemmology, non-coherent fibre optic light guides are used as a convenient means to channel light from a high-intensity source to the specimen under inspection (e.g. for microscopic or spectroscopic work).

**fibrolite** A rare stone which is polymorphous with andalusite and kyanite. Also called sillimanite, it comprises the mineral aluminium silicate. $Al_2SiO_5$. Orthorhombic. R.I. 1.658, 1.678; D.R. +0.02; S.G. 3.25; H. 6-7½. Transparent, blue, pale blue-green (chatoyant). Pleochroism, strong (green, dark green, blue). Occurrence: Burma, Sri Lanka, USA.

**fictile ivories** Castings made from plaster of Paris which are coloured with yellow ochre and coated with a mixture of wax, spermaceti or stearine.

**fictile mosaic** A mosaic used for walls and vaults in which pieces of opaque glass in small cubes are arranged to form a picture.

**filigree** Jewellery metalwork consisting of fine wires twisted into ornate patterns.

**filter** An optical component used to modify the spectrum or the polarization of light rays. Colour filters are used in spectroscopy to enhance spectral bands by eliminating unwanted sections of the spectrum. Polarizing filters are used with both the spectroscope and the refractometer to separate out the polarized rays emerging from doubly refracting gems. See also ***crossed filters, polarized light*** and ***UV lamps.***

**findings** The component metal parts which are used in the manufacture of jewellery.

**fine light brown** A colour grade for polished diamonds. See ***Colour Grading Standards*** in Appendix B.

**fine line spectra** See ***rare-earth spectra.***

**finest light brown** A colour grade for polished diamonds. See ***Colour Grading Standards*** in Appendix B.

**finest white** A UK colour grade for polished diamonds. See ***Colour Grading Standards*** in Appendix B.

**fine white** A UK colour grade for polished diamonds. See ***Colour Grading Standards*** in Appendix B.

**fingerprinting** A term used to describe various methods of positively identifying one polished diamond from another. These methods cover the use of a laser to produce a pattern of reflected and refracted light spots unique to the gem (Gemprint), the use of

X-ray topography to map its internal crystal features (De Beers), the photographing of surface-visible crystalline features by means of Nomarski interference contrast techniques (DGL Identiprint), and the printing of a metalized code on the table facet of the diamond (Okuda). See ***laser fingerprinting, X-ray topography*** and ***Nomarski interference contrast.***

**finish** The excellence of polish, freedom from external flaws and overall symmetry of a faceted diamond. Sometimes classified as the diamond's external clarity.

**fire** A term used to describe the effect of a gemstone's dispersion in splitting up white light into its spectral colours. Fire is particularly evident in highly dispersive colourless gems such as diamond and white zircon, although it can also be detected in coloured gems such as demantoid garnet and sphene. See ***dispersion.***

**fire agate** See ***chalcedony.***

**fired topaz** See ***heat treated stones.***

**fired zircon** See ***heat treated stones.***

**fire jade** A misleading name for a rock having the appearance of tiger's eye and containing mainly opal.

**fire marble** A rare fossil marble used for small ornamental objects. It is a dark brown marble containing small whitish shells which contain areas of iridescence similar to that of opal. Also known as lumachella (a word meaning little snail). Occurrence: Austria, USSR.

**fire marks** Small cracks seen at the edges of facets, particularly in corundum. They are caused by overheating due to too rapid polishing.

**fire opal** See ***opal.***

**fire pearl** A misleading trade name for billitonite.

**firestones** Rock crystal which has had cracks induced in it artificially by heating. Natural cracked quartz is known as ***rainbow quartz*** or ***iris quartz.***

**first bye** See ***bye.***

**first water** A comparative term used occasionally to denote a top colour / top quality diamond or other gemstone; a slightly lower quality stone is described as one of the second water.

**fisheye** An optical effect caused by the reflection of the girdle through the table facet in a diamond having a shallow pavilion.

**fish-eye stone** See ***apophyllite.***

**fissure** An elongated cavity, fracture or cleavage fault in the surface or in the body of a gemstone.

**FL** A clarity grade for polished diamonds meaning flawless. A similar grade IF means internally flawless. See ***Clarity Grading Standards*** in Appendix C.

**flame-fusion process** See ***Verneuil furnace.***

**flame spectrum** A spectrum produced by spectroscopic analysis of a bunsen flame coloured by a sample of the specimen. See ***bright-line spectrum.***

**flame spinel** An orange-red natural spinel.

**flash opal** An opal with a single-colour flash of iridescence.

**flats** A shape category for rough diamonds comprising flat irregular-shaped or triangular stones. See also ***chips, cleavages, macles, melée, shapes*** and ***stones.***

**flaw** A surface or internal fracture or cleavage in a gemstone. May also be applied to an inclusion or a polishing defect.

**flawless** A gemstone free from both external flaws and from internal flaws or inclusions. Also a clarity grade for polished diamonds, often abbreviated as IF (internally flawless) or FL. See ***Clarity Grading Standards*** in Appendix C.

**flêche d'amour** See ***sagenitic quartz.***

**flinder's diamond** A misleading name for colourless topaz.

**flint** Silica concretions.

**flint glass** A glass containing lead oxide, which produces a large dispersion. Also called lead glass, it is used for paste or imitation stones. See also ***crown glass*** and ***Bannister's graph.***

**Florence marble** See ***ruin marble.***

**Florentine mosaic** Also known as intasia and pietra dura, this is a mosaic made up from small pieces of coloured stone (coral, lapis lazuli, malachite, marble, turquoise). These are cemented into a recess cut into a slab of usually black marble to form a picture.

**flower agate** A chalcedony with flower-like inclusions.

**flowering obsidian** A variety of black obsidian containing rounded vitreous inclusions of a white mineral. Also known as snowflake obsidian. Occurrence: USA. See ***obsidian.***

**fluor** See ***fluorspar.***

**fluorescence** A form of luminescence which, like phosphorescence, can be stimulated in some gemstones by the application of energy (e.g. light, UV, X-rays, etc.). Fluorescence ceases immediately the source of energy is removed, but phosphorescence persists for some time afterwards. See ***luminescence.***

**fluoride coating** Used to improve the colour of a yellow diamond. See ***treated diamonds.***

**fluorite** The mineralogical name for fluorspar.

**fluorspar** A calcium fluoride. $CaF_2$. Cubic. R.I. 1.434; S.G. 3.18; H. 4. Transparent, colourless, blue, violet, green, yellow, orange, red. Fluorescence strong under LW UV in most varieties (none in the 'Blue John' variety from Derbyshire, England). Occurrence: Canada, Czechoslovakia, Germany, Italy, Poland, Switzerland, UK, USA.

**flux** A borax-based compound used to facilitate soldering and brazing by preventing the heated metal surface from becoming oxidized.

**flux-fusion process** See ***flux-melt process.***

**flux-melt process** Also known as flux-fusion, this is a method of growing synthetic crystals using a high melting point solvent or flux. The constituent or source materials are dissolved in the flux. Seed crystals of the material to be synthesized are then lowered into the flux, and its temperature reduced to a point where it becomes supersaturated. At this point the source material is precipitated out and grows on the seed crystals. Crystals grown by this method include synthetic emerald, ruby, spinel, quartz, alexandrite and the rare-earth garnets. *Figure F.1.* See also ***flame fusion process*** and ***Verneuil furnace.***

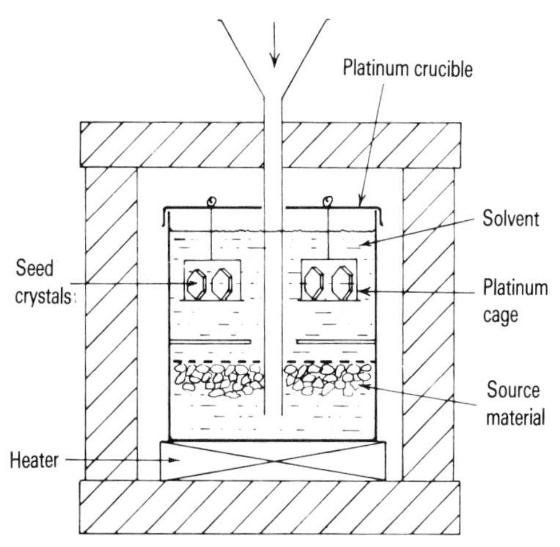


*Figure F.1* The flux melt process is used to grow synthetic emerald crystals from source material dissolved in a lithium molybdate flux. The source materials consist of beryllium and aluminium oxides, with chromium as a colouring agent, and slabs of silica glass, which is floated on top of the flux.

**focal length** When incident parallel rays are brought to a focus by a lens, the distance from the centre of the lens to the point of focus is called the focal length *(f)*. In a convex lens, the focal point is on the opposite side of the lens to the parallel incident light, and the lens is said to have a positive focal length. In a concave lens, the focal point is on the same side as the incident light and the lens has a negative focal length.

**foiled stone** A gemstone mounted with a backing of silver or coloured foil to improve its brilliance or enhance its colour. See also ***chatons.***

**fool's gold** See ***pyrites.***

**fortification agate** An agate containing markings which are similar in appearance to the outline of a fortress.

**form** A group of similar crystal faces. A form made up entirely of identical interchangeable faces is called a closed form (e.g. a cube or octahedron). A form which is only completed by the addition of other forms is called an open form.

**form birefringence** The small double refraction sometimes measured in a singly-refractive or cryptocrystalline substance which also contains a material of different refractive index (e.g. chalcedony).

**forsterite** A magnesium silicate forming an end member of an isomorphous series containing peridot. $Mg_2SiO_4$. See ***peridot.***

**fossil** Vestiges of an ancient animal or plant preserved (usually by petrification) in the Earth.

**fossil coral** A chalcedony pseudomorph in which the coral structure has been replaced by agate.

**fossil ivory** An ivory obtained from the tusks of mammoths (i.e. large extinct elephants) whose bodies have been preserved in frozen mud. Occurrence: Canada, USSR (Siberia). See also ***odontolite.***

**fossil marble** Marble containing the remains of shells, corals and crinoids or sea lilies.

**fossil opal** An opal pseudomorph of wood (also called petrified wood), freshwater shells, sea shells or bones.

**fossil pineapple** An opal pseudomorph replacing crystals of gay-lussite, glauberite or gypsum.

**fossil resin** See ***amber.***

**fossil turquoise** A misleading name for odontolite.

**fossil wood** A chalcedony pseudomorph in which the wood fibres have been replaced by agate. Also called petrified wood. See also *opal* (wood opal).

**four 'C's of diamond grading** Polished diamonds are graded, among other things, for *colour, clarity, cut* and *carat* weight.

**four-point** A cutting orientation for diamond where the table is polished parallel to a possible cube face (i.e. parallel to the octahedron's pyramid-based natural girdle). See ***three-point*** and ***two-point.***

**fowlerite** See ***rhodonite.***

**fracture** The manner in which a gemstone breaks (other than by cleavage or parting). The type of fracture can sometimes be a useful identifying feature. Typical types of fracture are:

*conchoidal* — a shell-like fracture seen in glass, quartz and the garnets, *splintery* — long fibrous splinters seen in jadeite, nephrite and ivory,

*hackly or uneven* — typical of the broken surface of rocks and of amber,

*smooth or even* — although not flat as with a cleavage, this type of fracture has no identifiable irregularities and can often be seen in rough diamonds.

**framesite** See ***boart.***

**Fraunhofer lines** If daylight is viewed through a spectroscope, its spectrum will contain a series of fine absorption lines. These lines are called Fraunhofer lines and are due mainly to the absorption of certain characteristic wavelengths by the vapour of various elements in the chromosphere surrounding the sun (see *Figure F.2*

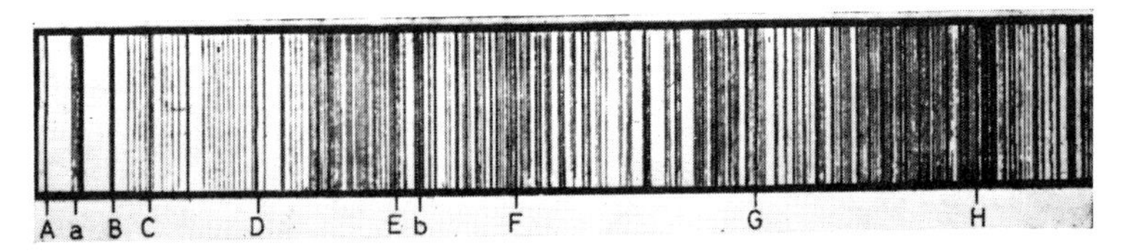


*Figure F.2* Reproduction of one of Fraunhofer's drawings of the solar spectrum.

and ***Table of Principal Fraunhofer Lines*** in Appendix J). In gemmology the Fraunhofer B line (caused by oxygen in the Earth's atmosphere) and G line (caused by calcium) are used as standard wavelengths for measuring the dispersion of a gem. The B line is in the red at 686.7 nm, and the G is in the blue at 430.8 nm.

**free pearls** Pearls not attached to the mollusc's shell. Also known as cyst or mantle pearls.

**French colour rubies** Light red rubies.

**French Gemmological Association** See ***Association Française de Gemmologie.***

**French jet** A black glass used as a jet simulant. Also called Vauxhall glass.

**frequency** A measure of the propagation characteristic of an electro-magnetic wave in terms of the number of cycles or oscillations per second (Hz).

$$\text{Frequency in megahertz (MHz)} = \frac{300 \times 10^9}{\text{nanometres}}$$

$$\text{Frequency} = \frac{\text{Velocity}}{\text{Wavelength}}$$

See ***electromagnetic spectrum.***

**freshwater pearls** Pearls found in various clam and mussel species in rivers and lakes in Canada, Scandinavia and the UK.

**Fresnel's reflectivity equation** A complex equation relating the reflectivity of a transparent isotropic mineral in air with the refractive index of the mineral. In a simplified version of the equation which gives the relationship for normal (i.e. 90 degree) incidence:

$$\text{Reflectivity} = \frac{I}{I_0} = \frac{(n-a)^2}{(n+a)^2}$$

where $I$ = intensity of reflected ray
$I_0$ = intensity of incident ray
$n$ = R.I. of gem
$a$ = R.I. of surrounding medium (for air = 1).

**frictional electricity** Also known as static or tribo-electricity, this is an electrostatic charge which can be generated on various materials by rubbing them. Amber, diamond, topaz and tourmaline are triboelectric materials.

**friedelite** A collector's stone comprising the mineral manganese silicate. $(Mn,Fe)_8(OH,Cl)_{10}Si_6O_{15}$. Trigonal. R.I. 1.63, 1.66; D.R. −0.03; S.G. 3.06-3.07; H. 4-5. Transparent to opaque, rose-red, orange-red. Occurrence: France, Sweden, USA.

**frit** A calcined mixture of sand and fluxes used in glass making. In ancient Egypt a frit consisting of a crystalline compound of silica, a copper compound, calcium carbonate and soda was used as a turquoise simulant.

**frost agate** An agate with white markings. Also called frost stone.

**frost stone** See ***frost agate.***

**frosted diamonds** Diamonds with a matt surface. Unlike coated diamonds, the surface of a frosted diamond is a thin film integral with the stone.

**fuchsite mica** A green chrome mica present in green aventurine quartz. See ***mica.***

**fukien jade** A misleading name for soapstone.

**fulgurites** Also known as lightning tubes, these are thin tubes of fused sand produced in the desert by the intense heat of a lightning strike.

**furnace slag** A lumpy vitreous material containing dark coloured stripes and patches, which may be mistaken for obsidian. S.G. in region of 2.82.

**fused beryl** See ***beryl glass.***

**fused quartz** An amorphous silica made by fusing crystalline quartz. R.I. 1.45; S.G. 2.21.

**fused sand glass** See ***fulgurites.***

**futuran** Trade name for a phenolic resin plastic.

**GA** See ***Gemmological Association of Great Britain.***

**GAA** See ***Gemmological Association of Australia.***

**GAAJ** See ***Gemmological Association of All Japan.***

**gabbro** A blackish-green basic rock of crystalline texture which is low in silica content but rich in magnesium.

**gadolinium gallium garnet** (GGG) A man-made diamond simulant (originally developed as a substrate for computer bubble memories) introduced in 1973. It has no counterpart in nature. $Gd_3Ga_5O_{12}$. Cubic. R.I. 1.97; S.G. 7.05; H. 6.

**gagat** See ***jet.***

**gahnite** A collector's stone comprising the mineral zinc alumina. $ZnOAl_2O_3$. Cubic. R.I. 1.794 - 1.805; S.G. 3.58-4.58; H. 7½-8. Transparent to opaque, blue, reddish-violet, green. Occurrence: Found in zinc deposits worldwide.

**gahnospinel** A blue spinel containing a high proportion of zinc. R.I. values of 1.725-1.753, and S.G. values of 3.58-4.06 are higher than for normal spinels.

**galalith** Trade name for a casein plastic sometimes used as an amber simulant.

**galliant** Trade name for the man-made diamond simulant gadolinium gallium garnet (GGG).

**gamma alumina** A cubic form of aluminium oxide used in the Verneuil flame-fusion production of synthetic corundum. It is produced by re-crystallizing ammonium alum from solution in water until it is pure, and then calcining it in a furnace at 1100 °C. The calcining drives off ammonia and sulphur dioxide gases to leave pure gamma alumina. See ***Verneuil furnace.***

**gamma radiation** Electromagnetic rays of very short wavelength with very high penetration properties. Gamma rays are indistinguishable from X-rays and differ only in the way they are produced (i.e. from radioactive substances). See also ***alpha particles*** and ***beta particles.***

**gangue** Unwanted residue from which a gem concentrate is extracted.

**garden** An inclusion effect produced by complicated combinations of liquid-filled droplets and threads together with variously shaped crystals.

**garnet** An isomorphous series of gem minerals forming (with the feldspar group) one of the two main groups of gemstones species comprising aluminium, calcium, chromium, iron, magnesium, manganese and iron silicates. Cubic. Species:

*almandine* (purplish-red). $Fe_3Al_2(SiO_4)_3$. R.I. 1.77-1.81; S.G. 3.8-4.2; H. 7½.

*andradite* $Ca_3Fe_2(SiO_4)_3$. Varieties, demantoid (green) yellow andradite, melanite (black). R.I. 1.89; S.G. 3.85; H. 6½.

*grossular* $Ca_3Al_2(SiO_4)_3$. Varieties, hessonite (orange-brown, green, pink), massive grossular or hydrogrossular (jade-green, also known as African jade), tsavolite (transparent green). R.I. 1.74; S.G. 3.63-3.68; H. 6½.

*pyrope* (blood-red). $Mg_3Al_2(SiO_4)_3$. R.I. 1.75-1.77; S.G. 3.7-3.8; H. 7½.

*spessartine* (orange, yellow, flame-red). $Mn_3Al_2(SiO_4)_3$. R.I. 1.80; S.G. 4.16; H. 7.

*uvarovite* (emerald-green). $Ca_3Cr_2(SiO_4)_3$. R.I. 1.87; S.G. 3.77; H. 7½.

Occurrence: *almandine,* Austria, Brazil, China, Czechoslovakia, Sri Lanka; *andradite,* Switzerland (yellow variety), USSR (demantoid); *grossular,* Canada, South Africa (hydrogrossular), Sri Lanka (especially hessonite); *pyrope,* Australia, Czechoslovakia, South Africa; *spessartite,* Brazil, the Malagasy Republic, Sri Lanka, USA; *uvarovite,* Canada, Finland, Poland, USA, USSR.

**garnet jade** A misleading name for massive green grossular garnet.

**garnet-topped doublets** See ***composite stones.***

**gauge plate** A device for estimating the weight of mounted and unmounted gemstones. See ***diamond gauge.***

**gava gem** Trade name for a synthetic rutile diamond simulant.

**gedanite** A soft light variety of amber found in Northern Germany. It contains very little succinic acid. S.G. 1.02; H. 1½-2.

**geiger counter** An instrument for detecting and counting ionizing particles emitted from radioactive materials, and used to measure the strength of their radioactivity. Can be used to detect radioactivity in ekanite and in some zircons.

**gel** A solid or semi-solid colloidal solution or jelly.

**gem** A material possessing the necessary qualities of beauty, rarity and durability for use in jewellery. Such material can be of inorganic (i.e. mineral) or organic origin.

**Gem and Mineral Society of Zimbabwe** Headquarters: P.O. Box 712, Harare (formerly Salisbury), Zimbabwe.

**gem cutter** See ***lapidary.***

**gem diamonds** Rough diamonds whose colour, quality and shape make them suitable for use in jewellery as polished stones. See also ***near gem*** and ***industrial diamonds.***

**gemerald** Trade name for a beryl doublet or a beryl coated with synthetic emerald.

**gem gravels** Alluvial gem deposits associated with existing or ancient river courses.

**geminair** Trade name for the man-made diamond simulant yttrium aluminium garnet.

**Gem Instruments Corporation** A subsidiary of the Gemological Institute of America. Headquarters: 1735 Stewart Street, P.O. Box 2147, Santa Monica, CA 90406, USA.

**Gemmological Association and Gem Testing Laboratory of Great Britain** Founded in 1908 as the Education Committee of the National Association of Goldsmiths, it was reconstituted in 1931 as the Gemmological Association. It is affiliated with the Gemmological Association of Australia, the Canadian Gemmological Association and the Gem and Mineral Society of Zimbabwe. Fellowship of the Association is gained by taking a two-year course (evening class or correspondence) and passing the Association's Preliminary and Diploma examinations. Headquarters: 27 Greville Street (Saffron Hill entrance), London EC1N 8SU, UK.

**Gemmological Association of All Japan** Headquarters: Tokyo Bihokaikan, 1-24 Akashi-cho, Chuo-ku, Tokyo, Japan. See also ***Gemological Association of Japan*** and ***Gemmological Society of Japan.***

**Gemmological Association of All Korea** Headquarters: c/o Mi Jo Gem Study Institute, No. 244-39 Hoo Am-Dong, Yong San Ku, Seoul, Korea. See also ***Gemmological Institute of Korea.***

**Gemmological Association of Australia** Qualified gemmologists in the Association use the suffix FGAA. Headquarters (Victoria branch): P.O. Box 5133AA, Melbourne 3001, Victoria, Australia.

**Gemmological Association of Hong Kong** Headquarters: University of Hong Kong, Department of Physics, Hong Kong.

**Gemmological Association of Switzerland** Headquarters: Multergasse 20, CH-9000, St Gallen, Switzerland.

**Gemmological Institute of India** Headquarters: 29/30 Gurukul Chambers, 187/9 Mumbaderi Road, Bombay 2, India.

**Gemmological Institute of Korea** Headquarters: 30-7, 3-ka, Namdaemunro, Chungku, Seoul, Korea. See also ***Gemmological Association of All Korea.***

**Gemmological Instruments Ltd** A subsidiary of the Gemmological Association of Great Britain. Headquarters: St Dunstan's House, Carey Lane, London EC2V 8AB, UK.

**Gemmological Society of Japan** Headquarters: Institute of Mineralogy, Petrology and Economic Geology, Tohoku University, Aoba, Sendai, Japan 980. See also ***Gemmological Association of All Japan*** and ***Gemological Association of Japan.***

**gemmologist** A qualified specialist in the science of gem materials. See ***CG, FGA, FGAA,*** and ***GG.***

**Gemmologists' Association of Sri Lanka** Headquarters: 63 Bristol

Buildings, York Street, Colombo 1, Sri Lanka.

**Gemological Association of Japan** Headquarters: Kaneku Building, 3-27-11 Yushima, Bankyo-ku, Tokyo 113, Japan. See also ***Gemmological Association of All Japan*** and ***Gemmological Society of Japan.***

**Gemological Institute of America** An endowed non-profit jewellers' organization founded in 1931, this has become the educational, research and testing centre of the jewellery industry in the USA. Correspondence and residential courses run by the Institute lead to the qualification Graduate Gemologist (GG). Headquarters: 1660 Stewart Street, P.O. Box 2110, Santa Monica, CA 90406, USA.

**gemmology** The science of gem materials.

**gem refractometer** See ***refractometer.***

**Gem Society of Ceylon** Headquarters: Melbourne Estate, Tummodera, Sri Lanka.

**gem stick** A wooden stick with a metal collet at the end which is used by a lapidary to hold a rough gemstone while cutting its facets on a rotating lap or grind-stone. The gemstone is held in the collet by a special cement.

**gemstone** A polished mineral which possesses the necessary qualities of beauty, rarity and durability for use in jewellery.

**gemstone constants** Constants such as refractive index, double refraction, specific gravity and hardness which enable a gemstone to be identified.

**gemstone cuts** See ***antique cut*** (cushion), ***brilliant cut*** (round, marquise/navette, oval, pear-shape), ***baguette*** (baton), ***cabochon, emerald cut*** (trap), ***rose cut*** (Antwerp rose/Brabant) and ***scissors cut*** (cross).

**Geneva rubies** Once thought to be made by fusing together smaller fragments of natural ruby, these were originally called *reconstructed* rubies. More recent analysis of surviving specimens has indicated that the rubies were more probably manufactured by an early form of flame-fusion process, using powdered alumina (or even powdered natural ruby) rather than fragments of the natural gemstone.

**geode** An igneous occurrence in which gem minerals are precipitated as crystals in almost spherical cavities formed by molten or aqueous residues trapped in the cooling magma. Owing to their shape when removed from the rock formation they are also called potato stones. See also ***druse*** and ***vug.***

**geological eras** See ***Precambrian, Palaeozoic, Mesozoic*** and ***Cenozoic.***

**geology** Science of the structure and composition of the Earth's crust.

**georgiatite** A variety of tektite found near Georgia, USA. See ***moldavite.***

**German diamond** A misleading name for the rock crystal variety of quartz.

**German Gemmological Association** See ***Deutsche Gemmologische Gesellschaft.***

**German lapis** Also called Swiss lapis, this is a blue-stained jasper used as a simulant for lapis lazuli.

**German mocoas** Trade name for a moss agate simulant.

**German silver** A misleading name for a white alloy of nickel, copper and zinc. Also called nickel silver.

**geschenite** An apple green beryl rich in sodium.

**geuda stones** 'Geuda' is a term applied to Sri Lankan stones (mainly blue sapphires, but also rubies) which have a milky-white opaline appearance due to a network of inclusions (usually rutile). With some of these stones (called 'diesel' geudas) it is possible to improve their colour dramatically by means of heat treatment, the rutile being absorbed into the crystal lattice to enhance the blue of the sapphire.

**GG** A suffix used by qualified gemmologists who have passed the examinations of the Gemological Institute of America.

**GGG** See ***gadolinium gallium garnet.***

**GIA** See ***Gemological Institute of America.***

**giant conch** A pearl-producing marine mollusc found along the coast of Florida and the West Indies, and in the Gulf of California, Mexico. The giant conch (*Strombus gigas*) is a source of pink pearls, and its shell is used for cameo carving.

**Gibraltar stone** A stalagmitic deposit found in limestone caves around the Rock of Gibraltar. The stone is a translucent calcite with brown and amber-coloured wavy veins. It is polished as cabochons and used for small ornamental objects.

**gibsonite** A pink variety of thomsonite.

**gibsonville emerald** A misleading name for green quartz.

**gidgee opal** An opal variety cut from the opal and ironstone impregnated roots of the gidgee (acacia) tree. S.G. 2.65-3.00.

**gilding** The application of a fine layer of gold to an article. Originally, this was effected by coating the article with a layer of gold/mercury amalgam, and then applying heat to drive off the mercury. Present-day gilding is mainly applied by electro-plating.

**Gilson synthetic stones** Stones manufactured by Pierre Gilson SA of Aire, France.

*Gilson synthetic emerald* — a synthetic emerald grown by the flux-melt process. R.I. 1.560, 1.563; D.R. −0.003; S.G. 2.65; H. 7½ (R.I., D.R. and S.G. may be higher in more recent material).

*Gilson synthetic lapis lazuli* — a synthetic lapis lazuli which has the mineral lazurite as its chief ingredient. S.G. 2.36.

*Gilson synthetic opal* — a synthetic black or white variety of opal made by dehydrating a sodium silicate or a silicon ester. H. 4½.

*Gilson synthetic turquoise* — a turquoise simulant made from a copper phosphate and calcite. R.I. 1.592; S.G. 2.635. (Recent analysis has shown calcite to be the main component, and this material is therefore more correctly designated as a simulant.)

**giogetto** A variety of black opal.

**girasol** A fire opal or water opal. See ***opal.***

**girasol** Trade name for glass used in the manufacture of imitation pearl beads.

**girasol pearl** An imitation glass pearl.

**girasol sapphire** A cat's eye sapphire.

**girdle** The outer circumference of a polished gemstone which separates the top, or crown, from the base, or pavilion.

**girdle facets** Small facets which are polished on the curved face of a diamond's girdle to improve the overall brilliance of the stone.

**girdle facets** The triangular facets which are adjacent to the girdle on a brilliant-cut stone. There are 16 such facets above the girdle and 16 below. Also called upper and lower girdle or break facets, skill facets, skew facets and cross facets. See ***brilliant cut.***

**glass** For man-made glasses, see ***Bannister's graph, crown glass*** and ***flint glass.*** For natural glasses, see ***obsidian, Libyan glass, moldavite*** and ***tektite.***

**glass agate** A misleading name for obsidian.

**glassies** A term used to describe well-shaped, transparent and clear octahedral diamond crystals.

**glass lava** See ***obsidian.***

**glass opal** See ***hyalite.***

**glass S.G. indicators** Small glass discs made in a range of specific gravity values for the purpose of blending heavy liquids to precise values of S.G. Also used to check the S.G. of these liquids before use. *Figure G.1.*

**glass stone** See ***axinite.***

**glets** A cleavage crack in a diamond which resembles a feather. Also called a gles.

**glyptography** The art and science of gem carving and engraving.

**gneiss** A coarse-grained banded metamorphic rock containing quartz, feldspar and mica.

**goethite** A hydrated iron oxide. $Fe_2O_3.H_2O$. Red or orange platy crystals of goethite when present as inclusions in plagioclase feldspar produce the sunstone variety.

**gold** A precious metallic element used in jewellery (especially as a

*Figure G.1* A set of calibrated glass specific gravity indicators. (Rayner/ Gemmological Instruments Ltd.)

mount for gems). Au. Atomic number, 79; atomic weight 197.2; melting point 1063 °C; S.G. 19.3. Because of the relative softness of the pure metal, gold is usually alloyed with silver and other metals when used in jewellery (see ***carat***).

**gold alloys** See ***carat.***

**gold amalgam** A plastic combination of gold and mercury used in gilding.

**golded jade** See ***hornbill ivory.***

**golden quartz** Heat treated amethyst, also known as *burnt amethyst. See* ***heat-treated stones.***

**gold filled** A misleading illegal description in the UK of a composite jewellery metal made by bonding a layer of gold alloy to each side of silver or a base metal alloy (usually brass). In the USA, the term gold filled is used for a higher grade of rolled gold in which the total thickness of the gold layers is at least 1/20th of the overall thickness (below 1/20th it is called rolled gold). See ***rolled gold.***

**gold foil** Gold beaten into a thin sheet (thicker than gold leaf).

**gold leaf** Gold beaten into a very thin almost translucent sheet (thinner than gold foil) and used for decorative purposes.

**gold opal** See ***opal*** (fire opal).

**gold quartz** A milky quartz containing flecks of native gold.

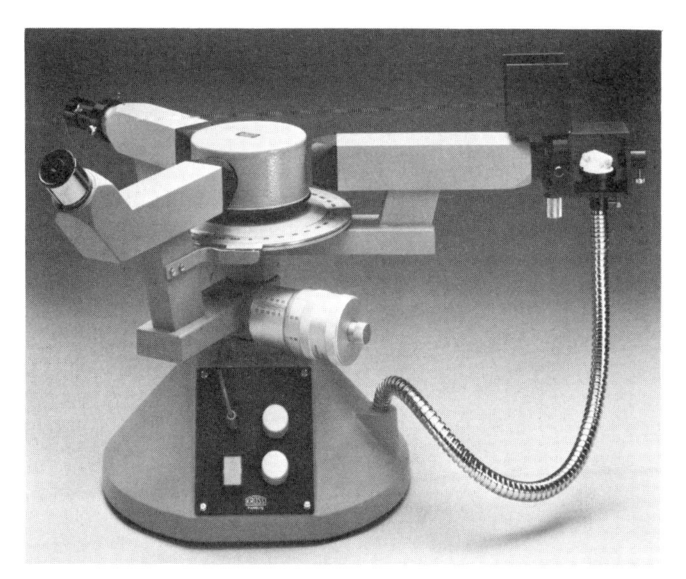

*Figure G.2* A modern version of the goniometer, with the addition of a wavelength scale (far side of shrouded table), and a gemstone holder (far right) which enables the instrument to be used as a spectroscope. The light source is built into the base unit, and light is channelled to the gemstone holder via a glass-fibre light guide. (Krüss).

**gold sapphire.** A misleading name for lapis lazuli.

**gold solder** Usually 2-4 carats lower in gold content than the gold it is used to solder, this is a gold-silver-copper alloy to which a small quantity of zinc (3.5-8%) and cadmium (5%) may be added to further lower the melting point. Variations in proportions are : gold (37.5-65%) silver (15-40%) and copper (14-25%).

**goldstone** Also called aventurine glass, this is a man-made glass simulant of the sunstone or aventurine variety of plagioclase feldspar and of aventurine quartz. It consists of a soda-lime glass coloured by cuprous oxide which precipitates out as thin triangular or hexagonal plates of crystalline copper. R.I. 1.53; S.G. 2.5-2.8.

**gold topaz** A misleading name for golden quartz.

**goniometer** An instrument for measuring angles between the faces of crystal specimens. Also called a reflecting goniometer and table spectrometer, it consists basically of a light source/collimator, a table for supporting the specimen, and a radially-pivoted telescope viewer having an eyepiece fitted with cross-wires. The position of the telescope, relative to the collimator, can be read off a scale on the table. The instrument is also used for measuring dispersion and R.I. (see ***angle of minimum deviation***). *Figure G.2.*

*Figure G.3* The GIA DiamondLite provides daylight-type illumination and a neutral background for the colour grading of polished diamonds (Gem Instruments Corp.)

**goshenite** See ***beryl.***

**grading of pearls** Pearls are graded for colour, which ranges from white to silver and yellowish. Fancy coloured pearls are those with a strong colour, such as rose-pink, green, blue, yellow, bronze and black. Pearls are also graded into shape categories which range from spherical and pear-shaped drop pearls, to irregularly-shaped baroque pearls. Drilled pearls are prepared for marketing by stringing each size on a silk thread. A number of sizes suitable for making up into graduated necklaces are strung together and are known as a Bombay bunch.

**grading standards (diamonds)** See under ***grading standards*** in Appendices B and C.

**grading lamps** Colour-corrected 'daylight' grading lamps are mainly used for colour grading diamonds (as an alternative to the use of 'north light'). The colour temperature of these lamps is chosen to simulate 'north sky' daylight. The lamps are sometimes enclosed in a cabinet which provides a neutral white background for comparison grading. *Figure G.3.* See also ***diamond grading lamp*** and *Figure 7* in Appendix B.

**Graduate Gemologist** (GG) A title awarded by the Gemological

Institute of America to candidates who have passed the qualifying examinations. See ***Gemological Institute of America.***

**grain** The grain of a diamond's crystal structure refers mainly to its cleavage direction. It is also used to refer to sawing and polishing directions. Diamonds are cleaved parallel to the four octahedral faces. Sawing is mainly done across the grain, parallel to the cubic plane.

**grain (diamond and pearl)** A unit of weight used with rough diamonds and pearls. 1 grain = 0.25 metric carat.

**grain (gold)** A unit of weight used for precious metals. 1 ounce troy = 480 grain. 1 tola = 0.375 ounce troy = 180 grain.

**gram** A unit of weight equivalent to five metric carats.

**grammatite** See ***tremolite.***

**grandidierite** A rare collector's stone comprising the mineral iron aluminium magnesium silicate. Orthorhombic. R.I. 1.602, 1.639; D.R. −0.037; S.G. 3.0 H. 7½. Transparent, bluish-green. Pleochroism, strong. Occurrence: The Malagasy Republic.

**granite** A granular igneous rock composed of feldspar, quartz and mica.

**graphite** One of the crystalline forms of carbon (diamond being another). Graphite crystallizes in the hexagonal system. Because of the loose bonding between its molecular layers, it has perfect cleavage. The 'slip' between these layers makes it useful as a lubricant. S.G. 2.25.

**grating spectroscope** See ***spectroscope.***

**grease belt** A development of the grease table to facilitate the continuous separation of diamonds from rock and gravel. Because diamond is non-wettable, it sticks to grease. The continuously rotating belt has a layer of grease applied to it at one end, and this is scraped off at the other end. The diamond bearing gravels are washed across the central span of the belt, the diamonds sticking to the grease and the bulk of the gravels washing over. The recovered grease is then melted to release the diamonds. See ***grease table.***

**grease table** An early method of recovering diamonds from gravel and crushed rock, which is still in use in some mines. Because diamond is non-wettable, it sticks to grease. The grease table consists of a series of vibrating wooden slats which are coated with grease (*Figure G.4*). The diamond-bearing concentrate is washed over the slats, the diamonds becoming embedded in the grease and the bulk of the gravels being washed over. The diamonds are then recovered from the grease by being loaded into a perforated metal container and heated. See also ***grease belt.***

**greasy** See ***lustre.***

**greened amethyst** Either a green synthetic quartz, grown in a

*Figure G.4* Removing individual diamonds from a grease table in Kimberley, South Africa. (De Beers).

reducing atmosphere with iron as the additive or a gem produced by heating naturally-occurring amethyst.

**green garnet** A misleading name for enstatite.

**green gold** A green-tinted gold alloy containing silver and zinc.

**green john** A massive green variety of fluorspar.

**green onyx** A misleading name for green stained chalcedony.

**Greenough microscope** A type of microscope which provides stereoscopic vision (and an upright image) by using paired objectives linked to inclined binocular eyepieces. See ***magnifiers.***

**green quartz** A misleading name for green fluorite.

**green rouge** A chromium oxide abrasive powder used for polishing gemstones.

**green starstone** See ***chlorastrolite.***

**greenstone** See ***nephrite.***

**green stone** A misleading name for chlorastrolite.

**grenalite** See ***staurolite.***

**grenz rays** Soft (i.e. low energy) X-rays of long wavelength (0.5-1.0 nm). Also called infra-röntgen rays.

**Griqualandite** See ***quartz*** (tiger's eye variety).

**grinding** The abrasive removal of material when preforming and polishing a gemstone.

**grit** Diamond powders produced for gemstone polishing and industrial uses. May be of natural (see ***bourt***) or synthetic origin.

**grossular garnet** See ***garnet.***

**grospydite** A rock consisting of the minerals grossular garnet, pyroxene and kyanite.

**groups** As an aid to classification, mineral species are gathered together into a series of groups, each of which contains species having similar features or characteristics. In gemmology there are two groups, and these contain the feldspar and garnet gemstones. See ***species*** and ***varieties.***

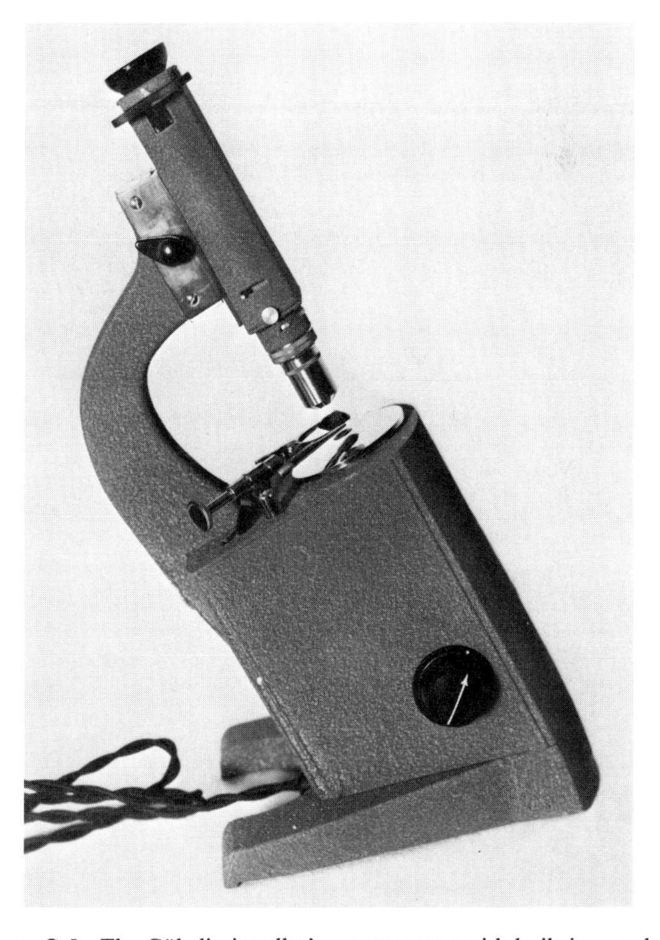

*Figure G.5* The Gübelin jeweller's spectroscope with built-in wavelength and specimen light sources. (Gübelin).

**GTD** See *composite stones.*

**Guadalcanal cat's eye** See *operculum.*

**guarnaccio** A yellowish-red garnet.

**Gübelin's jewellers' spectroscope** Designed by Dr E. Gübelin in 1950, this was the first spectroscope to be produced specifically for gemmological work and which also contained a built-in adjustable source of illumination for both the specimen and the wavelength scale. Constructed in the style of a microscope stand, this unit enabled the height of the spectroscope to be adjusted relative to the stone holder, and its angle varied. The eyepiece contained a series of five lenses which could be selected to suit the user's eye, and which were also useful to correct for focus differences between the blue and red ends of the spectrum. *Figure G.5.*

**gum animé** See *copal resin.*

**gypsum** A hydrated calcium sulphate, occurring in the varieties alabaster, satin spar and selenite. See ***alabaster.***

# H

**habit** The characteristic external shape commonly adopted by a crystalline material. Habits include acicular, bipyramid, botryoidal, columnar, dendritic, mamillary, massive, prismatic, tabular (see under appropriate heading).

**hackly fracture** See ***fracture.***

**haematite** An iron oxide used both as a gemstone and in powdered form as a polishing abrasive (jeweller's rouge). Because of its mamillary contours it is also known as kidney stone. $Fe_2O_3$. Trigonal. R.I. 2.94, 3.22; D.R. −0.28; S.G. 4.95-5.16; H. 5½-6½. Opaque, reddish-black. Occurrence: Elba, England, Switzerland.

**hailstone boart** See ***boart.***

**hair amethyst** Amethyst variety of quartz with hair-like inclusions.

**halbanita aquamarine** A maxixe-type indigo beryl whose colour is due to $CO_3$ impurity ions.

**half facets** See ***break facets.***

**haliotis pearl** A highly coloured, iridescent and often hollow baroque pearl from the *Haliotis* mollusc.

**Haliotis shell** See ***abalone.***

**halite** Common salt, NaCl. This mineral is too soft and soluble to be of use as a gemstone. It occurs as minute cubic crystals in liquid-filled cavities in, for example, emerald.

**hallmark** A mark embossed into gold and silver articles by an Assay Office indicating the maker's initials, the standard of purity of the metal, the place of assay and the year of hallmarking. See ***assay*** and ***carat.***

**halo** See ***zircon haloes.***

**halogen** Any of the group of non-metallic elements astatine, chlorine, bromine, fluorine and iodine.

**hambergite** A collector's stone comprising the mineral beryllium borate. $Be_2(OH)BO_3$. Orthorhombic. R.I. 1.553, 1.625 to 1.559, 1.631; D.R. +0.072; S.G. 2.35; H. 7½. Transparent, colourless. Occurrence: The Malagasy Republic, Norway.

**hammer pearls** Baroque pearls in the shape of a hammer head.

**hand lens** Also called a loupe, this is a basic inspection aid for magnifying the internal and external features of a gemstone. Hand lenses range from inexpensive uncorrected models to fully corrected triplets (see ***aberration***). The most useful magnification factor (particularly for diamond grading purposes) is 10×. *Figure H.1.* See ***head loupe*** and ***triplet (lens).***

**Hanneman balance** See ***hydrostatic weighing.***

**hard ivory** A commercial description of a type of hard or bright

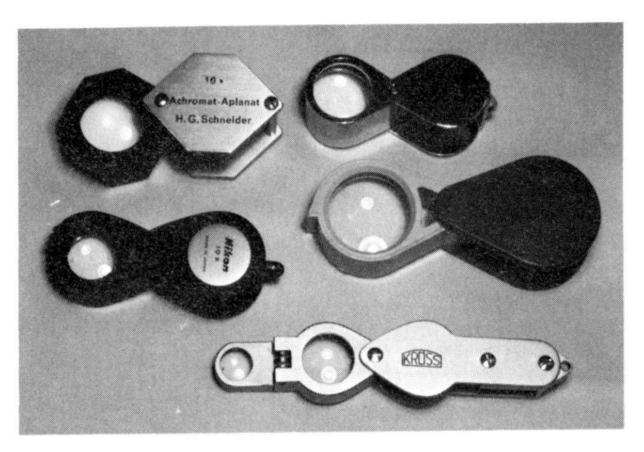


*Figure H.1* A range of hand lenses.

ivory which has a 'glassy' surface and is harder to cut than the 'soft' variety (e.g. Angola and Ambriz ivory). See ***soft ivory*** and ***bastard ivory.***

**hardness** The ability of a material to resist abrasion damage is measured in gemmology and mineralogy by means of the Mohs scale of comparative hardness. Ten minerals are used as standards as follows:

| | |
|---|---|
| 1. Talc | 6. Feldspar |
| 2. Gypsum | 7. Quartz |
| 3. Calcite | 8. Topaz |
| 4. Fluorspar | 9. Corundum |
| 5. Apatite | 10. Diamond |

Any substance with a particular Mohs hardness number will scratch another substance having a lower number and will itself be scratched by one having a higher number. See ***hardness pencils*** and ***indentation test.***

**hardness pencils** Metal holders set with pointed fragments of the standard minerals in the Mohs hardness scale. See ***hardness.*** *Figure H.2.*

**hardness test plates** Test plates made of polished sections of quartz, synthetic spinel and synthetic ruby. The hardness of gemstones can be assessed by checking their ability to scratch these plates.

**harlequin opal** See ***opal.***

**haüyne** See ***haüynite.***

**haüynite** A constituent of lapis lazuli, haüynite is a complex sodium aluminium silicate and is mainly cut as a collector's stone. Cubic. R.I. 1.496; S.G. 2.4; H. 6. Translucent, blue. Occurrence: Germany, Italy.

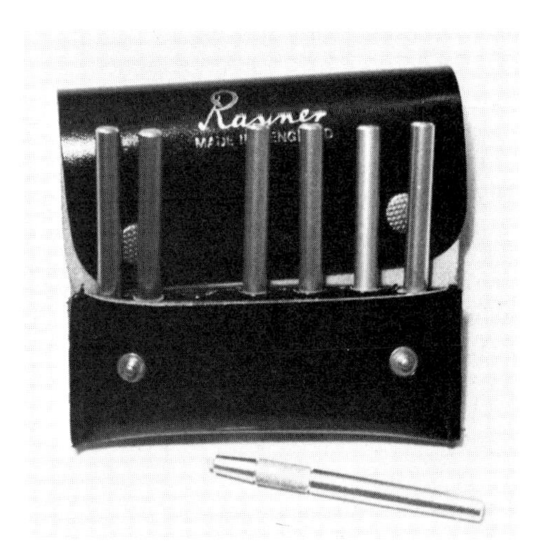


*Figure H.2* A set of seven hardness pencils. (Rayner/Gemmological Instruments Ltd.)

**Hawaiian diamonds** A misleading name for the rock crystal variety of quartz.

**hawaiite** Peridot from Hawaii.

**hawksbill turtle** A sea-turtle whose shell is the main source of the gem material known as tortoiseshell.

**hawk's eye** See ***quartz.***

**haytorite** Chalcedony pseudomorphous after datolite.

**head loupe** A binocular lens assembly mounted on a head band enabling both hands to be free when inspecting and sorting gemstones. See ***hand lens*** and ***triplet (lens).***

**head magnifier** See ***head loupe.***

**heat conduction** See ***thermal conduction.***

**heat treated stones** Gemstones which have their colour improved or changed by means of the controlled application of heat. Amethyst is heated to produce yellow and green quartz. Dark green tourmalines from Namibia are improved to emerald green by heating. Heating is used to change pale green beryl to an aquamarine colour, zoisite to a sapphire blue , and sapphires and rubies (containing excessive iron) to a more attractive shade. Brown and yellow topaz from Brazil turns pink after being heated to 500-600 °C, and becomes colourless if taken above this temperature. Brown zircons from Cambodia turn blue if heated to 900-1000 °C in a reducing (oxygen-free) atmosphere. If heated to 850-900 °C in air they turn golden brown, colourless or sometimes red. See also ***geuda stones.***

**heavily spotted** A UK clarity grade used for polished diamonds. See ***Clarity Grading Standards*** in Appendix C.

**heavy liquids** Used for measuring the specific gravity of gemstones; heavy liquids exploit Archimedes' principle (i.e. a body totally immersed in a fluid experiences an upward force equal to the weight of fluid it displaces). Commonest liquids in use for S.G. testing are:

| | | |
|---|---|---|
| *bromoform* | $CHBr_3$ | S.G. 2.89 |
| *methylene iodide* | $CH_2I_2$ | S.G. 3.32 |
| *Clerici's solution* | | S.G. 4.15 |

Intermediate S.G. values can be obtained by diluting bromoform and methylene with toluene (S.G. 0.88) or monobromonaphthalene (S.G. 1.49), and by diluting Clerici's solution with water. Clerici's solution contains thallium malonate and thallium formate, and is both poisonous and corrosive. *Care should be taken when using any of these liquids to avoid skin contact or inhalation of vapour.* See ***glass S.G. indicators*** and ***specific gravity.***

**heavy media separation** A technique used to separate diamond from crushed kimberlite (blue ground) and gravel. The separator uses a cone shaped tank containing a slurry, or heavy liquid, made up of a fine ferro-silicon powder suspended in water to give it a specific gravity of 2.7–3.1. This slurry floats off the lighter elements and allows the diamonds to be drawn off from the bottom of the tank.

**heavy spar** See ***barite.***

**hedgehog-stone** Quartz with goethite inclusions.

**heliocite** Aventurine feldspar.

**heliodor** See ***beryl.***

**heliolite** A red or green variety of labradorite, the red colour being due to flakes of haematite. R.I. around 1.57; S.G. 2.7; H. 6. Occurrence: Oregon, USA.

**heliotrope** See ***chalcedony*** (bloodstone).

**hematine** A man-made sintered simulant of haematite. It is distinguished from haematite because it is attracted by a magnet. Itaglios made with hematine are pressed instead of being carved as with haematite.

**hematite** See ***haematite.***

**hematite garnet** A synthetic iron-rich garnet.

**hemihedral** A term applied to crystals which only exhibit half the number of faces required by their crystal system.

**hemimorphic** A term applied to crystals which have different forms at either end of an axis of symmetry.

**hemimorphite** Usually associated with smithsonite, this consists of the mineral zinc silicate. $Zn_4(OH)Si_2O_7.H_2O$. Orthorhombic (crystals are hemimorphic when doubly terminated; otherwise massive botryoidal). R.I. 1.614, 1.636; D.R. +0.022; S.G. 3.4-3.5; H. 5. Opaque to translucent, blue, green, often banded. Occurrence: Greece, Mexico, Namibia, Spain, USA.

**herbeckite** Jasper variety of quartz.

**Herbert Smith refractometer** A gemstone refractometer designed in 1905 as an improved version of the Bertrand refractometer. It was further improved two years later by incorporating a scale calibrated directly in refractive indices. *Figure H.3.*

*Figure H.3* The Herbert Smith refractometer.

**herderite** A collector's stone comprising the mineral beryllium calcium fluo-phosphate. $CaBe(F,OH)PO_4$. Monoclinic. R.I. 1.594, 1.624; D.R. −0.03; S.G. 3.0; H. 5. Greyish. Occurrence: Brazil, Germany, USA.

**herkimer diamond** A misleading name for the rock crystal variety of quartz.

**herrerite** See ***smithsonite.***

**hessonite** See ***garnet.***

**hexagonal system** A crystal system having four axes, the three lateral ones being of equal length and intersecting each other at 60° in the same plane. The fourth (or principal) axis is at right-angles to the others and usually longer. There are seven axes of symmetry (six two-fold and one six-fold), seven planes of symmetry and a centre of symmetry. *Figure H.4.*

**hexagonite** See ***tremolite.***

**hexakis octahedron** A 48-sided crystal which is one of the seven basic forms belonging to the highest class of symmetry in the cubic crystal system. It consists of an octahedron with each face replaced by six triangular faces.

**hidaka jade** A chrome diopside, containing a small amount of uvarovite, chromite and pectolite, found in central Hokkaido, Japan.

**hiddenite** See ***spodumene.***

**high zircon** A zircon whose internal crystal structure is relatively

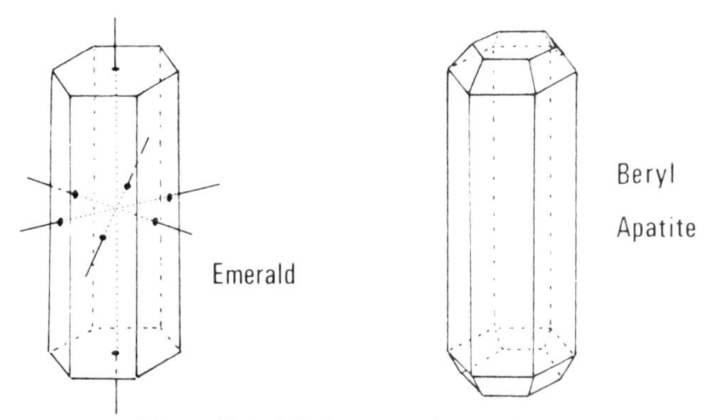


*Figure H.4* The hexagonal crystal system.

undamaged, and whose constants are at their maximum values. See ***zircon*** and ***low zircon.***

**hinge pearls** Pearls of irregular shape found near the hinge of shellfish from freshwater (also known as *dog tooth* and *wing pearl).*

**hinjosa topaz** A misleading name for yellow quartz.

**hippopotamus ivory** Dentine ivory from the teeth of the hippopotamus.

**hodgkinsonite** A very rare collector's stone consisting of a hydrated magnesium zinc silicate (found in only one location in the early part of this century). $MnZn_2SiO_5.H_2O$. Monoclinic. R.I. 1.720, 1.746; D.R. 0.026; S.G. 3.95 (mean); H. 4½-5. Transparent bright pink to purplish-pink. Occurrence: New Jersey, USA.

**hole gauge** See ***diamond gauge.***

**Holocene** (Recent) The smaller and later part of the Quaternary period of geological time from 10 000 years ago to the present day. See ***Quaternary.***

**holohedral** A term applied to a crystal which exhibits the full symmetry of its crystal system.

**holosymmetrical** See ***holohedral.***

**holstein** See ***fossil wood.***

**homogeneous** A term applied to a substance such as a gem mineral which is composed throughout of the same chemical element or compound.

**honan jade** A misleading name for soapstone.

**honey opal** A yellow translucent non-iridescent opal similar to fire opal. Occurrence: Western Australia. See ***opal.***

**Hong Kong Gemmological Association** See ***Gemmological Association of Hong Kong.***

**hope sapphire** A misleading trade name for synthetic blue spinel.

**horatio diamond** A misleading name for the rock crystal variety of quartz.

**horn** A carving material derived from the horn of the rhinoceros and the antler of the deer. Rhinoceros horn consists of a closely packed mass of hairs or horny fibres having a low hardness and a density of 1.29. Deer horn more closely resembles bone, but is usually brownish. R.I. 1.56; S.G. 1.70-1.85; H. 2½.

**hornbill ivory** A rare organic material obtained from the beak and casque of the helmeted hornbill bird of southeast Asia. R.I. 1.55; S.G. 1.28-1.29; H. 2½.

**hornblende** A dark brown, black or green ferro-magnesium silicate present in many rocks including granite.

**horn coral** A black variety of coral.

**horn of the unicorn** See ***whale ivory.***

**hornstone** See ***jasper.***

**horsetail inclusion** See ***inclusion.***

**hot-point tester** An instrument (marketed by the GIA) having an electrically heated probe which is used to test for wax- and plastic-impregnated turquoise, amber simulants, tortoiseshell and jet. The test relies on the characteristic smell given off when the tip of the heated probe is brought into contact with the gem material.

**hot springs diamond** A misleading name for the rock crystal variety of quartz.

**howlite** A massive ornamental stone comprising a complex silico-borate of calcium. Believed to be monoclinic. Mean R.I. 1.59; S.G. 2.58; H. 3½. Opaque white, veined with black. Occurrence: USA.

**hübnerite** A rare collector's stone comprising the mineral manganese tungstate. $MnWO_4$. Monoclinic. R.I. 2.1 to 2.2; S.G. 7.25; H. 4-4½. Transparent, deep red. Occurrence: Peru.

**hue** A term applied to the colour or wavelength of light. See ***saturation.***

**humite** The name given to a group of minerals comprising norbergite, humite, chondrodite and clinohumite.

**Hungarian cat's eye** Quartz cat's eye from Bavaria.

**Hungarian opal** Opal from the Cervencia mines in Hungary.

**hyacinth** A former name applied to orange-brown zircons or hessonite garnets.

**hyacinth of compostella** Reddish quartz.

**hyaline** An opalescent milky quartz.

**hyalite** See ***opal.***

**hyalithe** Trade name for a red, brown, green or black opaque glass.

**hydrochloric acid** A mineral acid, HCl, which is a constituent, with nitric acid, of aqua regia.

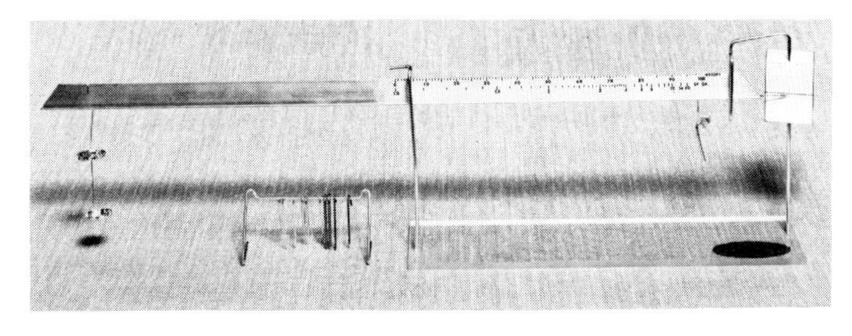

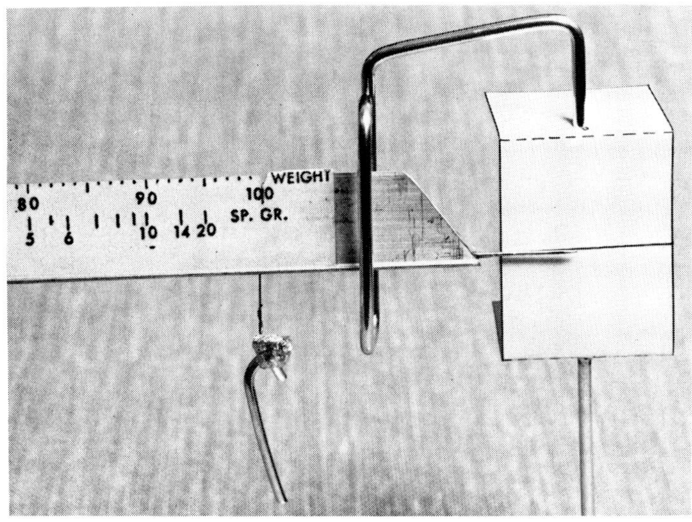


*Figure H.5* A direct-reading specific gravity balance. Two gemstone weighpans are provided (top left) for in-air and in-water weighings. The counterweight slide (bottom centre) is set to 100 for the in-air weighing and is loaded by means of hooked weights to achieve equilibrium. The gemstone is then transferred to the lower weighpan for the in-water weighing, and the counterweight moved down the scale to restore equilibrium. Its new position on the scale indicates the stone's S.G. (Hanneman)

**hydro-cyclone** A method of separating diamond from crushed kimberlite (blue ground) and gravel. The hydro-cyclone consists of a cone-shaped tank. The diamond-rich material is fed in from the side and subjected to the centrifugal action of a continuously circulating ferro-silicon slurry. The heavy diamond fraction moves to the outside of the tank, sinks, and is drawn off, the light fraction migrates to the centre and is forced upwards and floated off.

**hydrogrossular garnet** See *garnet*.

**hydrometer** An instrument incorporating a calibrated float which is used to measure the specific gravity of liquids.

**hydrophane** See *opal.*

**hydrostatic weighing** A method of determining the S.G. of a gemstone by weighing it first in air, and then when it is totally immersed in water.

$$\text{S.G.} = \frac{\text{Weight in air}}{\text{Weight in air} - \text{Weight in water}}$$

Direct-reading balances, such as the Westphal, Penfield and Hanneman balances (*Figure H.5*), can be used (or modified) to give a direct indication of S.G. without the need for calculation. The balance is first set to zero while weighing the gemstone in air. A subsequent reading (or zero adjustment) when weighing the gemstone in water then provides the S.G. value.

**hydrothermal process** A process for growing synthetic crystals by dissolving their constituents in superheated water. Seed crystals are suspended in the mineral-rich water and the temperature gradient adjusted so that the solution becomes supersaturated and precipitates out on the seed crystals. The water is superheated to around 400° C in a pressure vessel called an autoclave. *Figure A.6.*

**hypersthene** Related to enstatite and bronzite, this is an iron-magnesium silicate. $(Fe,Mg)SiO_3$. Orthorhombic. R.I. 1.673, 1.715 to 1.683, 1.731; D.R. −0.045; S.G. 3.4-3.5; H. 5-6. Opaque to translucent, dark brown. Occurrence: India.

**Iceland agate** A misleading name for an obsidian.
**Iceland spar** See ***calcite.***
**icosi tetrahedron** A 24-sided crystal (also called a trapezohedron) which is one of the seven basic forms belonging to the highest class of symmetry in the cubic crystal system. It consists of an octahedron whose faces have each been replaced by three four-sided faces.
**ideal cut** The name given to the modern brilliant cut whose proportions and angles are designed to produce an optimum blend of brilliance and fire in a diamond. See ***brilliant cut.***
**identification** (of polished diamonds) See ***breath test, dot-ring test, fingerprinting, light spill test, reflectivity meter, thermal conductivity diamond tester, water contact angle*** and ***X-ray diamond tester.***
**idiochromatic gems** Gem minerals which owe their colour to their basic chemical constituents rather than to impurities (the term idiochromatic meaning 'self coloured'). See also ***allochromatic.***
**idiomorphic** Term applied to a crystal which exhibits its normal habit. See ***xenomorphic*** and ***pseudomorphic.***
**idocrase** A collector's stone comprising a complex calcium aluminium silicate, which may also contain beryllium, boron, fluorine and titanium. $Ca_6Al(Al,OH)(SiO_4)_5$. Tetragonal. R.I. 1.700, 1.705 to 1.716, 1.721; D.R. −0.005 (lower values), +0.005 (higher values); S.G. 3.32-3.47; H. 6½. Transparent, olive green, yellowish-brown. Occurrence: Austria, Canada, Norway, Pakistan, Switzerland, USA, USSR.
**igmarald** Trade name for a German synthetic emerald grown by I.G. Farbenindustrie, using the flux-melt process but never produced commercially.
**igneous intrusion** The intrusion of molten rock magma into pre-existing rock which produces a thermal or contact metamorphism of the earlier rock. See ***contact metamorphism.***
**igneous rock** A rock which solidified from the molten magma either within the Earth or on its surface. Igneous rocks which solidified deep inside the Earth are called intrusive or plutonic (e.g. granite). Those which solidified rapidly on the surface are called extrusive or volcanic (e.g. lava). See also ***metamorphic rock*** and ***sedimentary rock.***
**illam** A term applied to the gem gravels of Sri Lanka.
**illumination** See ***dark-field illumination, incident illumination*** and ***light-field illumination.***
**illusion setting** A setting consisting of a large polished mount

designed to increase the apparent size of a small diamond.

**ilmenite** A common minor constituent of basic igneous rocks. An industrial source of titanium and iron. $FeTiO_3$. Trigonal. S.G. 4.7; H. 5–6. Opaque dull black. Occurrence: France, Switzerland, USA. USSR.

**image stone** An Indian variety of steatite. Alternative name for agalmatolite.

**imitation pearls** Usually solid glass spheres, mother-of-pearl spheres, or hollow glass spheres filled with wax. Imitation pearls are given a lustrous outer coating by dipping them in a fish scale preparation called 'essence d'orient'.

**imitation stones** See ***composite stones, simulants*** and ***synthetic stones.***

**immersion cell** Also called a cuvette, this consists of a small transparent glass container which is used to facilitate the internal inspection of gemstones by reducing surface reflections. The cell is filled with a liquid having an R.I. close to that of the gemstone under inspection, and the gemstone is immersed in the liquid. Unwanted surface reflections are minimized because the reflectivity of a surface is reduced when surrounded by a medium of similar R.I. See ***Fresnel's reflectivity equation.***

**immersion contact photography** A technique developed by B.W. Anderson to reveal the differences between the R.I.s of gemstones by placing them on a piece of photographic paper which is immersed in a shallow dish containing a liquid of known R.I. The stones are then exposed to visible light. In the developed paper stones with a higher R.I. than the liquid display a white marginal rim and the facet edges are marked by dark lines. With stones having a lower R.I. than that of the liquid, these effects are reversed. This method can also be used to reveal internal features such as growth stria in synthetics. Norman Day extended the technique by using UV light to distinguish between natural and synthetic emeralds and rubies. The test specimen is placed together with a natural stone (as a reference), table facet down on a piece of photographic paper in a darkened room. The stones and the paper are placed in the bottom of a shallow dish containing water, and exposed to SW UV light for a few seconds. When the photographic paper is developed, the reference stone will appear white (i.e. it will have absorbed the UV light) while the test specimen, if it is a synthetic, will appear black with a white rim. Later synthetics, containing iron oxides, fail this test.

**immersion contrast** Composite and coated stones can be identified by immersion in a liquid of similar R.I.

**immersion estimation of R.I.** See ***Becke line method*** and ***immersion liquids.***

**immersion liquids** Liquids having known R.I.s which are used in an immersion cell either to reduce reflections from the surface of a gemstone, or to approximate its R.I. R.I.s of suitable immersion fluids are as follows:

| | | | |
|---|---|---|---|
| Water | 1.33 | Bromoform | 1.59 |
| Alcohol | 1.36 | Iodobenzene | 1.62 |
| Petrol | 1.45 | Monobromonaphthalene | 1.66 |
| Benzene | 1.50 | Iodonaphthalene | 1.70 |
| Clove oil | 1.54 | Methylene iodide | 1.74 |
| | | Refractometer contact fluid | 1.81 |

See also ***immersion cell*** and ***Becke line method.*** *Care should be taken when using benzene because it is a suspect carcinogenic liquid.*

**imori stone** See ***victoria stone.***

**imperial jade** Emerald green translucent jadeite.

**imperial Mexican jade** A misleading name for green-dyed calcite.

**imperial sodden snow jade** White nephrite.

**imperial topaz** Sherry-brown topaz.

**imperial Yu stone** Green aventurine quartz.

**inamori padparadscha** A synthetic orange sapphire marketed by Kyocera International Inc., Kyoto, Japan.

**inanga** Grey nephrite.

**inca emerald** Emerald from Ecuador.

**inca rose** See ***rhodochrosite.***

**inca stone** See ***pyrites.***

**incident illumination** Illumination in which the light rays are incident to that surface of the gemstone nearest to the viewer's eye (or to the microscope objective). See also ***dark-field illumination*** and ***light-field illumination.***

**inclusions** These consist of a variety of features contained within a gemstone:

*pre-existing* inclusions are of materials which were present before the host crystal began to form (e.g. solid particles and small crystals). Also called protogenetic.

*contemporary* inclusions consist of substances which were present at the same time as the host crystal (e.g. minute droplets of aqueous solution from which the host crystal grew). Also called syngenetic.

*post-contemporary* inclusions occurred after the formation of the host crystal (e.g. various types of fissure). Also called epigenetic.

Inclusions are often given descriptive names:

*feather* or *veil* — a plane of minute cavities (usually liquid filled),

*silk* — a series of fine parallel rutile needles,

*horsetail* — a group of asbestos fibres,
*negative crystal* — a void within the gem having a crystalline shape,
*three-phase* — a liquid-filled cavity containing a bubble and a crystal,
*two-phase* — a liquid-filled cavity containing a bubble or a crystal,
*treacle* — wisps and swirls of colour,
*zircon halo* — a zircon crystal inclusion surrounded by a stress crack.

See also ***colour zoning*** and *Figure I.1.*

**indentation test** An alternative to the use of a scratch test to evaluate the hardness of a mineral. One version, the Knoop

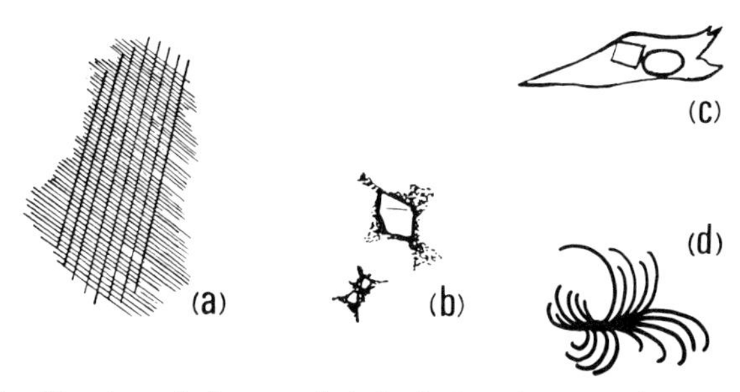


*Figure I.1* Sketches of characteristic inclusions in natural gemstones. (a) Rutile needles, seen as 'silk' in rubies and sapphires. (b) Zircon crystals surrounded by 'haloes' seen in Sri Lankan sapphires, spinels and garnets. (c) Three-phase inclusion (liquid, bubble, crystal) in Colombian emeralds. (d) Asbestos fibres forming a 'horsetail' inclusion in demantoid garnet.

indentation test, involves the measurement of the deformation produced in the surface of the specimen when a diamond-pointed indenter is applied to it with a known load. Another method is the micro-abrasion test which uses a small cone-shaped grinding wheel coated with diamond dust to measure the depth of abrasion over a preset time. Both these techniques produce a measurement of hardness based on an approximately linear scale (e.g. on the Knoop scale of hardness, topaz is 766, corundum is 1000 and diamond is 5180).

**index of refraction** See ***refractive index.***

**Indian agate** Moss agate.

**Indian cat's eye** Chrysoberyl cat's eye.

**Indian cut** An imperfect version of the eight cut designed to retain the maximum weight in the polished diamond.

**Indian emerald** A misleading name for green-dyed cracked quartz.

**Indian Gemmological Institute** See ***Gemmological Institute of India.***

**Indian jade** A misleading name for green aventurine quartz.

**Indian topaz** A misleading name for yellow sapphire.

**indicators** Glass or pure gemstone specimens used as S.G. indicators when blending heavy liquids. See ***heavy liquids*** and ***glass S.G. indicators.***

**indicolite** See ***tourmaline.***

**industrial diamonds** Rough diamonds whose colour, quality or shape make them unsuitable for gem use. See also ***gem diamonds*** and ***near gem.***

**inert** A material which shows no detectable reaction either to stimuli such as UV or X-ray irradiation, or to chemical reagents.

**infra red** The band of electromagnetic energy whose wavelengths lie between the deep red end of the visible spectrum (750 nm) and the microwave end of the radio spectrum (1 million nm or 1 mm).

**infra red spectrophotometer** See ***spectrophotometer.***

**inorganic** A term applied to substances not derived from living or once-living organisms.

**Instituto Gemologico Español** Headquarters: Victor Hugo 1, Floor 3, Madrid 28004, Spain

**intaglio** An incised gemstone carving produced for use as a seal.

**intarsia** See ***Florentine mosaic.***

**interference** (of light rays) Light rays reflected from a thin transparent layer, or from a surface containing a series of fine regular surface indentations, travel over differing path lengths and mutually interfere with each other to produce spectral colours. *Figure I.2.*

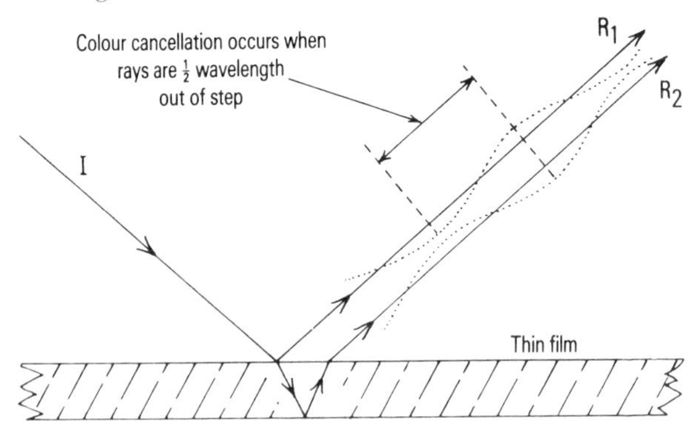


*Figure I.2* Sketch showing how colour is produced in a thin film by the mutual interference between reflected rays. A particular colour is reinforced when the extra distance travelled by $R_2$ brings it into phase with $R_1$. The same colour is cancelled when the rays are out of step by a half wavelength of that colour.

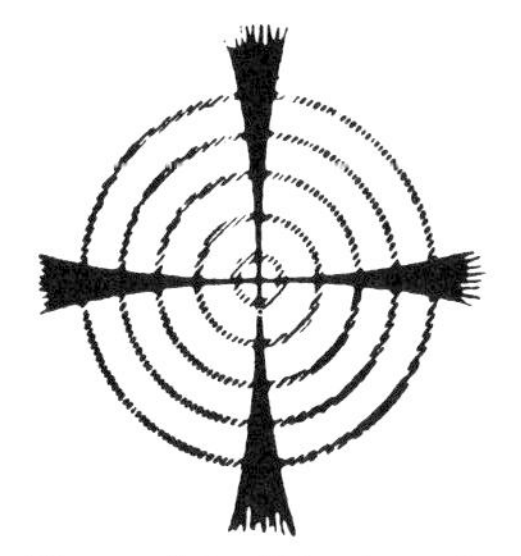
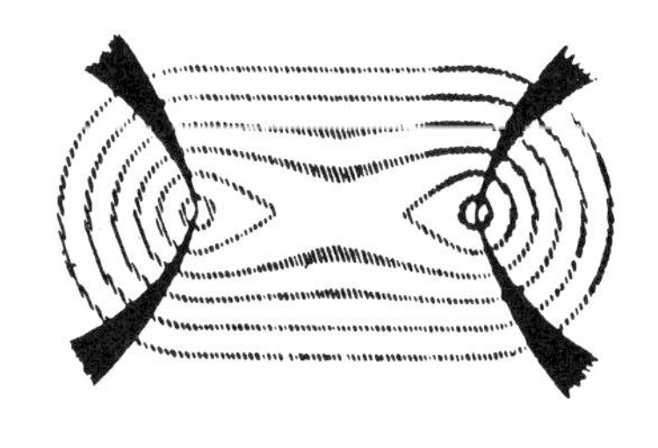

*Figure I.3* The interference figures seen (left) in a uniaxial stone, and (right) in a biaxial stone.

**interference figures** Figures produced when transparent doubly-refracting materials are viewed in polarized light under a strongly convergent lens. The figures are indicative of the optical character of the material. *Figure I.3.* See ***konoscope.***

**interference filter** A colour filter which consists of a plate of glass on which are deposited thin metallic films interlayered with films of a low refractive index mineral such as magnesium fluoride. Light incident to the filter experiences internal reflection and interference in the different layers (see *Figure I.2*) which results in the transmission of only a narrow band of wavelengths. Interference filters are used in gemmology to simulate yellow monochromatic light (centred on the sodium emission lines at 589.3 nm) for refractive index measurements. They are also used to produce light at the B and G Fraunhofer wavelengths in the measurement of dispersion. As only a small portion of the incident light is transmitted through the filter, it is necessary to use it in conjunction with a high-intensity light source.

**intermediate zircon** A zircon whose constants lie between those of high zircon and low zircon.

**internally flawless** A clarity grade (IF) for polished diamonds indicating that no internal features are visible at 10× magnification. See ***Clarity Grading Standards*** in Appendix C.

**interpenetrant twins** Two (or more) crystals which have grown in proximity and have penetrated each other. With multiple twinning, the result is often a cross, star or hexagonal form. See also ***contact twin*** and ***polysynthetic twinning.***

**intrusive rock** See ***igneous rock.***

**invelite** Trade name for phenolic resin.

**iodobenzene** A liquid used as an immersion fluid. R.I. 1.62. See ***Becke line method*** and ***immersion cell.***

**iolanthite** A banded reddish jasper. See ***quartz.***

**iolite** See ***cordierite.***

**ion** An electrically charged atom or molecule. Certain substances such as salts, acids and alkalies **ionize** when dissolved in water and produce a solution which conducts electricity. Neutral atoms become **ionized** when they lose or gain an electron. Negatively charged ions are called *anions*, and positively charged ones *cations*.

**iridescence** See ***sheen.***

**iridium** A member of the platinum group of metals sometimes alloyed with gold or platinum. Ir. Atomic number 77; atomic weight 193.1; melting point 2443 °C; S.G. 22.4.

**iris** A mechanical device fitted above the substage illuminator in a microscope. It consists of an aperture whose diameter can be varied to control the area of light projected onto the specimen. Also used as an intensity control in the output of quartz halogen light sources.

**iris agate** An agate in which the concentric bands are packed so close that they form a diffraction grating and split transmitted light up into spectral colours.

**iris diamond** A diamond which has been coated to cause it to iridesce, this effect giving the impression of increased dispersion.

**iris quartz** A clear colourless quartz containing a series of thin cracks which produce spectral colours by interference effects.

**Irish diamonds** A misleading name for the rock crystal variety of quartz.

**Irish black marble** A variety of marble found in County Carlow, Eire.

**Irish green marble** Also known as Connemara marble, this is found in County Galway, Eire.

**iron** One of the eight transition metals mainly responsible for colour in gemstones (e.g. almandine garnet, amethyst, aquamarine, peridot, sinhalite). Fe. Atomic number 26; atomic weight 55.84; melting point 1539 °C; S.G. 7.87.

**iron opal** Red or yellow common opal.

**iron roses** Rosettes of platy haematite crystals found in Switzerland.

**irradiation of diamond** See ***treated diamonds.***

**Isle of Wight diamonds** A misleading name for the rock crystal variety of quartz.

**ISO** International Standards Organization.

**isochrome** The interference-produced coloured circle seen around the optic axis of a doubly-refractive gem under convergent polarized light. See ***konoscope*** and ***isogyre.***

**isogyre** The dark 'brushes' produced in interference figures as seen in doubly-refracting materials under converging **polarized light.** See ***interference figures.***

**isometric** A crystal system having equal length axes (e.g. cubic).

**isomorphic replacement** The replacement of one element in a mineral by another element having the same valency, and resulting in the same form and crystal structure. Such replacement may cause wide variations in the mineral's constants (e.g. gems in the garnet group).

**isomorphism** Minerals exhibit isomorphism when they have identical external forms but differ chemically from each other (e.g. gems in the garnet group).

**isotopes** Forms of an element which differ from each other in atomic weight and nuclear properties while remaining the same chemically. These dissimilarities are due to differences in the number of neutrons in the atomic nucleus.

**isotropic** A singly-refracting material in which light rays travel at the same velocity in any direction. All amorphous gems and gemstones in the cubic crystal system are isotropic. See also ***double refraction*** and ***optical character.***

**Istituto Gemmologico Italiano** Headquarters: Viale Gramsci 228, 1-20099 Sesto S. Giovanni, Milano, Italy.

**itali** Aztec name for obsidian.

**Italian chrysolite** See ***idocrase.***

**Italian Gemmological Institute** See ***Istituto Gemmologico Italiano.***

**Italian lapis** A stained jasper (variety of quartz).

**ivorine** A plastic ivory simulant.

**ivory** See ***dentine ivory, corozo nut, doom palm nut.***

**ivory pearls** A misleading name for ivory spheroids found in tusk cavities.

**ivory turquoise** A misleading name for odontolite.

# J

**jacinth** Reddish-brown zircon or hessonite garnet.

**jade** See ***jadeite*** and ***nephrite.***

**jade-albite** A rock containing a mixture of chrome-rich jadeite and albite feldspar. Also called maw-sit-sit. Cryptocrystalline. R.I. 1.52-1.54 S.G. 2.46-3.15. Opaque, green with black markings. Occurrence: Burma.

**jadeite** A sodium aluminium silicate jade mineral comprising an aggregate of granular crystals $NaAl(SiO_3)_2$. Monoclinic (cryptocrystalline). R.I. 1.65-1.68; S.G. 3.30-3.36; H. 6½-7. Opaque to translucent, white, green, pink, lilac, violet, brown, black. Occurrence: Burma, USA. See also ***nephrite.***

**jade matrix** A rock containing a mixture of tremolite and albite feldspar. Also called snowflake jade. Cryptocrystalline. R.I. 1.56; S.G. 2.80-2.95.

**jade tenace** A misleading name for saussurite.

**jadine** A misleading trade name for Australian chrysoprase.

**jager** A diamond having a blue tint which is usually caused by a strong blue fluorescence. See ***overblue.***

**jamb peg** An upright wooden-capped metal post containing holes which is used by a lapidary to anchor one end of the gemstone holder (called a gem stick) when polishing side facets. The jamb peg acts as a guide enabling the lapidary to set the angles of these facets correctly.

**Japanese coral** Dark red coral with a white core.

**Japanese gemmological associations** See ***Gemological Association of Japan, Gemmological Association of All Japan*** and ***Gemmological Society of Japan.***

**Japan pearl** A cultured blister pearl.

**Japan twinning** Twinning of crystals with inclined axes. *Figure J.1.*

**jardin** A term (from the French, meaning garden) applied to the inclusions found in emeralds.

**jargon** A term applied to a low quality yellow diamond.

**jargoon** Pale or colourless zircon.

**jarra gem** A trade name for a synthetic rutile diamond simulant.

**jasp agate** A microcrystalline quartz, midway between jasper and agate. When banded this is called jasponyx.

**jaspe fleuri** See ***jasp agate.***

**jasper** See ***quartz.***

**jasperine** A banded variety of jasper.

**jasper jade** A misleading name for green jasper and serpentine.

**jasper opal** A red, reddish-brown or yellow-brown opal resembling jasper.

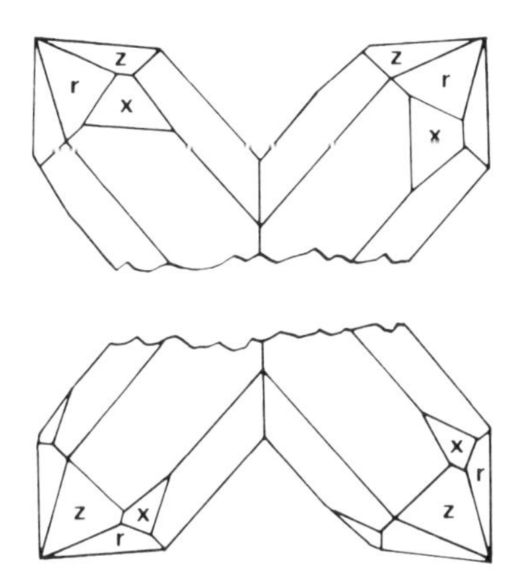


*Figure J.1* Idealized shapes of Japan-law twins.

**jaspillite** A banded variety of jasper containing haematite.
**jasponal** A gem material intermediate between jasper and opal.
**jasponyx** See ***jasp agate.***
**java gem** Trade name for a synthetic rutile diamond simulant.
**java onyx** An opaque stalagmitic marble. Off-white or variegated with amber-coloured wavy bands. Occurrence: Java.
**jeremejevite** A rare gemstone comprising the mineral aluminium borate. Hexagonal (blue), orthorhombic (yellow, colourless). $AlBO_3$. R.I. 1.639, 1.648; D.R. −0.009; S.G. 3.28. Transparent, pale yellow, aquamarine blue. Pleochroism, medium (colourless, blue). Occurrence: Namibia, USSR.
**jet** A variety of fossilized wood, similar to lignite or brown coal, and halfway in formation between peat and bituminous coal. Also called gagat. Amorphous. R.I. 1.64–1, 68; S.G. 1.3–1.35; H. 3½. Opaque, black, dark brown. Occurrence: France, Spain, UK (Whitby), USA.
**jet stone** Black tourmaline, also called schorl.
**jewel** An unmounted gemstone or an ornament worn for personal adornment which contains gemstones.
**jewelite** Trade name for the man-made diamond simulant strontium titanate.
**jeweller** A manufacturer or dealer in gemstones or jewellery.
**jeweller's rouge** A brownish-red abrasive powder (made from crushed haematite) used for polishing gemstones. Also called ferric oxide. See ***haematite.***
**johannes gem** Trade name for a synthetic rutile diamond simulant.
**johnite** A vitreous scaly turquoise.
**Johnson and Rösch brilliant cut** One of the earlier of several 'ideal' cuts for diamond. It has a table facet width, crown depth and

pavilion depth of 56.1%, 19.2% and 40% respectively compared with the girdle diameter. The crown angle is 41.08°, and the pavilion angle is 38.67°. See ***Eppler brilliant cut, Scan DN brilliant cut, Parker brilliant cut*** and ***Tolkowsky brilliant cut.***

**joule** An SI unit of energy, work or quantity of heat expressed in newtons per metre (i.e. force × distance). Force (in newtons) = mass (in kilograms) × acceleration (in metres per s per s).

**jourado diamond** A misleading trade name for a colourless synthetic spinel used as a diamond simulant.

**Jurassic** A rock system on the Earth's surface comprising the rocks laid down during the Jurassic period, 195-135 million years ago. The Jurassic period was the middle part of the Mesozoic era. See ***Mesozoic.***

**kahurangi** A pale green translucent variety of New Zealand nephrite.

**kakortokite** An ornamental rock consisting of a whitish nepheline syenite and containing red crystals of eudialite (a rare zirconium mineral) and black arfvedsonite. S.G. 2.7-2.8. Occurrence: Greenland.

**kalmuck agate** Also known as cacholong. See ***opal.***

**kandy spinel** A misleading name for a reddish-violet garnet found in Sri Lanka.

**kan huang jade** A light yellowish jade.

**kaolin** A fine white clay comprising a hydrated aluminium silicate derived from decomposed feldspar in pegmatite rocks. Used as a lapidary abrasive and in the manufacture of porcelain.

**kaolite** Trade name for imitation cameos, etc., moulded in clay and baked.

**karat** See ***carat.***

**karlsbad spring stone** A banded gypsum used for carvings.

**Kashan synthetic ruby** A synthetic ruby grown by the flux-melt process (and containing variable amounts of iron oxide). Kashan Laboratories, Texas, USA.

**kashgar jade** A low quality nephrite.

**Kashmir sapphire** A deep cornflower blue sapphire, having a milky semi-transparent appearance caused by minute liquid inclusions. See ***corundum.***

**kauri gum** See ***copal resin.***

**kawakawa** The normal green variety of New Zealand nephrite.

**keisel** Quartz.

**kelvin temperature scale** See ***absolute temperature scale.***

**kenneth lane jewel** Trade name for the man-made diamond simulant strontium titanate.

**Kenya gem** Trade name for a synthetic rutile diamond simulant.

**Kerez effect** An effect, discovered by Dr C. J. Kerez, seen in some green tourmalines which show four instead of two shadow edges on a critical-angle refractometer. The two extra anomalous shadow edges disappear if the stone is repolished, and the effect is thought to be due to skin-deep alterations caused by local overheating during polishing.

**kerf** The small groove scratched in the surface of a rough diamond (by another diamond) prior to cleaving. The kerf is positioned parallel with a cleavage plane, its radius being made smaller than that of the cleaving blade tip which then acts as a wedge to part the stone. See *Figure C.3.*

**keshi pearls** Naturally occurring non-nucleated pearls which form in a mollusc when it is returned to the water after the removal of a crop of non-nucleated cultured pearls. See also ***Biwa pearls.***

**keweenaw agate** A variety of agate found near Lake Superior, Canada.

**keystone** A trap cut stone having a keystone or trapezium outline.

**keystoneite** A blue chalcedony coloured by chrysocolla.

**khoton jade** A poor quality nephrite.

**kidney stone** See ***nephrite*** and ***haematite.***

**kiku-ishi** See ***xenotime.***

**Kilkenny black fossil marble** An Irish black marble containing white circles formed by the fossilized remains of brachiopod shells.

**killiecrankie diamond** A misleading name for colourless topaz from Australia.

**kima gem** Trade name for a synthetic rutile diamond simulant.

**kimberlite** An igneous rock rich in olivines (a type of peridot), which is found in volcanic-type pipes or vents. In diamond-bearing pipes, kimberlite is thought to be the medium which transported the diamond crystals from deep inside the Earth's crust. Kimberlite is also called blue ground. This weathers on the surface to become the more friable yellow ground.

**kimberlite gem** Trade name for a synthetic rutile diamond simulant.

**Kimmeridge shale** A highly bituminous shale containing marine fossils. S.G. 1.285. Used as a jet simulant.

**kimpi** A red or brown variety of jadeite.

**king cut** An 85-facet diamond cut consisting of 49 crown facets (including a 12-sided table facet) and 36 pavilion facets (plus a culet). *Figure K.1.*

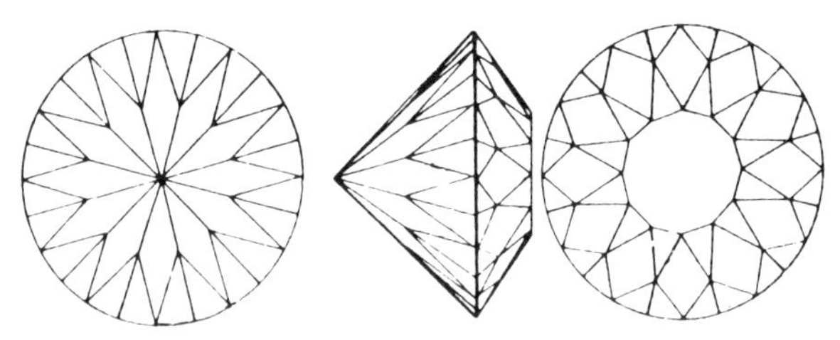

*Figure K.1* The king cut.

**kingfisher jade** A bluish-green jadeite.

**king's coral** A black coral also called akabar.

**king topaz** A misleading name for yellow sapphire.

**kinradite** An orbicular variety of jasper containing circular markings.

**kismet pearls** Trade name for imitation pearls.

**kite** A trap-cut stone having the profile of a kite.

**kite facets** The eight kite-shaped crown facets on a brilliant-cut stone (also called bezel facets and top main facets). See ***brilliant cut.***

**Klein's solution** A heavy liquid consisting of a solution of cadmium borotungstate in water. S.G. 3.28.

**Knischka synthetic rubies** Synthetic rubies grown by a flux-melt process developed by Professor P. O. Knischka of Steyr, Austria. They have constants substantially the same as the natural gemstone, but unlike the majority of natural rubies, lack any trace of iron as detected with an X-ray spectrometer or by SW UV transparency.

**Knoop indentation hardness test** See ***indentation test.***

**knot** A major distortion or discontinuity of the crystal lattice within a diamond which often creates problems in cleaving and polishing the stone. May sometimes be an included crystal, or a twinning plane (see ***macles***). Also called a naat.

**Koh-i-nur** An historic diamond (the name meaning 'mountain of light'), reputed to have been found in the Indian Kollur diamond mines. Originally a 186-carat Indian rose-type cut, it was reduced to a 105.6-carat oval diamond when incorporated in the British Crown Jewels. It is now traditionally set in the crown of the Queen Consort, and never in the crown of the monarch. When Elizabeth II became the reigning monarch, the Koh-i-nur remained in the crown of Queen Elizabeth the Queen Mother.

**kollin garnet** An almandine garnet.

**konoscope** A polariscope fitted with a strongly convergent lens which enables the optical character of doubly-refracting materials to be identified by making visible optical axis interference patterns. See ***interference figures*** and ***polariscope.***

**kopje** An Africaaner word for a small flat-topped hill. This is one of the geological formations associated with the yellow ground top of a kimberlite pipe. See ***kimberlite.***

**koranna stone** A variety of pyrophyllite, also known as South African wonderstone and Ottosdal G stone, used for ornamental objects. R.I. 1.58; S.G. 2.72; H. 1½-2. Opaque, dark grey. Occurrence: South Africa. See ***pyrophyllite.***

**Korea jade** A misleading name for green serpentine.

**Korean Gemmological Association** See ***Gemmological Association of All Korea.***

**Korean Gemmological Institute** See ***Gemmological Institute of Korea.***

**korite** Trade name for ammolite.

**kornerupine** A rare collector's stone comprising a complex borosilicate of aluminium, iron and magnesium. Orthorhombic.

R.I. 1.665, 1.678 to 1.668, 1.680; D.R. −0.013; S.G. 3.28-3.35; H. 6½. Transparent to translucent (occasionally chatoyant), green, greenish-brown. Pleochroism, strong (green, yellow, brown). Occurrence: Burma, Canada, East Africa, the Malagasy Republic, South Africa, Sri Lanka.

**kurnakovite** A collector's stone consisting of a hydrated magnesium borate. $Mg_2B_6O_{11}.15H_2O$. Triclinic. S.G. 1.86; H. 4½. Transparent, colourless, pink.

**kunzite** See ***spodumene.***

**kupfernickel** See ***niccolite.***

**kyanite** A collector's stone (polymorphous with andalusite and sillimanite) comprising the mineral aluminium silicate. Also called disthene (meaning double strength). $Al_2SiO_5$. Triclinic. R.I. 1.715, 1.732; D.R. −0.017; S.G. 3.65-3.69; H. 7 (across width), 5 (across length). Transparent to translucent (occasionally chatoyant), colourless, blue, blue-green. Pleochroism, strong (colourless, light blue, dark blue). Occurrence: Austria, Burma, India, Kashmir, Kenya, Switzerland, USA.

**kyauk-ame** A black jadeite.

**kyauk-átha** A white translucent jadeite.

**Kyropoulos synthesis method** This is a variation of the Czochralski 'pulling' method of crystal growth. The crystal itself is not moved, but the temperature of the melt is lowered from the seed downwards. This is accomplished by lowering the crucible down a temperature gradient so that, as the material solidifies, the crystal grows from the seed. This method produces good crystals with a large diameter in proportion to length. Czochralski crystals have the opposite shape characteristic.

**la beau pearls** Trade name for imitation pearls.
**labradorescence** See ***sheen.***
**labradorite** See ***feldspar.***
**labrador moonstone** The labradorite variety of plagioclase feldspar. See ***feldspar.***
**labrador spar** The labradorite variety of plagioclase feldspar. See ***feldspar.***
**lace agate** A blue and white banded chalcedony, also called blue lace agate.
**lactoid** Trade name for a casein plastic.
**laguna pearls** Trade name for imitation pearls.
**Lake George diamond** A misleading name for the rock crystal variety of quartz.
**Lake Superior fire agate** A misleading name for a glass opal simulant.
**Lake Superior greenstone** See ***chlorastrolite.***
**lamachella** See ***fire marble.***
**lamellar** A crystalline habit or structure composed of straight or curved plates or leaves.
**landerite** A pink grossular garnet in a matrix of white marble. Also called xalostocite and rosolite. Occurrence: Mexico.
**landscape agate** An agate containing dendritic 'tree'-like inclusions resembling a landscape. Also called moss agate.
**landscape marble** A marble comprising a light grey rock having dark brown or black dendritic markings resembling a landscape. Also called Cotham marble. See also ***ruin marble.***
**lap** The rotary metal or wooden disc (sometimes surfaced with cloth or leather) used by lapidaries for polishing gemstones. For diamond polishing the lap is made of cast iron and is called a scaife or a mill (see *Figure T.1*).
**lapidary** A craftsman who cuts and polishes gemstones (other than diamond). See also ***diamond cutter.***
**lapis crucifer** Staurolite crystals.
**lapis lazuli** A complex rock containing several minerals including calcite, hauynite (mainly responsible for the stone's colour), lazurite, noselite, sodalite and flecks of iron pyrites. R.I. 1.5; S.G. 2.7-2.9; H. 5½. Opaque, purple blue to greenish-blue. Occurrence: Afghanistan, Canada, Chile.
**lapper** See ***cross cutter.***
**lardite** See ***agalmatolite.***
**laser** A laser (light amplification by stimulated emission of radiation) is a generator of UV to infra red electromagnetic energy, that is monochromatic, collimated and coherent (i.e. all of

the emitted rays are in step, or in phase). Because of these features it is possible to concentrate the energy of the laser beam into a very small cross-section.

**laser drilling of diamonds** A method by which a diamond's clarity is improved by drilling a fine hole (less than 0.005 inch diameter) through the diamond into an inclusion by means of a laser beam. A bleaching agent is leached via the hole into the inclusion to whiten it. The hole may then be filled with a transparent gel. Because diamond is transparent to the infra red laser beam, and therefore cannot be directly vapourized by its heat, drilling is initiated by placing a spot of amorphous carbon or graphite on the diamond's surface to absorb the laser energy. As the carbon vapourizes it converts the diamond beneath it to carbon, and the drilling process continues.

**lasered diamond** See ***laser drilling of diamonds.***

**laser fingerprinting** A commercial instrument called a Gemprint produces a 'fingerprint' identification picture of a diamond by using the gem to reflect and refract the light from a laser beam onto a Polaroid film. The unique pattern of light spots recorded on the film is caused by minute and individualistic differences in the symmetry and polish on the stone's facets. *Figure L.1.* See also ***fingerprinting.***

**laser gem** Trade name for a diamond simulant doublet having a synthetic sapphire crown and a strontium titanate base.

*Figure L.1* The Gemprint produces a 'fingerprint' picture of a polished diamond by using the gem to reflect and refract the light from a laser beam onto Polaroid film.

**lasque diamond** A flat diamond used by Indian cutters to cover miniature paintings. Also called a portrait stone.

**la tausca pearls** Trade name for imitation pearls.

**lateral axes** Horizontal crystal axes which are at right-angles to the vertical or principle axis in tetragonal, hexagonal, trigonal and orthorhombic crystal systems. See ***crystal axes.***

**lathi** A Burmese weight equal to 1.75 carats. See also ***bali, rati, tickal*** and ***viss.***

**lattice** See ***crystal lattice.***

**lat yay** A cloudy variety of jadeite.

**Laue diffraction** An X-ray technique used to distinguish between natural and cultured pearls. In natural pearls, the aragonite crystals are aligned radially round the pearl with their major axes at right-angles to the surface. When the pearl is placed in a narrow beam of X-rays, these crystals scatter some of the rays and produce a Laue diffraction pattern of spots which can be recorded on a photographic film. Because of the atomic structure within the aragonite crystals, this diffraction pattern will have a hexagonal symmetry for any orientation of the natural pearl. With the nucleated cultured pearl, this hexagonal pattern is only produced in one position where the crystals in the mother-of-pearl bead are parallel to the line of the X-rays. In all other positions of the pearl a four-point symmetry pattern is produced. *Figure L.2.*

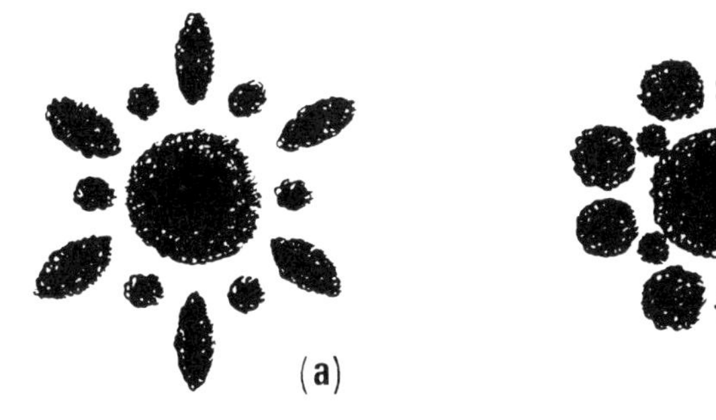


*Figure L.2* The hexagonal Laue diffraction pattern produced when a narrow beam of X-rays penetrates a natural pearl is shown at (a). With a cultured nucleated pearl, both the hexagonal and the four-point pattern, as shown at (b), can occur, depending on the orientation of the bead.

**lauegram** The characteristic pattern of spots produced on a photographic film by passing a narrow X-ray beam through a crystalline material. The pattern is caused by the diffraction of the X-ray beam by the crystal lattice. See ***Laue diffraction.***

**laurelite** See ***idocrase.***

**Laurvikite** A feldspar-rich Norwegian rock used for cladding building facades. Sometimes incorrectly called labradorite. It has a pearl-grey iridescence.

**lava** See ***igneous rock.***

**lava cameo** An opaque grey or brownish-yellow fine-grained limestone marble.

**lavendrine** See ***quartz*** (amethyst variety).

**lavernite** Trade name for synthetic periclase.

**law of reflection** The angle of incidence of a light ray striking a polished surface is equal to its angle of reflection, and both the incident ray, the normal (at the point of incidence), and the reflected ray lie in the same plane.

**law of refraction** Snell's Law states that:

1. When a ray of light passes from one medium into another there exists a definite ratio between the sines of the angle of incidence and the angle of refraction, which is dependent only on the two media and the wavelength of the light.
2. The incident ray, the normal (at the point of incidence) and the refracted ray are all in the same plane.

From *Figure L.3:*

$$\text{Refractive Index} = \frac{\sin \text{ION}}{\sin \text{MOR}}$$

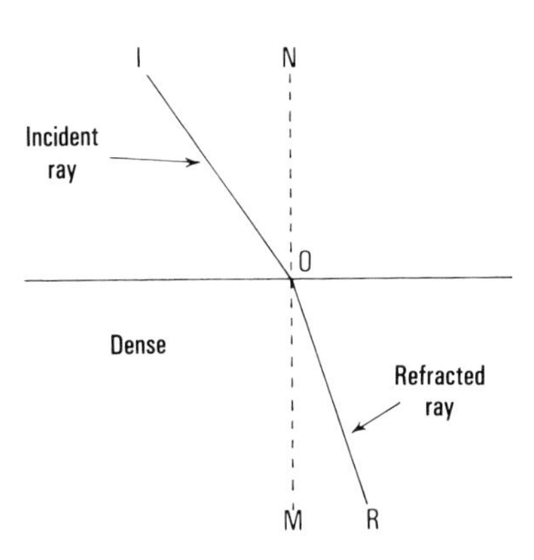


*Figure L.3* An incident ray entering an optically denser medium, such as a gemstone, at an angle other than the normal, is refracted towards the normal. A ray leaving the gemstone and passing into the less dense medium, such as air, will be refracted away from the normal.

In gemmology, R.I. values are quoted in terms of a reference wavelength of 589.3 nm (i.e. sodium light).

**lawsonite** A rare gemstone comprising the mineral calcium aluminium silicate. $CaAl_2(OH)_2Si_2O_7.H_2O$. Orthorhombic. R.I. 1.665, 1.684; D.R. +0.019; S.G. 3.08-3.09; H. 7-8. Transparent, colourless, pale blue. Occurrence: Italy, Scotland, USA.

**laxey diamond** A trade term for very shallow-cut diamond brilliants.

**lazulite** A phosphate of magnesium iron and aluminium. $(Mg,Fe)Al_2(PO_4)_2(OH)_2$. Monoclinic. R.I. 1.615, 1.645; D.R. −0.03; S.G. 3.1-3.2; H. 5½. Transparent to opaque, colourless to dark blue. Pleochroism, strong (colourless, blue). Occurrence: Austria, Brazil, India, the Malagasy Republic, Sweden, USA.

**lazurapatite** A variety of apatite with lapis lazuli. Occurrence: USSR.

**lazurfeldspar** A bluish orthoclase feldspar from the USSR.

**lazurite** An isomorphous combination of hauynite and sodalite present in lapis lazuli.

**lazurquartz** Blue chalcedony.

**lead glass** See ***flint glass.***

**lechatelierite** Silica glass.

**Lechleitner emerald simulants** Faceted beryls coated with a hydrothermally deposited layer of synthetic emerald by Lechleitner of Innsbruck, Austria. Constants are similar to those of natural emerald. Later Lechleitner emeralds consist of alternating layers of colourless and green synthetic beryl, also grown hydrothermally.

**lechosos opal** A variety of opal having deep green and red iridescence.

**legrandite** A rare gemstone consisting of the mineral hydrated zinc arsenate. Monoclinic. R.I. 1.675, 1.735; D.R. +0.06; S.G. 3.98-4.04; H. 5. Transparent, bright yellow. Occurrence: Mexico.

**Lennix synthetic emeralds** Synthetic flux-melt emeralds grown by M. Lens of France. The process was developed by M. Lens in the De Beers Diamond Research Laboratory, Johannesburg, South Africa, and produces four-sided rather than hexagonal crystals. R.I. 1.562–1.566; D.R. −0.004; S.G. 2.65.

**lens** A polished piece of glass or transparent material with one or both sides curved, to converge, disperse or collimate light rays. See ***hand lens.***

**lens cut** A gemstone cut in which the crown is cut in a series of long parallel facets forming a cylindrical dome-shape, and the pavilion is step cut.

**lepidocrocite** A brown hydrated iron oxide with the same chemical composition as goethite ($Fe_2O_3.H_20$). It commonly occurs in fibrous or tabular form. Orthorhombic. S.G. 4.3; H.5. Translucent, red to reddish-brown.

**lepidolite** An ornamental stone comprising a complex silicate of potassium, lithium and aluminium. Also called lithia mica. Monoclinic. Mean R.I. 1.55; S.G. 2.8-2.9; H. 3½. Opaque, rose red. Occurrence: the Malagasy Republic, Namibia, USA, USSR, Zimbabwe.

**lestergem** Trade name for a synthetic spinel diamond simulant.

**leucite** A collector's stone comprising the mineral potassium aluminium silicate. $KAl(SiO_3)_2$. Cubic. R.I. 1.51; S.G. 2.45–2.50; H. 5½–6. Transparent, colourless. Occurrence: Germany, Italy, USA.

**leuco-sapphire** A colourless sapphire.

**leveridge gauge** See ***caliper gauge.***

**Libyan glass** A nearly pure silica glass found in the Libyan desert. $SiO_2$. Amorphous. R.I. 1.46; S.G. 2.21; H. 6. Transparent to translucent, greenish-yellow.

**liddicoatite** A brown, blue or pink/green parti-coloured elbaite-type tourmaline, having (unlike elbaite) a high calcium content and little sodium.

**life** (of a diamond) A term used to describe the overall brilliance of a polished diamond resulting from its surface lustre and from the total internal reflection of light from its pavilion facets.

**light** A form of visible electromagnetic energy spanning the wavelengths of the spectrum from 400 nm to 750 nm. (See *Figure E.1.*) White light is composed of an approximately equal mixture of all the colours, or wavelengths, that make up the visible spectrum. Non-white light is specified in terms of its hue (i.e. colour of predominant wavelength), saturation (depth or strength of dominant colour) and lightness (shade). The velocity of light waves is 300 000 kilometers per second.

**light brown** A colour grade for polished diamonds. See ***Colour Grading Standards*** in Appendix B.

**light cape** A UK colour grade for polished diamonds. See ***Colour Grading Standards*** in Appendix B.

**light-field illumination** Illumination in which light is transmitted through the specimen to the eye. See also ***dark-field illumination*** and ***incident illumination.***

**light guide** See ***fibre optics.***

**lightning tubes** See ***fulgurites.***

**light spill test** A simple method of distinguishing a brilliant-cut diamond from a simulant (*provided they are modern ideal cuts*). The stone is viewed against a dark background, with the table facet at right-angles to the line of vision. It will appear uniformly bright because its pavilion facets will act as reflecting mirrors. If the stone is a diamond, it will be possible to tilt it (so that the eye begins to look into the table facet at increasingly shallow angles) without losing the uniformly bright appearance of the pavilion facets, even when this angle becomes very small (5 to 10°). If the stone is a simulant, and has a lower refractive index than

*Figure L.4* Five diamond simulants photographed at an angle to illustrate the 'light spill' test. The centre stone is a YAG, and shows the greatest light leakage from its pavilion facets due to its relatively low R.I. (1.83). The top left stone is a GGG (R.I. = 1.97), top right is a lithium niobate (R.I. = 2.25), bottom left is a cubic zirconia (R.I. = 2.16) and bottom right is a strontium titanate (R.I. = 2.41) which, like diamond (R.I. = 2.42) shows no light leakage.

diamond, the pavilion facets furthest from the eye will begin to look black as the stone is tilted below 60° (i.e. light will 'spill' out of these facets instead of being reflected back — see *Figure L.4*). The lower the refractive index of the stone, the more marked will be the effect. This test will not distinguish strontium titanate (R.I. 2.41) or synthetic rutile (R.I. 2.75) from diamond, but these two diamond simulants are recognizable by their excessive dispersion or fire.

**light yellow** A colour grade for polished diamonds. See ***Colour Grading Standards*** in Appendix B.

**lignite** A brown coal intermediate between peat and bituminous coal. Used as a jet simulant.

**lily pad** A form of inclusion consisting of more or less discoidal films of liquid surrounding small grains of chromite. Found only in peridot.

**limestone** A sedimentary rock composed mainly of calcium carbonate.

**limonite** A brown hydrated iron oxide forming the matrix in which turquoise often occurs.

**Linde A** See ***aluminium oxide.***

**Linde simulated diamond** Trade name for the man-made diamond simulant yttrium aluminium garnet.

**Linde synthetic emeralds** Synthetic emeralds produced by the hydrothermal process. R.I. 1.571, 1.578; D.R. −0.007; S.G. 2.678. Linde Division of the Union Carbide Corporation, East Chicago, USA. Now produced by Vacuum Ventures Inc. as Regency synthetic emerald.

**Linde synthetic star corundum** A synthetic star corundum in which asterism is induced by adding titanium oxide to the alumina powder in the Verneuil flame-fusion process. The finished boule is then re-heated to precipitate the titanium oxide as rutile needles along the planes of the three lateral crystal axes. See ***Verneuil furnace.***

**lines of Retzius** Term used to describe wavy parallel lines visible in dentine ivory. As these are not growth lines, but an optical effect produced by the dentine substructure, the term 'engine turned' is a more correct description.

**linobate** Trade name for the man-made diamond simulant lithium niobate.

**lintonite** A plain green variety of thomsonite (also called winchellite).

**liquid inclusion** A fissure or void within a gemstone which contains a liquid (often the remains of the aqueous 'mother' solution from which the gem crystallized).

**lithia amethyst** A misleading name for the kunzite variety of spodumene.

**lithia emerald** A misleading name for the hiddenite variety of spodumene.

**lithia mica** See ***lepidolite.***

**lithium amethyst** See ***lithia amethyst.***

**lithium niobate** A man-made diamond simulant (introduced in 1969) which has no counterpart in nature. $LiNbO_3$ (niobium, Nb, has the alternative name columbium, Cb). Trigonal. R.I. 2.21, 2.30; D.R. +0.09; S.G. 4.64; H. 5½. Transparent, colourless or green, red, blue/violet, yellow (coloured crystals are doped with transition metal oxides). Pleochroism, distinct in all colours. Crystals are grown by the Czochralski process.

**lithium tantalate** A man-made scientific crystal suitable for use as a diamond simulant. $LiTaO_3$. R.I. 2.175, 2.180; D.R. +0.005; S.G. 7.454; H. 5½-6. Transparent, colourless.

**lithosphere** The outer layer of the Earth comprising the crust and upper mantle and having a thickness of 30-40 miles. The outer section of the lithosphere contains aluminium silicate rocks (e.g. feldspars) and is the most important area in the genesis of gemstones.

**lithoxylite** An opalized wood.

**litoslazuli** A massive purple fluorspar.

**liver opal** See ***menilite.***

**lode** A vein of metallic ore in a rock.

**lodestone** Name given to a magnetite sample having a natural magnetic polarity which makes it suitable for use as a magnet. See ***magnetite.***

**long wave UV** See ***ultra violet light.***

**lonsdaleite** A diamond-like polymorph of carbon found in meteorites. Lonsdaleite has a hexagonal crystal structure, and was discovered by Dame Kathleen Lonsdale.

**lost-wax casting** A method of producing a cast metal object from a wax pattern. The wax pattern is encased in a gypsum-based moulding material, and then melted out, the vacated space forming the casting mould.

**lotus leaf** See *lily pad.*

**loupe** See ***head loupe, triplet (lens)*** and ***hand lens.***

**loupe clean** A misleading clarity grading term for polished diamonds. Its use is prohibited by the American Gem Society. Loupe clean implies 'flawless' under 10× magnification, and this is the preferred term.

**love stone** Aventurine quartz.

**lower break facets** See ***break facets.***

**low zircon** A variety of zircon in which alpha-particle bombardment from once radioactive uranium and thorium impurities have almost completely broken down the stone's internal crystalline structure. As a result, low zircons have lower constants than normal 'high' zircons and are virtually amorphous. R.I. 1.78-1.84; S.G. 3.9-4.1; H. 6½. Such zircons are usually green or brown, and are described as metamict. See also ***high zircon*** and ***zircon.***

**lucidoscope** An apparatus used before the introduction of the endoscope for viewing the zonal structure in some thin-skinned cultured pearls by means of an intense beam of light directed through the immersed pearl.

**lucinite** A variety of variscite from Utah, USA.

**ludlamite** A hydrated phosphorous oxide. $(Fe,Mg,Mn)_3(PO_4)_2 4H_20$. R.I. 1.653, 1.697; D.R. 0.044; S.G. 3.1; H. 3-4. Green. Occurrence: Cornwall (UK), West Germany, USA.

**lumachella** See ***fire marble.***

**luminescence** When some substances acquire surplus energy in one form or another (below the level which would cause incandescence) they emit a visible 'cold' radiation which is often characteristic for that substance. The mechanism producing this cold radiation, or luminescence, is associated with the excitation of atoms within the substance. Of the many varieties of luminescence, photoluminescence is the most useful in gemmology, and results from the application of energy in the form of electromagnetic radiation (i.e. visible light, UV light or X-rays). Some gem materials luminesce with different characteristic colours when irradiated with SW UV, LW UV or X-rays, and this can form a useful means of identification (see ***Table of Fluorescence of Principal Gemstones*** in Appendix I). See also ***bioluminescence, cathodoluminescence, electroluminescence, fluorescence, thermophosphorescence, triboluminescence*** and ***ultra violet light.***

**lunette** A step-cut stone having a half moon profile.

**lussatite** Chalcedony.

**luster** See ***lustre.***

**lusterite** Trade name for a synthetic rutile diamond simulant.

**lustigem** Trade name for the man-made diamond simulant strontium titanate.

**lustre** The lustre of a gemstone is the characteristic reflective property of its surface. The following terms are used to describe gemstone lustres:

*adamantine* — the high surface reflectivity of diamond, high zircons and demantoid garnet.

*greasy* — the surface of soapstone and nephrite.

*metallic* — the high lustre associated with metals, and seen in some metallic compounds (e.g. pyrites).

*pearly* — the lustre seen with mother-of-pearl.

*resinous* — the lustre of amber.

*silky* — the fibrous lustre of satin spar.

*vitreous* — the glass-like lustre typical of the majority of gemstones.

*waxy* — the almost matt surface of turquoise and jadeite.

**lux sapphire** A misleading name for cordierite.

**LW UV** See ***ultra violet light.***

**lydian stone** See ***basanite.***

**lynx eye** A variety of labradorite with green iridescence.

**lynx sapphire** A misleading name for cordierite.

**mabe pearls** Cultured blister pearls produced by cementing a small pellet of mother-of-pearl to the inside surface of the mollusc's shell. The resulting blister pearl is sawn out of the shell and a dome-shaped piece of mother-of-pearl cemented to its base to cover the area lacking in nacre. In a later production method, a soft bead is used in place of the mother-of-pearl pellet. This bead is subsequently removed from the grown pearl, and a smaller glass bead cemented in its place. S.G. 2.72-2.78.

**maccle** See ***macles.***

**macles** A shape category for rough diamonds consisting of a contact-twin diamond crystal in which the two halves have grown with one half rotated through 180° to the other. A macle usually takes the form of a flat triangular crystal, the junction between the two halves being visible as a 'herring bone' pattern round the edge of the triangle. See also ***chips, cleavages, melée, shapes*** and ***stones.***

**macro axis** See ***brachy axis.***

**macro pinacoid** The faces of a macro pinacoid are cut by the longer (macro) axis in an orthorhombic or triclinic crystal. See ***basal pinacoid, brachy pinacoid*** and ***pinacoid.***

**macroscopic** Visible to the naked eye. See ***microscopic.***

**Madagascar aquamarine** A blue variety of beryl from the Malagasy Republic.

**Madeira topaz** A misleading name for the citrine variety of quartz.

**magalux** Trade name for a synthetic spinel diamond simulant.

**magic eye** Trade name for a honey-coloured simulant of cat's eye chrysoberyl. $MgTiO_3$.

**magma** The molten or semi-molten material beneath the Earth's crust which, on cooling, solidifies to form igneous rocks.

**magna cut** A 101 facet (plus culet) diamond consisting of a ten-sided table surrounded by 60 crown facets and backed by 40 pavilion facets. *Figure M.1.*

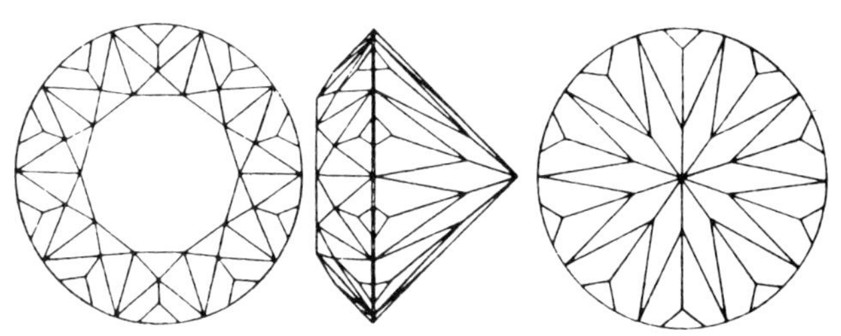

*Figure M.1* The magna cut.

**magnesioaxinite** A colour-change magnesium calcium aluminium silicate member of the axinite group. Triclinic. R.I. 1.656, 1.668; D.R. +0.012; S.G. 3.178; H. 6½. Transparent, pale blue (in daylight), pale violet (under tungsten light). Pleochroism, strong (pale blue, pale violet, pale grey). Occurrence: Tanzania.

**magnesite** A collector's stone comprising the mineral magnesium carbonate. $MgCO_3$. Trigonal. R.I. 1.515, 1.717; D.R. −0.202; S.G. 3.0-3.12; H. 4. Transparent, colourless. Occurrence: World-wide (gem quality from Brazil).

**magnetism** The magnetic phenomenon produced by an electric current and inherent in some materials. The two main types of magnetism are paramagnetism (magnetism induced in materials such as cobalt, iron, nickel, steel, etc., which are attracted towards the inducing field), and diamagnetism in which the induced magnetism tends to repel the material transversely away from the inducing field (e.g. bismuth).

**magnetite** One of the members of the spinel group and a magnetic component of crystalline schists and basalts. $Fe_3O_4$. Cubic. S.G. 4.9-5.2 H. 5½-6½. Black opaque. Occurrence: Widespread, but specimen crystals mainly from Austria, Canada, Italy, Mexico, Sweden, Switzerland, USA. Because of its magnetic properties it is also called lodestone.

**magnetite-jade** An opaque jade coloured black by magnetite inclusions. Sometimes electrolytically plated with swathes of gold. S.G. (depending on magnetite content) 3.4-4.4; H. 5½-7.

**magneto-hydrostatic separation** A technique used for the final separation of diamond from a concentrate of crushed aggregate and gravels.

**magnification** A term usually expressed as a linear (i.e. length or diameter) magnification factor of lenses and microscopes. The overall magnification factor of a microscope is the product of the magnification of its eyepiece and its objective lens. Doubling the magnification of the objective will halve the microscope's working distance (i.e. the distance between the objective and the specimen). The magnification factor of the eyepiece does not affect the working distance.

**magnifiers** See ***hand lens, head loupe, compound microscope, binocular microscope, monocular microscope, Greenough microscope, microscope*** and ***triplet (lens).***

**main facets** A general term which refers to the large crown and pavilion facets of a brilliant-cut stone.

**make** See ***cut.***

**makeables** Rough diamonds which can be polished without the need for preliminary sawing (e.g. chips, cleavages and macles). See ***sawables.***

**making up** The weighing and sizing of rough gem diamonds in the De Beers Central Selling Organization which follows the sorting operations, and precedes the splitting operation (prior to the sights). See ***splitting*** and ***sights.***

**malachite** A hydrated copper carbonate. $Cu_2(OH)_2CO_3$. Monoclinic. R.I. 1.655, 1.909; D.R. −0.254; S.G. 3.8; H. 4. Opaque, light and dark greens with concentric banding. Occurrence: Australia, Chile, Namibia, South Africa, USA, USSR, Zaire.

**malacolite** See ***diopside.***

**malacon** A glassy brown variety of zircon.

**malaya garnet** See ***umbalite garnet.***

**malleability** A property of a metal which allows it to be hammered, stretched or pressed into a shape without the formation of stress cracks or factures.

**mamillary** An external mineral shape or habit consisting of rounded intersecting surfaces (a larger form of botryoidal) e.g. haematite.

**mammoth ivory** See ***fossil ivory.***

**manchandi** A Sri Lankan weight equal to 1.15 carats. See also ***chevvü.***

**manchurian jade** A misleading name for soapstone.

**manganese** One of the eight transition metals which are mainly responsible for colour in gemstones. Mn. Stones coloured by manganese include rhodochrosite, rhodonite, rose quartz and spessartine. Atomic number 25; atomic weight 54.93; melting point 1250°C; S.G. 7.4.

**manganese dioxide** An abrasive powder used by lapidaries for gemstone polishing.

**manganese spar** See ***rhodochrosite.***

**manganotantalite** A collector's stone comprising the mineral manganese tantalum oxide. $MnTa_2O_6$. Orthorhombic. R.I. 2.14, 2.22 to 2.17, 2.25; D.R. +0.08; S.G. 7.52-7.92; H. 5½-6. Transparent, red. Occurrence: Mozambique.

**mangelin** An Indian weight equivalent to 1.75 carats. See also ***rati*** and ***tola.***

**Manilla shell** Pearl shell from the Philippines.

**man-made stones** The term generally applied to synthesized gemstones which have no counterpart in nature (e.g. lithium niobate, gadolinium gallium garnet, yttrium aluminium garnet). See ***synthetic stones.***

**mantle** The protective inner tissues of the pearl-producing mollusc which secretes nacre.

**mantle** That portion of the Earth's structure, 1780 miles thick, between the Earth's crust and its core.

**mantle quartz** A quartz in which a deposit of silica took place forming a transparent coating 1-2mm thick which has the appearance of a cloak or mantle. *Figure M.2.*

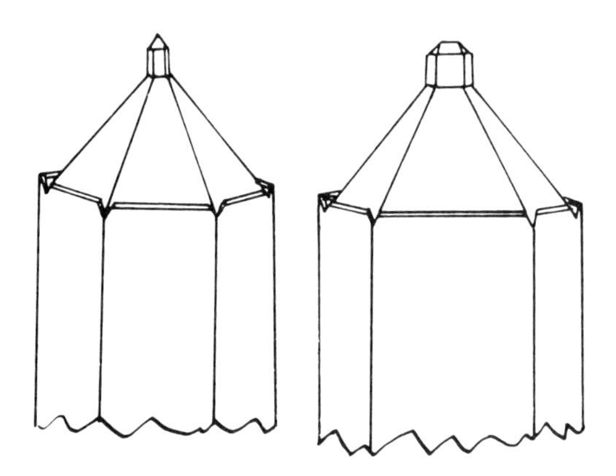

*Figure M.2* Mantle growth disturbance in quartz crystals found in fissures at Safien, Grisons, Switzerland.

**manufactured stones** See ***composite stones*** and ***synthetic stones.***
**man yu** A blood-red variety of jade.
**Maori stone** New Zealand nephrite.
**marble** A crystalline aggregate of calcite (often having a lustrous granular texture) derived from compacted or metamorphosed limestone. Commercially the term marble includes a number of ornamental stones which depart from the foregoing definition. Occurrence: World-wide.
**marcasite** A dimorphous form of pyrites which, unlike pyrites, is rarely used in jewellery. $FeS_2$. Orthorhombic. S.G. 4.85-4.90. Opaque, bronze-yellow. Occurrence: World-wide.
**marekanite** A smoky-brown, grey or black obsidian. Occurrence: Mexico, USSR.
**Margaritifera** A genus of freshwater pearl-bearing mussel.
**marialite** See ***scapolite.***
**mari diamond** A misleading name for the rock crystal variety of quartz.
**marine terrace** A wave-cut coastal shelf or raised beach.
**mariposite** A foliated rock containing green streaks of mica.
**marmarosch diamond** A misleading name for the rock crystal variety of quartz.
**marmora diamond** A misleading name for the rock crystal variety of quartz.

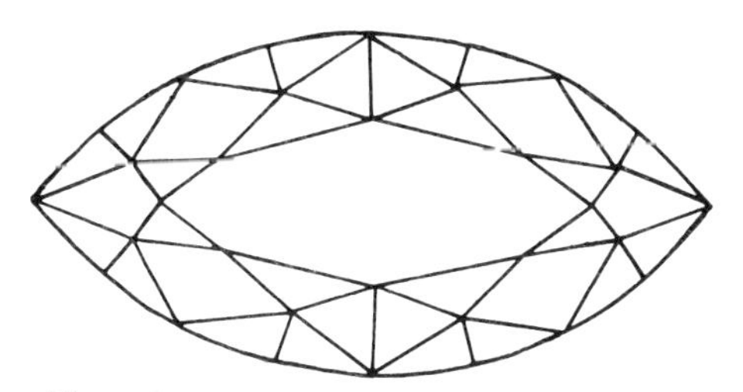

*Figure M.3* The marquise or navetter cut.

**marquise** A variant of the 57-facet brilliant-cut (also called a navette), having a boat-shaped profile with pointed ends. *Figure M.3.*

**marvelite** Trade name for the man-made diamond simulant strontium titanate.

**marvella pearls** Trade name for imitation pearls.

**masai anyolite** See ***anyolite.***

**mascot emerald** A misleading name for a soudé emerald made from three pieces of natural beryl.
See ***composite stones.***

**mass** The standard unit of mass is the kilogram (kg). Mass is the measure of the inertia of a body (i.e. its acceleration when a force is applied to it), while *weight* is the force exerted on that body by the Earth's gravity. The weight of an object varies slightly from place to place on the Earth's surface (being greater at the poles than at the equator because of the Earth's flattened spheroid shape), while the mass of a body remains constant. An object having a mass of 1 kg, which weighs 1 kg on Earth, would, for example, have a *weight* of 1/6 kg on the moon, although its *mass* would still be 1 kg. *Figure M.4.*

**mass aqua** A misleading name for a glass simulant of aquamarine.

**massive** Without external crystalline shape.

**massive grossular** A hydrogrossular garnet, also misleadingly called Transvaal jade and African jade. See ***garnet.***

**master stones** Carefully selected polished stones which are used as standards for comparison colour grading.

**mastodon ivory** Dentine fossil ivory from the extinct mastodon elephant. Occurrence: Alaska.

**matrix** The 'mother rock' in which gemstones crystallize.

**matura diamond** A misleading name for colourless zircon.

**maw-sit-sit** See ***jade-albite.***

**maxixe** See ***beryl.***

**maxixe-type beryl** A beryl whose colour is due to $CO_3$ impurity ions.

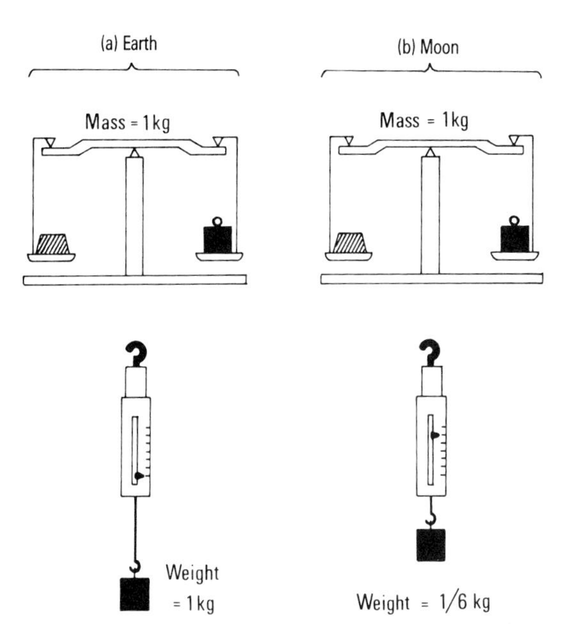


*Figure M.4* Sketch illustrating the difference between mass and weight.

**mayaite** A diopside-jadeite.
**mazarin cut** An early diamond cut having a cushion-shaped girdle, with seventeen crown facets (including the table) and sixteen pavilion facets (plus a large culet).
**mecca stone** The cornelian variety of chalcedony.
**mechanical dop** See ***dop.***
**mechanical faceting head** See ***faceting head.***
**medfordite** A moss agate variety of chalcedony.
**medina emerald** A misleading trade name for a green glass emerald simulant.
**meerschaum** A decomposition product of serpentine comprising a complex hydrous magnesium silicate. Also known as sepiolite. Used for pipe bowls, cigarette holders and jewellery. Orthorhombic (cryptocrystalline). R.I. 1.53; S.G. 2.0; H. 2-2½. Opaque (very porous), white, creamy-white, grey, reddish. Occurrence: Turkey.
**meionite** See ***scapolite.***
**melange** An assortment of polished diamonds of mixed sizes and/or qualities over 0.25 carats.
**melanite** See ***garnet*** (andradite).
**melatope** A dark spot in the centre of the interference figure seen around the optic axis of a doubly-refractive gem under

convergent, polarized light. This spot is absent in quartz. See also ***konoscope, isogyre*** and ***isochrome.***

**melée** An assortment of small polished diamonds of mixed sizes and/or qualities (usually under 0.25 carat). See ***melange.***

**melée** A shape category for rough diamonds consisting of unbroken octahedral crystals (or distorted octahedra) under 2 carats. See ***cleavages, macles, shapes*** and ***stones.***

**melichrysos** A yellow zircon.

**melinophane** A collector's stone comprising the mineral beryllium calcium sodium fluo-silicate. Tetragonal. R.I. 1.593, 1.612; D.R. −0.019; S.G. 3.0; H. 5. Transparent, yellow. Occurrence: Norway.

**menilite** An impure common opal with grey and brown banding.

**mercury-vapour lamp** A mercury discharge lamp having strong emission lines ranging from yellow to the far ultra-violet. When used as a source of UV, these lamps are filtered to remove all but the 366 nm (LW) or 254 nm (SW) UV emission lines.

**meru sapphire** A misleading name for blue zoisite.

**mesolite** A collector's stone consisting of a silicate of sodium, calcium and aluminium, this is one of the zeolite group of minerals, midway between natrolite and scolecite $(Na_2,Ca)Al_2Si_3O_{10}.2H_2O$. Monoclinic (fibrous). R.I. 1.5; S.G. 2.29; H. 5. Translucent to opaque (silky), white or colourless. Occurrence: World-wide.

**meson** An unstable elementary particle present in atomic nuclei and cosmic rays. It has a positive or negative charge equal to that of an electron, but its mass is about 150 times greater.

**Mesozoic** The third era of geological time between 225 and 65 million years ago and comprising the ***Triassic, Jurassic*** and ***Cretaceous*** periods. See also ***Cenozoic, Palaeozoic*** and ***Precambrian.***

**meta-jade** A misleading name for a Japanese glass jade simulant.

**metallic lustre** See ***lustre.***

**metameric** The term applied to materials or surfaces which appear as different colours in different types of lighting. This colour-change effect is strongest in the alexandrite variety of chrysoberyl, which appears red in tungsten light and green in daylight. The effect is due to absorption bands in the material. In the case of alexandrite, the cause is a broad band centered on 580 nm.

**metamict** A term used to describe a mineral whose crystalline structure has been broken down to an amorphous state by alpha-particle bombardment. See ***ekanite*** and ***low zircon.***

**metamorphic rock** Pre-existing igneous or sedimentary rocks which have been subjected to high pressures and temperatures, and as a result have undergone changes of chemistry and shape without passing through a liquid phase.

**metamorphism** An alteration in the structure and chemistry of rocks brought about by natural agencies (e.g. heat and pressure).

**meteoric diamond** See ***lonsdaleite.***

**meteorites** Extra-terrestrial objects (mainly composed of iron and nickel or of olivine, pyroxene and feldspar) which on impact with the Earth are suspected as being possible sources of tektites. Diamond crystals are also found in meteorites.

**methylene iodide** A volatile 'heavy' liquid used in the approximation of specific gravity, and as an immersion fluid for gemstone inspection and for the estimation of refractive index. $CH_2I_2$. R.I. 1.74; S.G. 3.32.

**metric carat** See ***carat weight.***

**metric grain** See ***grain*** (diamond and pearl).

**Mexican agate** A banded calcite or aragonite.

**Mexican diamond** A misleading name for the rock crystal variety of quartz.

**Mexican fire opal** See ***opal.***

**Mexican jade** A misleading name for green-dyed calcite.

**Mexican onyx** A misleading name for banded calcite.

**Mexican water opal** See ***opal.***

**miarolitic** A coarse-grained granite containing irregular cavities lined with crystals.

**mica** An aluminium silicate which, when it occurs in crystals, can be separated into thin transparent sheets. Also found as small lustrous particles in granite and aventurine quartz.

**micatite** Trade name for a phenolic resin plastic.

**microcline** See ***feldspar.***

**micro-diamonds** Rough diamonds of grit size which are too small to be recovered commercially, but are sometimes extracted for scientific research work.

**microlite** A collector's stone comprising the mineral calcium pyrotantalate. $(Na,Ca)_2Ta_2O_6(O,OH,F)$. Cubic. R.I. 1.93–2.02; S.G. 5.5; H. 5½. Transparent, green, brownish-green, yellowish-brown to hyacinth-red. Occurrence: Elba, Sweden, USA.

**micrometer** A precision engineering instrument for the measurement of small dimensions. A digital electronic version has been used to measure the proportions of polished diamonds when grading them for cut.

**micrometre** A unit of length measurement. One micrometre (μm) is equal to one millionth of a metre. In the measurement of wavelengths, 1 μm = 1000 nm = 10 000 Å. See ***Ångström unit, electron volt, nanometre*** and ***wave number.***

**micron** A unit of length measurement. One micron (μ) is equal to one millionth of a metre. The unit is now superseded by the

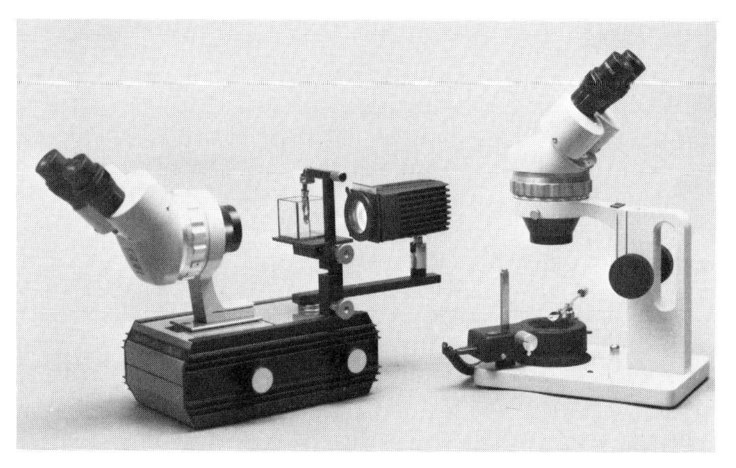

*Figure M.5* Horizontal and vertical-format stereo zoom microscopes. (Eickhorst)

micrometre.

**microphotography** See ***photomicrograph.***

**microprobe** See ***electron microprobe.***

**microscope** An optical instrument designed to produce enlarged images of objects by means of lenses. For gemmological purposes, the most useful range of magnification is 10× to 40×. Microscopes are designed in monocular and binocular/stereo versions. Magnifications can be changed by replacing the eyepieces, by adding supplementary lenses to the objective, by using a multi-objective lens turret, or by means of a zoom lens. See ***compound microscope, Greenough microscope, dark-field illumination, immersion cell, incident illumination*** and ***light-field illumination.*** *Figure M.5.*

**microscopic** Too small to be visible to the naked eye. See ***macroscopic.***

**midge stone** A moss agate variety of chalcedony in which the dendritic inclusions resemble a swarm of mosquitoes. Also called mosquito agate.

**milkama pebbles** Trade name for jasper pebbles. See ***quartz.***

**milk opal** Milky-white common opal.

**milky quartz** A white translucent crystalline quartz whose milky appearance is due to minute liquid-filled cavities.

**mill** The diamond cutting bench containing the scaife (see *Figure T.1*). The term is also used to describe the plant which separates diamonds from kimberlite rock by crushing.

**Miller indices** Indices used to define crystallographic planes, faces and habits. Crystal faces are often parallel to one or more axes,

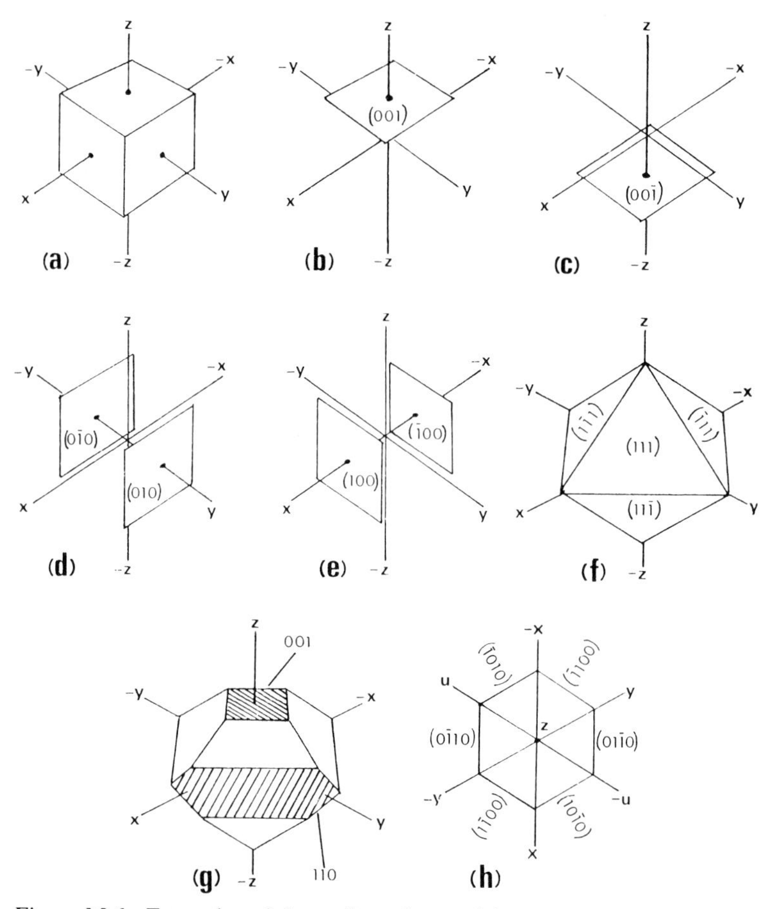


*Figure M.6* Examples of the coding of crystal faces and planes by Miller indices.

and therefore only meet them at infinity. Miller indices are based on reciprocals of ratios of the distances between the crystal origin and the point at which a face is cut by an axis (the reciprocal of infinity being conveniently zero).

Miller indices consist of three numbers for a three-axis crystal. In a cubic crystal, the six crystal faces are cut by the axes x, y, z (*Figure M.6[a]*). The crystal face (*Figure M.6[b]*) is given the Miller index (001) because it is parallel to the x axis (intercept ratio = infinity, reciprocal = 0), and to the y axis (= 0), but is intersected by the z axis (= 1). The same face on the opposite side of the crystal (*Figure M.6[c]*) is identified as ($00\bar{1}$), because with the Miller system an intercept on an axis pointing away from the observer is given a negative index ($\bar{1}$). The two faces intercepted by the y, -y axis are coded (010) and (0$\bar{1}$0). The remaining two faces, intercepted by the x, -x axis, are identified as (100) and ($\bar{1}$00).

Four of the eight faces of an octahedron are similarly identified in *Figure M.6(f),* and *Figure M.6(g)* shows the Miller indices for cubic and rhombic dodecahedron *planes* in the same crystal.

When an index is enclosed by brackets this indicates a crystal face, as in (100). If the index is enclosed in *braces,* this indicates a form comprising all the faces generated by that index. For example, {100} denotes a cube, and {111} denotes an octahedron. Used without brackets or braces, an index indicates a plane within the crystal (as illustrated by 001 and 110 in *Figure M.6[g]).*

The system was adapted by A. Bravais to suit the four-axes hexagonal/trigonal system. With Miller-Bravais indices, the sequence of the four axes is x, y, u, z, and their polarities are arranged as shown in *Figure M.6(h).*

**millerite** A rare collector's stone comprising the mineral nickel sulphide. Sometimes called capillary pyrites. Trigonal. S.G. 5.3-5.65; H. 3-3½. Translucent, cloudy yellowish-green. Occurrence: Namibia.

**millimicron** A thousandth part of a micron; this unit of length is now called a nanometre.

**mimetite** A collector's stone comprising the mineral lead arsenate. $Pb_5(AsO_4)_3Cl$. Hexagonal. S.G. 7.1; H. 3½. Transparent to opaque, pale yellow to bright orange. Occurrence: Mexico.

**mine** An excavation in the Earth made for the purpose of extracting minerals. See ***diamond mine.***

**mineral** A homogeneous substance, formed in the Earth's crust by the forces of inorganic nature, whose chemical composition and physical characteristics are constant within narrow limits.

**mineraloid** A mineralogical term applied to those organic materials, such as amber and jet, which are mined from the Earth.

**mineralogy** The science of minerals.

**minimum deviation** See ***angle of minimum deviation.***

**Miocene** A division of the Tertiary period of the Cenozoic era of geological time, 26-7 million years ago. See ***Cenozoic.***

**miridis** Trade name for a synthetic rutile diamond simulant.

**mirror foiling** See ***chaton*** and ***foiled stone.***

**miscal** An Iranian weight equal to 36.44 carats or 40 Indian ratis. See also ***dirhem.***

**mispickel** Arsenical pyrites.

**mixed cut** A gemstone cut used mainly for coloured stones in which the crown is brilliant cut and the pavilion step or trap cut.

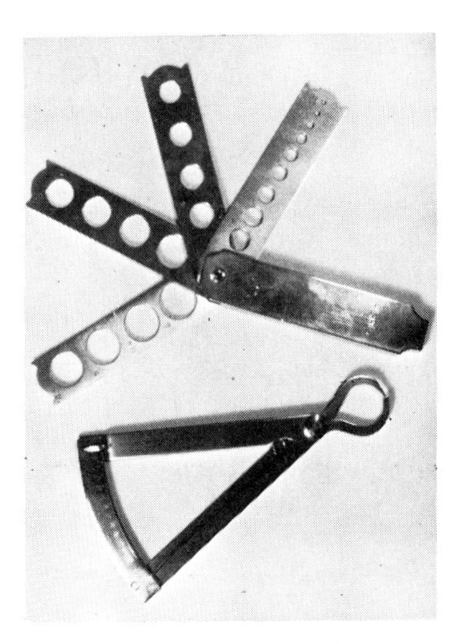

*Figure M.7* Diamond hole gauges (top) and the Moe diamond gauge (bottom).

**mixte** A composite stone, consisting of a natural crown, and a glass or synthetic pavilion. See ***composite stones.***

**mizzonite** See ***scapolite.***

**mocha stone** A variety of agate containing dendritic inclusions. Also called moss agate in the UK and America. Translucent, green, brown and black.

**Moe diamond gauge** A caliper gauge for estimating the weight of brilliant-cut diamonds. *Figure M.7.* See ***caliper gauge.***

**mogok diamond** A misleading name for a colourless Burmese topaz.

**Mohs' hardness scale** See ***hardness.***

**moldavite** A variety of tektite consisting of 75% silica. Amorphous. R.I. 1.488-1.503; S.G. 2.34-2.39; H. 5½. Transparent to translucent, bottle-green to brown-green. Occurrence: Australia (australite), Czechoslovakia (moldavite), USA (georgiaite).

**molecular weight** The sum of the atomic weights of the elements in a molecule of a substance. See ***atomic weight.***

**molecule** A molecule is formed when two or more elements combine together, their atoms joining to form a stable molecule of a new substance or compound. The resulting molecule is the smallest part of the new substance which can have a separate stable existence (e.g. oxygen atoms are more stable when combined together in pairs to form the *diatomic* molecule $O_2$). However many elements are stable as single atoms (and can therefore be regarded as both atom and molecule). Such elements are called *monatomic.*

**mollusc** A phylum (Mollusca) of soft-bodied hard-shelled animals which includes cuttlefish, limpets, mussels, oysters, scallops and snails.

**molochites** A green jasper variety of quartz.

**momme** A Japanese cultured pearl weight. 1 momme = 75 pearl grains or 3.75 gram, or 18.75 carat.

**mona marble** A serpentine marble found on Holy Island off the coast of Wales, UK.

**monatomic** See ***molecule.***

**monazite** A rare colour-change phosphate exhibiting radioactivity and containing thorium, lanthanum and cerium, together with traces of other rare earths. $(Ce,La,Th)PO_4$. Monoclinic. R.I. 1.795, 1.845; D.R. +0.05; S.G. 4.9-5.4; H. 5½. Transparent, reddish-orange (tungsten light), bright green (mercury vapour lamp or fluorescent lighting). Occurrence: the Malagasy Republic, Sri Lanka.

**monobromonaphthalene** A volatile liquid used as a dilutant for the 'heavy' liquids bromoform and methylene iodide, and as an immersion fluid for gemstone inspection and for the estimation of refractive index. $C_{10}H_7Br$. R.I. 1.66; S.G. 1.49.

**monochromatic light** A light containing only a very narrow waveband of electromagnetic energy. The standard yellow monochromatic light used for refractometer measurements is derived from a sodium vapour lamp (this actually consists of two very closely spaced emission lines, whose mean value is 589.3 nm).

**monoclinic system** A crystal system having three axes, all of different lengths. Two axes are inclined to each other (at an angle other than 90°), the third one is at right-angles to the other two. There is one axis of symmetry (two-fold), a plane of symmetry and a centre of symmetry. *Figure M.8.*

**monocular microscope** A microscope fitted with a single eyepiece and objective. See ***magnifiers.***

**Montana ruby** A misleading name for red garnet.

**Mont Blanc ruby** A misleading name for rose quartz.

**moonstone** See ***feldspar.***

**morganite** See ***beryl.***

**morion** A black variety of smoky quartz.

**moro** A Japanese blood-red coral.

**moroxite** A bluish-green apatite from Norway.

**morse ivory** Dentine ivory derived from the tusks of the walrus.

**mosaic** A pattern or picture made by fitting together small pieces

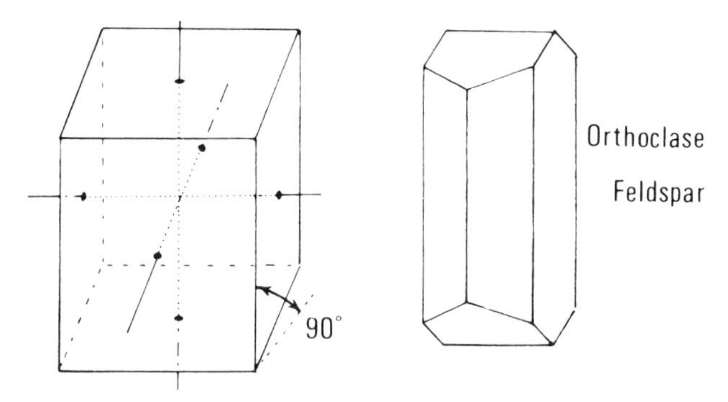


*Figure M.8* The monoclinic crystal system.

of coloured ornamental stones (see ***Florentine mosaic***). Alternatively it may consist of a series of coloured glass rods cemented together (see ***Roman mosaic***). See ***fictile*** and ***tessellated mosaic.***

**mosaic triplet** A composite gemstone formed by cementing a transparent segment (made from colour film) between a crown and pavilion of synthetic spinel. The film segment contains a mosaic of three colours.

**mosquito agate.** See ***midge stone.***

**moss agate** A variety of chalcedony containing brownish-green dendritic inclusions.

**mother-of-emerald** A misleading name for prase.

**mother-of-pearl** The smooth iridescent nacreous layers which cover the inside surface of mollusc shells. Mother-of-pearl consists mainly of the aragonite variety of calcium carbonate.

**mother rock** See ***matrix.***

**moukaite** A pink and white banded Australian jasper.

**mount** The metalwork or frame into which a gemstone is set.

**mountain crystal** The rock crystal variety of quartz.

**mountain jet** A misleading name for black obsidian.

**mountain mahogany** A banded black and red obsidian.

**mountain ruby** A misleading name for red garnet.

**mtorodite** A green chalcedony coloured by chromium. Also called mtorolite. Occurrence: Zimbabwe.

**mtorolite** See ***mtorodite.***

**müller's glass** See ***opal*** (hyalite).

**multifacet diamond** An American trademark used to describe a brilliant-cut diamond whose girdle has been faceted.

**muscle pearls** Pearls found in the muscular tissue of a mollusc near its attachment to the shell.

**muscovite mica** A potassium mica, often with sodium and iron. S.G. 2.8; H. 2–2½. Colourless, yellowish, greenish.

**mussite** See ***diopside.***

**mutton fat jade** A creamy-coloured variety of nephrite.

**mutzschen diamond** A misleading name for the rock crystal variety of quartz.

**mya yay** Best quality green jadeite.

**myrickite** A translucent white chalcedony coloured bright red or pink by inclusions of cinnabar (mercuric sulphide).

**naat** See ***knot.***

**Nacken synthetic emeralds** An early (1928) synthetic emerald grown by the hydrothermal process.

**nacre** A secretion produced by the mantle of some molluscs, which forms the iridescent layers of both the pearl and the mother-of-pearl surface inside the mollusc shell. This nacreous deposit consists of a very thin network of organic conchiolin cells whose interstices are filled with minute crystals of aragonite (an orthorhombic form of calcite).

**naif** The unpolished surface or skin of a diamond crystal.

**nanometre** (nm) A length measurement used to quantify the wavelength of light rays and X-rays. One nanometre is equal to one millionth of a millimetre. See ***ångström unit, electron volt*** and ***wave number.***

**narwhal ivory** A dentine ivory derived from the incisor tooth or tusk of the narwhal (a dolphin-like arctic mammal).

**nassau pearls** Pink conch pearls found in waters around the West Indies.

**natrolite** A collector's stone consisting of a hydrated sodium aluminium silicate, this is one of the zeolite group of minerals. $Na_2Al_2Si_3O_{10}.2H_2O$. Orthorhombic. R.I. 1.480, 1.493; D.R. +0.013; S.G. 2.2-2.25; H. 5½. Transparent, colourless. Occurrence: Czechoslovakia, Norway, Scotland.

**natural** A portion of the surface or 'skin' of a rough diamond crystal which has been left on the girdle of a polished diamond (this is often left to indicate that maximum yield has been achieved from the rough crystal).

**natural grit** Abrasive powder made by crushing poor quality natural diamond such as boart.

**natural glasses** See ***basalt glass, Libyan glass, moldavite, obsidian, pit glass*** and ***tektites.***

**nautilus** A cephalopod mollusc having a multi-chambered shell. Its central whorl is used to fabricate a pearl simulant called a *coque de perle.*

**navette** A step-cut gemstone having a boat-shaped profile with pointed ends. A marquise-cut stone is sometimes referred to as a navette. See ***marquise.***

**near gem** A category of rough diamonds which contains crystals of marginal colour or quality. These become either top grade industrial stones, or low grade gem diamonds depending on which market is the most favourable in demand or price.

**needle stone** See ***sagenitic quartz.***

**negative crystal** A crystal-shaped cavity or void within a gemstone. It may take the shape of a habit occurring in the host mineral's crystal system.

**negative reading** If a gemstone is tested on a critical-angle refractometer, and has a higher refractive index than the measuring prism's contact fluid, all of the light rays will pass out through the gemstone, and no shadow edge (other than that of the contact fluid) will be visible.

**neodymium** One of two rare-earth elements neodymium and praseodymium which occur together in nature and share the collective name of didymium. See ***didymium.***

**neolite** Trade name for turquoise simulant.

**neolith** Trade name for a German turquoise simulant comprising a mixture of bayerite and copper phosphate.

**neo-turquoise** Trade name for a turquoise simulant.

**nepheline syenite** See ***kakortokite.***

**nephelite** A collector's stone comprising the mineral sodium aluminium silicate. Hexagonal (massive). R.I. 1.539, 1.544; D.R. −0.005; S.G. 2.55-2.65; H. 5½-6. Translucent to opaque, bluish-green, brownish-red, with chatoyance. Occurrence: Italy, Norway, USA, USSR.

**nephrite** A calcium magnesium/iron silicate jade mineral consisting of an interlocking mass of fibrous crystals. Also called kidney stone (because of its alleged curative properties). $Ca_2(Mg,Fe)_5(OH)_2(Si_4O_{11})_2$. Monoclinic (crypto-crystalline). R.I. 1.600, 1.627 to 1.614, 1.641; D.R. −0.027; S.G. 2.90-3.02; H. 6½. Opaque, white, green, grey, yellowish, brown. Occurrence: Canada, China, New Zealand, Taiwan, USA, USSR.

**nerchinsk aquamarine** A misleading name for blue topaz.

**netsuke** A carved button-like ornament or toggle worn by the Japanese as a means of hanging articles from a girdle.

**neutron** An electrically neutral particle in the nucleus of an atom having a mass slightly greater than that of a proton. See ***isotope.***

**neutron-treated diamonds** See ***treated diamonds.***

**Nevada black diamond** A misleading name for obsidian.

**Nevada diamond** A misleading name for obsidian.

**Nevada topaz** A misleading name for smoky obsidian.

**Nevada turquoise** A misleading name for variscite.

**Nevada wonderstone** A volcanic rock, weathered into alternate bands of red and buff, which is used as an ornamental stone. S.G. 2.53. Occurrence: Nevada, USA.

**new jade** A misleading name for bowenite.

**New Zealand greenstone** A variety of nephrite found in New Zealand.

**niccolite** A collector's stone, also known as kupfernickel, comprising the mineral nickel arsenide. NiAs. Hexagonal (massive). S.G. 7.33-7.67; H. 5–5½. Opaque, pale red with metallic lustre. Occurrence: Canada, Europe, USA.

**nickel** One of the eight transition metals which are mainly responsible for colour in gemstones. Ni. Stones coloured by nickel include chrysoprase and synthetic green and yellow sapphires. Atomic number 28; atomic weight 58.69; melting point 1453 °C; S.G. 8.8.

**nickel silver** See ***german silver.***

**nicolo** A black or dark brown onyx with a thin bluish-white vein.

**nicol prism** A prism consisting of two sections of optically pure calcite (Iceland spar) which are cemented together with Canada balsam. Light entering the prism is split into two plane polarized rays. The refractive index of the balsam layer (1.53) is such that it produces total internal reflection of the 'ordinary' polarized ray (R.I. 1.65), while allowing the extraordinary ray (R.I. 1.49) to pass through. See ***polarizing filters.***

**nifty gem** A composite stone comprising a pavilion of strontium titanate covered by a crown of synthetic sapphire (see ***laser gem***) or synthetic spinel (see ***carnegie gem***).

**night emerald** A misleading name for peridot.

**nigrine** A black variety of rutile.

**nitric acid** A highly corrosive mineral acid, $HNO_3$, which is a constituent, with hydrochloric acid, of aqua regia.

**nitrogen** A colourless gaseous element. N. Atomic number 7; atomic weight 14.008; boiling point −196 °C. Its most important relationship to gems occurs with diamond, where nitrogen dispersed within the crystal lattice (replacing carbon atoms) produces absorption bands in the blue end of the spectrum. These bands are the cause of the yellow tints in Cape Series stones. Diamonds containing only dispersed nitrogen are classified as Type Ib. Diamonds may also contain nitrogen atoms which are not dispersed with the lattice, but exist as groups of atoms within the stone. Nitrogen aggregates of this type do not produce yellow tints, and diamonds containing only this form of nitrogen are classified as Type Ia. Most diamonds are mixtures of Type Ia and Ib. Diamonds completely free of nitrogen are classified as Type IIa and IIb (the latter contain boron, are usually blue, and have semi-conductor properties).

**nixonoid** Trade name for a cellulose plastic.

**nm** See ***nanometre.***

**noble gases** Gaseous elements forming a group which rarely combine with any other elements (e.g. helium, neon, argon, krypton, xenon and radon).

**noble metals** A group of metallic elements which resist chemical action and do not tarnish in air or water (e.g. gold, platinum and the platinum group metals).

**noble opal** Precious opal. See ***opal.***

**nodule** A small rounded lump or outcrop of mineral material.

**noir belge** A black marble found in the Hainault and Namur provinces of Belgium.

**noir français** A black marble found in the Pas de Calais area of northern France.

**Nomarski interference contrast** A technique for increasing the surface contrast of a specimen, as viewed through a microscope, by means of polarizing filters and phase interference between light rays reflected off the specimen from a co-axial source of illumination. A modified version of this technique has been used to produce a photograph 'fingerprint' of a diamond showing characteristic crystallographic surface features for identification purposes. See ***fingerprinting.***

**non-nucleated pearls** See ***Biwa pearls.***

**norbide** Trade name for a boron nitride abrasive.

**normal** In optics, this is an imaginary line drawn perpendicular to the boundary between two media at the point of incidence of a ray.

**north light** In the northern hemisphere this is the natural daylight from the north sky by which diamonds are traditionally colour graded. This is not a sufficiently reliable or constant illumination standard for present-day grading requirements, and most national and international grading nomenclatures specify a colour-balanced daylight grading lamp of a particular colour temperature (i.e. between 5000 K and 6200 K). See ***grading lamps.***

**Norwegian Gemmological Association** Headquarters: Dronningsgatan 27, Oslo, Norway.

**noselite** A constituent mineral of lapis lazuli. $Na_8(SO_2)(Al_6Si_6O_{24})$.

**nucleon** A general term for both proton and neutron.

**nucleus** The positively-charged central mass of an atom (also the central core of a pearl).

**nunkirchner jasper** A grey-brown fine-grained variety of jasper found near Idar-Oberstein, Germany.

**nyf** See ***naif.***

# O

**objective** (optics) The lens system, or object glass, at the specimen end of a microscope's body tube. See ***microscope.***

**objective** When applied to gemstone grading, the term implies the use of quantitative (i.e instrumental), rather than subjective techniques in the assessment of colour, clarity or cut.

**oblong cut** See ***emerald cut.***

**obsidian** A natural glass formed by the rapid cooling of volcanic lava and consisting of approximately 70% silica (the name 'obsidian' is sometimes incorrectly applied to moldavite). Amorphous. R.I. 1.48-1.51; S.G. 2.33-2.42; H. 5. Translucent to opaque, black, brown, grey, green — rare (sometimes with a silver or golden iridescence caused by minute bubbles or inclusions). Occurrence: Iceland, Mexico, USA.

**occidental agate** A poor quality agate.

**occidental amethyst** The amethyst variety of quartz.

**occidental cat's eye** The cat's eye variety of quartz.

**occidental chalcedony** A poor quality chalcedony.

**occidental cornelian** A poor quality cornelian.

**occidental diamond** A misleading name for the rock crystal variety of quartz.

**occidental emerald** A term used to distinguish genuine emerald from green sapphire (i.e. oriental emerald).

**occidental topaz** A misleading name for citrine. See ***quartz.***

**occidental turquoise** See ***odontolite.***

**occurrence** The locality and geology of the deposit or find from which gemstones are recovered.

**octahedral cleavage** A cleavage plane parallel to any of the four pairs of triangular faces on an octahedral crystal (e.g. diamond and fluorspar have octahedral cleavage). See also ***cleavage.***

**octahedrite** See ***anatase.***

**octahedron** An eight-sided crystal, each face being an equilateral triangle. It is one of the seven basic forms belonging to the highest class of symmetry in the cubic crystal system.

**octavo** See ***oitava.***

**ocular** The eyepiece lens system of an optical instrument such as a microscope or goniometer. See ***microscope.***

**odontolite** A bluish fossil bone or ivory obtained from prehistoric animals such as the mammoth (see also ***fossil ivory***). The bone owes its colour to vivianite, an iron phosphate. It is also known as *bone* or *fossil turquoise* and is used as a turquoise simulant. Amorphous. R.I. 1.57–1.63; S.G. 3.0–3.2 H. 5. Occurrence: France.

**off-colour diamond** A diamond having an obvious and

unattractive tinge of yellow, brown or green.

**oiled emeralds** Emeralds containing flaws which reach the surface, are sometimes 'oiled' to conceal these flaws (as are other gemstones). This is effected by immersing them for several days in a gently-warmed fine oil. With emeralds, the addition of green colouring matter to the oil also improves the colour of the stone. Cleaning such a stone in a detergent solution will leach out the oil and reveal the flaws. Gently warming the stone under a lamp will also 'sweat' the oil out of the flaws and make it visible under hand lens inspection.

**oil pearl** See ***antilles pearl.***

**oitava** A Mexican weight equal to approximately 17.5 carats.

**okkolite** An ornamental stone containing various colours of epidote. Occurrence: South Africa.

**Okuda diamond-photometer** See ***diamond colorimeter.***

**old English cut** See ***eight cut.***

**old European cut** A round brilliant-cut diamond having a small table, and a deep crown and pavilion.

**old mine cut** A brilliant-cut diamond with a cushion-shaped girdle profile, a small table facet and a deep crown and pavilion.

**Oligocene** A division of the Tertiary period of the Cenozoic era of geological time, 38–26 million years ago. See ***Cenozoic.***

**oligoclase** See ***feldspar.***

**olivene** A misleading name for demantoid garnet.

**olive oil** A vegetable oil which is mixed with diamond dust to produce the abrasive paste used for sawing and polishing diamonds. See also ***castor oil.***

**olivine** The mineralogical name for the mineral iron magnesium silicate (of which peridot is the gem variety). See ***peridot.*** Also misleadingly applied to demantoid garnet.

**onegite** A type of amethyst with needle-like inclusions.

**onyx** See ***chalcedony.***

**onyx marble** A whitish marble, veined by bands of yellow, orange and green, used for carvings and small ornamental objects. Also applied incorrectly to a banded travertine or stalagmitic calcite.

**onyx obsidian** A variety of obsidian with parallel banding.

**onyx opal** A banded opal.

**oölitic opal** A variety of opal having circular areas of iridescence.

**opal** A hardened compound of silica and water. $SiO_2nH_2O$. Amorphous. R.I. 1.44–1.46; S.G. 2.0 (fire opals), 2.1 (black and white opals); H. 5½–6½. Varieties:

*common or 'potch' opal* — opaque, without iridescence, see also ***cacholong.***

*milk opal* — yellowish, milk-white or greenish common opal.

*white opal* — white background with iridescence.

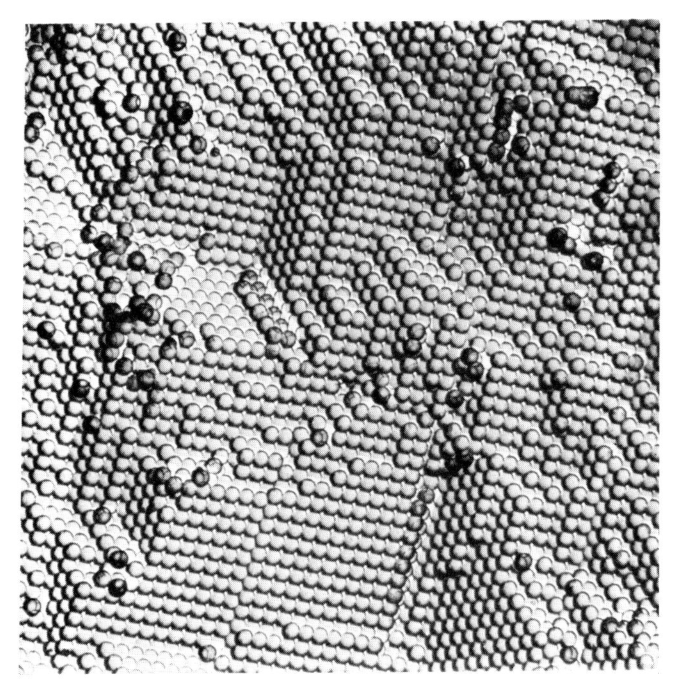

*Figure O.1* The symmetrical pattern of cristobalite spheres in iridescent opal. (Pierre Gilson)

*black opal* — dark background with iridescence.
*fire opal* — transparent to translucent, orange, occasionally with iridescence.
*prase opal* — similar in appearance to chrysoprase.
*cherry opal* — transparent to translucent, cherry-red without iridescence.
*pink, yellow, green and blue opal* — translucent, without iridescence.
*water opal* — translucent to transparent, colourless or brownish-yellow with adularescence.
*hyalite* — a colourless glass-like opal without iridescence.
*hydrophane* — light-coloured opaque opal which becomes transparent and iridescent when soaked in water.
*materials petrified by opal* — e.g. wood.
*opal pseudomorphs* — shells, bones and minerals.

See also ***gidgee opal, lechosos opal, oölitic opal*** and ***vermilite.*** Occurrence: Australia, Czechoslovakia ('Hungarian opal'), Indonesia (black opal), Mexico (fire opal).

The iridescence in opal is described by terms such as harlequin, rolling flash, flash and pinfire, and is caused by a combination of interference and diffraction of the light reflected from submicroscopic cristobalite spheres. *Figure O.1.*

**opal agate** A gem material consisting of alternate bands of opal and chalcedony.

**opal doublet** See ***composite stones.***

**opalescence** See ***sheen.***

**opal glass** A milky-white translucent man-made glass used as a light diffuser.

**opaline** See ***opal matrix.***

**opalite** A term applied to varieties of common opal.

**opalized wood** An opal-petrified wood.

**opal matrix** A mixture of opal vein and the supporting rock matrix (sometimes called opaline).

**opal triplet** See ***composite stones.***

**opaque** Impenetrable to light rays. See also ***transparent*** and ***translucent.***

**open cast mining** See ***diamond mine.***

**open form** See ***form.***

**open culet** An over-large culet, easily visible to the naked eye.

**open setting** A gemstone mount in which the pavilion facets are easily visible.

**open table** A term used to describe a brilliant-cut diamond having a 'spread' table (i.e. one whose width is significantly greater than 58% of the girdle diameter).

**operculum** The closure flap found in certain types of shellfish which is sometimes used in jewellery (under the name of Chinese cat's eye, Guadalcanal cat's eye, Pacific cat's eye or shell cat's eye).

**ophicalcite** A clouded white to green serpentine rock containing calcite and dolomite. Also called Connemara marble. Amorphous. R.I. 1.56; S.G. 2.48-2.77; H. 3.

**ophicite** See ***ophicalcite.***

**optical character** A general term used in connection with specific optical properties of a gemstone. The optical character of a stone is described as *isotropic* if the gem is amorphous or belongs to the cubic crystal system, as *anisotropic* if it belongs to any of the other six crystal systems, as *uniaxial* if it is in the tetragonal, hexagonal or trigonal systems or as *biaxial* if it is orthorhombic, monoclinic or triclinic. See also ***optic axes*** and ***optic sign.***

**optical density** See ***refractive index.***

**optical separator** An equipment designed to separate rough diamonds from gravel or crushed rock by using the high reflective properties of the diamond crystals. A modification of the Gunson's Sortex optical separator is used to colour-sort small

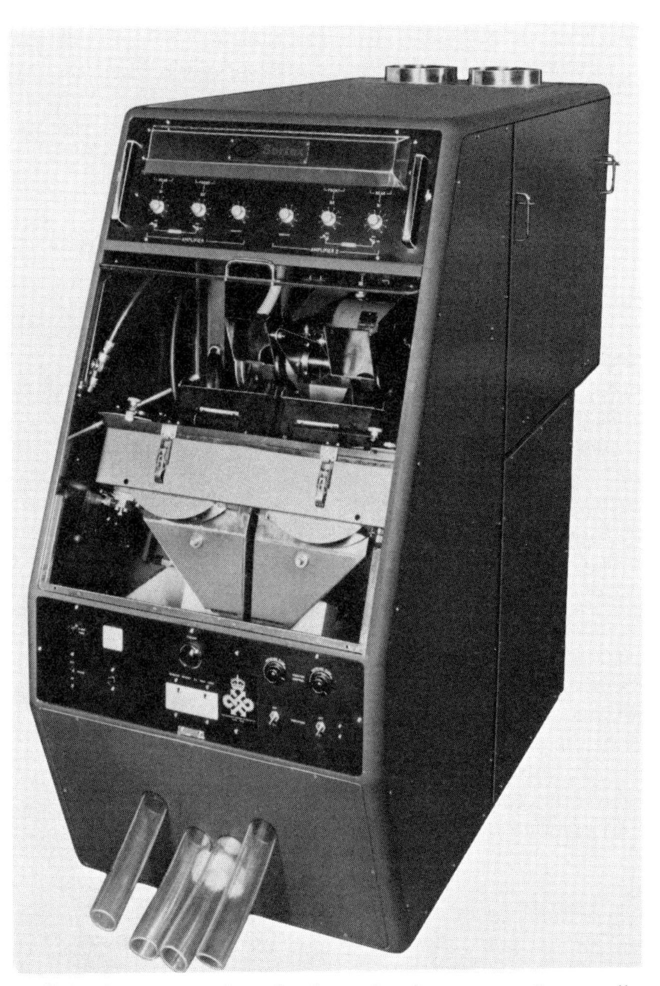


*Figure O.2* An automatic twin-channel colour sorter for small rough diamonds. (Gunson's Sortex)

rough diamonds. *Figure O.2.*

**optic axes** Directions of single refraction in an otherwise doubly-refracting material. Gemstones in the tetragonal, hexagonal and trigonal crystal systems have one such axis and are described as *uniaxial.* Gemstones in the orthorhombic, monoclinic and triclinic systems have two optic axes and are therefore *biaxial.*

**optic sign** The convention of designating birefringent crystals as optically positive or negative is based on the following relative values of the two refractive indices as measured on a critical-angle refractometer.

1. With uniaxial stones, if, on rotation of the stone, the moving extraordinary ray R.I. is greater in value than the fixed ordinary ray R.I., the gem is optically positive. If the ordinary ray R.I. is greater than the extraordinary ray R.I., the gem is optically negative. *Figure O.3.*

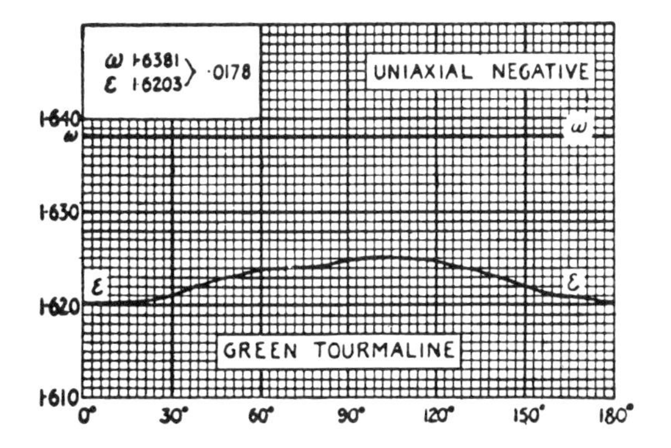


*Figure O.3* Refractometer shadow-edge movements for green tourmaline, a uniaxial stone which has a negative optic sign.

2. With biaxial stones, if rotation causes the higher R.I. index to move more than halfway from its highest-reading position towards the lowest-reading position of the other index, the gem is optically positive. *Figure O.4.* If the lower-reading R.I. moves more than halfway towards the higher R.I. the stone is optically negative.

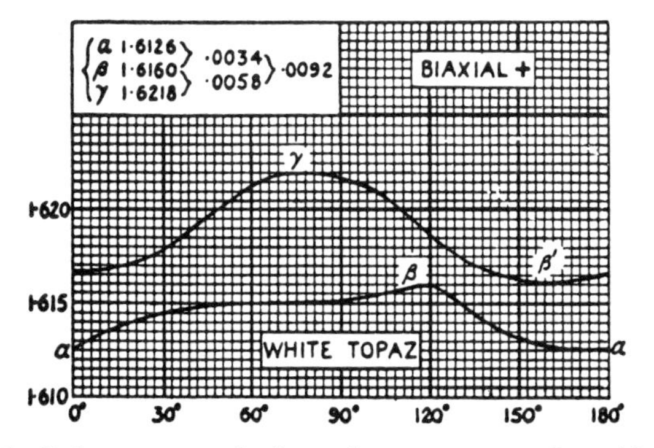


*Figure O.4* Refractometer shadow-edge movements for white topaz, a biaxial stone which has a positive optic sign.

**orange topaz** A misleading name for brownish-yellow quartz.

**orbicular** A term used to describe an opaque material containing spheroid inclusions (e.g. shells).

**orbicular diorite** See ***diorite.***

**orbicular jasper** A jasper containing white or grey circular areas in a red matrix, or, conversely, white/red or black/red circles in a white or yellow matrix.

**ordinary ray** Of the two polarized rays passing through a uniaxial crystal (i.e. one belonging to the tetragonal, hexagonal or trigonal system), the ordinary ray is the one whose velocity and associated R.I. ($\omega$) remains the same whatever its orientation in the crystal. See ***extraordinary ray*** and ***optic sign.***

**Ordovician** A rock system on the Earth's surface comprising the rocks laid down during the Ordovician period, 500–430 million years ago. The Ordovician period is part of the Palaeozoic era. See ***Palaeozoic.***

**Oregon jade** A misleading name for the dark green plasma variety of chalcedony.

**Oregon moonstone** A misleading name for chalcedony.

**organic** A term applied to materials derived from living or once-living organisms (e.g. amber, coral, ivory, jet, pearl, tortoiseshell).

**organ-pipe fluorescence** The emission lines seen in the spectrum of a synthetic red spinel when irradiated by LW UV light.

**orient** (of pearl) The iridescent sheen of pearl caused by the interference and diffraction effects on light rays reflected from thin surface layers of nacre.

**oriental alabaster** See ***Egyptian alabaster.***

**oriental emerald** A misleading name for green sapphire or green chlorospinel.

**oriental agate** A good quality agate.

**oriental almandine** A misleading name for purple-red sapphire.

**oriental amethyst** A misleading name for violet sapphire.

**oriental aquamarine** A misleading name for light blue sapphire.

**oriental cat's eye** The cat's eye (cymophane) variety of chrysoberyl.

**oriental chalcedony** A good quality chalcedony.

**oriental chrysoberyl** A misleading name for yellowish-green sapphire.

**oriental chrysolite** A misleading name for greenish-yellow chrysoberyl or sapphire.

**oriental cornelian** A deep coloured cornelian.

**oriental pearl** A pearl from the true oyster genus *Pinctada.* The term was first applied to pearls from the Indian seas.

**oriental topaz** A misleading name for yellow sapphire.

**orletz** The name for rhodolite in the USSR.

**ornamental stones** Those minerals or rocks which, although opaque, are valued for the beauty of their surface colours and markings and are used for carvings and ornamental objccts.
**ortho axis** The lateral axis in the monoclinic crystal system which is at right-angles to the vertical axis. See ***clino axis.***
**orthoclase feldspar** See ***feldspar.***
**orthorhombic system** A crystal system having three axes, all at right-angles to each other and all of different lengths. There are three axes of symmetry (all two-fold), three planes of symmetry and a centre of symmetry. *Figure O.5.*

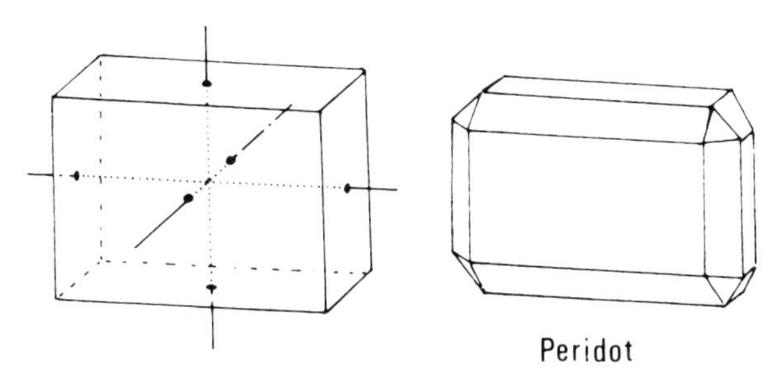


*Figure O.5* The orthorhombic crystal system.

**osmenda pearl** See ***coque de perle***
**osseous amber** A variety of amber having the appearance of dried bone.
**Ottasdal G stone** See ***koranna stone*** and ***pyrophyllite.***
**ounce Avoir** A unit of weight equal to 28.349 grams or 141.747 carats.

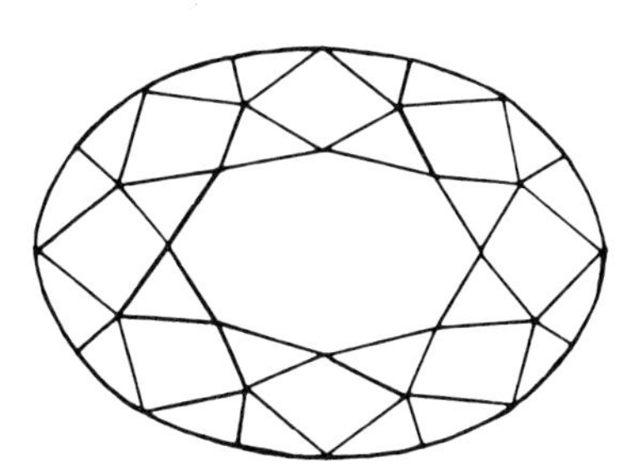

*Figure O.6* The oval cut.

**ounce Troy** A unit of weight (used for precious metals) equal to 31.103 grams or 155.517 carats.
**oval cut** A variant of the 57-facet brilliant cut. *Figure O.6.*

**overblue** A term applied to both rough and polished diamonds having a faint blue tint (usually caused by a marked blue fluorescence).

**owl eye** Eye agate with two similar eyes.

**oxalite** A trade name for an ivory or a jade simulant made from calcined beef bone.

**ox eye** A chatoyant labradorite feldspar.

**oxidized diamonds** Rough diamonds completely or partially covered with a thin yellow or orange-brown oxide film. The bulk of this film is usually removed by means of an acidizing process.

**oxitol** Trade name for ethylene glycol mono-ethyl ether, a volatile low-residue liquid (R.I. 1.4) suitable for use as an immersion fluid.

**oxolite** See ***oxalite.***

**ozarkite** A snow-white variety of thomsonite from Arkansas, USA.

# P

**Pacific cat's eye** See ***operculum.***

**padparadschah** An orange-pink variety of corundum found in Sri Lanka. The name is Singhalese for 'lotus flower'.

**pagoda stone** A translucent agate whose opaque white bands resemble a Burmese pagoda.

**painite** A collector's stone comprising a calcium boro-zirconium aluminate. $CaAl_9ZrO_{15}(BO_3)$. Hexagonal. R.I. 1.787, 1.816; D.R. −0.029; S.G. 4.01; H. 7½. Transparent, deep red. Pleochroism, medium (red, pale brownish-orange). Occurrence: Burma.

**painted diamonds** See ***treated diamonds.***

**pai yu** White jadeite or nephrite.

**Palaeozoic** The second era of geological time between 570 and 225 million years ago and comprising the ***Cambrian, Ordovician, Silurian, Devonian, Carboniferous*** and ***Permian*** periods. See also ***Cenozoic, Mesozoic*** and ***Precambrian.***

**palladium** A member of the platinum group of metals, sometimes used in jewellery as an alternative to platinum. Pd. Atomic number 46; atomic weight 106.7; melting point 1552 °C; S.G. 11.4.

**palmeira topaz** A misleading name for brown synthetic sapphire.

**palmyra topaz** A misleading name for a pale yellow heat-treated amethyst/citrine.

**paludina limestone** A blue-grey to reddish-brown marble containing the fossilized shells of freshwater snails. Also known as Purbeck marble. Occurrence: Dorset, England.

**pampille cut** A drop-shaped cut similar to the briolette.

**Panama pearls** Slate-blue to black pearls found in the Gulf of California, Mexico.

**panning** A technique for separating heavy minerals (such as gold, diamonds and other gemstones) from their associated gravels or silt. The gravels are placed in a shallow metal pan or, in the case of gem gravels, a hemispherical basket, and partially immersed in water. By means of a cyclic rotary motion of the pan, the water is swirled over the edge, carrying with it the lighter non-gem materials.

**pantha** White translucent jadeite.

**paphros diamond** A misleading name for the rock crystal variety of quartz.

**paragon pearls** Large spherical pearls. Also a trade name for imitation pearls.

**parallel growth** A multiple crystal growth in which all the edges and faces of one crystal are parallel to those of its neighbour. Parallel growth should not be confused with twinned growth, in which the faces of the adjoining crystals are not parallel but are symmetrically orientated to each other.

**paramagnetism** See ***magnetism.***

**paramorphous** Having different chemical compositions but the same form.

**Paris jet** A black glass simulant of jet.

**Paris pearls** Trade name for imitation pearls.

**Parker brilliant cut** One of several 'ideal' cuts for diamond, having a table facet width, crown depth and pavilion depth of 55.9%, 10.5% and 43.4% respectively compared with the girdle diameter. The crown angle is 25.5°, and the pavilion angle is 40.9°. See ***Eppler brilliant cut, Johnson and Rösch brilliant cut, Scan DN brilliant cut*** and ***Tolkowsky brilliant cut.***

**parquetry** The setting of geometrically shaped pieces of coloured stone in a metal mount.

**parrot wing** Trade name for a mainly cryptocrystalline quartz, similar to agate or jasper. The red and yellow colours are due to quartz, green-blue to chrysocolla and brown to limonite. Occurrence: USA.

**parti-coloured stones** Stones cut from allochromatic crystals whose colour has changed during their growth (due to a change in the chemistry of the matrix). Tourmaline crystals often exhibit two or three changes of colour (e.g. from pink through colourless to green), and parti-coloured stones are cut from the colour-change sections.

**parting** The splitting of a mineral along twinning planes.

**parure** A suite of matching jewellery which became fashionable during the Renaissance. Typically it consists of a necklace, two bracelets, earrings and a brooch or pendant. A demi-parure has fewer items, e.g. a pendant and matching earrings.

**passau pearl** A freshwater pearl from Central Europe.

**paste** Gemstone simulants made from glass (usually flint glass).

**pâte de riz** A glass jade simulant.

**patricia pearls** Trade name for imitation pearls.

**paua shell** See ***abalone.***

**pauline trigere** Trade name for the man-made diamond simulant strontium titanate.

**paulite** Blackish hypersthene with coppery inclusions.

**pavé setting** A setting in which a group of small stones are set as close together as possible with the minimum of mount visible.

**pavilion** That section of a polished stone beneath the girdle. See ***crown.***

**pavilion angle** The angle between the plane of the girdle and the main facets of the pavilion. See ***brilliant cut.***

**pavilion depth** The perpendicular distance between the plane of the girdle and the culet, measured as a percentage of the girdle diameter. See ***brilliant cut.***

**pavonazzo marble** A group of white or pale yellow marbles traversed with purple veins.

**peacock stone** See ***malachite.***

**pearl** An organic gem produced by pearl-bearing molluscs which consists of a central small nucleus surrounded by concentric layers of nacre (see ***mantle***). Composition of the pearl is 86% calcium carbonate (in the form of orthorhombic aragonite crystals), 12% conchiolin, 2% water. R.I. 1.52-1.66 (black, 1.53-1.69); S.G. 2.6-2.78; H. 3-4. Varieties and Occurrence: See under the following headings, ***baroque, black, blister, cultured (Biwa, mabe), cyst, freshwater*** and ***pink.***

**pearl doctor** A skilled technician who improves pearls by removing surface blemishes. See ***skinning***.

**pearl doublet** A cultured blister pearl. See ***mabe pearls.***

**pearl opal** See ***cacholong.***

**pearl spar** See ***dolomite.***

**pearly** See ***lustre.***

**pear-shaped cut** See ***pendeloque.***

**pecos diamonds** A misleading name for the rock crystal variety of quartz.

**pectolite** A sodium calcium silicate usually cut as cabochons, and in its massive form used a simulant of jade. $NaCa_2Si_3O_8OH$. Monoclinic. R.I. 1.595, 1.633; D.R. +0.038; S.G. 2.74-2.88; H. 5. Translucent, white or grey with a silky lustre. Occurrence: Italy, Scotland, USA.

**pectolite jade** A misleading name for pectolite.

**pedrara onyx** A misleading name for a stalagmitic marble from Mexico, comprising a white or green translucent rock veined with dark orange, yellow or brown.

**peganite** See ***variscite.***

**pegmatite** A coarse-grained granite (i.e. a granular igneous rock comprising quartz, feldspar and mica).

**Peiping (Peking) jade** Any true jade, but usually nephrite.

**pelhamine** A gem quality serpentine.

**pendeloque** A varient of the 57-facet brilliant cut having a pear or drop profile. *Figure P.1.*

**penetration twins** See ***interpenetrant twins.***

**Penfield balance** See ***hydrostatic weighing.***

**pennyweight** Equal to 24 grains (gold weight), 1/20 ounce troy and 7.776 carats.

**pentelicum marble** A pure white granular marble from Greece.

**pentlandite** A collector's stone comprising the mineral nickel iron sulphide. $(Fe, Ni)_9S_8$. Cubic. S.G. 5.0; H. 3½-4. Bronze-yellow.

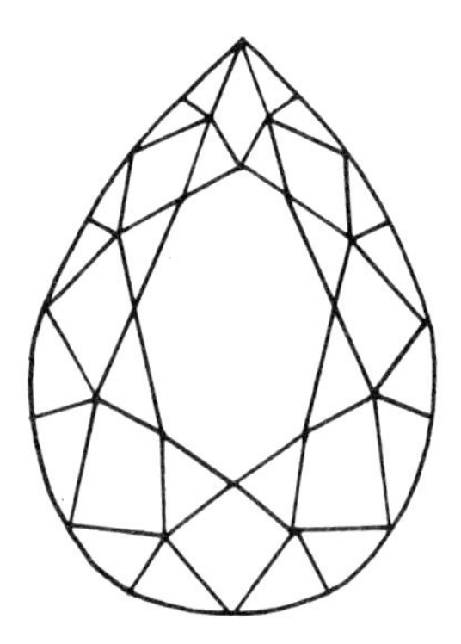

*Figure P.1* The pendeloque or pear-shaped cut.

Occurrence: Canada, Finland.

**perdine** The name given to amethyst from the Montezuma mine in Brazil which turns milky green when heated to around 650°C. The change of colour is due to the reduction of ferric iron to ferrous iron.

**peredell topaz** A greenish variety of topaz.

**periclase** A magnesium oxide mineral. MgO. Cubic. R.I. 1.737; S.G. 3.55–3.60; H. 5. Transparent to translucent, colourless, yellowish, grey-green. A synthetic periclase has been marketed under the trade name 'lavernite' and used as a spinel simulant.

**peridine** Trade name for green heat-treated quartz.

**peridot** A magnesium iron silicate also called olivine (by mineralogists) and chrysolite. $(Mg,Fe)_2SiO_4$. Orthorhombic. R.I. 1.654, 1.690; D.R. +0.036; S.G. 3.34; H. 6½. Transparent, yellow-green, olive-green, brown (rare). Occurrence: Brazil, Burma, China, Hawaii, Norway, USA, Zeberget or the Isle of St John (Red Sea).

**perigem** Trade name for a synthetic light yellow-green spinel.

**peristerite** An opaque albite variety of feldspar with bluish iridescence on a white or brown body colour. H. 6½.

**Permian** A rock system on the Earth's surface comprising the rocks laid down during the Permian period, 280–225 million years ago. The Permian period is the last part of the Palaeozoic era. See ***Palaeozoic.***

**perspex** Trade name for a transparent acrylic resin from which faceted gemstone simulants are moulded. R.I. 1.5; S.G. 1.18.

**perthite** An intergrowth of albite or oligoclase in orthoclase or microcline feldspar, used as an ornamental stone. Opaque, white, red, reddish-brown with golden labradorescence. Occurrence: Canada, Scotland.

**peruzzi cut** Thought to be the origin of the modern brilliant cut, the peruzzi cut had 57 facets (plus a culet), and was developed towards the end of the 17th century. It is attributed to the Venetian cutter Vincenzio Peruzzi.

**petalite** A collector's stone comprising the mineral lithium sodium aluminium silicate. $LiAlSi_4O_{10}$. Monoclinic (massive). R.I. 1.504, 1.518; D.R. +0.014; S.G. 2.39-2.46; H. 6. Transparent to translucent, colourless, pink. Occurrence: Australia, Brazil, Namibia, Sweden, USA.

**petal pearls** Pearls having a distorted flattened shape.

**petoskey stone** A patterned marble derived from a fossil coral limestone. Occurrence: USA.

**petrified dinosaur bone** A fossil bone used for ornamental purposes. Occurrence: USA. See also ***dinny bone.***

**petrified wood** See ***fossil wood.***

**petrology** The study of the origin, structure and mineralogy of rocks.

**Petworth marble** A marble similar to paludina limestone but containing larger shells. Occurrence: England.

**pewter** Originally an alloy of tin with lead, it now is mainly made from a tin, copper, antimony alloy resembling silver (also called britannia metal).

**phianite** Trade name for the diamond simulant cubic zirconium oxide manufactured by the Lebedev Physical Institute in Moscow, USSR.

**phase-difference microscopy** See ***Nomarski interference contrast.***

**phenacite** See ***phenakite.***

**phenakite** A collector's stone comprising the mineral beryllium silicate, $BeSiO_4$. Trigonal. R.I. 1.654, 1.670; D.R. +0.016; S.G. 2.95-2.97; H. 7½-8. Transparent, colourless, greenish-blue, wine-yellow, pink. Occurrence: Brazil, Mexico, Namibia, Switzerland, USA, USSR.

**phosgenite** A collector's stone (which has a strong yellow fluorescence under UV light and X-rays) comprising the mineral lead chlorocarbonate. $Pb_2(Cl_2CO_3)$. Tetragonal. R.I. 2.114, 2.140; D.R. +0.026; S.G. 6.2; H. 3. Transparent, colourless, yellow-white, greenish, brownish-yellow. Occurrence: Australia, Namibia, Sardinia.

**phosphophyllite** A rare collector's stone comprising a hydrated zinc phosphate. Monoclinic. R.I. 1.595, 1.616; D.R. +0.021; S.G. 3.1; H. 3½. Transparent, bluish-green. Occurrence: Bolivia, Germany.

**phosphorescence** See ***fluorescence*** and ***luminescence.***

**photoconductivity** A property possessed by some gemstones, such as diamond, in which their normally high electrical resistance falls when they are exposed to UV light. Semiconductor Type IIb diamonds (containing boron) are photoconductive to gamma radiation, and are used (like a geiger tube) as radioactive counters in situations which call for a strong corrosion-resistant sensor material.

**photoluminescence** See ***luminescence.***

**photometer** See ***diamond colorimeter*** and ***spectrophotometer.***

**photomicrograph** Photograph taken of a specimen through a microscope. Depth of focus can be increased by stopping down the microscope objective (by means of a small aperture in an opaque mask) and increasing the exposure time to compensate. Some microscopes are provided with an extra 'trinocular' port for the attachment of a camera. Camera adaptors are also provided for use in place of an ocular.

**photon** A unit quantity or 'packet' of electromagnetic radiation, whose energy is proportional to the frequency of radiation and which forms the mechanism by which light is emitted according to the quantum theory. See also ***wave theory of light.***

**phylum** Major division of plant or animal kingdom, containing species having the same general form.

**picotite** A black variety of spinel.

**picrolite** See ***serpentine.***

**picture jasper** A jasper containing banding or dendritic inclusions which produce a scenic picture. Occurrence: Namibia, USA.

**piedmontite** An opaque cherry-red variety of epidote found in Italy.

**pierre des Incas** See ***pyrites.***

**pietersite** Trade name for a cabochon-cut disorientated pseudo-crocidolite containing limonite, found in Namibia. See ***quartz (tiger's eye).***

**pietra dura mosaic** See ***Florentine mosaic.***

**piezoelectric effect** A property possessed by some gem mineral crystals such as tourmaline and quartz, which become electrically charged when stressed or bent in certain directions. Conversely, if an electric potential is applied across the crystal, this sets up mechanical stresses in the form of minute dimensional changes. *Figure P.2.*

**pigeon blood agate** The cornelian variety of chalcedony.

**pigeon's blood** A colour description applied to the best quality Burmese rubies.

**pigeon stone** See ***peristerite.***

**pile-irradiated diamonds** Diamonds coloured by neutron bombardment in an atomic pile or reactor. See ***treated diamonds.***

**pinacoid** A pair of crystal faces which are parallel to two crystal axes, and are cut by the third. In a prismatic crystal, these are the terminating faces. See ***basal pinacoid, brachy pinacoid*** and ***macro***

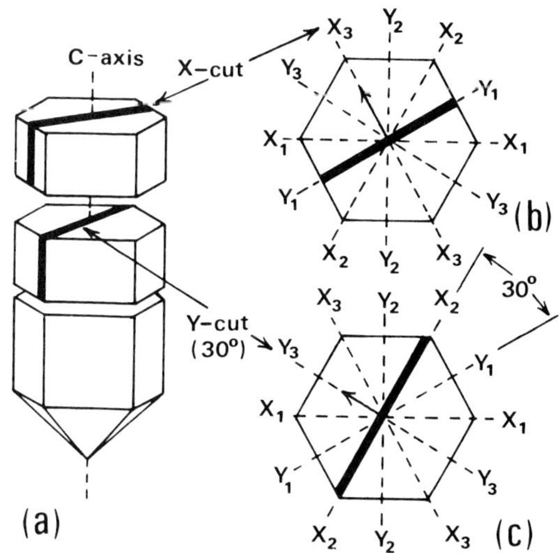


*Figure P.2* The piezoelectric effect in quartz produces mechanical stress across the Y axes when an electrical charge is applied across the X axes. Plates are cut as shown for use in electrical resonators.

***pinacoid.***

**pineapple opal** An opalized glauberite pseudomorph.

**pinchbeck** A gold-like alloy of copper and zinc (83% Cu, 17% Zn).

**Pinctada** A genus of pearl-bearing oyster.

**pink moonstone** A misleading name for the opalescent pink variety of scapolite.

**pink pearls** Pearls fished off the coast of Florida and the Gulf of California, Mexico. S.G. 2.85.

**pinna pearls** Pearls from the pinna mussel in the Mediterranean Sea. They are lack-lustre and have a radiating structure of prismatic crystals as opposed to the concentric structure of oriental pearls.

**pipe** A core of rock that has solidified in the vent shaft of a volcano. Pipes composed of kimberlite sometimes contain diamonds. See ***diamond mine*** and ***kimberlite.***

**piqué (pk)** A term used in the clarity grading of polished diamonds. See ***Clarity Grading Standards*** in Appendix C.

**piqué work** The inlaying of pin-head dots of silver into tortoiseshell objects.

**pistacite** See ***epidote.***

**pit amber** See ***amber.***

**pit glass** A glass, thought to be a natural glass similar to obsidian, but because the properties of known samples are dissimilar to those of any of the natural glasses, their origin is still a mystery.

**pi yu** A vegetable-green jade.

**PK synthetic rubies** See ***Knischka synthetic rubies.***

**placer deposit** A deposit of mineral-rich gravels which have been carried downstream by river currents and then trapped in a depression in the river bed.

**plagioclase** See ***feldspar.***

**planchéite** A hydrated copper silicate having the appearance of turquoise or azurite. $2CuSiO_3H_2O$. Monoclinic (fibrous). R.I. around 1.75; S.G. 3.8. H. 3½-4. Opaque, blue. Occurrence: USA, Zaire.

**plane of symmetry** A plane through a crystal which divides it into two mirror-image halves. A cube has nine such planes. *Figure P.3.*

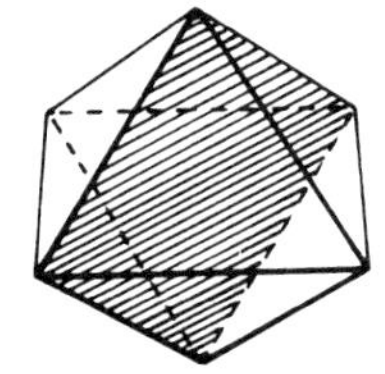
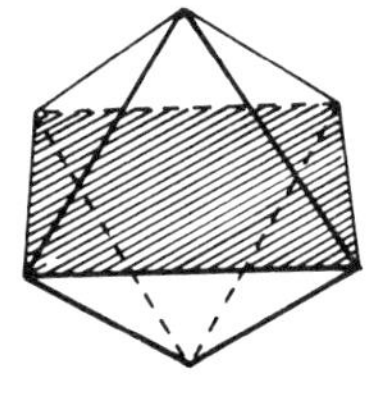

*Figure P.3* Two of the planes of symmetry in an octahedron.

**plasma** See ***chalcedony.***

**plastics** A general term for a man-made material (usually a resin based polymer) that can be extruded or moulded by heat or pressure.

**platinum** A white ductile metallic element, resistant to common acids, which is used in jewellery, particularly as a diamond setting. Pt. Atomic number 78; atomic weight 195.23; melting point 1769°C; S.G. 21.4.

**Plato test** A method, developed by Dr W. Plato, for identifying synthetic Verneuil corundum containing no inclusions or detectable curved stria. The direction of the stone's optic axis is first detected by using a polariscope (see ***konoscope***). The stone is then viewed under crossed polars at 20-30× magnification while immersed in methylene iodide. If two sets of lines intersecting at 60° are visible when viewing the stone in a direction parallel to the optic axis, the stone is a synthetic Verneuil corundum. See ***Verneuil corundum.***

**play of colour** The iridescent sheen seen in precious opal and labradorite. See ***sheen.***

**Pleistocene** The larger and earlier part of the Quaternary period of the Cenozoic era of geological time, 2 million to 10 thousand years ago, the later part being classed as the *Holocene* or *Recent*. Deposits from this epoch are mostly sands and clays deposited by Ice Age glaciers. See ***Quaternary.***

**pleochroism** See ***dichroism.***

**pleonaste** See ***spinel.***

**Pliocene** A division of the Tertiary period of the Cenozoic era of geological time, 7-2 million years ago. See ***Cenozoic.***

**plume agate** A variety of moss agate in which the markings resemble ostrich feathers.

**plutonic rock** See ***igneous rock.***

**plutons** Rocks which have crystallized slowly in large masses deep in the Earth.

**pneumatolytic rocks** Rocks altered by the action of chemically-active vapours.

**pocket lens** See ***hand lens, loupe*** and ***head loupe.***

**point** A unit of weight used for polished diamonds. 1 carat equals 100 points.

**point chalcedony** A grey variety of chalcedony with red spots.

**point-cut diamonds** An early cutting style in which the natural faces of an octahedral crystal were polished, but the basic shape left intact.

**polariscope** An optical instrument consisting of two polarizing filters which enables gemstones to be inspected under plane polarized light, usually from a built-in light source. The lower filter is provided with a rotateable glass specimen platform, and the top viewing or 'analyser' filter is set for extinction of the polarized light from the bottom filter. A doubly-refracting gem 'rotates' the polarized light from the lower filter, making it visible through the top filter at four positions when the stone is orientated through 360°. Singly-refracting stones do not produce this marked effect, and cryptocrystalline stones transmit light through the top filter in all positions. Internal strains in glass imitation stones appear as a strong cross-pattern of dark lines, while strains in some man-made materials, such as synthetic spinel, produce an effect known as anomalous double refraction, which is never as clearly defined as true double refraction. ***Figure P.4.***

**polarized light** Light in which the majority of rays are vibrating in the same direction or plane. With unpolarized light, the rays vibrate in all directions at right-angles to the line of transmission. With plane polarized light, the rays vibrate only in one direction or plane. Light entering a doubly-refracting gemstone is split into two sets of rays which are plane polarized at right-angles to each other. See also ***polarizing filters.***

**polarizing angle** See ***Brewster angle.***

**polarizing filters** The majority of polarizing filters consist of a

*Figure P.4* The Rayner polariscope (Rubin).

plastic sheet containing either microscopic crystals of quinine iodosulphate or, more recently, 'long' molecules, which are orientated so that they transmit light with minimum absorption only when it is vibrating in one plane, and are optically opaque to rays which are polarized at right-angles to this plane. Filters are often protected by being sealed between plates of glass. See ***nicol prism.***

**polaroid** Trade name for a plastic polarizing filter.

**polishing** The technique of achieving a lustrous surface finish on a gemstone. See ***lapidary, diamond cutter*** and ***Beilby layer.***

**polka dot agate** A variety of translucent chalcedony with small red, brown or yellow dots.

**pollucite** A rare collector's stone containing caesium. $(Cs,Na)AlSi_2O_6.H_2O$. Cubic. R.I. 1.517–1.525; S.G. 2.85-2.94; H. 6½. Transparent to translucent, colourless, white, mauve-white. Occurrence: Afghanistan, Elba, Sweden, USA.

**polybern** Trade name for a German amber simulant consisting of small pieces of natural amber in a coloured polyester resin.

**polycrystalline diamond** A natural diamond which is composed of a mass of small or microscopic crystals. This type of diamond is normally only suitable for crushing as an industrial grit. See ***boart.***

**polymorphism** A term used where minerals have the same chemical composition but differ in their crystalline form (e.g. andalusite, kyanite and sillimanite). See also ***dimorphism.***

**polystyrene** A hard thermoplastic styrene polymer from which faceted gemstone simulants are moulded. R.I. 1.59; S.G. 1.05; H. 2½. Dissolves in hydrocarbon liquids such as toluene, bromoform, monobromonaphthalene and methylene iodide.

**polysynthetic twinning** The repeated twinning of a crystal which results in a series of thin plates of alternate orientation. This repeated or lamellar twinning often results in a symmetrical habit uncharacteristic of the gem's crystal system (e.g. the pseudo-hexagonal twinning of chrysoberyl). It also produces parting or planes of false cleavage. See also ***contact twin*** and ***interpenetrant twins.***

**pomegranate ruby** A misleading name for red spinel.

**pompadour pearls** Trade name for imitation pearls.

**Pong Kham quartz** A rock crystal variety of quartz found in the Pong Kham mountain range of Northern Thailand.

**poppy stone** See ***orbicular jasper.***

**porcelain** A type of fine earthenware made from white kaolin clay. It has been used as a simulant for gems such as turquoise. S.G. 2.1-2.5. See also ***streak plate.***

**porphyry** An igneous rock containing comparatively large well-formed crystals embedded in a homogeneous fine-grained matrix. The red porphyry mined in Egypt consisted of crystals of white and pink feldspar in a dark red matrix. An unstratified or igneous rock with a homogeneous structure containing micro-crystals of one or more minerals.

**portrait stones** See ***bevel cut*** and ***lasque diamond.***

**Portugese cut** A modified brilliant cut occasionally used on large stones. It consists of two rows of rhomboid facets and two rows of triangular facets on both crown and pavilion.

**positron** An elementary particle with the same mass as an electron and an equal but opposite charge.

**post-contemporary inclusions** See ***inclusions.***

**potato stone** See ***geode.***

**potch opal** A poor quality opal showing little or no iridescence.

**pounamu** A Maori name for New Zealand nephrite.

**powder diffraction analysis** An X-ray technique for producing a lauegram from powder scrappings taken from a specimen. See ***lauegram.***

**practical fine cut** See ***Eppler brilliant cut.***

**prase** See *quartz.*

**prasemalachite** Chalcedony filled with malachite.

**praseodymium** One of two rare-earth elements neodymium and praseodymium which occur together in nature and share the collective name of didymium. See ***didymium.***

**prase opal** A non-iridescent green opal (coloured by nickel) found in Poland.

**prasiolite** Trade name for green quartz produced by heat treating a variety of Brazilian amethyst.

**Precambrian** The first era of geological time stretching from the origin of the Earth to about 570 million years ago. It may be divided into the ***Archaean,*** in which no life existed, and the ***Proterozoic*** in which the earliest life-forms were present. See also ***Cenozoic, Mesozoic*** and ***Palaeozoic.***

**precious metals** A general term which includes high-value jewellery metals such as gold, silver, platinum, iridium and palladium.

**precious stones** An imprecise term, now little used, which encompassed such high-value gems as diamond, emerald, ruby and sapphire.

**pre-existing inclusions** See ***inclusions.***

**preforming** The grinding of the basic profile of a gem prior to faceting.

**prehnite** A hydrated calcium aluminium silicate carving material, also cut as cabochons. $Ca_2Al_2.(OH)_2Si_3O_{10}$. Orthorhombic. R.I. 1.61, 1.64; D.R. +0.03; S.G. 2.88-2.94; H. 6. Transparent to translucent, yellow-green, brown-yellow. Occurrence: Australia, China, France, Scotland, South Africa, USA.

**pressed amber** See ***ambroid.***

**Primary group of rocks** An obsolete term for rocks of the Palaeozoic era. See ***Palaeozoic.***

**Primer Instituto Gemologico Latin Americano** Headquarters: Sourdeaux 1312, Bella Vista, F.C.S.M., Buenos Aires, Republic of Argentina.

**princess cut** The original name for what is now called the profile cut.

**principal axis** The vertical axis of a crystal or prism. The remaining axes are called laterals.

**prism** An optical component used to bend or disperse light rays. In a microscope, prisms are used to bend and invert the rays to produce an 'upright' image for viewing by the ocular(s). In the prism type spectroscope the prism is used to disperse light into its spectral colours so that those parts of the spectrum absorbed by a gemstone can be made visible as dark bands or lines.

**prismatic** A crystal habit consisting of parallelogram faces. See *prism (form).*

**prismatic cleavage** A cleavage direction parallel to the principal axis (i.e. length) of a prism.

**prismatic emerald** A misleading name for euclase.

**prismatic moonstone** A misleading name for chalcedony.

**prismatic quartz** A misleading name for cordierite.

**prismatine** See ***kornerupine.***

**prism (form)** A crystal form whose faces are parallel to the principal axis, and are cut by the lateral axes. In *first-order* prisms each prism face is cut by two lateral axes; in *second-order* prisms each face is cut by only a single lateral axis.

**prism spectroscope** See ***spectroscope.***

**profile cut** A diamond cut, designed for the economic use of flat crystals, which provides a large table area for little weight. Flat crystals are sawn and polished into various shapes having a polished top and a series of narrow V-shaped parallel grooves on the underside. Originally known as the princess cut. *Figure P.5.*

*Figure P.5* The profile or princess cut.

**profiled bubbles** Distorted gourd-shaped bubbles occurring as typical inclusions in synthetic spinel.

**propagation of light** See ***wave theory of light.***

**proportion** A term used when grading polished stones, particularly diamond, for cut. The proportions of an ideally-cut diamond are based on the width of the table facet, the depth of the crown and pavilion and the thickness of the girdle as percentages of the girdle diameter, together with the crown and pavilion facet angles. See ***brilliant cut.***

**prosopite** A turquoise simulant comprising gem-quality calcium aluminium hydroxide fluoride. Monoclinic. R.I. around 1.50; S.G. 2.69-2.85; H. 4½. Opaque, blue. Occurrence: Mexico, USA.

**Proterozoic** The later part of the Precambrian era. See ***Precambrian.***

**protogenetic inclusions** See ***inclusions*** (pre-existing).

**proton** An elementary particle in the nucleus of an atom with a unit positive charge and a mass slightly less than that of a neutron.

**proustite** A collector's stone which darkens on exposure to light. $3Ag_2S.As_2S_3$. Trigonal R.I. 2.881–3.084; D.R. +0.203; S.G. 5.57–5.64; H. 2½. Transparent, red. Occurrence: Canada, Chile, Czechoslovakia, France, Mexico, USA.

**pseudochrysolite** A misleading name for moldavite.

**pseudo-cleavage** See ***false cleavage.***

**pseudocrocidolite** A quartz pseudomorph of crocidolite, better known as tiger's eye. See ***crocidolite*** and ***quartz.***

**pseudomalachite** A copper phosphate similar in habit and colour to malachite. $Cu_3P_2O_83Cu(OH)_2$. Monoclinic. Mean R.I. 1.80; S.G. 3.6; H. 4½. Opaque, green. Occurrence: Germany, USSR, Zambia.

**pseudomorphic** Term applied to a mineral which has adopted an external form other than its normal habit by copying, for example, the shape of a pre-existing crystal or organic structure.

**pseudophite** A variety of aluminous serpentine used for small ornamental objects. R.I. 1.57; S.G. 2.69; H. 2½. Opaque, green. Occurrence: Austria.

**psilomelane** A colloidal manganese oxide used as a haematite simulant. S.G. 4.35; H. 5½–6½. Opaque, silvery lustre (can be distinguished from haematite by its strong electroconductivity and brownish-black streak).

**pudding stone** A conglomerate formed by pebbles cemented together by secondary mineralization (e.g. Hertfordshire pudding stone).

**pulling method of crystal growth** See ***Czochralski process.***

**pumice powder** A powdered volcanic rock used as a polishing abrasive.

**Purbeck marble** See ***paludina limestone.***

**pure melt method of crystal growth** See ***Bridgeman-Stockbarger process.***

**purity** See ***clarity*** and ***quality.***

**purpurite** An ornamental material comprising the mineral manganese iron phosphate. $(Mn,Fe)PO_4$. Orthorhombic. R.I. 1.87; S.G. 3.69; H. 4–4½. Opaque, deep rose to purplish-red. Occurrence: Namibia.

**putty powder** A creamy-white abrasive polishing powder, containing mainly tin oxide, which is used for polishing gemstones (also called stannic oxide and tin oxide).

**pyknometer** See ***specific gravity bottle.***

**pyoene** Silicate minerals with two directions of cleavage intersecting at a little less than 90 degrees.

**pyralspite garnet series** An isomorphous series of garnets encompassing the pyrope-almandine-spessartite species. See also ***ugrandite garnet series.***

**pyramid** A form consisting of a group of triangular faces whose planes are cut by three crystal axes (e.g. an octahedron).

**pyrandine** See ***pyrope-almandine.***

**pyrites (iron pyrites)** Also known as 'Fool's gold' and inca stone, this iron sulphide is dimorphous with marcasite. $FeS_2$. Cubic. S.G. 4.84-5.10; H. 6½. Opaque, brass yellow. Occurrence: World-wide. See also ***marcasite.***

**pyroclastic rock** Igneous rock fragments ejected by an erupting volcano.

**pyroelectric effect** A property possessed by some gemstones, such as tourmaline and quartz, which become electrically charged when heated.

**pyroemerald** A misleading name for green fluorite.

**pyrope** See ***garnet.***

**pyrope-almandine** A violet variety of garnet with a composition between that of pyrope and almandine. R.I. 1.76; S.G. 3.84; H. 7¼. Occurrence: Brazil, Sri Lanka, Tanzania, USA, Zambia.

**pyrophyllite** An aluminium silicate similar in appearance and composition to soapstone. $H_2Al_2(SiO_3)_4$. R.I. around 1.6; S.G. 2.8; H. 1½. Opaque, white, grey or greenish. Also called South African wonderstone, Ottosdal G stone and koranna stone, it has been used both as an ornamental stone and as a container for the reaction constituents in the synthesis of industrial diamonds (the melting point of pyrophyllite rises from 1360 °C to 2720 °C under high pressure). Occurrence: Brazil, South Africa, USA, USSR.

**pyroxene** A group of silicate minerals linked by similar physical and optical characteristics (e.g. diopside, enstatite, jadeite and spodumene).

**pyroxmangite** A rare collector's stone comprising the mineral manganese/iron silicate. $(Mn,Fe)SiO_3$. Triclinic. R.I. 1.726, 1.744 to 1.748, 1.764; D.R. +0.016 to +0.018; S.G. 3.61-3.90; H. 5½-6. Transparent, bright pink/purple. Occurrence: Japan.

**pyrrhotite** A mineral similar to pyrites, but of duller colour and containing more sulphur in its composition.

# Q

**quality** A term used in the sorting of rough diamonds which is equivalent to clarity for polished diamonds (i.e. freedon from internal flaws and inclusions). See ***Sorting Standards for Rough Diamonds*** in Appendix D.

**quartz** A crystalline form of silica. $SiO_2$. Trigonal. R.I. 1.544, 1.553; D.R. +0.009; S.G. 2.65; H. 7. Varieties:

*rock crystal* — transparent, colourless.

*milky quartz* — translucent, white.

*amethyst* — transparent, purple.

*citrine* — transparent, yellow.

*rose quartz* — translucent, pink.

*aventurine quartz* — opaque, green or golden-brown with spangles of mica.

*jasper* — impure multi-crystalline quartz; opaque, brown, green (called *prase*), pink, yellow.

*hornstone* — a form of jasper.

*cairngorm* — transparent, brown.

*blue quartz* — called *siderite,* opaque.

*smoky quartz* — called *morion*; transparent, greyish.

*quartz cat's eye* — translucent, light greenish or brownish chatoyant.

*quartz tiger's eye* — opaque, golden brown chatoyant.

*quartz hawk's eye/falcon's eye* — opaque, blue/green chatoyant.

*rutilated quartz* — called *venus hair stone, fleche d'amour*; transparent, colourless with rutile needle inclusions.

*tourmalated quartz* — called *thetis hair stone*; transparent, colourless with needle-like tourmaline inclusions.

Pleochroism, medium in amethyst (bluish-violet, reddish-violet). Occurrence: World-wide except for tiger's eye and hawk's eye which come mainly from South Africa, and quartz cat's eye which comes mainly from Sri Lanka and India.

**quartz en chemise** A milky white quartz in which the milkyness is only skin deep.

**quartz glass** A fused amorphous quartz. R.I. 1.46; S.G. 2.21.

**quartzite** A rock consisting of a granular interlocking mass of quartz crystals (when small crystals of mica are present it forms aventurine quartz). R.I. around 1.55; S.G. 2.64-2.69. Occurrence: India, Spain, Tanzania, USSR.

**quartz-schist** An opaque quartzite heavily impregnated with fuchsite mica.

**quartz topaz** A misleading name for the citrine variety of quartz.

**quasima diamond** A misleading name for the rock crystal variety of quartz.

**Quaternary** The period of geological time representing the last 2 million years. It is the later part of the Cenozoic era and comprises the ***Pleistocene*** and ***Holocene (Recent)*** epochs. See also ***Cenozoic*** and ***Tertiary.***

**Quebec diamond** A misleading name for the rock crystal variety of quartz.

**queen conch** See ***giant conch.***

**queenstownite** A slaggy natural glass grouped with those glasses associated with meteorite craters. Transparent to opaque, colourless, yellowish-green, olive-green, black. R.I. 1.47-1.50; S.G. 2.27-2.29. Occurrence: Tasmania.

**quetzalztli** A variety of translucent green jade found in Mexico.

**quincite** A pink sepiolite or a pink common opal.

**quoin facets** Four of the bezel facets and four of the pavilion facets on a brilliant-cut stone. See ***brilliant cut.***

**radiant cut** This is a 70-facet mixed cut for diamond. It has emerald-cut facets on top, and triangular facets on the pavilion. The radiant cut has some of the fire and scintillation of a round brilliant in the centre. In this respect it is superior to the emerald cut. *Figure R.1.*

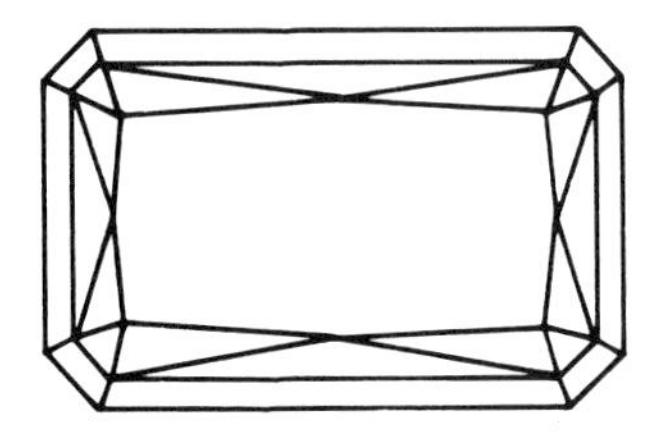
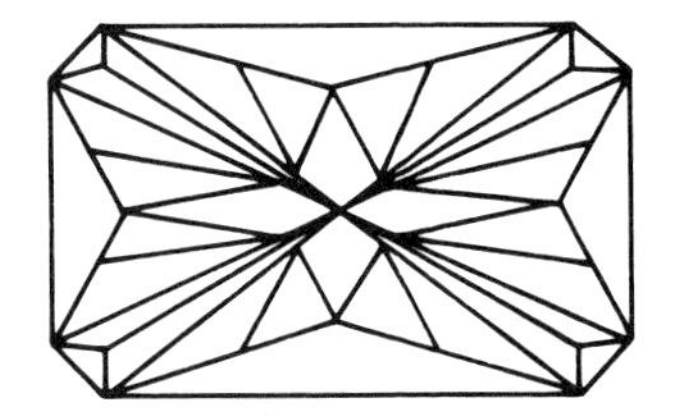

*Figure R.1* The radiant cut.

**radient** Trade name for a synthetic colourless spinel.

**radioactive** A material which emits elementary particles or rays as a result of the spontaneous disintegration of atomic nuclei. See ***ekanite*** and ***zircon.***

**radiograph** An X-ray or gamma ray shadowgraph for the internal inspection of materials transparent or translucent to those rays (e.g. pearls). Also used to distinguish diamonds, which are transparent to X-rays, from diamond simulants, which are either opaque or translucent to X-rays. See ***X-rays*** and ***X-ray diamond tester.***

**radioisotope** A radioactive isotope such as cobalt-60 which emits gamma rays and is used in the artificial colour treatment of diamonds. See ***treated diamonds.***

**radium diamond** A misleading name for smoky quartz.

**radium-treated diamonds** See ***treated diamonds.***

**rain** Inclusions consisting of a parallel arrangement of thin, elongate tubules which may contain liquid and minute crystals.

**rainbow agate** An iridescent agate. See also ***fire agate.***

**rainbow diamond** A misleading name for a synthetic rutile diamond simulant.

**rainbow gem** Trade name for a synthetic rutile diamond simulant.

**rainbow magic diamond** A misleading trade name for a synthetic rutile diamond simulant.

**rainbow obsidian** An iridescent obsidian.

**rainbow quartz** See ***iris quartz.***

**Raman spectroscopy** When a high intensity light (such as a laser beam) falls on a surface, a minute amount of it undergoes Raman scattering. This scattered light is shorter in wavelength than the incident beam, the effect being caused by the excitation of molecular vibrations in the surface of the material. The degree of wavelength difference, or Raman shift, between the incident beam and the scattered light depends on the nature of the surface atoms and their structural bonding. This spectral shift enables diagnostic absorption spectra in the infra red to be seen in the visible region of the spectrum by means of a standard spectrometer.

**ramaura** A synthetic flux-grown ruby incorporating a tell-tale dopant which causes a distinctive fluorescence under LW UV in uncut material.

**rape seed oil** An oil derived from the seed of the rape or colza plant which is used to clarify cloudy amber. The warmed oil penetrates the amber and enters the air cavities causing the cloudiness. Overheating of the amber produces stress cracks known as sun spangles.

**rare-earth elements** The lanthanide group of 15 rare metallic elements, which includes rare-earths such as cerium (Ce), erbium (Er), holium (Ho), neodymium (Nd), praseodymium (Pr), terbium (Tb) and thulium (Tm), and whose oxides are used as colour dopants in various man-made gems. Praseodymium occurs in nature with neodymium (with a collective name of didymium) and these elements are the cause of the colour in yellow apatite. See *Table of Elements* in Appendix H.

**rare-earth garnets** Man-made garnets containing rare-earth elements as part of their composition (e.g. yttrium aluminium garnet, gadolinium gallium garnet).

**rare-earth spectra** When rare-earths are present in a gemstone they give rise to characteristic absorption spectra called 'fine line' spectra.

**rare white/rarest white** Colour grades for polished diamonds. See ***Colour Grading Standards*** in Appendix B.

**raspberry spar** See ***rhodochrosite.***

**rati** An Indian/Burmese unit of weight equal to 0.911 carat. See also ***mangelin*** and ***tola.***

**Rayner Prize** A prize (of gemmological equipment) once awarded to the top candidate in the annual Preliminary Examination of the Gemmological Association of Great Britain, whose papers also meet the required standards for this award and who also derives his or her main income from activities essentially connected with the jewellery trade. See also ***Anderson Medal*** and ***Tully Medal.***

**Recent** (Holocene) See ***Quaternary.***

**reconstructed rubies** See ***Geneva rubies.***

**reconstructed stones** Stones fabricated by fusing together small pieces of the natural gem. See ***ambroid*** and ***Geneva rubies.***

**recovery plant** A plant, usually comprising a series of units, which is used to separate rough diamonds from crushed rock or gravel. See ***heavy media separation, hydro-cyclone, grease belt, grease table, magneto-hydrostatic separation, optical separator*** and ***X-ray separator.***

**red gold** A red tinted gold made by alloying gold with either copper or copper and silver.

**red jade** A misleading name for a reddish quartzite, and the reddish variety of dumortierite in quartz.

**red ogwell marble** A red limestone marble from Devon, England, containing white fossilized coral known as favosites.

**red sea pearls** A misleading name for coral beads.

**reflectivity** The light reflected from a surface (or from an interface between two media) is a measure of that surface's reflectivity or lustre. See ***Fresnel's reflectivity equation, law of reflection*** and ***lustre.***

**reflectivity meter** An instrument for measuring the reflectivity of a surface. Reflectivity meters developed for the purpose of gemstone identification are based on the Fresnel relationship between reflectivity and refractive index (see ***Fresnel's reflectivity equation***). Such instruments do not measure absolute reflectivity, but are calibrated in terms of comparative reflectivity, and are particularly useful in the identification of diamond and those man-made diamond simulants whose R.I. is above the range of the critical-angle refractometer. The first reflectivity instrument for gemstone identification (using a visual-optical comparator) was built by L. C. Trumper, FGA, in 1959. Modern instruments use infra-red light-emitting diodes and photo-detectors, and display the result either by means of an analogue meter or on a digital display. Important criteria are cleanliness of the stone and a scratch-free flat test surface (more recent developments with focused fibre optics have made it possible to test cabochons). *Figure R.2.*

**refraction** The bending of light rays as they pass through the interface (at angles other than the normal) of media having different optical densities. The greater the difference in the optical densities of the two media, the greater will be the angle of refraction. See ***angle of refraction, double refraction*** and

---

*Figure R.2* (right) The 'Jeweller's Eye' (top) is a two-range reflectivity meter whose lower range covers from glass up to garnet. (Hanneman). The 'Diamond Checker' (middle) is a single-range meter designed specifically for diamond identification. (Culti Corp.) The 'Gemlusta 400× (bottom) uses a digital display and can detect the small difference in reflectivity between machine-cut synthetic corundums and hand-cut natural corundums.

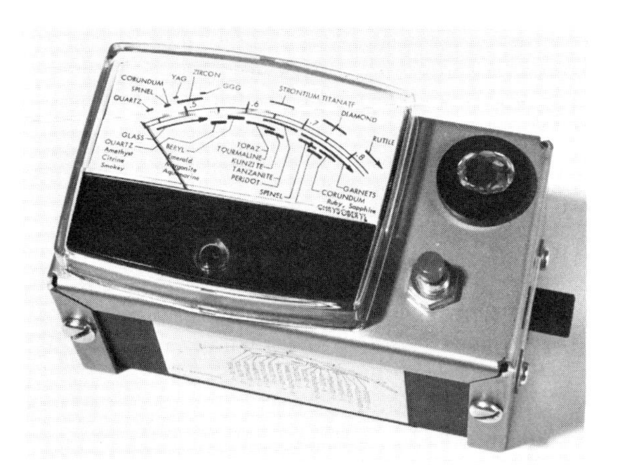
CORUNDUM
SPINEL
QUARTZ
YAG
ZIRCON
GGG
STRONTIUM TITANATE
DIAMOND
RUTILE
GLASS
QUARTZ
Amethyst
Citrine
Smokey
BERYL
Emerald
Aquamarine
TOPAZ
TOURMALINE
KUNZITE
TANZANITE
PERIDOT
SPINEL
GARNETS
CORUNDUM
Ruby, Sapphire
CHRYSOBERYL

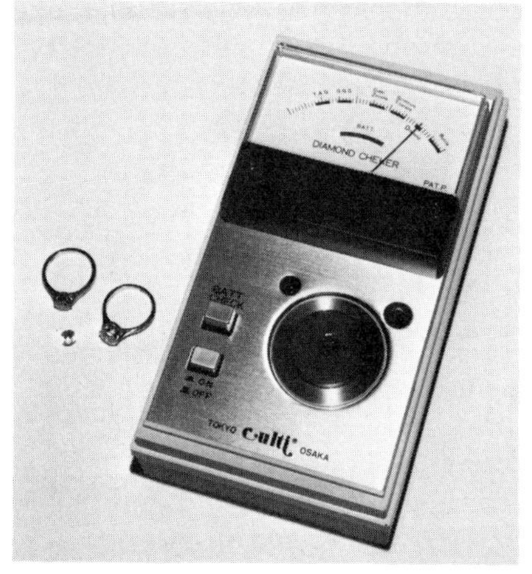
DIAMOND CHECKER
PAT.P.
BATT CHECK
ON
OFF
TOKYO
OSAKA

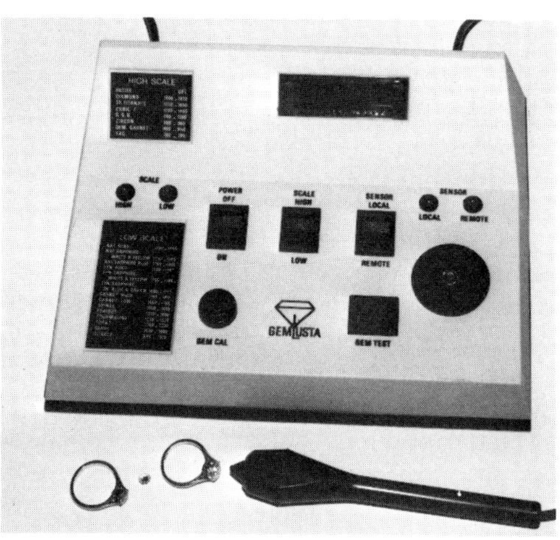
HIGH SCALE
SCALE
HIGH
LOW
POWER OFF
ON
SCALE HIGH
LOW
SENSOR LOCAL
REMOTE
SENSOR
LOCAL
REMOTE
LOW SCALE
GEM CAL
GEM TEST

***refractive index.***

**refractive index** (R.I.) A measure of the degree by which a material bends or refracts the light rays entering it from the surrounding medium (air) at angles other than the normal. The refractive index of a material can be expressed as the ratio between its optical density and that of air (the standard medium for all practical gemmological purposes).

$$\text{R.I.} = \frac{\text{Optical density of material}}{\text{Optical density of air}}$$

As the velocity of light is decreased in an optically dense material (and is inversely proportional to optical density), R.I. can also be expressed as the ratio of the velocity of light in air to that in the material.

From ***Snell's law***, the refractive index of a material can also be obtained from the relationship between the angle of incidence of a light ray in air, and its angle of refraction in the material. From *Figure L.3:*

$$\text{R.I.} = \frac{\text{Sine of angle ION}}{\text{Sine of angle MOR}}$$

Because the refractive index of a material varies with the wavelength of light, monochromatic sodium light, with a wavelength of 589.3 nm, is chosen as the standard for gemmological work.

In doubly-refracting biaxial stones, the maximum value index is designated the *gamma* index ($\gamma$), and the minimum value is called the *alpha* index ($\alpha$). An intermediate value *beta* ($\beta$) corresponds either with the lowest value for the higher index or the highest value for the lower index (see ***extraordinary ray*** and ***ordinary ray***). See also ***refractometer, Becke line method*** and ***direct method.***

**refractometer** An optical instrument designed to measure the refractive indices of various substances. For gem identification purposes, a specialized instrument is used which enables the refractive index of a stone to be measured as a shadow line on a scale. This shadow line is produced as the result of the critical angle of total reflection at the interface between the gemstone and refractometer's measuring prism (see *Figure R.3* and ***critical angle***). Because of the difficulty in obtaining a good optical contact between the gemstone facet and the surface of the prism, use is made of a contact liquid (see ***contact liquid***). To achieve higher ranges, special refractometers have been marketed using blende, diamond or strontium titanate prisms (the latter using a thermo-plastic contact paste and a heated prism. *Figure R.4.).* The refractive index of curved surface gems (cabochons) can also be measured on a refractometer (see ***distant vision method).***

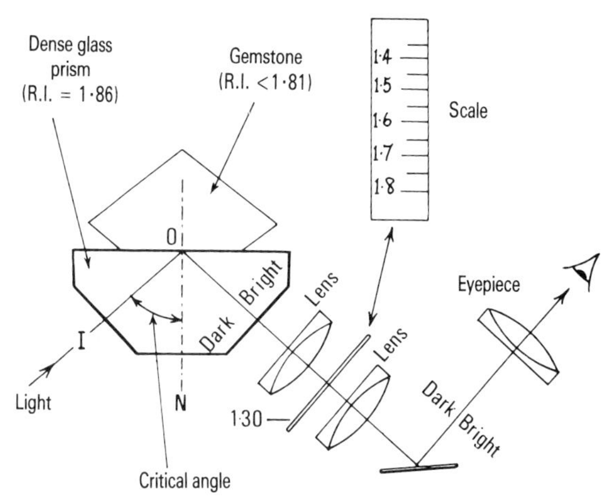


*Figure R.3* Sketch showing the optical design of a modern critical angle refractometer.

This is facilitated by an instrument such as the Rayner Dialdex refractometer *(Figure R.4.)* which uses a calibrated control in place of a calibrated internal scale. See also ***Abbé refractometer, Bertrand refractometer, Erb and Gray refractometer, Herbert Smith refractometer, spinel refractometer*** and ***Tully refractometer.***

**Regency synthetic emerald** A synthetic emerald produced by the hydrothermal process (Vacuum Ventures Inc.) using the Linde process and Union Carbide patents. R.I. 1.570, 1.576; D.R. −0.006; S.G. 2.67–2.69.

**relative density** A term used instead of specific gravity in connection with liquids. See ***specific gravity.***

**reniform** See ***mamillary.***

**repeated twinning** See ***polysynthetic twinning.***

**repoussé** A technique in silver- and gold-smithing of pushing metal into a raised design from the reverse side.

**resinoid** Trade name for a phenolic resin plastic.

**resinous lustre** See ***lustre.***

**resistivity** The electrical resistance (per cm) which limits the passage of an electric current through a conductor. Basic unit of measurement is the ohm (kilo-ohm, mega-ohm). See ***electro-conductivity.***

**retinalite** A honey yellow variety of serpentine.

**Retzius** See ***lines of Retzius.***

**Rhine diamond** A misleading name for the rock crystal variety of quartz.

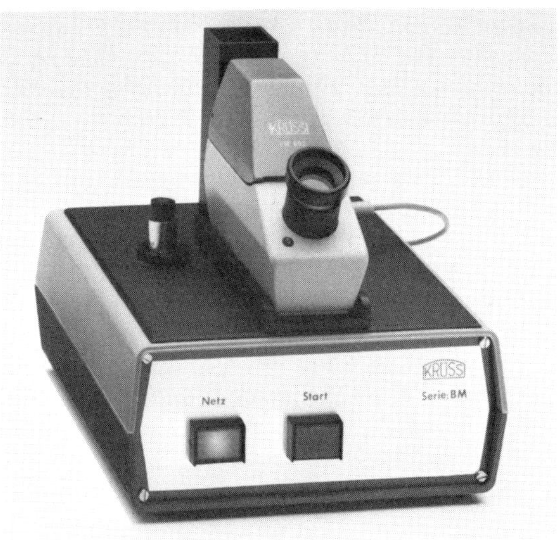


*Figure R.4* The Rayner Dialdex critical-angle refractometer (top) is fitted with a calibrated control in place of a calibrated internal scale. (Rubin.) The Krüss ER602 extended-range refractometer (bottom) uses a heated strontium titanate measuring prism. The bottle of thermo-plastic contact paste is heated to liquid temperature (40°C) in a special socket on the control plinth. A sodium light source is fitted at the rear of the plinth. The R.I. of the contact paste is 2.22, and the range of the refractometer is 1.79–2.21.

**rhinestone** A coloured (sometimes multicoloured) glass gemstone simulant.

**Rhodesian Gem and Mineral Society** See ***Gem and Mineral Society of Zimbabwe.***

**Rhodesian moonstone** A bluish-white translucent quartz.

**rhodium** A member of the platinum group of metals, used for plating jewellery. Rh. Atomic number 45; atomic weight 102.91; melting point 1960 °C; S.G. 12.44.

**rhodizite** A rare collector's stone comprising the mineral potassium aluminium borate. $KAl_2B_3O_8$. Cubic. R.I. 1.69; S.G. 3.4; H. 8. Transparent, pink, light-yellow, greenish. Occurrence: the Malagasy Republic, USSR.

**rhodochrosite** An ornamental stone comprising the mineral manganese carbonate (also called inca rose). $MnCo_3$. Trigonal (crystals and massive crystalline aggregate). R.I. 1.60, 1.82; D.R. −0.22; S.G. 3.50-3.65; H. 4. Transparent (crystals) to opaque (massive), rose red. The opaque ornamental material is banded with white and shades of pink. Occurrence: Argentine, India, Southern Africa (Kalahari), USA.

**rhodoid** Trade name for a non-flammable variety of celluloid.

**rhodolite** A violet variety of garnet with a composition between that of pyrope and almandine. R.I. 1.76; S.G. 3.84; H. 7¼. Occurrence: Brazil, Sri Lanka, Tanzania, USA, Zambia.

**rhodonite** An ornamental stone comprising the mineral manganese silicate $MnSiO_3$. Triclinic (crystals and massive crystalline aggregate). R.I. 1.733, 1.744; D.R. +0.011; S.G. 3.6-3.7; H. 6. Transparent (crystals) to opaque (massive), red with black inclusions or veining of oxidized manganese. Pleochroism, medium (orange-red, brownish-red). Occurrence: Australia, Mexico, South Africa, Sweden, USA, USSR.

**rhombic** See ***orthorhombic.***

**rhombic dodecahedron** See ***dodecahedron.***

**rhombohedron** A crystal form consisting of six identical rhombus (four-sided) faces.

**rhombus** An oblique equilateral parallelogram (i.e. a 'diamond' shape).

**rhyolite** A fine grained granitic rock.

**ribandagate** A banded agate variety of chalcedony.

**riband jasper** See ***ribbon jasper.***

**ribbon jasper** A jasper containing ribbon-like colour stripes. See ***quartz.***

**richlieu pearls** Trade name for imitation pearls.

**ricolite** A banded variety of fine-grained serpentine from Mexico.

**river** A colour grade for polished diamonds. See ***Colour Grading Standards*** in Appendix B.

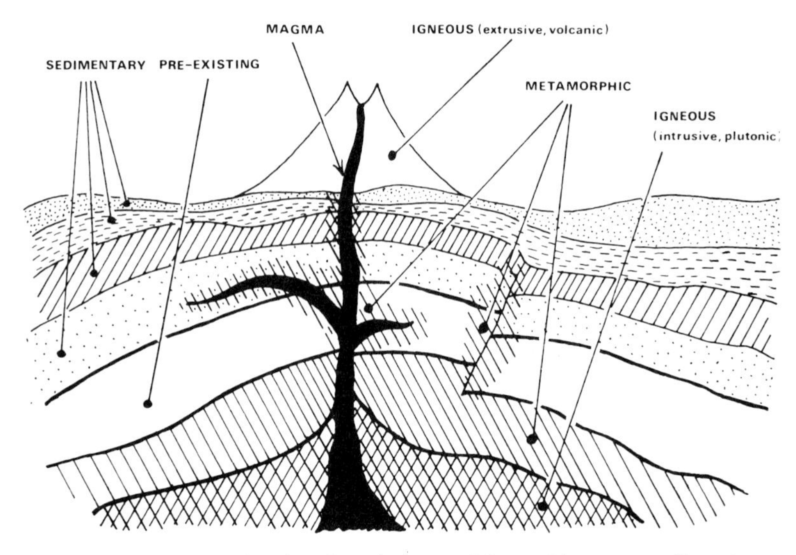


*Figure R.5* Sketch showing the relative positions of igneous, sedimentary and metamorphic rocks. Quartz occurs widely in igneous and metamorphic rocks.

**river agate** Water worn pebbles of moss agate.

**river pearl** A natural pearl from a freshwater mussel.

**rock** A naturally-occurring solidified mixture of various minerals (e.g. granite is a rock consisting of feldspar, quartz and mica). See also ***igneous rock, metamorphic rock*** and ***sedimentary rock.*** *Figure R.5.*

**rock crystal** See ***quartz.***

**rock glass** See ***obsidian.***

**rock ruby** A misleading name for pyrope garnet.

**rock systems** See ***geological eras.***

**rogueite** A greenish variety of jasper.

**rejection** A clarity grade for polished diamonds. See ***Clarity Grading Standards*** in Appendix C.

**rolled gold** A thin layer of gold or gold alloy (not less than 9 carat) thermally bonded to silver or a base metal alloy (usually brass), which is then rolled to reduce it to the required overall thickness. See also ***gold filled.***

**Roman mosaic** A mosaic made not from natural stones but from small coloured-glass rods. These are cut to length and cemented in an upright position in a frame so as to make a picture. Also called Byzantine mosaic.

**Roman pearls** A misleading name for glass-bead imitation pearls.

**romanzovite** A brown grossular garnet.

**rondel** A polished gem, usually rock crystal, cut in the form of a flat circular disc, centrally pierced and faceted round the perimeter. It is used for separating beads in a necklace.

**rondisting** See ***bruting.***

**röntgen rays** See ***X-rays.***

**rosaline** See ***zoisite.***

**rose cut** An ancient cutting style used for diamonds, which consists of a flat base and a dome of triangular facets. *Figure R.6.* See also ***Antwerp rose cut*** and ***Dutch rose cut.***

**rose de France** Trade name for a pinkish amethyst or a pink synthetic sapphire.

**rosée pearl** A much prized pink-tinted pearl.

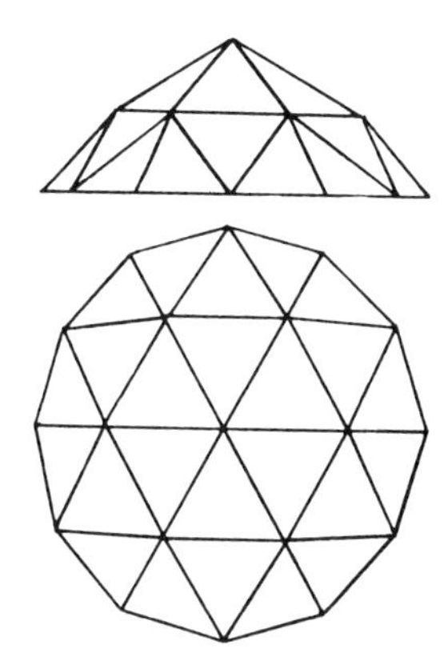

*Figure R.6* The rose cut.

**rose garnet** See ***landerite.*** Also a misleading name for rhodonite.

**roseki** See ***agalmatolite.***

**rose kunzite** A misleading name for synthetic pink sapphire.

**rose quartz** See ***quartz.***

**rose moonstone** A misleading trade name for pink scapolite.

**rosinca** See ***rhodochrosite.***

**rosolite** See ***landerite.***

**rossini jewel** Trade name for the man-made diamond simulant strontium titanate.

**rosterite** A variety of rose-red beryl from Elba.

**rothoffite** A yellow-brown variety of andradite garnet.

**rottenstone** A white to pale-brownish silica-based 'soft' abrasive powder used for polishing gemstones, and derived from decomposed limestone (also called silicon dioxide and tripoli).

**rouge** Powdered haematite (jeweller's rouge) or chromium oxide (green rouge).

**rough diamond** A diamond crystal in its natural unpolished state.
**roumanite** A variety of amber from Romania.
**round brilliant cut** See ***brilliant cut.***
**royal azel** Trade name for sugilite.
**royalite** Trade name for a purplish-red glass.
**royal lavulite** Trade name for sugilite.
**royal topaz** Blue topaz.
**royite** A rock crystal variety of quartz.
**rozircon** A misleading trade name for rose-coloured synthetic spinel.
**rubace** Trade name for red-stained cracked quartz.
**rubellite** A misleading name for pink tourmaline.
**rubicelle** A misleading name for yellow-orange spinel.
**rubolite** A red-coloured common opal.
**ruby** See ***corundum.***
**ruby balas** A misleading name for red spinel.
**ruby powder** See ***aluminium oxide.***
**ruby spinel** A misleading name for red spinel.
**ruin agate** Brecciated or dendritic agate with markings resembling ruins.
**ruin marble** A yellow marble with brown markings resembling ruins.
**run-of-mine** A normal month's production from a diamond mine.
**Russian jade** A spinach-green variety of nephrite.
**ruthenium** A member of the platinum group of metals. Rh. Atomic number 44; atomic weight 101.7; melting point 2400 °C; S.G. 12.3.
**rutilated quartz** See ***quartz.***
**rutile** A naturally-occurring titanium oxide. $TiO_2$. Tetragonal. R.I. 2.616, 2.903; D.R. +0.287; S.G. 4.2-4.3; H. 6-6½. Transparent, red, red-brown, black. Occurrence: Brazil, France, Italy, the Malagasy Republic, Scandinavia, Switzerland, USA, USSR. Synthetic rutile crystals, having the same constants as natural rutile but yellowish in colour, are grown in a modified Verneuil furnace by the flame-fusion process, and cut as diamond simulants.

**sabalite** A variety of banded green variscite found inthe USA.
**sac pearl** See ***cyst pearl.***
**saffronite** Citrine variety of quartz.
**safirina** A blue spinel or blue quartz.
**safranite** Citrine variety of quartz.
**sagenitic agate** An agate variety which contains needle-like inclusions of other minerals.
**sagenite** A quartz containing needle-like inclusions. Also an acicular rutile.
**sagenitic quartz** A variety of rock crystal quartz containing needle-like inclusions (e.g. rutilated quartz, known as 'Venus hair stone' and 'Flêches d'amour'; tourmalated or actinolated quartz, known as 'Thetis hair stone').
**Saint Stephen's stone** A red-spotted white chalcedony.
**salamanca topaz** A misleading name for a fiery-coloured citrine variety of quartz.
**salininha emeralds** Brazilian beryl coloured green by vanadium. Because of this they are more correctly classified as green beryl, because emerald is coloured by chromium.
**samarskite** A complex mixture of tantalum, niobium (columbium) and rare-earth oxides. S.G. 4.1-6.2; H. 5-6. Opaque, velvet-black with a semi-metallic lustre.
**San Diego ruby** A misleading name for red tourmaline.
**sandstone** A sedimentary rock formed from the compacted debris of pre-existing rock masses. See ***sedimentary rock.***
**sang-i-yeshan** A dark green bowenite.
**sanidine** A glassy variety of orthoclase feldspar found in Germany. R.I. 1.516, 1.522 to 1.520, 1.526; D.R. −0.006; S.G. 2.57-2.58; H. 6. Transparent, light grey to light brown.
**sapphire** See ***corundum.***
**sapphire powder** See ***aluminium oxide.***
**sapphire quartz** A misleading name for blue chalcedony or the hawk's eye variety of quartz.
**sapphire spinel** A misleading name for blue spinel.
**sapphirine** A misleading name for blue chalcedony, blue spinel and a blue glass sapphire simulant.
**sapphirine** A rare silicate containing magnesium and aluminium. Monoclinic. R.I. 1.711, 1.718; D.R. −0.007; S.G. 3.5; H.7½. Transparent dark green or dark blue. Occurrence: Thailand.
**sapphirized titania** Trade name for a synthetic rutile.
**sarcolite** A rare collector's stone comprising a complex aluminium silicate. $(Ca,Na)_4Al_3(Al,Si)_3Si_6O_{24}$. Tetragonal. R.I. 1.604, 1.615; D.R. 0.011-0.017; S.G. 2.92; H.6. Transparent pale red to rose.

Occurrence: Italy (Mount Vesuvius).

**sard** See ***chalcedony.***

**sardium** Artificially coloured sard.

**sardoine** A dark variety of cornelian.

**sardonyx** See ***chalcedony.***

**sarium** Dyed sard.

**satelite** A fibrous serpentine.

**satin spar** A fibrous white or pink variety of calcite. Occurrence: England, Scotland, USA. Also a white fibrous variety of gypsum.

**saualpite** Original name for the mineral zoisite.

**saussurite** A rock consisting mainly of decomposed plagioclase feldspar and zoisite (plus some mica and calcite) sometimes used as a jade simulant. R.I. 1.57-1.70; S.G. 3.0-3.4; H. 6½. Opaque, variegated white/green, grey-green, yellow-green or moss-green. Occurrence: Switzerland.

**sawables** Rough diamonds having a blocky shape (e.g. whole crystals such as stones and shapes) which are sawn before being polished. See ***makeables.***

**sawing** A method used to divide rough gem material. With rough diamonds it is used to part a crystal in two, in directions other than those of the cleavage planes. The diamond cutting saw consists of a clamped thin phosphor-bronze blade which is coated with a mixture of olive oil and diamond dust and rotated at 5000 to 10 000 rev/min.

**sawyer** A diamond cutter who operates a bank of diamond sawing machines, often comprising up to 40 individual saws.

**saxon diamond** A misleading name for colourless topaz.

**saxon chrysolite** A misleading name for topaz.

**saxon topaz** A misleading name for the citrine variety of quartz.

**scaife** A cast iron lap used for polishing diamonds. The scaife has a porous surface which is coated with a mixture of olive (or castor) oil and diamond dust. It is rotated at 2500 rev/min, and the diamond, secured in a holder or dop, is brought into pressure contact with the treated surface. See *Figure T.1.*

**SCAN** A scanning laser acoustic microscope.

**Scan DN** The Scandinavian nomenclature and grading standards for polished diamonds. See ***Grading Standards*** in Appendices B and C.

**Scan DN brilliant cut** One of several 'ideal' cuts for diamond, which together with the Eppler cut is mainly favoured in Europe (see *Figure B.6.*). See ***Eppler brilliant cut, Johnson and Rösch brilliant cut, Parker brilliant cut*** and ***Tolkowsky brilliant cut.***

**scanning electron microscope** (SEM) See ***electron microscope.***

**scapolite** A member of the scapolite isomorphous series whose end members are marialite, $Na_4Cl(AlSi_3O_8)_3$, and meionite

$Ca_6(Al_2Si_2O_8)_3(SO_4CO_3)$. Scapolite is an aluminium-calcium-sodium-silicate combination of these two end members. Tetragonal. R.I. (blue) 1.544, 1.560; R.I. (yellow) 1.548, 1.568; R.I. (pink and colourless) 1.540, 1.549; D.R. −0.009 to −0.02; S.G. (blue) 2.634; S.G. (yellow) 2.70; S.G. (pink and colourless) 2.63; H. 6. Transparent, colourless, blue (chatoyant), violet, yellow, pink (chatoyant). Pleochroism, strong in pink (colourless, pink) and violet (dark blue, pale blue), medium in yellow (colourless, yellow). Occurrence: Brazil, Burma, Canada (opaque yellow), the Malagasy Republic, Mozambique.

**schaumberg diamond** A misleading name for the rock crystal variety of quartz.

**scheelite** A collector's stone comprising the mineral calcium tungstate. $CaWO_4$. Tetragonal. R.I. 1.918, 1.934; D.R. +0.016; S.G. 5.9-6.1; H. 4½-5. Transparent to translucent, colourless, yellowish-white, brownish, orange. Occurrence: Mexico, USA. Synthetic scheelite has been grown by the Czochralski and Bridgeman-Stockbarger processes.

**schiller** See ***sheen.***

**schiller spar** Also known as bastite, this is a leek-green altered enstatite. S.G. 2.6; H. 3½-4. Opaque. Occurrence: Germany.

**schist** A metamorphic rock consisting of layers of different minerals which split up into thin irregular plates.

**schlossmacherite** A complex hydrated calcium alumina sulphur arsenide belonging to the alunite-jerosite series. Hexagonal. R.I. around 1.597. Opaque, green. Occurrence: Chile.

**schnide** A blue glassy common opal.

**schorl** See ***tourmaline.***

**scientific brilliant** A misleading name for colourless synthetic corundum.

**scientific emerald** A misleading name for a beryl glass simulant of emerald.

**scientific hematite** A misleading name for a metallic alloy made to imitate haematite. See ***hematine.***

**scientific topaz** A misleading name for a synthetic pink corundum.

**scintillation** The multiple and alternating reflections of light from the facets of a polished gemstone when there is relative movement between the observer and the light source or the gemstone.

**scissors cut** A rectangular gemstone cut, also called a cross cut. *Figure S.1.*

**scolecite** A collector's stone consisting of a hydrated silicate of calcium and aluminium, this is one of the zeolite group of minerals. $CaAl_2Si_3O_{10}.3H_2O$. Monoclinic. R.I. around 1.49; S.G. 2.3; H. 5-5½. Opaque to translucent, colourless to white, yellowish, greenish, reddish.

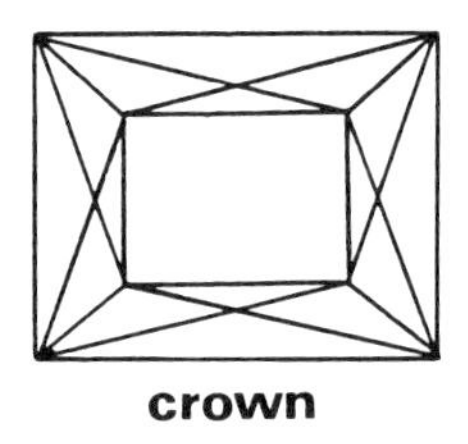

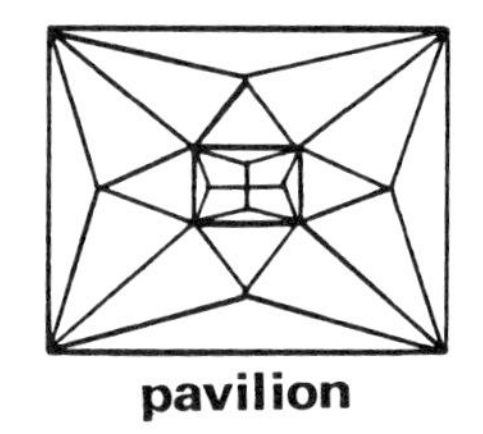


*Figure S.1* The scissors or cross cut.

**scorodite** A rare collector's stone comprising a hydrated ferric arsenate. $FeAsO_4.2H_2O$. Orthorhombic. R.I. 1.785, 1.816; D.R. +0.031; S.G. 3.29; H. 3½-4. Transparent to translucent, dark blue. Pleochroism, strong. Occurrence: Namibia.

**Scotch pearls** Freshwater pearls from mussels found in the rivers of Scotland.

**Scotch topaz** A misleading name for cairngorm, citrine or smoky quartz.

**Scottish topaz** A misleading name for yellow-brown quartz.

**scratch hardness** See ***hardness.***

**sea amber** See ***amber.***

**sea horse ivory** Ivory from the teeth of the hippopotamus.

**secondary deposit** See ***alluvial deposit.***

**secondary group of rocks** An obsolete term for rocks of the Mesozoic era. See ***Mesozoic.***

**second water** See ***first water.***

**sedimentary rock** A rock formed from deposits of the fine fragments of sand, grit and clay eroded from pre-existing rocks, or by natural chemical precipitation on the sea bed, e.g. sandstone and limestone.

**seed pearls** Very small pearls (less than ¼ grain) found mainly in the Gulf of Mannar, between India and Sri Lanka.

**Seiko synthetic corundum** Pink, orange and blue sapphires and ruby produced by the floating zone method. Stones contain Verneuil-type bubbles and tadpole-shaped inclusions. The ruby has curved zoning. Stones contain a swirled structure which is characteristic of the floating zone process.

**Seiko synthetic emerald** R.I. 1.561, 1.565; D.R. 0.004; S.G. 2.66. Stones appear dusty due to internal dust-like particles and contain two-phase feathers and 'Venetian blind' zoning.

**selective absorption** The suppression or absorption of certain wavelengths or colours in white light by a gemstone. See also ***differential selective absorption.***

**selenite** A crystalline variety of gypsum. See ***alabaster.***

**semi-conductor diamonds** See ***Type II diamonds.***

**semi-genuine doublet** A composite stone in which a crown of the genuine gem material is backed by a pavilion of another material such as glass or a synthetic gem.

**semi-precious stones** An imprecise term (whose use is prohibited by CIBJO) which once encompassed the majority of less costly gems (i.e. gems other than, for instance, diamond, emerald, ruby and sapphire).

**senaille** Small diamond chips cut with a flat base and irregular triangular facets.

**sepiolite** See ***meerschaum.***

**serandite** Na(Mn,Ca)SiO(OH). Triclinic. R.I. 1.660, 1.688; D.R. 0.028; S.G. 3.32; H. 4½–5. Orange. Occurrence: Canada.

**serpentine** A hydrated silicate of magnesium. $Mg_6(OH)_8(Si_2O_5)_2$. Monoclinic. R.I. 1.56 (mean); S.G. 2.5-2.7; H. 2½. Opaque, mottled dark green, leafy-green (antigorite). Occurrence: Found in many countries including Austria, England, Scotland, South Africa. See also ***bowenite, verd antique*** and ***williamsite.***

**serra stone** Brazilian agate.

**setter** A craftsman who sets gemstones in rings and other jewellery.

**shadow method of R.I. approximation** With this technique, the gemstone under test is immersed in turn in a series of liquids of known R.I.s in an immersion cell placed on a white surface. A black straight edge is slid under the cell so that it obscures the light passing through one edge of the stone. If the stone and the liquid have the same R.I., the image of the straight edge will appear unbroken by the stone. If the R.I. of the liquid is higher than that of the stone, the black edge will appear to advance into the stone. If the R.I. of the liquid is lower, the outline of the stone will appear to cut into the black straight edge.

**shaft mining** See ***diamond mine.***

**shale** A solidified mud or clay forming a stratified sedimentary rock which splits readily into thin plates.

**Shanghai jade** A misleading name for steatite (i.e. soapstone) or talc.

**shape categories (rough gem diamonds)** See ***chips, cleavages, macles, melée, shapes*** and ***stones.***

**shapes** Distorted (but unbroken) rough gem diamond octahedrons over 2 carats in size are called shapes. Under 2 carats these are called melée. See also ***chips, cleavages, macles, stones,*** and *Figure C.3*.

**shatter marks** See ***fire marks.***

**shattuckite** See ***planchéite.***

**sheen** The optical effect created by light rays reflected back from beneath the surface of a gemstone.

*chatoyancy* — the cat's eye effect caused by the reflection of light from parallel groups of fibres, crystals or channels within the stone (e.g. as in the tiger's eye variety of quartz and the cymophane variety of chrysoberyl).

*asterism* — a star effect present in a few gemstones such as ruby and sapphire (which are polished as cabochons to show the effect to best advantage). Asterism is caused by sets of fine parallel fibres or crystals which have aligned themselves along the crystal axes (in star corundum there are three sets intersecting at 60°). In star diopside and some garnets a four-pointed star is produced as the result of two sets of inclusions intersecting at approximately right-angles.

*iridescence* — the 'play' of rainbow-coloured light caused by extremely small regular structures beneath the surface of the gemstone which 'interfere' with the reflected light (see ***interference***). In precious opal, iridescence is caused by millions of microscopic spheres of cristobalite (*Figure O.1*) which colour the reflected light by a combination of interference and diffraction effects.

*labradorescence* — a particular form of iridescence seen in the labradorite and spectrolite varieties of feldspar which is caused by thin layers or flakes beneath the surface.

*adularescence* — also known as Schiller and opalescence, this is the bluish iridescence seen in moonstone, and is caused by lamellar twinning.

**shell** The hard outer casing of a mollusc.

**shell cat's eye** See ***operculum.***

**shell marble** A marble containing fossil shells. See ***paludina limestone, Petworth marble, Kilkenny black fossil marble*** and ***fire marble.***

**Shipley colorimeter** See ***diamond colorimeter.***

**short wave UV** See ***ultra violet light.***

**shot boart** See ***boart.***

**shoulders** The parts of a ring shank adjacent to the stone mount.

**Siam aquamarine** A misleading trade name for heat-treated blue-green zircon.

**Siberian chrysolite** A misleading name for demantoid garnet.

**Siberian ruby** A misleading name for the pink variety of tourmaline.

**siberite** A violet variety of tourmaline.

**Sicilian marble** A misleading name for a white Italian marble which is clouded with greyish veins.

**siderite (blue quartz)** See ***quartz.***

**siderite** A collector's stone comprising the mineral iron carbonate (also called chalybite). $FeCO_3$. Trigonal. R.I. 1.633, 1.873; D.R. −0.24; S.G. 3.83-3.88; H. 3½-4. Transparent, gold-brown, red-brown. Occurrence: Portugal.

**sights** The five-weekly sale of parcels of rough gem diamonds by the Diamond Trading Company (the principal company in De Beers Central Selling Organization). See also ***splitting.***

**sign of refraction** See ***optic sign.***

**silex** A variety of brown jasper having red spots. Occurrence: Egypt.

**silica glass** For natural silica glasses see ***Libyan glass, moldavite, pit glass*** and ***tektites.*** Man-made silica glass is produced by melting rock crystal at 1700 °C. The resulting change from crystalline quartz to amorphous silica glass causes a fall in R.I. and S.G. to 1.46 and 2.21 respectively.

**silicified wood** See ***fossil wood.***

**siliciophite** Chrysotile in common opal.

**silicon carbide** See ***carborundum.***

**silicon dioxide** See ***rottenstone.***

**silk** See ***inclusions.***

**silky** See ***lustre.***

**sillimanite** See ***fibrolite.***

**Silurian** A rock system on the Earth's surface comprising the rocks laid down during the Silurian period, 430-395 million years ago. The Silurian period is part of the Palaeozoic era. See ***Palaeozoic.***

**silver** A precious white metallic element used in jewellery. Ag. Atomic number 47; atomic weight 107.88; melting point 961 °C; S.G. 10.5.

**silver cape** A UK colour grade for polished diamonds. See ***Colour Grading Standards*** in Appendix B.

**silver peak jade** A misleading name for malachite.

**silver solder** A silver-copper-zinc alloy used as a solder for joining silver components in jewellery. There are five basic grades, 'extra-easy' with a melting point of 680-700 °C, 'easy' (melting point of 705-723 °C), 'medium' (melting point of 720-765 °C), 'hard' (melting point of 745-778 °C) and 'enamelling' (with a melting point of 730-800 °C, i.e. a solder which does not soften during the enamelling process). The constituents vary from 67-82% for silver, 14-24% for copper and 4-9% for zinc.

**simetite** A reddish-brown variety of amber found in Sicily.

**simpsonite** A rare aluminium tantalate. Hexagonal. R.I. 1.994-2.04; D.R. −0.046; S.G. 5.9-7.3; H. 7. Bright orange-yellow. Occurrence: Brazil.

**simulant** A term used to describe materials which simulate or imitate a gemstone. A gemstone simulant, while having a superficial resemblance to the gem it imitates, differs from it either in composition, structure or physical constants (often in all three). See also ***composite stones*** and ***synthetic stones.***

**single-cut** See ***eight cut.***

**single refraction** The refraction of light which occurs in an amorphous material or with a crystalline substance belonging to the cubic system. Unlike doubly-refracting materials, these do not polarize the light into two separately refracted rays, but transmit it as a single refracted ray.

**sinhalite** A magnesium aluminium iron borate (until 1952 classified as a brown peridot). $Mg(Al,Fe)BO_4$. Orthorhombic. R.I. 1.67, 1.71; D.R. −0.038; S.G. 3.47-3.49; H. 6½. Transparent, yellow, brown. Pleochroism, medium (pale brown, greenish-brown, dark brown). Occurrence: Sri Lanka.

**sinopal** A misleading name for a reddish aventurine quartz.

**Sioux Falls jasper** A quartzite from South Dakota, USA.

**sizes** A category for rough diamonds over 2 carats.

**sizing** The separation of rough diamonds into weight categories.

**skaif** See ***scaife.***

**skeif** See ***scaife.***

**skew facets** See ***break facets.***

**skill facets** See ***break facets.***

**skinning** A technique for improving the appearance of a badly-coloured or blemished pearl by carefully polishing or filing away the outer layer.

**skull crucible process** A method, originated in the Lebedev Physical Institute, Moscow, which is used to grow crystals of cubic zirconium oxide (manufactured as a diamond simulant). Because of the high melting point of zirconia powder, the process uses a cold 'skull' crucible, which consists of a cylindrical arrangement of water-cooled copper pipes. The zirconia powder (plus a stabilizer to maintain the cubic crystal structure of the material as it cools) is melted within the crucible by means of radio frequency induction heating. The bulk of the powder melts, except for a thin crust next to the cooled copper tubes, which then acts as a high-temperature crucible for the molten zirconia. After several hours, the R.F. heating power is slowly reduced, and the cubic zirconium oxide crystals form as the melt cools.

**slate** A fine-grained grey metamorphic rock which can be easily split into flat sheets.

**slightly tinted white** A CIBJO colour grade for polished diamonds. See ***Colour Grading Standards*** in Appendix B.

**slocum stone** An opal simulant made from a form of sodium-rich silicon glass containing some calcium and magnesium. The manufacturing process produces extremely thin parallel layers within the glassy matrix, and these are the cause of the material's iridescence. R.I. 1.49-1.52; S.G. 2.4-2.5; H. 6.

**smalls** A size category for rough diamonds under 2 carats.

**smaltite** A collector's stone comprising the mineral cobalt arsenide. $CoAs_3$. Cubic (massive). S.G. 6.0-6.3; H. 5½. Opaque, tin-white to steel-grey. Occurrence: Canada, Chile, Europe.

**smaragdite** A jade-like variety of actinolite (also called edenite). $Ca_2(Mg,Fe)_5(Si_4O_{11})_2(OH)_2$. Monoclinic. R.I. 1.608, 1.630; D.R. −0.022; S.G. 3.25; H. 6½. Translucent to opaque, grass-green to emerald-green.

**smaragdolin** Trade name for a green beryl glass.

**smaryll** Trade name for an emerald simulant comprising a crown and pavilion of poor quality beryl cemented together with an emerald-coloured cement.

**smithsonite** A zinc carbonate cut as cabochons. Also called bonamite. $ZnCO_3$. Trigonal. R.I. 1.621, 1.849; D.R. −0.228; S.G. 4.3; H. 5. Translucent to opaque, pale green, pale blue, pink. Occurrence: Greece, Mexico, Namibia, Spain, USA.

**smoky quartz** See ***quartz.***

**smoky topaz** A misleading name for smoky quartz.

**Snell's law** The law of refraction, which states that:

1. When a ray of light passes from one medium into another, there exists a definite ratio between the sines of the angle of incidence and the angle of refraction, which is dependent only on the two media and the wavelength of the light.
2. The incident ray, the normal (at the point of incidence) and the refracted ray are all in the same plane. See ***refractive index.***

**snowflake jade** See ***jade matrix.***

**snowflake obsidian** See ***flowering obsidian.***

**soapstone** See ***steatite.***

**sobrisky opal** A variety of opal from California.

**Société Belge de Gemmologie** Headquarters: Rue du Midi 118, 1000 Bruxelles, Belgium.

**sodalite** One of the principal components of lapis lazuli, it is a complex chloric sodium aluminium silicate. Cubic. R.I. 1.48; S.G. 2.28 H. 5½-6. Opaque to translucent, blue, grey. Occurrence: Brazil, Canada, Namibia, USA.

**sodium light** The standard illuminant used when specifying the refractive indices of gemstones. Sodium light is monochromatic and has a wavelength of 589.3 nm. Because of the cost of sodium discharge lamps, yellow colour filters and interference filters (centered on 589.3 nm) are often used, in conjunction with a white light source, as an alternative when measuring gemstone R.I.s. Yellow light-emitting diodes (LEDs) with an emission peak at 585 nm are also used.

**soft ivory** A commercial description for a type of ivory which is easier to cut than the hard more 'glassy' variety. It is also more tolerant to changes in temperature and does not crack so easily (e.g. Zanzibar and Mozambique ivory). See ***hard ivory*** and ***bastard ivory.***

**sogdianite** A complex aluminium/lithium silicate with potassium, sodium, zircon, titanium and iron. R.I. 1.606, 1.608; D.R. +0.002; S.G. 2.765; H. 6–7. Opaque, violet. Occurrence: South Africa.

**solar spectrum** See ***Fraunhofer lines*** and ***Table of Principal Fraunhofer Lines*** in Appendix J.

**solder dop** A metal holder containing a low melting-point solder which is used to secure a diamond during polishing. See ***dop.***

**soldered emerald** A soudé emerald. See ***composite stones.***

**soldier's stone** Amethyst variety of quartz.

**solitaire** A ring mounted with a single gemstone, usually a diamond.

**soochow jade** A misleading name for bowenite or steatite (soapstone).

**sorella** Trade name for the man-made diamond simulant strontium titanate.

**sorting** A general term covering the sorting of rough diamonds for colour, quality and shape. See ***Sorting Standards for Rough Diamonds*** in Appendix D.

**soudé emeralds** See ***composite stones.***

**soudé spinels** Composite simulants made from a coloured centre layer (often a sintered glass) fused to a crown and pavilion of colourless synthetic spinel.

**sousmansite** See ***wardite.***

**South African emerald** A misleading name given to a faceted emerald-green fluorspar from Namibia.

**South African jade** See ***garnet (grossular).***

**South African wonderstone** See ***koranna stone*** and ***pyrophyllite.***

**Spanish emerald** A misleading name for a green glass emerald simulant.

**Spanish emerald** Green glass.

**Spanish Gemmological Association** See ***Association Españia de Gemologia.***

**Spanish Gemmological Institute** See ***Instituto Gemmologico Español.***

**Spanish lazulite** A misleading name for cordierite.

**Spanish topaz** A misleading name for orange-brown quartz.

**sparklite** Trade name for colourless heat-treated zircon.

**spat** Spawn of the pearl oyster.

**species** A classification of minerals which are separated into individual species by their chemical composition and crystal system. See ***groups*** and ***varieties.***

**specific gravity** The ratio of the mass of a substance to the mass of an identical volume of pure water at 4 °C (by definition, the specific gravity of water is 1). See also ***density, density bottle, relative density, heavy liquids*** and ***hydrostatic weighing.***

**specific gravity bottle** See ***density bottle.***

**specific gravity indicators** Small samples of inclusion-free gem minerals (having known stable S.G. values) which are used to blend and check the specific gravity of heavy liquids (e.g. rock crystal, fluorspar and corundum). See also ***glass S.G. indicators.***

**spectra** See ***absorption spectrum, emission spectrum, flame spectrum, rare-earth spectra.***

**spectrolite** Finnish variety of labradorite feldspar.

**spectrometer** See ***goniometer.***

**spectrophotometer** An instrument for measuring the absorption spectrum of a specimen, often as a means of objectively (and precisely) specifying its colour. It consists of a light source (which may cover the UV and IR as well as the visible section of the spectrum), a monochromator which can be tuned over the spectral range, a detector unit for sampling the transmitted or reflected

*Figure S.2* The 6010 spectrophotometer, comprising a light source, a scanning monochromator using a diffraction grating disc rotating at 10 Hz, with a sample holder, photoelectric detector and wavelength marker. The absorption spectrum of the specimen is displayed on a standard oscilloscope. (Rofin)

light from the specimen and a control unit to amplify and display the output of the detector unit. Spectrophotometers may also contain the means for automatic scanning and recording of an absorption spectrum, and the computing ability to translate this

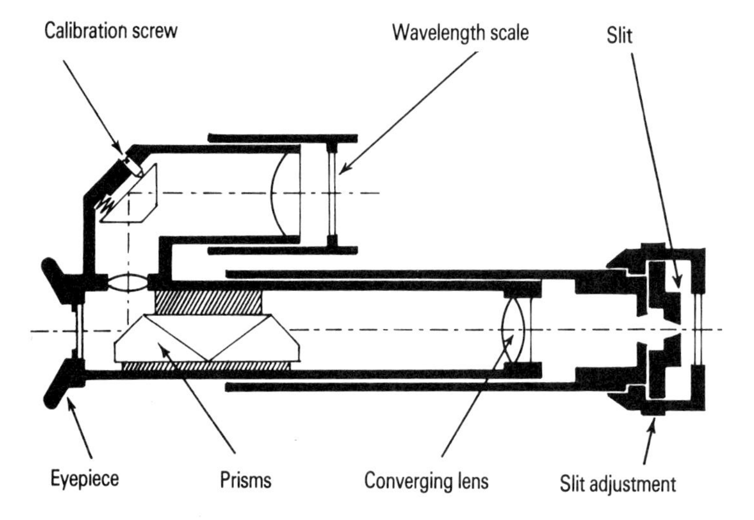


*Figure S.3* Sketch showing the construction of a prism-type spectroscope with a built-in wavelength scale.

into tristimulus values and CIE colour co-ordinates. See ***diamond colorimeter***. *Figure S.2.*

**spectroscope** An optical instrument which makes those sections of white light absorbed by a gemstone visible by dispersing or spreading out the resultant reflected or transmitted light into its spectral colours (see ***absorption spectrum***). Two methods of light dispersion are used in these instruments: a compound prism which produces a bright spectrum, but one which is cramped at the red end and spread out at the violet end, and a diffraction grating, which produces a weaker, but evenly spaced, spectrum (see ***diffraction grating***). Prism spectroscopes often incorporate a superimposed wavelength scale (*Figure S.3.*). Spectroscope units may also contain built-in light sources (*Figure S.4.*). See also ***Gübelin's jewellers' spectroscope.***

**specularite** See ***haematite.***

**speed of light** See ***velocity of light.***

**spessartine** See ***garnet.***

**spessartite** See ***garnet.***

**sphalerite** A collector's stone comprising the mineral zinc sulphide (also called blende and zinc blende). ZnS. Cubic. R.I. 2.37; S.G. 4.09; H. 3½-4. Transparent to translucent, dark brown, green, colourless. Occurrence: Central Africa (green), Mexico, Spain.

**sphene** A titanium calcium silicate (also called titanite). $CaTiSiO_5$. Monoclinic. R.I. 1.885, 1.990 to 1.915, 2.050; D.R. +0.105 to +0.135; S.G. 3.52-3.54; H. 5½. Transparent, yellow, brown,

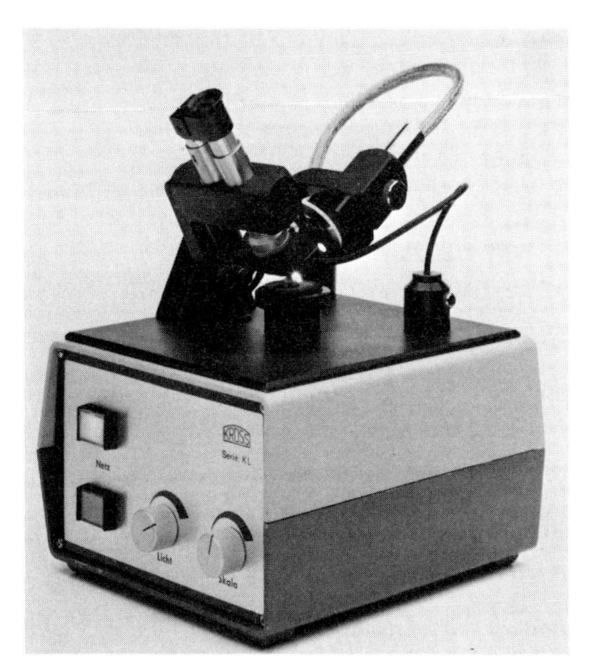


*Figure S.4* A unit combining a variable-intensity self-contained light source, a colour filter disc and a prism-type wavelength spectroscope. (Krüss)

green. Pleochroism, strong (green, colourless, yellow; and yellow, colourless, reddish). Occurrence: Austria, Brazil, Canada, the Malagasy Republic, Sri Lanka, Switzerland, USA.

**spherical aberration** See ***aberration.***

**spinach jade** See ***nephrite.***

**spinel** An isomorphous magnesium aluminate in which the magnesium may be replaced by manganese or iron, and the aluminium by iron or chromium. $MgO.Al_2O_3$. Cubic. R.I. 1.718; S.G. 3.6; H. 8. Transparent, colourless (rare), red, pink, brownish, grass-green (called chlorospinel), dark green/black (called ceylonite and pleonaste), yellowish, blue, violet, purple. Occurrence: Brazil, Burma, Sri Lanka, Thailand, USA. See also ***ceylonite*** and ***gahnospinel.***

**spinel refractometer** A critical-angle Rayner refractometer with a measuring prism made from synthetic spinel. Although spinel restricts the measuring range of the instrument (1.3 to 1.68), it has a similar dispersion to the majority of gemstones. This latter feature makes it possible to use a white light source without producing strong colour fringing of the shadow edges. Another advantage of the spinel refractometer is its open scale which enables more accurate readings to be taken.

**spinel ruby** A misleading name for red spinel.

**splintery fracture** See ***fracture.***

**splitting** A stage in the preparation of rough diamonds for the De Beers sights in which diamonds from all the sorted categories of weight, shape, colour and quality are allocated or split into parcels for the individual buyers. Each buyer, depending on the value of his allocation and his requirements, is offered an equitable selection of diamonds from each available category. See also ***sights.***

**spodumene** A lithium aluminium silicate. $LiAl(SiO_3)_2$. Monoclinic. R.I. 1.660, 1.675; D.R. +0.015; S.G. 3.17–3.19; H. 7. Transparent, yellow, yellowish-green, pink (kunzite), emerald-green (hiddenite, coloured by chromium — rare). Pleochroism, strong in kunzite and hiddenite (violet, deep violet, colourless and bluish-green, emerald-green, yellowish-green respectively). Occurrence: Brazil, Burma, the Malagasy Republic, USA.

**spot method** (of R.I. measurement) See ***distant vision method.***

**spotted** A UK clarity grade for polished diamonds. See ***Clarity Grading Standards*** in Appendix C.

**spread stone** See ***open table.***

**spread table** See ***open table.***

**Sri Lankan Gemmologists' Association** See ***Gemmologists' Association of Sri Lanka.***

**stalactite** A deposit (usually of calcium carbonate) shaped like a hanging icicle, and formed by the evaporation of dripping water in a cave or cavern.

**stalagmite** A deposit, similar to a stalactite, formed by the evaporation of dripping water but growing upwards from the floor of a cave, and often uniting with a hanging stalactite.

**stannic oxide** See ***putty powder.***

**star facets** The eight triangular facets immediately adjacent to the table facet on a brilliant-cut stone. See ***brilliant cut*** and *Figure B.6.*

**starilian** Trade name for the man-made diamond simulant strontium titanate.

**Star of India** A 536-carat star sapphire which originated from Ceylon (now Sri Lanka), and is now in the Museum of Natural History in New York.

**star stones** See ***sheen*** (asterism).

**starlite** Trade name for a blue zircon.

**starolite** Trade name for a star rose quartz doublet.

**starred agate** An agatized coral, found on the south-west coast of England, which consists of a pale brown chalcedony containing a pattern of chalk-white stars. See also ***fossil coral.***

**star-tania** Trade name for a synthetic rutile diamond simulant.

**star topaz** A misleading name for a yellow star sapphire.

**staurolite** A collector's stone, but mainly prized as a mineral specimen for its cross-shaped interpenetrant twin crystals (also called a 'cross stone', or 'fairystone', and grenalite). The mineral is a hydrated aluminium iron silicate. $Fe_2Al_9Si_4O_{22}(OH)_2$. Orthorhombic. R.I. 1.739, 1.750 to 1.747, 1.762; D.R. +0.011 to +0.015; S.G. 3.65-3.78; H. 7-7½. Transparent, reddish-brown. Pleochroism, medium (colourless, yellow or red). Occurrence: Brazil, France, Scotland, Switzerland, USA, USSR. See also ***zincian staurolite.***

**steatite** A variety of the mineral talc, an acid metasilicate of magnesium. In its massive form it is used as a carving material and called 'soapstone'. $Mg_3Si_4O_{10}(OH)_2$. Monoclinic. R.I. 1.54-1.59 (around 1.54 for soapstone); D.R. 0.05; S.G. 2.2-2.8; H. 1 (often higher due to impurities). Opaque, yellow, greenish, brown, reddish. Occurrence: Canada, Central Africa, India, Zimbabwe.

**stellarite** Trade name for a blue quartz with blue/green and metal grey/black veins due to a copper matrix, chrysocolla and haematite. Interference colours are caused by the presence of planchéite. Occurrence: USA.

**step cut** See ***emerald cut.***

**stereo microscope** See ***binocular microscope.***

**sterling silver** An alloy consisting of 92.5% silver and 7.5% copper.

**stewartite** See ***boart.***

**stibiotantalite** A collector's stone consisting of a niobate and tantalate of antimony. $SbO_2(Ta,Nb)_2O_6$. (note: niobium, Nb, has the alternative name columbium, Cb). Orthorhombic. R.I. 2.39, 2.46; D.R. +0.07; S.G. around 7.4; H. 5½-6. Transparent, brownish-yellow. Occurrence: USA.

**stichtite** A collector's stone comprising a decomposition product of chrome-serpentine. $Mg_6Cr_2(OH)_{16}CO_3.4H_2O$. Trigonal (massive, fibrous). R.I. around 1.53; S.G. 2.15-2.22; H. 2½. Opaque, rose-red, lilac. Occurrence: Algeria, Canada, South Africa, Tasmania.

**Stokes Law** A law associated with photoluminescent phenomena which states that the luminescent glow from a material is always of a longer wavelength than that of the exciting radiation.

**stolberg diamond** A misleading name for the rock crystal variety of quartz.

**stone gauges** See ***caliper gauge*** and ***diamond gauge.***

**stone paper** A folded paper container for gemstones, often containing a tissue paper inner lining. See diagram under ***Stone Papers*** in Appendix E.

**stones** A term used in the shape sorting of rough gem diamonds to denote well-shaped octahedral crystals over 2 carats in size. Under 2 carats these crystals are called melée. See also ***chips, cleavages, macles, shapes,*** and *Figure C.3.*

**stone tongs** See ***tweezers.***

**stoping** An underground mining technique used in diamond mines, involving the progressive step-cutting of the gem-bearing rock.

**strass** A highly dispersive glass, containing lead or thallium, used for gemstone simulants.

**strawberry pearl** A pink-coloured baroque freshwater pearl with a pimpled surface.

**streak** The mark produced when a mineral is rubbed on the unglazed surface of a plate of white porcelain (called a 'streak plate'). As the colour of a mineral's powder is sometimes quite different from its body colour, this forms a useful identification feature in mineralogy.

**stremlite** Trade name for a blue zircon.

**striae** Roughly parallel or concentric lines or channels on the surface of crystals, or within stones.

**strongite** Trade name for a synthetic spinel.

**strontium titanate** A man-made diamond simulant (introduced in 1953) which has no counterpart in nature. $SrTiO_3$. Cubic. R.I. 2.41; S.G. 5.13; H. 6. Transparent, colourless (yellow, brown or red when doped with transition metal oxides). Crystals are grown by the flame-fusion process using a special burner which supplies extra oxygen to the boule. The blackened boules are then annealed in an oxidizing atmosphere to produce a colourless crystal.

**Sturmlechner emerald simulants** Faceted beryls coated with a hydrothermally deposited layer of synthetic emerald by Sturmlechner of Vienna, Austria.

**styles of cutting** See ***antique cut*** (cushion), ***brilliant cut*** (round, marquise/navette, oval, pear-shape), ***baquette*** (baton), ***cabochon, emerald cut*** (trap or step cut), ***rose cut*** (Antwerp/Brabant) and ***scissors cut*** (cross).

**Styrian jade** A misleading name for pseudophite.

**subjective** When applied to gemstone grading the term implies the comparative assessment of colour, clarity or cut by eye rather than by quantitative (i.e. objective or instrumental) techniques.

**succinic acid** A constituent of amber.

**sugar stone** A pink variety of datolite from Michigan, USA.

**sugilite** A complex sodium/lithium silicate similar to sogdianite but containing no aluminium or zircon. R.I. 1.607–1.610; D.R. +0.003; S.G. 2.74. Opaque, blue-purple, red-purple, magenta. Occurrence: South Africa.

**sun opal** See ***opal*** (fire opal).

**sun-spangled amber** Amber clarified by heating it in oil. See ***rape seed oil.***

**sunstone** See ***feldspar.***

**surface colour-treated amber** Amber which has been made colourless by overheating and then oxidized to produce a surface colour.

**surface tension** The tension existing in the surface film of a liquid which acts to minimize the area of that surface.

**sweetwater agate.** A fluorescent moss agate from Wyoming, USA.

**swirl marks** Curved and convoluted internal marks due to imperfect mixing of materials. Commonly seen in glass (paste) gems.

**Swiss cut** A simplified version of the 57-facet brilliant-cut designed for small diamonds. It consists of an eight-sided table surrounded by 16 triangular facets. There are eight triangular lower girdle facets and eight four-sided main facets on the pavilion.

**Swiss Gemmological Association** See ***Gemmological Association of Switzerland.***

**Swiss jade** A misleading name for green-stained jasper. See ***quartz.***

**Swiss lapis** See ***German lapis.***

**SW UV** See ***ultra violet light.***

**syenite** See ***kakortokite.***

**symant** Trade name for the man-made diamond simulant strontium titanate.

**symerald** Trade name for a faceted beryl gemstone coated hydrothermally with synthetic emerald. See ***Lechleitner emeralds.***

**symmetry** (crystallography) There are three principal 'elements' of symmetry. See ***axis of symmetry, centre of symmetry*** and ***plane of symmetry.***

**symmetry** (polished stones) The correct facet alignment and overall balance and proportions of a polished gemstone.

**syndite** Trade name for a material made from sintered diamond particles for use in machine tool tips and marketed by De Beers Industrial Diamond Division.

**syngenetic inclusions** See ***inclusions*** (contemporary).

**synthetic 'alexandrite'** A misleading trade name for a colour-change synthetic corundum or spinel.

**synthetic 'aquamarine'** A misleading trade name for synthetic blue corundum or spinel.

**synthetic stones** Synthetically-produced materials which have the same composition, structure and physical constants as their naturally-occuring counterparts (e.g. corundum, chrysoberyl, emerald, opal and rutile). Synthetically-grown products which have no counterpart in nature are more accurately described as man-made. See ***lithium niobate, gadolinium gallium garnet, yttrium aluminium garnet*** and ***strontium titanate.***

*synthetic alexandrite* — see *synthetic chrysoberyl.*

*synthetic corundum* — grown mainly by the flame-fusion process. Synthetic rubies are also grown by the flux-melt process (e.g. Kashan, Chatham, and Knischka synthetic rubies). See ***Linde synthetic star corundum*** and ***Seiko synthetic corundum.***

*synthetic chrysoberyl* — the alexandrite (colour change) variety of chrysoberyl is grown synthetically by both the flux-melt and the Czochralski 'crystal pulling' processes.

*synthetic cubic moissanite* — a possible diamond and coloured gemstone simulant. Cubic. SiC. R.I. 2.651; S.G. 3.218; H. 9½.

*synthetic diamond* — industrial synthetic diamond grits are produced by dissolving graphite in molten iron or nickel at high temperatures and pressures (i.e. 3300 °C and 110 000 atmospheres) in special presses. Experimental gem quality synthetic diamonds, grown from synthetic diamond 'seeds' using a diffusion technique, have been produced up to 1 carat in size, but are not commercially viable.

synthetic emerald — see ***Biron synthetic emeralds, Chatham synthetic emeralds, Lechleitner emerald simulants, Lennix synthetic emeralds, Linde synthetic emeralds, Nacken synthetic emeralds, Regency synthetic emeralds, Seiko synthetic emeralds, Sturmlechner emerald simulants*** and ***Zerfass synthetic emeralds.***

*synthetic lapis lazuli* — see ***Gilson synthetic lapis lazuli.***

*synthetic opal* — see ***Gilson synthetic opal.***

*synthetic quartz* — for the jewellery industry, the amethyst variety of synthetic quartz is grown by both the hydrothermal and flux-melt processes.

*synthetic rutile* — introduced as a diamond simulant in 1948. See ***rutile.***

*synthetic spinel* — because synthetic spinel boules (grown by the flame-fusion process) are brittle if they are made from constituents in precisely the same proportions as the natural stone ($MgO.Al_2O_3$), extra alumina is added ($MgO.3Al_2O_3$). This increases the R.I. and S.G. of the material to 1.727 and 3.65 respectively. H. 8. Transparent, colourless, blue, green, pink, red (rare).

*synthetic turquoise* — see ***Gilson synthetic turquoise.***

# T

**taaffeite** A rare beryllium magnesium aluminate. $BeMg_3Al_8O_{16}$. Hexagonal, R.I. 1.717, 1.721 to 1.719, 1.723; D.R. −0.004; S.G. 3.60–3.61; H. 8. Transparent, pale, commonly mauve. Occurrence: Sri Lanka.

**tabby extinction** A term describing the anomalous double refraction seen typically when rotating a synthetic spinel on a polariscope. The 'tabby cat' stripes are caused by strains within the material.

**table-cut diamonds** An early cutting style (developed from the point-cut) in which one of the points of an octahedral diamond crystal was truncated and polished to form a table facet, and the opposite point was polished to form a large culet of about half the width of the table facet. The remaining faces of the crystal were also given a surface polish.

**table facet** The large central facet on the crown of a polished gemstone.

**table spectrometer** See ***goniometer.***

**tabular** A crystal having a flattened tablet-like habit.

**tachylyte** See ***basalt glass.***

*Figure T.1* Mechanical claw-type dops holding diamonds on a scaife or lap. The dops are mounted in the end of tangs, which are weighted to achieve the necessary polishing pressure. (De Beers)

**tailings** The gravel, rock and silt residue of a mine's output once the gem content has been extracted.

**Taiwan cat's eye** A chatoyant tremolite. R.I. 1.613, 1.637; S.G. 3.05; H. 6-7. Translucent to opaque, greenish-yellow, pale yellow, dark green, dark brown, black. Occurrence: Taiwan.

**takara pearls** Imitation pearls cut from the shell of a mussel.

**talc** A hydrated magnesium silicate used as a carving material. R.I. around 1.54; S.G. 2.7-2.8; H. 1. Opaque, white, silvery-white. Occurrence: World-wide. See ***steatite.***

**tallow-topped cabochon** A cabochon with a very flat dome.

**tang** A metal tong-shaped holder for a diamond dop which is weighted to produce the correct grinding pressure between the diamond and the surface of the scaife. *Figure T.1.*

**tangiwaite** Maori name for New Zealand bowenite.

**tania-59** Trade name for a synthetic rutile.

**tantalite** A collector's stone comprising the mineral iron/manganese tantalate. $(Fe,Mn)Ta_2O_6$. Orthorhombic. R.I. 2.24, 2.41; D.R. +0.17; S.G. 5.18–8.20; H. 5–6. Translucent, reddish-brown.

**tantalite** Trade name for lithium tantalate.

**tanzanite** See ***zoisite.***

**taprobanite** Provisional name for a transparent red beryllium-containing mineral found in Sri Lanka in 1978. This was later identified as taaffeite.

**tare** Allowance made for the container or packet in which goods are weighed. Electronic balances are often fitted with a tare control to set the balance to zero against the empty packet or container.

**Tasmanian diamond** A misleading name for the rock crystal variety of quartz.

**tawmawite** A deep green chrome epidote found in Burma and Zimbabwe.

**Tay pearls** Freshwater pearls found in the River Tay, Scotland, UK.

**tecali marble** A Mexican marble, also known as 'Mexican onyx', which is sometimes used as a jade simulant.

**tektite** A collective name for natural glasses which have a high silica content and are similar to the volcanic glass obsidian. See ***basalt glass, Libyan glass, moldavite*** and ***pit glass.***

**television stone** See ***ulexite.***

**templet** An alternative name for the first four bezel facets which are polished immediately after the table facet on a brilliant-cut diamond.

**termination** The crystal form found at the end of a prism.

**temperature scales** See ***absolute temperature scale, Celsius tem-***

*perature scale* and ***Fahrenheit temperature scale.***

**tempering** Altering the hardness of metals by controlled heating and cooling.

**Tertiary** A rock system on the Earth's surface comprising the rocks laid down 65-2 million years ago. The Tertiary period, consisting of the ***Eocene, Oligocene, Miocene*** and ***Pliocene*** divisions, constitutes the bulk of the Cenozoic era. See also ***Cenozoic*** and ***Quaternary.***

**tessellated mosaic** A pavement mosaic whose design is formed from small cubes, generally of marble.

**tetragonal system** A crystal system having three axes. Two of these are of equal length and at right angles to each other. The third or principal axis is either shorter or longer than the other two, and is at right-angles to them. There are five axes of symmetry (four two-fold and one four-fold), five planes of symmetry and a centre of symmetry. *Figure T.2.*

**tetrahedron** A crystal form having four triangular faces, which is one of the seven basic forms belonging to the highest class of symmetry in the cubic crystal system.

**tetraiodoethylene** A constituent of the contact liquid used to provide an air-free optical seal between a gemstone and the

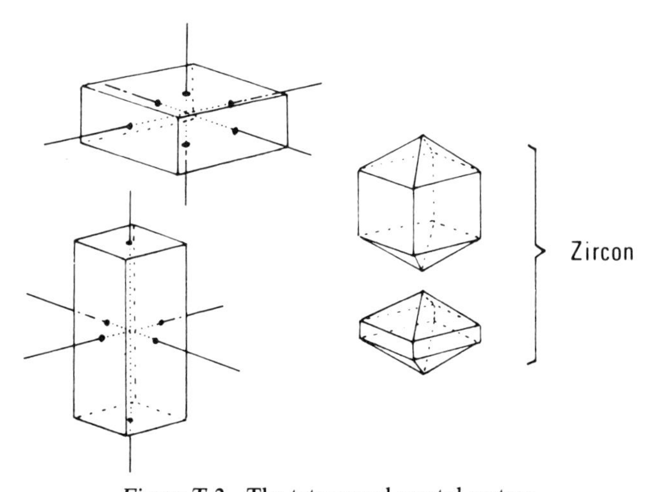


*Figure T.2* The tetragonal crystal system.

measuring prism of a critical-angle refractometer. See ***contact liquid.***

**tetrakis hexahedron** A 24-sided crystal which is one of the seven basic forms belonging to the highest class of symmetry in the cubic crystal system. It consists of a cube whose faces have each been replaced by four triangular faces. See ***triakis octahedron.***

**thermal conductivity** The capability of a material to conduct heat. At room temperature, Type I diamonds have twice the thermal conductivity of copper. Type IIa diamonds have six times the thermal conductivity of copper, and for this reason are used as a substrate to conduct heat away from semiconductor devices and thereby increase their power ratings. Thermal conductivity ($k$) is measured (in SI units) in watts per metre per °C (i.e. the rate of heat flow through a unit thickness of the material per unit temperature gradient). $k = 1000$ for Type I diamond, 430 for silver, 320 for gold, 40 for corundum, 10 for cubic zirconium oxide, 1 for glass.

**thermal conductivity diamond tester** An instrument which identifies diamond by its high thermal conductivity (all of the natural and man-made simulants of diamond are bad thermal conductors). The tester consists of a control unit and a pen-like probe. The probe contains a miniature heating element in thermal contact with a metal tip. When this tip is held against the surface of a diamond, heat is conducted away, and the electronic circuits in the control unit detect the lowering of the tip temperature. With diamond simulants, the tip temperature remains high. *Figure T.3.*

**thermal metamorphism** See ***contact metamorphism.***

**thermal reaction tester** See ***hot-point tester.***

**thermoluminescence** See ***thermophosphoresence.***

**thermophosphorescence** The phenomenon exhibited by some materials which are able to store energy acquired from electromagnetic radiation and then release it in the form of a luminous glow when heated.

**thetis hair stone** See ***quartz.***

**thomsonite** A banded hydrated calcium sodium aluminium silicate belonging to the zeolite group of minerals. $NaCa_2(Al_5Si_5O_{20}).6H_2O$. Orthorhombic. R.I. around 1.52-1.54; S.G. 2.3-2.4; H. 5. Translucent (occasionally with chatoyance or schiller), white, yellow, reddish, brown, greenish. Occurrence: USA.

**three-phase inclusions** See ***inclusions.***

**three-point** A cutting orientation for diamond where the table has been polished nearly parallel to a possible octahedral crystal face. See ***four-point*** and ***two-point.***

**thulite** See ***zoisite.***

**thunder eggs** Agate-filled nodules found in the USA. The spherical nodules, when cut, often show a 'star' profile agate filling.

**tickal** A Burmese unit of weight equal to 80 carats. See also ***Bali,***

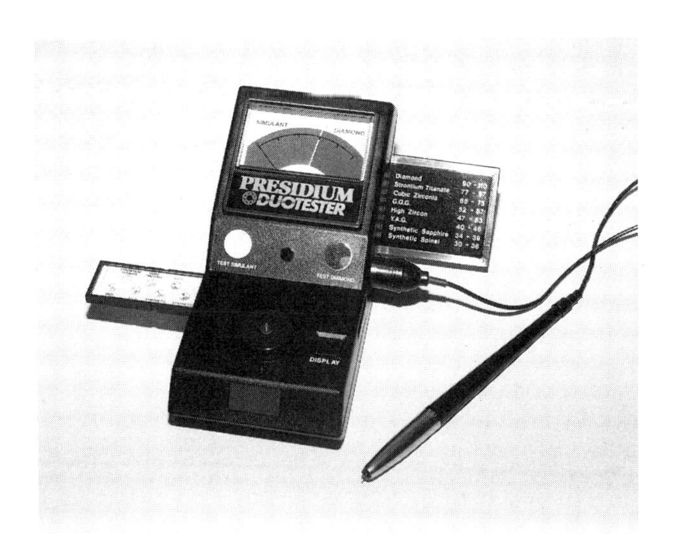


*Figure T.3* The Duotester is a combined reflectivity and thermal tester. The slide drawer on the left contains diamond simulants for calibration checking. The right-hand pull-out panel indicates typical reflectance readings displayed on the unit's LED front edge panel. (Presidium)

***lathi, rati*** and ***viss.***

**tigerite** See ***quartz*** (tiger's eye).

**tiger's eye** A quartz pseudomorph of crocidolite. See ***quartz.***

**till** Stiff clay containing boulders, sand, etc.

**tilt test** See ***light spill test.***

**tin cut** Cast glass gemstone simulants whose facets are polished on a tin lap using tin oxide as a polishing powder.

**tin oxide** See ***putty powder.***

**tinstone** See ***cassiterite.***

**tinted colour** A CIBJO colour grade for polished diamonds. See ***Colour Grading Standards*** in Appendix B.

**tinted white** A colour grade for polished diamonds. See ***Colour Grading Standards*** in Appendix B.

**tinting** See ***treated diamonds.***

**tiree marble** A variety of marble found on the island of Tiree off the west coast of Scotland.

**tirum gem** Trade name for a synthetic rutile diamond simulant.

**titangem** Trade name for a synthetic rutile diamond simulant.

**titania** Trade name for a synthetic rutile diamond simulant.

**titania brilliante** Trade name for a synthetic rutile diamond simulant.

**titania midnight stone** Trade name for a synthetic rutile diamond simulant.

**titanite** See ***sphene.***

**titanium** One of the eight transition metals which are mainly responsible for colour in gemstones. Ti. A stone coloured by titanium is the blue sapphire. Atomic number 22; atomic weight 47.9; melting point 1680 °C; S.G. 4.5.

**titanium** Trade name for a synthetic rutile diamond simulant.

**titanium rutile** Trade name for a synthetic rutile diamond simulant.

**titanstone** Trade name for a synthetic rutile diamond simulant.

**tokay lux sapphire** A misleading name for Hungarian obsidian.

**tola** An Indian unit of weight used for gold. One tola = 58.32 carats. See also ***mangelin*** and ***rati.***

**Tolkowsky brilliant cut** One of several 'ideal' cuts for diamond, mainly favoured in America (see *Figure B.6.*). See also ***Eppler brilliant cut, Johnson and Rösch brilliant cut, Parker brilliant cut*** and ***Scan DN brilliant cut.***

**toluene** A volatile hydrocarbon used for the dilution of methylene iodide and bromoform in the heavy liquid determination of specific gravity (S.G. 0.8737 at 10°C; 0.637 at 20°C). Because of its low surface tension it is used in place of water in hydrostatic weighing (the results are adjusted to allow for its lower S.G.).

**tomb jade** A buried jade which has changed colour to reddish-brown.

**tongue test** A test for glass gemstones which, because of their poorer thermal conductivity, feel warmer against the tongue than, for instance, quartz stones.

**tooth turquoise** A misleading name for odontolite.

**topaz** A fluosilicate of aluminium. $Al_2(F,OH)_2SiO_4$. Orthorhombic. Blue, yellow and colourless stones — R.I. 1.61, 1.62; D.R. +0.01; S.G. 3.56; H. 8. Brown and pink stones — R.I. 1.63, 1.64; D.R. +0.008; S.G. 3.53; H. 8. Transparent, blue, brown, yellow, colourless, pink (the latter two produced by heat treatment — see ***heat treated stones***). Pleochroism, strong in heat-treated pink stones (colourless and two shades of pink); medium in brown stones (two shades of yellow, pinkish-yellow), and blue stones (colourless, pale pink, blue). Occurrence: Australia, Brazil, Burma, Sri Lanka, Tasmania, USA, USSR.

**topaz cat's eye** A misleading name for chatoyant yellow sapphire.

**topazolite** A misleading name for the yellow variety of andradite garnet.

**topaz quartz** A misleading name for brownish-yellow quartz.

**topaz saffronite** A misleading name for brownish-yellow quartz.

**top cape** A colour grade for polished diamonds. See ***Colour Grading Standards*** in Appendix B.

**top crystal** A colour grade for polished diamonds. See ***Colour Grading Standards*** in Appendix B.

**top main facets** See ***bezel facets.***

**top silver cape** A colour grade for polished diamonds. See ***Colour Grading Standards*** in Appendix B.

**top wesselton** A colour grade for polished diamonds. See ***Colour Grading Standards*** in Appendix B.

**torrelite** A jasper variety of quartz.

**tortoiseshell** An organic gem material derived mainly from the shell of the Hawksbill sea turtle. The individual plates, or *blades,* of the shell are a mottled yellow-brown. The front blades are called *shoulder plates,* the centre ones *cross-backs,* the side ones *main plates* and the rear ones *tail plates.* A clear yellow tortoiseshell is obtained from the turtle's under-shell. R.I. 1.55; S.G. around 1.3; H. 2½. Occurrence: Most tropical and subtropical seas, particularly around Malaysia, the West Indies and Brazil.

**tosa coral** A Japanese coral.

**total internal reflection** An optical condition by which the light rays entering a gemstone are reflected back from the pavilion facets to re-emerge from the crown facets (see *Figure D.8.).* This total internal reflection of light rays enhances the brilliance of the gemstone. It is achieved by adjusting the angles of the crown and pavilion facets so that the majority of rays meet the interior faces of the pavilion facets at angles to the normal which are *greater* than the critical angle of the gem material (see *Figure T.4.*). It is also important that the rays reflected back from the pavilion facets meet the crown facets at angles *less* than the critical angle. See also ***critical angle.***

**touchstone** A fine-grained dark schist or jasper used to check precious metals. The metals are rubbed on the touchstone, and the resulting streak tested with various acids.

**tourmalinated quartz** See ***quartz.***

**tourmaline** A complex borosilicate of aluminium and alkalies with calcium, fluorine, lithium, magnesium, manganese, potassium and water. Alkali-rich tourmalines (containing sodium, lithium or potassium) are colourless, red or green (elbalite — see also ***liddicoatite***). Iron-rich tourmalines are dark blue (indicolite), bluish-green or black (schorl). Manganese tourmalines are colourless or yellow-brown to brownish-black (dravite — see also ***uvite***). Trigonal. R.I. around 1.62, 1.64; D.R. −0.014 to −0.021; S.G. 3.02-3.26 (pink 3.03; red and pale green 3.05; brown 3.06; dark green 3.08; blue and yellow 3.10; black 3.15-3.26); H. 7-7½. Transparent, single- and parti-coloured. Pleochroism, strong in deeper colours (two shades of body colour). Occurrence: Brazil,

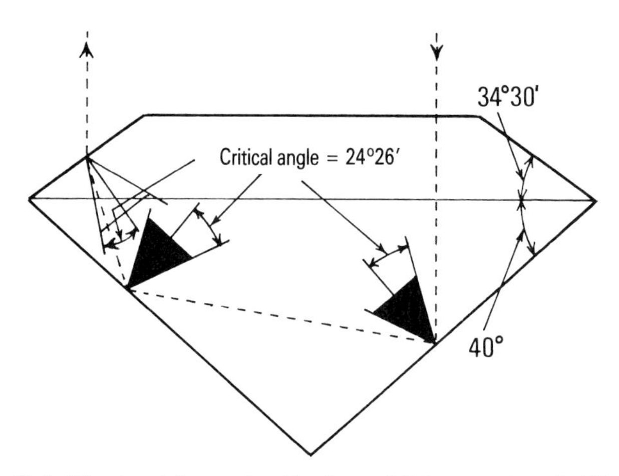


*Figure T.4* The total internal reflection of light rays in a brilliant-cut diamond is achieved by arranging the crown and pavilion angles so that as many rays as possible meet the interior faces of the pavilion facets at angles greater than the critical angle. The exit rays must meet the crown facts at angles less than the critical angle if they are to emerge.

Burma, the Malagasy Republic, Namibia, Sri Lanka, USA, USSR.

**tourmaline green** A misleading name for synthetic dark-green spinel.

**tourmaline tongs** An early form of hand polariscope consisting of two small slabs of pale brown or green tourmaline mounted in rotatable wooden discs which are held in wire pincettes. This device exploited the strong dichroism found in brown and green tourmaline in which the ordinary ray is almost totally absorbed.

**trainite** A banded variscite found in Utah, USA.

**transition elements** The eight metallic elements which are the main cause of colour in gemstones. See ***titanium, vanadium, chromium, manganese, iron, cobalt, nickel*** and ***copper.***

**translucent** A term used to describe a material which passes some light, but does not transmit a clear image of any object. See also ***opaque*** and ***transparent.***

**transparent** A term used to describe a material which transmits light freely without distortion. The opposte of transparent is opaque. See also ***translucent.***

**Transvaal jade** A misleading name for massive green grossular garnet.

**trap cut** See ***emerald cut.***

**trapeze cut** A gemstone whose profile is a trapezium (i.e. having two parallel sides and two inclined sides).

**trapiche emeralds** Emerald crystals from Colombia which contain central hexagonal crystals whose faces extend outwards as radial 'spokes'. The spaces between these radial arms are filled with a fine-grained white beryl. *Figure T.5.*

*Figure T.5* End and side views of two trapiche emeralds from Colombia.

**traversellite** A green variety of diopside.

**travertine** A white or light-coloured sedimentary rock composed mainly of crystalline calcium carbonate which has been precipitated from calcium bicarbonate-rich spring waters by the action of heat and pressure.

**treacle inclusion** See ***inclusions.***

**treated diamonds** The artificial coloration of a diamond is aimed at either improving its colour by making its appear whiter, or changing its colour to a more attractive and valuable 'fancy' hue. The simplest technique of improving the colour of a yellow diamond is to apply a thin translucent coat of blue dye to its pavilion facets to complement the body colour. A bluish fluoride coating (as applied to camera lenses) has been used for this purpose. Diamonds can also be artificially coloured by irradiating them with neutrons in an atomic reactor. This produces a homogeneous green body colour which can be changed to yellow or a cinnamon brown by a subsequent heat treatment. Some rarer types of diamond can be changed to red or purple by this method. The stones are intensely radioactive after treatment, but this dies away rapidly. Diamonds were first artifically coloured by irradiation in the early part of this century by Sir William Crookes who used a radium source to turn diamonds green. This was only a skin-deep colour, and surviving specimens have remained radioactive up to the present day. A colour change can also be produced by means of electron bombardment in an electron accelerator. With this process, some diamonds turn a pale blue or a bluish-green. The colour is only skin-deep and can be polished off if not suitable. The protons, deuterons and alpha particles generated by a cyclotron can also be used to change the colour of a diamond, the resulting hues after heat treatment being only skin-deep, and the diamonds rapidly losing their initial radioactivity. Detection of artificial coloration of diamonds by irradiation is mainly by means of spectroscopic analysis, usually at very low temperatures. See also ***umbrella effect.***

**treated opal** A poor quality opal which has been stained black to improve its iridescence.

**treatment of pearls** See ***skinning.***

**treatment plant** See ***recovery plant.***

**tree stone** A moss agate.

**tremolite** A calcium magnesium silicate (also called grammatite) occurring in fibrous form as mutton-fat jade (nephrite), also as a greenish chatoyant variety, and as a transparent lilac-pink variety called hexagonite. Tremolite is one end member of the amphibole series. The other end member is actinolite. Monoclinic. R.I. 1.60, 1.62-1.63; D.R. −0.02 to −0.028; S.G. 2.976 (chatoyant variety), 2.980 (hexagonite); H. 5½-6. Opaque, greenish, lilac-pink, emerald-green. Occurrence: Burma, Canada, USA.

**trenton diamond** A misleading name for the rock crystal variety of quartz.

**triakis octahedron** A 24-sided crystal which is one of the seven basic forms belonging to the highest class of symmetry in the cubic crystal system. It consists of an octahedron whose faces have each been replaced by three triangular faces. See ***tetrakis hexahedron.***

**triamond** Trade name for the man-made diamond simulant yttrium aluminium garnet.

**Triassic** A rock system on the Earth's surface comprising the rocks laid down during the Triassic period, 225-195 million years ago. The Triassic period is the first part of the Mesozoic era. See ***Mesozoic.***

**triboelectric effect** A property possessed by some gem materials, such as amber and plastic, whose surfaces develop an electrical charge when rubbed.

**triboluminescence** A property possessed by a material which causes it to luminesce or glow when it is rubbed or abraded (i.e. frictional luminescence).

**trichroism** See ***dichroism.***

**triclinic system** A crystal system having three axis, all of different lengths and all inclined to each other at angles other than right-angles. There is a centre of symmetry, but no axes or planes of symmetry. *Figure T.6.*

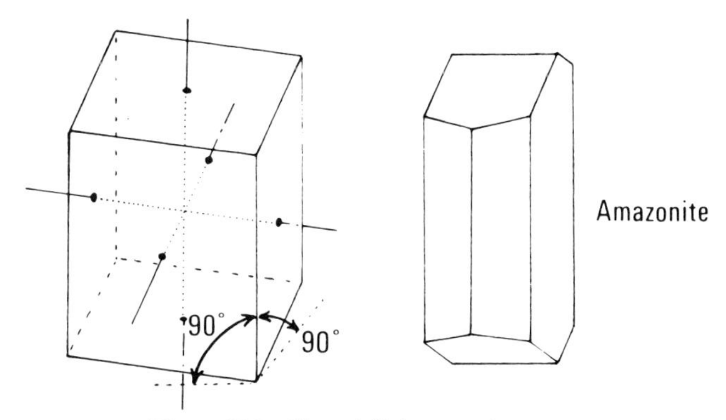


*Figure T.6* The triclinic crystal system.

**trigon** A triangular growth or etch mark on the face of a diamond crystal. The 'points' of the trigon are always orientated towards the straight edges of the crystal's octahedral face.

**trigonal system** A crystal system having four axes which are arranged in the same manner as in the hexagonal system. The symmetry of the trigonal system is, however, lower than that of the hexagonal system. A trigonal crystal with *maximum* symmetry has four axes of symmetry (three two-fold and one three-fold), three planes of symmetry and a centre of symmetry. The bulk of trigonal crystals have *normal* symmetry, and this consists of one axis of symmetry (three-fold), three planes of symmetry and a centre of symmetry.

**trilliant cut** A 43-facet (plus culet) diamond cut, having a polished and rounded triangular girdle. It is designed for macles and consists of 25 crown facets and 18 pavilion facets.

**trillings** Forms produced by triple twinning (e.g. the pseudo-hexagonal trilling produced by chrysoberyl).

**trillium** Trade name for gem quality green apatite from Canada.

**trinitite** A vesicular greenish fused sand glass formed by the first experimental atomic bomb exploded in New Mexico, USA, in 1945. Samples of trinitite are still strongly radioactive.

**triplet** See ***composite stones.***

**triplet** (lens) A compound-lens hand loupe which achieves distortion-free magnification by the use of three separate lenses. *Figure T.7.* See ***hand lens*** and ***head loupe.***

**tripletine** Trade name for an emerald-coloured beryl triplet.

**tripoli** See ***rottenstone.***

**troida** A triangular diamond cut designed for macles. It has 47 facets plus a culet.

**Troy weight** See ***ounce Troy.***

**tsavolite** A transparent green grossular garnet coloured by

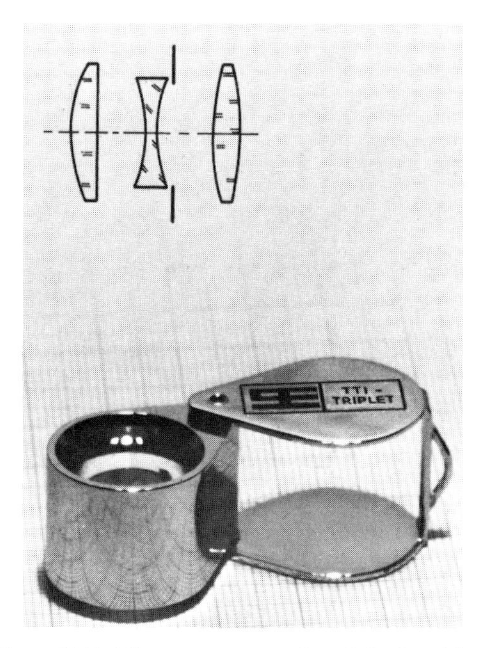


*Figure T.7* The components of a triplet hand lens.

chromium and vanadium. $Ca_3Al_2(SiO_4)_3$. R.I. 1.734-1.744; S.G. 3.68; H. 6½-7. Occurrence: Kenya, Tanzania.

**tsavorite** See ***tsavolite.***

**tsavolithe** See ***tsavolite.***

**tsilaisite** A manganese-rich tourmaline.

**tube agate** A variety of agate containing tubes, or channels, often liquid-filled.

**tufa** See ***aragonite.***

**tuff** A rock formed by consolidation of volcanic ash.

**tugtupite** An ornamental mineral close to sodalite in composition. Tetragonal. R.I. 1.496, 1.502; D.R. +0.006; S.G. 2.30-2.57 (depending on impurities); H. 6½. Transparent to opaque, cyclamen-red (massive material is light and dark red, mottled with white). Pleochroism, strong (bluish-red, orange-red). Occurrence: Greenland, USSR.

**Tully Medal** A medal awarded to the candidate submitting the best papers in the annual Fellowship Examination of the Gemmological Association of Great Britain, which also meet the required standard set for the award. See ***Anderson Medal.***

**Tully refractometer** The first table refractometer for gemstone use which employed a rotateable hemisphere of glass and an erect scale. Designed by B. G. Tully in 1925.

**tumbling** The polishing of gemstones into rounded and irregular shaped 'pebbles' by tumbling them (first with a coarse abrasive and then with a polishing powder) in a rotating drum. A technique used mainly by hobbyists.

**turbid** An unclear muddy translucency.

**turkey-fat ore** A yellow smithsonite coloured by cadmium.

**turquoise** A hydrous copper aluminium phosphate with some iron oxide replacing the alumina. $CuAl_6(PO_4)_4(OH)_8.5H_2O$. Triclinic (crypto-crystalline). R.I. around 1.62; S.G. 2.6-2.9 (2.6-2.7 for porous USA stones; 2.7-2.9 for Iranian stones); H. 5½-6. Opaque (sometimes veined with sandstone or limonite matrix), sky-blue, blue-green, green. Occurrence: Afghanistan, Australia, China (Tibet), Iran, Israel (Sinai), USA.

**turquoise matrix** A turquoise cut complete with a section of its associated dark grey sandstone or brown limonite matrix.

**turtle back** A turquoise or variscite matrix, or a chlorastrolite.

**turtle-back pearl** A natural oval blister pearl with a high dome.

**turritella agate** An ornamental orbicular stone consisting of agatized turritella shells.

**tweezers** Metal tongs for handling gemstones, which may take a variety of forms from self-locking and reverse-action types to spring-loaded prong versions. *Figure T.8.*

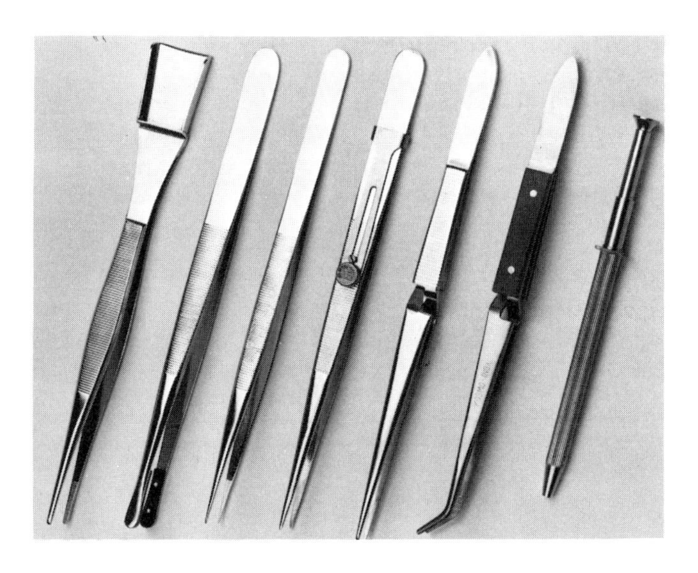

*Figure T.8* A selection of tweezers. (Rubin and Son)

**twinning** See *contact twin, interpenetrant twins* and *polysynthetic twinning.*

**two-phase inclusions** See *inclusions.*

**two-point** A cutting orientation for diamond where the table has been polished parallel to a possible dodecahedron crystal face (i.e. parallel to the edge of the octahedron's pyramid-based natural girdle). See *four-point* and *three-point.*

**Type I diamond** A category of diamonds which contain nitrogen as the main impurity. This is further sub-divided into Type Ia diamond, containing clusters of nitrogen atoms (which do not affect the colour of the stone) and Type Ib diamond in which the nitrogen atoms are dispersed throughout the crystal lattice and replace carbon atoms (this causes the stone to absorb light at the violet end of the spectrum and produces the yellow body colour of Cape series diamonds). Natural diamonds are normally a mixture of Type Ia and Type Ib. Synthetic diamonds containing nitrogen are all Type Ib.

**Type II diamond** A category of diamonds which contain no nitrogen impurities. This is further sub-divided into Type IIa which contains no other impurity, and Type IIb which contains boron. The boron atoms in Type IIb diamonds replace carbon atoms in the crystal lattice and make the stone electrically semi-conducting. Type IIb diamonds often have a blue body colour (blue diamonds artificially coloured by irradation are not semi-conductors).

**Type III diamond** See *lonsdaleite.*

**tyrolese onyx** A slightly translucent onyx marble with orange-coloured veins found in Austria.

# U

**ugrandite garnet series** An isomorphous series of garnets encompassing the uvarovite — grossularite — andradite species. See also ***pyralspite garnet series.***

**uigite** A variety of chlorastrolite found on the island of Skye off the coast of Scotland.

**ulexite** A collector's stone comprising a fibrous hydrated borate of calcium and sodium. $NaCaB_5O_9.H_2O$. Ulexite is not strictly a gemstone, but is of interest because when a slab of the material is cut and polished with both faces at right-angles to the stone's fibres, an image presented to one face is transmitted to the other face (as with coherent fibre optics). Because of this phenomenon it is called a 'television stone'. R.I. around 1.51; S.G. 1.65-1.99; H. 1-2. Occurrence: USA.

**ultrabasic rock** A low silica–content rock which is usually rich in iron, magnesium and alumina.

**ultralite** Trade name for reddish-violet synthetic corundum.

**ultramafic** A term used to describe rocks having a low silica content but which are unusually rich in magnesium and iron.

**ultramarine** A blue pigment originally produced from powdered lapis lazuli.

**ultrasonic cleaning** An efficient method of cleaning gemstones and jewellery which employs ultrasonic vibrations. Ultrasonic baths or tanks designed for this purpose consist of a container for the

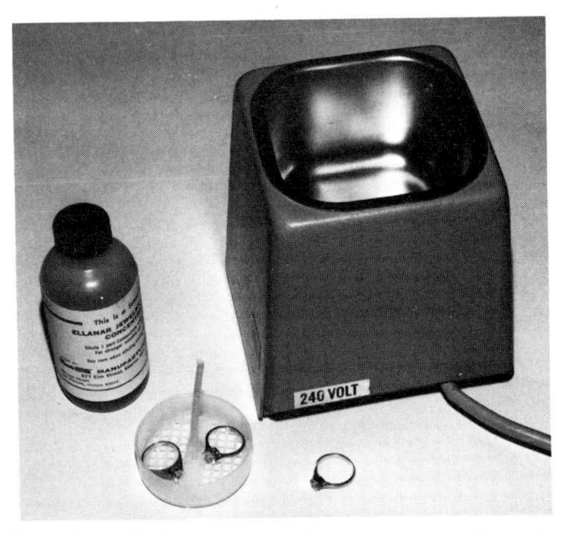


*Figure U.1* A small ultrasonic bath for cleaning jewellery. (Dawe)

cleaning fluid, and a piezo-electric transducer (e.g. a slab of zirconate titanate) which vibrates the tank at frequencies in the region of 50 000–100 000 Hz. The ultrasonic energy produces cavitation of the cleaning fluid. This is the creation of thousands of minute cavities or bubbles which, when they collapse, release enough mechanical energy to dislodge particles of dirt. On no account should gemstones containing stress flaws, such as emeralds, opals, zoisites or strontium titanate diamond simulants, be cleaned by ultrasonics as the cleaning energy could damage the stone. *Figure U.1.*

**ultra violet light** Electromagnetic radiation having wavelengths which range from just beyond the violet end of the visible spectrum at roughly 380 nm down to the longest X-ray wavelengths at around 20 nm. Because of the visible emission peaks in the mercury discharge lamps and low-pressure mercury vapour lamps used to produce UV light for gem testing, these lamps are filtered to produce light at 365 nm (LW UV) and 254 nm (SW UV). See ***UV lamps.***

**umbalite garnet** Provisional name for an orange or dark orange to brown garnet of the pyrope-spessartine series. Some stones contain vanadium and show a colour change (bluish-mauve under daylight, magenta under tungsten light). R.I. 1.74–1.76. Occurrence: Kenya, Tanzania.

**umbrella effect** Diamonds artificially coloured by cyclotron

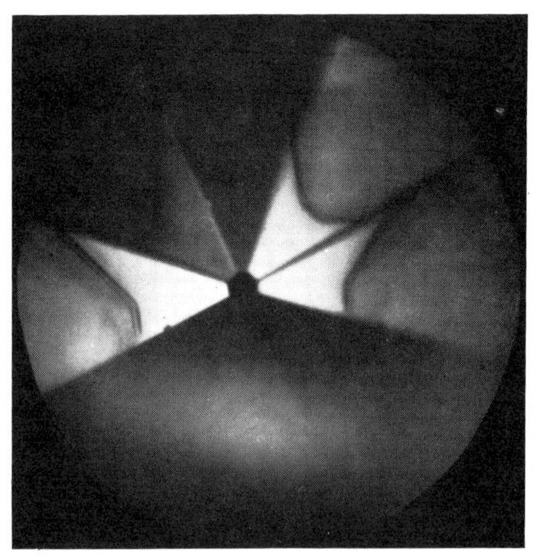

*Figure U.2* The 'umbrella' effect as seen round the culet of a cyclotron-treated diamond.

irradiation through the pavilion (at right-angles to the plane of the girdle) show a pattern round the culet which, when viewed through the table facet, looks like an opened umbrella. *Figure U.2.*

**unakite** A type of granite rock containing quartz, pink feldspar and green epidote, usually cut in cabochon form or tumbled. R.I. varies from 1.52 for the pink sections to 1.76 for the green areas; S.G. 2.85-3.2. Occurrence: Eire, South Africa, USA, Zimbabwe.

**uniaxial** The term used to describe a doubly-refracting crystal having a single optical axis along which it is singly-refractive. In the seven crystal systems, tetragonal, hexagonal and trigonal crystals all have uniaxial optical characters. See ***biaxial.***

**unionite** See ***zoisite*** (thulite).

**unit cell** The smallest part of a crystalline structure which still exhibits all the characteristic properties of the crystal.

**univalve mollusc** A shellfish such as the abalone and giant conch which has a shell in one piece, rather than in two halves as in bivalve molluscs such as the oyster.

**unripe pearls** A term used to describe poor quality pearls.

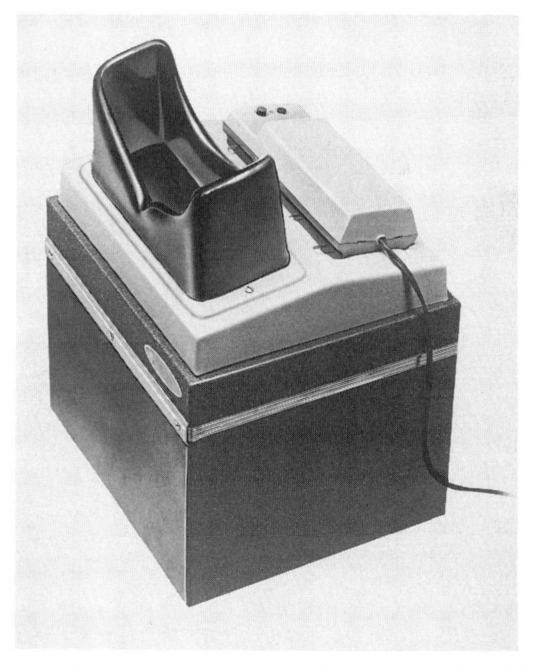

*Figure U.3* A darkroom viewing cabinet fitted with a dual LW/SW UV lamp. (U–V Products Inc.)

**upper break facets** See ***break facets.***

**upper girdle facets** The triangular facets adjacent to the girdle on the crown of a brilliant-cut stone. See ***brilliant cut.*** *Figure B.6.*

**uralian emerald** A misleading name for a demantoid garnet.

**uralian sapphire** A misleading name for blue tourmaline.

**uraninite** A radioactive mineral containing uranium and thorium.

**uranium glass** A yellow glass, also called canary glass, sometimes used as a gemstone simulant.

**utahlite** See ***variscite.***

**utah onyx** A misleading name for a translucent lemon-coloured stalagmitic marble containing orange veins, and found in Utah, USA.

**utah turquoise** A misleading name for variscite.

**uvarovite** See ***garnet.***

**uvite** A brown dravite-type tourmaline having (unlike dravite) a high calcium content and little sodium. Occurrence: Brazil, Burma, Sri Lanka.

**UV lamps** For gem testing purposes these are either LW or SW types, and are often combined in one unit. The LW version uses a mercury discharge lamp whose dominant mercury emission line at 366 nm is separated from the lamp's visible emission spectrum by means of a Wood's glass filter (e.g. a Chance OX1 filter) which contains cobalt and nickel. The SW UV lamp uses a low-pressure mercury lamp whose dominant 254 nm emission line is separated out by a Chance OX7 filter. *Figure U.3.*

# V

**vabanite** A reddish-brown jasper speckled with yellow, from California, USA.

**valencianite** An adularia variety of orthoclase feldspar.

**valency** A unit of combining power between elements, based on the number of hydrogen atoms with which it can combine or which it can replace. Carbon has a valency of four and its atom can link with four other atoms by sharing common orbital electrons. See ***Table of Elements*** in Appendix H.

**vallum diamond** A misleading name for the rock crystal variety of quartz.

**vanadium** One of the eight transition metals which are mainly responsible for colour in gemstones. V. Stones coloured by vanadium are green beryls, natural and synthetic colour-change sapphires. Atomic number 23; atomic weight 50.95; melting point 1920 °C; S.G. 6.0.

**vanadium emerald** A misleading name for a green beryl coloured with vanadium. The emerald variety of beryl is coloured by chromium. Occurrence: Brazil. Synthetic vanadium beryl is grown by the hydrothermal process.

**varieties** A mineral species may have several varieties which differ from each other in appearance (e.g. ruby and sapphire are colour varieties of the mineral species corundum). See also ***groups*** and ***species.***

**variolite** A variety of dark green orthoclase feldspar with light green orbicular inclusions.

**variscite** A hydrous aluminium phosphate with replacement of some of the aluminium by chromium and iron. $AlPO_4.2H_2O$. Orthorhombic (fibrous). R.I. around 1.56; S.G. 2.4-2.6; H. 5. Translucent to opaque, green to greenish-blue. Occurrence: Australia, USA.

**vashegyrite** A yellow or brown aluminium phosphate, similar to variscite.

**Vauxhall glass** See ***French jet***

**vega gem** Trade name for a synthetic corundum diamond simulant.

**vegetable ivory** See ***corozo nut*** and ***doom plam nut.***

**veils** Inclusions formed by concentrations of minute bubbles on a plane within a crystal. Similar to, but less restricted in extent than, 'fingerprints'.

**velocity of light** Light travels at a speed of 300 000 kilometres per second in air. In a gemstone or any other medium this is modified by the factor:

$$\frac{1}{\text{R.I. of medium}}$$

**venus hair stone** See *quartz.*

**verd antique** See *serpentine.*

**verdelite** A misleading name for green tourmaline.

**verdite** An ornamental muscovite-mica rock formed from compacted clay. R.I. around 1.58; S.G. 2.80–2.99; H. 3. Opaque, green (the colour is due to chrome mica). Occurrence: South Africa, Swaziland, USA.

**vermeil** A misleading name for orange-red zircons, garnets or spinels.

**vermilite** A variety of opal containing cinnabar.

**Verneuil corundum** A synthetic corundum produced by the flame-fusion process. See *Verneuil furnace.*

**Verneuil furnace** An oxy-hydrogen blowpipe-type furnace designed mainly to grow boules of synthetic corundum by the flame-fusion process. The furnace consists of an inverted blowpipe burner, a powder dispenser and a ceramic pedestal. When corundum is being synthesized, the dispenser is filled with high-purity alumina powder, which is dropped at a controlled rate down the blowpipe's central oxygen feed tube. As the powder drops through the 2200 °C oxy-hydrogen flame, it melts and recrystallizes on the ceramic pedestal. As the crystalline boule starts to grow, the height of the pedestal is adjusted so as to maintain the top of the crystal in the hottest part of the flame. Synthetic spinel, synthetic rutile and strontium titanate boules are also grown in the Verneuil furnace, extra oxygen being supplied for the latter two by use of a tricone burner. *Figure V.1.* See also *boule.*

**vespa gem** Trade name for a synthetic corundum diamond simulant.

**vesuvian garnet** A misleading name for leucite.

**vesuvianite** See *idocrase.*

**vesuvianite jade** A misleading name for californite.

**victoria stone** Trade name for a glass-like Japanese gemstone simulant having a fibrous aggregate structure, which gives it a chatoyant effect. Made in various colours, it is also produced to imitate jade, and is manufactured by fusing together minerals such as quartz, calcite, fluorspar, magnesite and feldspar to form a reconstructed stone. R.I. 1.62; S.G. 3.02; H. 6.

**victron** Trade name for polystyrene.

**Vienna turquoise** A misleading name for a glass simulant of turquoise. Also a turquoise simulant made from compacted aluminium phosphate powder coloured with copper oleate.

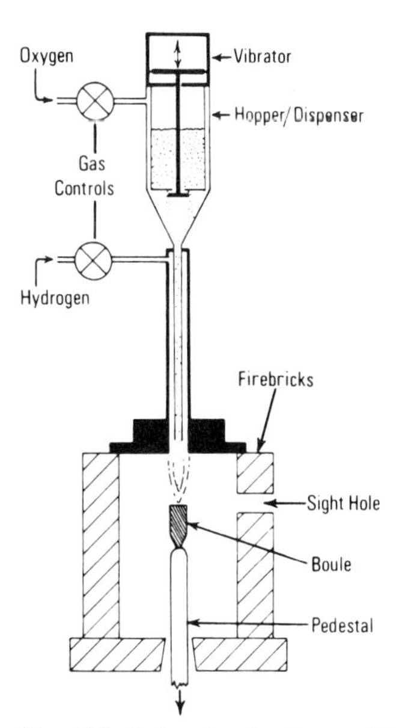


*Figure V.1* Simplified sketch of a Verneuil furnace.

**vigorite** Trade name for a phenolic resin plastic.
**viluite** See ***idocrase.***
**vinegar spinel** A yellowish-orange variety of spinel.
**violet stone** See ***cordierite.***
**violan** See ***violane.***
**violane** A massive violet-blue diopside. Translucent to opaque. R.I. around 1.69; S.G. 3.23; H. 6. Occurrence: Italy.
**violite** Trade name for a synthetic corundum.
**viridine** A manganese-rich variety of andalusite from Brazil, but originally found in West Germany. R.I. 1.640, 1.647; D.R. –0.007; S.G. 3.174. Semi-transparent, dark green with brownish tint.
**viscoloid** Trade name for a cellulosic plastic.
**viss** A Burmese unit of weight equal to 880 carats. See also ***rati, bali, tickal*** and ***lathi.***
**visual colorimeter** An instrument in which the eye is used to compare and match the colour of a specimen with an image produced by selecting the appropriate combination of hue, brightness and colour saturation. See *Figure V.2.*
**vitreous lustre** See ***lustre.***
**vivianite** A collector's stone comprising the mineral hydrous iron phosphate. $Fe_3(PO_4)_2.8H_2O$. Monoclinic. R.I. 1.580, 1.627; D.R. +0.047; S.G. 2.6; H. 2. Transparent, colourless, blue-green.

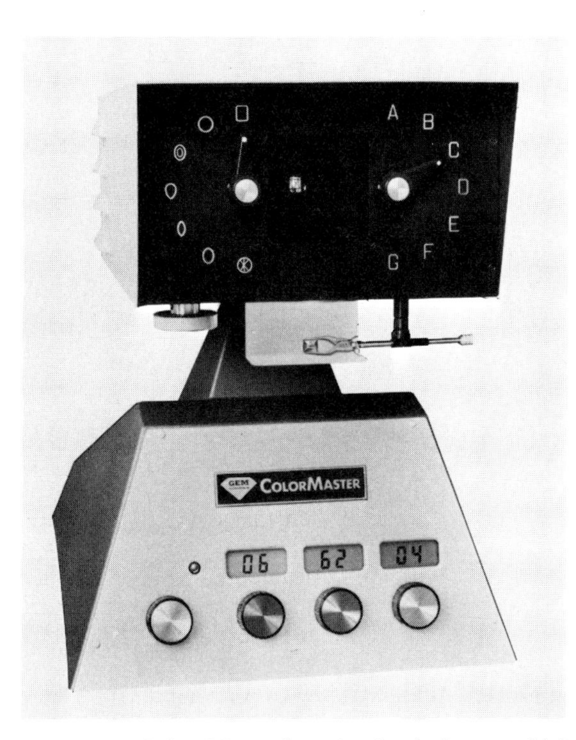


*Figure V.2* The GIA ColourMaster is a visual colorimeter which can be used to match and code coloured stones for hue, brightness and colour saturation. (Gem Instruments Corp.)

Occurrence: Australia, Bolivia, England, Romania, USA.

**volcanic chrysolite** A misleading name for idocrase.

**volcanic glass** See ***obsidian.***

**volcanic rock** See ***igneous rock.***

**vorobievite** A pink variety of beryl.

**vug** A rock cavity or fissure often lined with crystals which have grown from trapped mineral-rich water, and which are of a different composition to the surrounding rock. See also ***druse*** and ***geode.***

**vulcanite** A hard black vulcanized rubber (also called ebonite) used as a simulant for jet.

**vulpinite** A granular variety of anhydrite found in Vulpino, Italy. S.G. 2.90-2.92.

**walderite** A synthetic colourless corundum.
**walrus ivory** An ivory derived from the teeth of the walrus.
**wardite** A complex hydrous phosphate of sodium, calcium and aluminium. Tetragonal. R.I. 1.590, 1.599; D.R. +0.009; S.G. 2.81; H. 5. Translucent to opaque, bluish-green (resembling turquoise).
**wart pearls** See ***blister pearls.***
**washita diamond** A misleading name for the rock crystal variety of quartz.
**water agate** See ***enhydros.***
**water chrysolite** A misleading name for moldavite.
**water contact angle** The degree of wettability of a material can be assessed by measuring the contact angle formed by the edges of a droplet of pure (distilled) water deposited on a clean, flat and horizontal surface polished on the material. As diamond has a much lower water contact angle than all of its man-made simulants, this forms a practical method of identification.

For the water droplet test to succeed it is important that the surface of the specimen is first thoroughly cleaned. This is best done with a polishing powder, such as Linde A, to remove any surface coating (sometimes produced by irradiation). The water can be applied with a hypodermic syringe or a glass dropper with a fine tip, taking care that the resulting droplet is round and is not touching the edges of the table facet. Typical water contact angles are as follows (measured as included angles within the droplet):

| | | | |
|---|---|---|---|
| corundum | 95° | rutile | 73° |
| YAG | 93° | zircon | 60° |
| strontium titanate | 91° | diamond | 55° |
| cubic zirconium oxide | 91° | quartz | 0° (wets surface) |
| GGG | 84° | glass | 0° (wets surface) |

The effect of the relatively low water contact angle of diamond compared with the majority of its simulants is exploited in the GIA gem diamond pen. *Figure W.1.*
**water droplet test** See ***water contact angle.***
**water-melon tourmaline** A variety of bi-coloured tourmaline in which the crystal prism has a central colourless core surrounded by a green rim.
**water opal** See ***opal.***
**water sapphire** A misleading name for cordierite.
**water stone** A glassy orthoclase feldspar, or the hyalite variety of opal.
**wavelength** The distance between successive crests in a wave train. In the electromagnetic radiation of light this distance is very small,

*Figure W.1* The difference between the water contact angle of cubic zirconia (left) and diamond (right) is revealed by drawing an 'ink' line across their table facets with a GIA Gem Diamond Pen. The pen uses a draughting-type nib/dispenser, and a reservoir filled with a non-drying viscous fluid containing inert chemicals and a blue dye. The ink gathers into droplets on diamond simulants which have an R.I. greater than 1.8, but remains as a continous line on the surface of a diamond.

and wavelengths are measured in nanometres or ångström units (one nanometre = ten ångström units = one millionth of a millimetre). See also ***electron volt*** and ***wave number.***

**wavelength spectroscope** See ***spectroscope.***

**wave number** A method of indicating the frequency, or wavelength of an electromagnetic radiation, such as light or X-rays, in terms of the number of waves per centimetre:

$$\text{i.e. wavelength in nm} = \frac{10\,000\,000}{\text{wave number}}$$

$$\text{wave number} = \frac{10\,000\,000}{\text{wavelength (nm)}}$$

See also ***electron volt.***

**wave theory of light** This theory is based on the wave-motion propagation of light through an all-pervading hypothetical medium called the *ether.* It was modified by Maxwell's electromagnetic theory which suggested that the ether vibrations which transmitted light were caused by oscillation in the electrical and magnetic condition of the ether. Hertz later experimentally confirmed the existence of electromagnetic waves. A more complete picture of the emission and absorption of light was provided by Max Planck's quantum theory. See ***photon.***

**wax agate** A yellow to yellowish-red variety of agate with a waxy lustre.
**wax opal** A yellowish-brown common opal with a waxy lustre.
**waxed turquoise** A turquoise whose colour has been deepened by soaking it in paraffin wax.
**waxy lustre** See ***lustre.***
**weight** See ***mass.***
**weight estimation of polished stones** See ***caliper gauge, diamond gauge*** and ***moe diamond gauge.***
**wellington** Trade name for the man-made diamond simulant strontium titanate.
**wernerite** See ***scapolite.***
**wesselsite** A variety of sugilite found in the Wessels mine in South Africa.
**Wessex starred agate** See ***starred agate.***
**Westphal balance** See ***hydrostatic weighing.***
**West's solution** An 8:1:1 mixture of yellow phosphorus and sulphur in methylene iodide having an R.I. of 2.05. It is used as a contact liquid for extended range refractometers (e.g. diamond prism versions). As it contains phosphorus it must be handled with care, as the dried residue is spontaneously combustible.
**wet diggings** Diamond mining associated with alluvial rather than pipe deposits. See ***dry diggings.***
**whale ivory** An ivory derived from the incisor tooth or tusk of the narwhal, a species of arctic whale and the teeth of the cachalot or sperm whale.
**whewellite** A collector's stone comprising the mineral hydrated calcium oxalate. $CaC_2O_4.H_2O$. Monoclinic. R.I. 1.490, 1.650; D.R. +0.16; S.G. 2.23; H. 2½. Transparent, colourless. Occurrence: Czechoslovakia, France, Germany.
**Whitby jet** The jet mined from the sea cliffs near Whitby in Yorkshire, England.
**white** A colour grade for polished diamonds. See ***Colour Grading Standards*** in Appendix B. Also a commercial name for transparent colourless stones.
**white emerald** Goshenite variety of beryl.
**white garnet** A misleading name for leucite.
**white gold** Gold alloyed with nickel, silver, platinum or palladium.
**white graphite** A white abrasive powder consisting of hexagonal boron nitride.
**white light** Light containing an approximately equal mixture of all the colours or wavelengths that make up the visible spectrum.
**white opal** An iridescent opal having a whitish background.
**wilconite** A purplish-red variety of scapolite.
**wild pearl** A naturally initiated pearl.

**willemite** A collector's stone comprising the mineral zinc silicate. $Zn_2SiO_4$. Trigonal. R.I. 1.69, 1.72; D.R. +0.028; S.G. 3.89-4.18; H. 5½. Transparent, greenish-yellow, orange-brown. Occurrence: USA.

**williamsite** See ***serpentine.***

**wilsonite** A purplish-red variety of scapolite.

**wiluite** A variety of idocrase found in Siberia, USSR.

**winchellite** A plain green variety of thomsonite (also called lintonite).

**window** A facet polished on a coated or frosted (i.e. matt-surfaced) diamond crystal to enable its interior to be inspected for inclusions or flaws.

**wing pearl** A baroque pearl in the shape of a wing.

**Wisconsin pearls** Freshwater pearls from the Mississippi, USA.

**witherite** A collector's stone comprising the mineral barium carbonate. $BaCO_3$. Orthorhombic. R.I. 1.532, 1.680; D.R. −0.148; S.G. 4.27-4.35; H. 3½. Transparent, pale yellow, colourless. Occurrence: Canada, England, Japan, USA.

**wolf's eye** The moonstone variety of orthoclase feldspar, or the tiger's eye variety of quartz.

**wollastonite** A collector's stone comprising a calcium metasilicate. $CaSiO_3$. Monoclinic. R.I. 1.61, 1.63; D.R. −0.02; S.G. 2.8-2.9; H. 4½-5. Opaque, white. Occurrence: Finland, Mexico, Romania, USA.

**wonderstone** See ***pyrophyllite.***

**wood agate** See ***fossil wood.***

**Wood's glass filter** See ***UV lamps.***

**wood opal** See ***opal.***

**wood stone** See ***fossil wood.***

**work-hardening** An effect which occurs when 'working' metals (i.e. hammering, bending or stretching). They can be restored to their soft condition by heat treatment. See ***annealing.***

**wulfenite** A collector's stone comprising the mineral lead molybdate. $PbMoO_4$. Tetragonal. R.I. 2.304, 2.402; D.R. −0.098; S.G. 6.7-7.0; H. 3. Transparent to translucent, yellow, orange, red, green, grey, white. Occurrence: Australia, Austria, Germany, Mexico, Morocco, USA, Yugoslavia, Zaire.

**Wyoming jade** A variety of nephrite from Wyoming, USA. See also ***jade matrix.***

# X

**xalostocite** See ***landerite.***

**xanthite** A yellowish-brown variety of idocrase from New York State, USA.

**xenomorphic** Term applied to a crystal having a crystal form alien to its normal habit. See ***idiomorphic*** and ***pseudomorphic.***

**xenolith** A fragment of rock which is foreign to its host rock.

**xenotime** An yttrium phosphate ($Y_2O_3.P_2O_5$) present with zircon as flower-like radiating crystals in an ornamental basaltic rock. The rock is called kiku-ishi. Xenotime is sometimes found as an inclusion in diamond. Occurrence: Japan, Canada (Vancouver Island).

**X-ray diamond tester** An instrument for distinguishing between diamonds (which are transparent to X-rays) and diamond simulants (which are translucent or opaque). The stone under test is placed on a fluorescent plate inside the unit, and low-energy X-rays reveal the transparency or opacity of the stone as a shadow profile. *Figure X.1.*

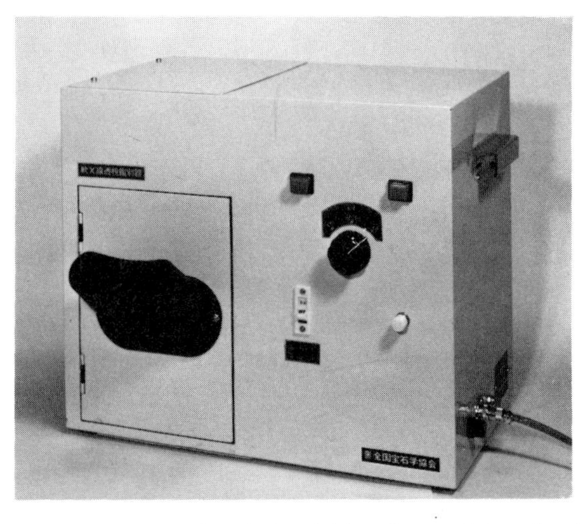

*Figure X.1* An X-ray tester for distinguishing diamond from its simulants by its transparency to X-rays. (GAAJ)

**X-ray luminescence** See ***luminescence*** and ***Table of Fluorescence*** in Appendix I.

**X-rays** Highly penetrating electromagnetic radiation having a range of wavelengths extending from the vicinity of the shortest ultra-violet rays at about 20 nm down to around 0.001 nm (i.e. a millionth of a micrometre). X-rays are produced in a vacuum tube by first accelerating electrons in a high-potential electric field, and then using them to bombard a tungsten target. X-rays are emitted as the high-energy electrons rapidly decelerate on striking the tungsten atoms. See ***lauegram, radiograph*** and ***X-ray diamond tester.***

**X-ray separator** An equipment which uses the X-ray fluorescent property of diamonds to separate them from crushed rock and gravels at the mine. The diamond concentrate is passed under an X-ray beam, and any fluorescing stone is detected by a photomultiplier which activates an air jet to eject the stone from the main stream. See ***recovery plant.***

**X-ray spectroscopy** See ***electron microprobe.***

**X-ray topography** A technique used in the experimental fingerprinting of diamonds which makes visible the unique lattice structure defects inside the gem. A vertical ribbon-like beam of collimated X-rays is used to scan the diamond, which is positioned

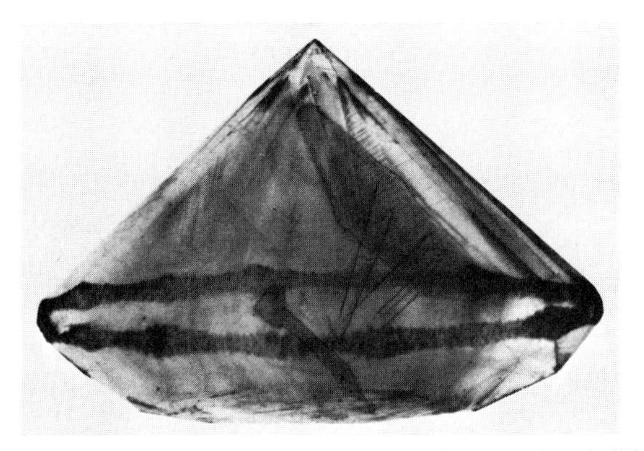

*Figure X.2* An X-ray projection topograph picture of a brilliant-cut diamond which reveals distinguishing crystal defects. (De Beers)

so that the beam is diffracted by the atomic layers in the crystal lattice. The emerging X-rays fall on a photographic plate to produce a projection topograph showing a pattern of crystal defects within the stone. *Figure X.2.* See also ***fingerprinting.***

**xyloid jasper** A jasper fossil wood.

**xylonite** Trade name for a cellulosic plastic.

**xylopal** An opalized fossil wood.

# Y

**YAG** See ***yttrium aluminium garnet.***

**yakutite** An impure dark-coloured diamond or boart, similar to carbonado, found in Yakutia, Siberia, USSR. See ***boart.***

**yanolite** A violet-coloured variety of axinite.

**yaqui onyx** A misleading name for a marble found in Baja California, Mexico.

**yava onyx** A misleading name for a marble found in Yavapai County, Arizona, USA.

**yellow ashover spar** A yellow fluorspar found in Derbyshire, England.

**yellow ground** See ***kimberlite.***

**yellow pearls** Pearls from the *Pinctada carcharium* mollusc fished off the coast of Shark Bay, Western Australia.

**yield** The yield of a diamond mine is quoted in terms of carats of diamonds recovered per 100 tons of rock processed. When a diamond is polished, the yield is given as a percentage of the weight of polished diamond against the weight of the original rough crystal.

**YIG** See ***yttrium iron garnet.***

**yttralox** Trade name for a man-made material originally developed for the optical industry. It is a transparent ceramic produced by heating powdered yttrium oxide ($Y_2O_3$) under high pressure. Ten percent of thorium oxide ($ThO_2$) is added to stabilize the material in the cubic form. R.I. 1.92; S.G. 5.3; H. 6½.

**yttrium aluminate** A man-made crystal (produced for the laser industry). $YA10_3$. Orthorhombic. R.I. 1.938, 1.955; D.R. −0.017; S.G. 5.35; H. 8. Transparent, red, pink, orange-pink, bluish-violet (coloured by rare-earth oxides). Crystals are grown by the Czochralski process.

**yttrium aluminium garnet** A man-made diamond simulant (introduced in 1969) which has no counterpart in nature. $Y_3Al_5O_{12}$. Cubic. R.I. 1.832; S.G. 4.58; H. 8½. Transparent, colourless and yellow, green, blue, red, lilac (produced by doping the crystal with transition element oxides and rare-earth oxides). Crystals are grown by the Czochralski and flux-melt processes.

**yttrium iron garnet** A man-made crystal, grown for its magnetic properties (as a modulator for infra-red laser beams) but too dark for gem use.

**yttrium oxide** A man-made crystal with potential as a diamond simulant. $Y_2O_3$. Cubic. R.I. 1.92; S.G. 4.84; H. 7½-8.

**yttro garnet** Trade name for an yttrium aluminium garnet.

**yu** The Chinese name for jade.

**yui ko lu jade** A tomb jade coloured green by bronze articles buried near it.

**yunnan jade** Burmese jadeite marketed through the Chinese province of Yunnan.

**yu yen stone** A massive greenish-grey variety of serpentine.

## Z

**zaba gem** Trade name for a synthetic rutile diamond simulant.

**zabeltitzten diamond** A misleading name for the rock crystal variety of quartz.

**zarafina** A blue variety of spinel or a blue chalcedony.

**zeasite** See ***opal*** (wood opal).

**zeathite** Trade name for a strontium titanate.

**zebra crocidolite** A parti-coloured blue/brown silica pseudomorph of crocidolite. See ***quartz*** (tiger's eye variety).

**zektzerite** A collector's stone comprising the mineral lithium sodium zirconium silicate. $LiNaZrSi_6O_{15}$. Orthorhombic. R.I. 1.582, 1.585; D.R. –0.003; S.G. 2.79; H. 6. Transparent, colourless to pale pink. Occurrence: USA.

**zenithite** Trade name for the man-made diamond simulant strontium titanate.

**zeolites** A group of minerals having the basic formula $X.Al_2Si_3O_{10}.nH_2O$. (e.g. natrolite, mesolite and scolecite).

**Zerfass synthetic emeralds** Synthetic emeralds grown by the flux-melt process. R.I. 1.560, 1.563; D.R. –0.003; S.G. 2.65. Zerfass of Idar-Oberstein, Germany.

**zeuxite** A variety of green tourmaline from Brazil.

**Zimbabwe Gem and Mineral Society** See ***Gem and Mineral Society of Zimbabwe.***

**zinc blende** See ***sphalerite.***

**zincian staurolite** A collector's stone comprising the colour-change zinc-rich variety of staurolite. R.I. 1.721, 1.731; D.R. +0.01; S.G. 3.79; H. 7. Transparent, yellowish-green (under fluorescent light), red-brown (under tungsten light). Pleochroism, medium (green, yellow, red). See ***staurolite.***

**zincite** A collector's stone comprising the mineral zinc oxide. ZnO. Hexagonal. R.I. 2.013, 2.029; D.R. +0.016; S.G. 5.66; H. 4–4½. Transparent, red, orange-yellow. Occurrence: USA.

**zircolite** Trade name for a synthetic corundum diamond simulant.

**zircon** A zirconium silicate. $ZrSiO_4$. Tetragonal. R.I. 1.929–1.990; D.R. +0.059; S.G. 4.67–4.70; H. 7–7½. Transparent, yellow, green, brown, red, orange, sky-blue, golden-brown, colourless (the latter three produced by heat treatment — see ***heat-treated stones***). Pleochroism, medium in blue stones (colourless, blue). Constants for zircon vary from those given above to the much lower values measured in metamict zircons. See ***high zircon, intermediate zircon*** and ***low zircon.*** Occurrence: Australia, Burma, Cambodia, France (red zircon), Indo-China, Norway, Sri Lanka, Thailand.

**zircon cut** A style, based on the brilliant cut, which is designed to improve the brilliance of a zircon. The zircon cut reduces light leakage from the rear of the stone by having an additional eight facets placed between the culet and the main pavilion facets.

**zircon haloes** A crystalline defect or stress crack seen in Sri Lankan sapphires, spinels and garnets, and caused by once radioactive zircon crystal inclusions, or by the unequal thermal expansion between these crystals and the host stone (or even by the transition of the zircon inclusions to a more bulky metamict state). See also ***inclusions.***

**zirconia** Trade name for the man-made diamond simulant cubic zirconium oxide manufactured by Swarovski & Co., of Wattens, Austria. Also the name of a reddish-brown abrasive powder used for polishing gemstones.

**zirconium dioxide** See ***cubic zirconium oxide.***

**zircon spinel** A misleading trade name for a synthetic blue spinel.

**zirctone** Trade name for a synthetic bluish-green sapphire.

**zoisite** A calcium aluminium silicate member of the epidote group of minerals. $Ca_2(OH)Al_3(SiO_4)_3$. Orthorhombic. Varieties:

*green zoisite* — also called anyolite, and originally called saualpite. Opaque chrome-rich with black hornblende inclusions, found with large opaque ruby crystals. R.I. 1.692, 1.700; D.R. +0.008; S.G. 3.35; H. 6.

*blue zoisite* — also called tanzanite. Transparent, blue to violet, occasionally chatoyant. R.I. 1.696, 1.703; D.R. +0.007; S.G. 3.38; H. 6.

*yellow zoisite* — transparent, turns colourless on heating.

*thulite* — also called rosaline. Opaque, pink. R.I. around 1.70; S.G. 3.10; H. 6.

Pleochroism strong in blue zoisite (purple, blue, slate-grey; less pronounced after heat treatment). Occurrence: Kenya (dark blue), Tanzania.

**zonite** A chert or jasper found in Arizona, USA. See ***quartz.***

**zoom microscope** A microscope employing a lens system which by variation of focal length provides a stepless change of magnification factors. See also ***microscope.***

**zylonite** Trade name for a cellulosic plastics material.

**spring balance** This operates by relating the known extension or compression properties of a helical spring to the weight of an object suspended from it (*Figure 1*). Unlike the beam balance, which is self-compensating for variations in gravity (and therefore measures *mass*), the spring balance indicates the gravitational force acting upon the load (i.e. its *weight*. See also under ***mass*** in dictionary section).

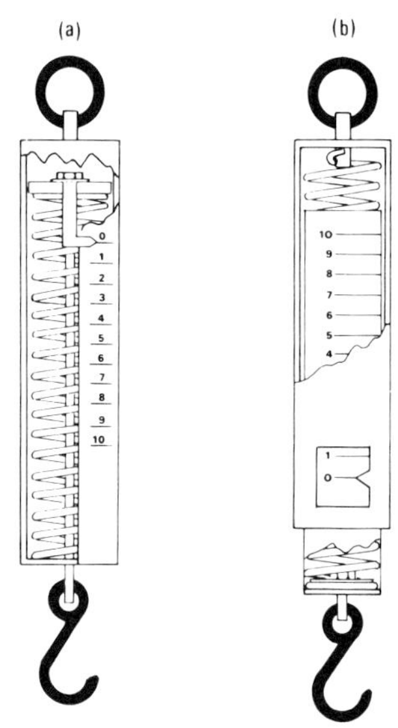


*Figure 1* (a) The construction of a compression spring balance and (b), an extension spring balance.

**beam balance** This uses one of the oldest of mechanical systems, the lever. In its simplest form, it consists of an equal-arm beam balance with a central fulcrum or pivot and a weighpan suspended from each arm of the beam (*Figure 2*).

**substitutional beam balance** An improved version of the simple beam balance designed to reduce the latter's inherent errors by providing a constant load. When an object is placed on the weighpan ($M_s$ in *Figure 3),* the appropriate substitutional weights ($M_x$) are removed (usually by means of calibrated control knobs which provide remote manipulation of the weights) until the balance pointer is within the range of its scale. Total weight of the object is then arrived at by the addition of the scale reading to that of the control knobs.

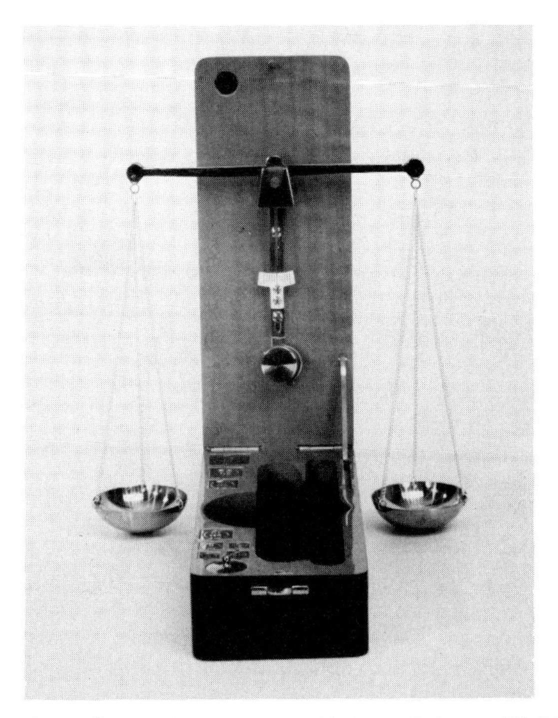

*Figure 2* A diamond dealer's portable beam balance. (Haigis)

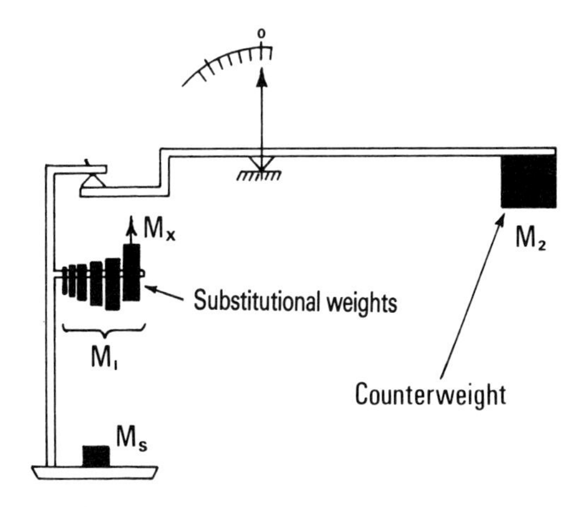


*Figure 3* A simplified sketch of a substitutional beam balance. A constant pivot load is maintained by making $M_s + M_1$ always equal to $M_2$.

**top pan balance** This was developed from the substitutional balance and the Roberval counter balance to facilitate rapid weighing. The top pan design sacrifices a degree of sensitivity in return for convenience (*Figure 4*).

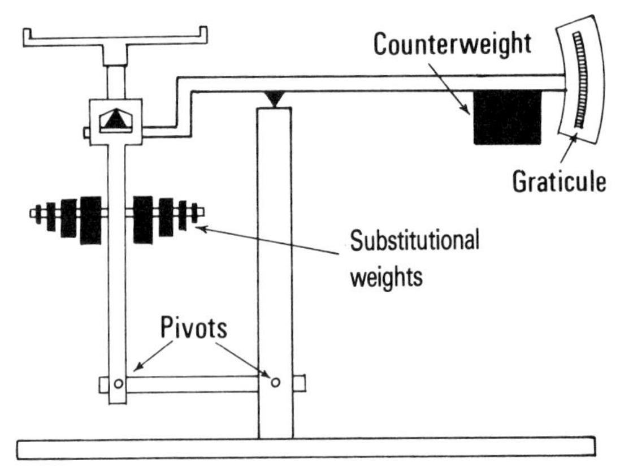


*Figure 4* A simplified sketch of a top pan substitutional balance.

**electronic balance** This instrument uses some of the components of the beam balance, but replaces the substitutional weights with a magnetic force-balance system. When an object is placed on the weighpan, an out-of-balance detector adjusts the current in a counter-balance coil to restore the beam to equilibrium. This

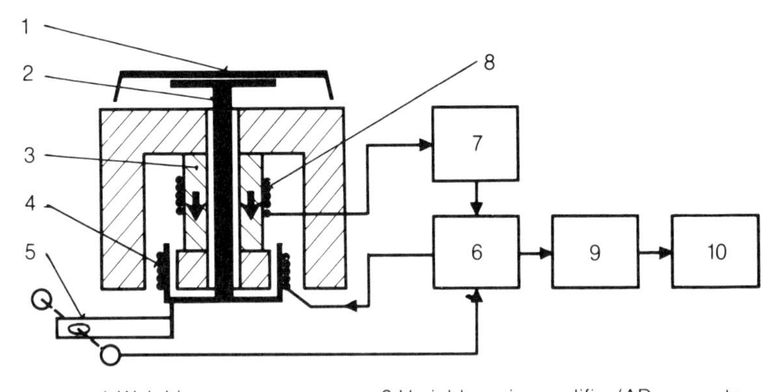


*Figure 5* Diagrammatic representation of a beamless all-electronic balance. (Mettler)

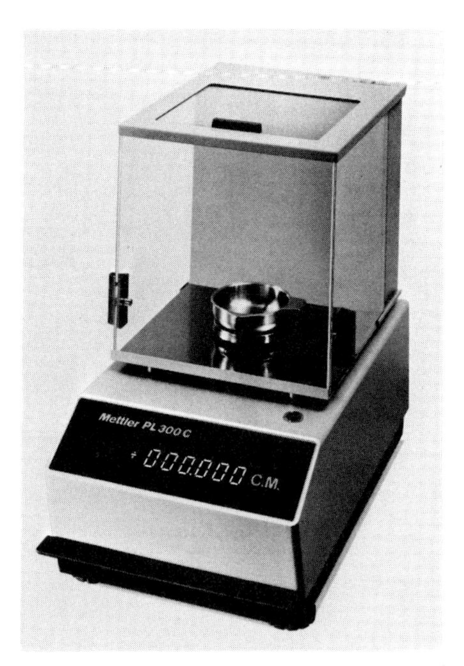


*Figure 6* An all-electronic carat balance with a digital display. (Mettler)

current is then measured and displayed as a weight reading. The latest designs dispense with pivots and beams, and suspend the weighpan/force coil assembly from centering flexures (*Figures 5* and *6*). The advent of the microprocessor has made it possible to incorporate such features as weight unit change (e.g. gram to carat), automatic tare, weight integration (averaging of several successive weighings to guard against vibration errors), and stand-still operation (inhibition of read-out until the weighpan has stopped moving).

**balances for hydrostatic weighing** Several manufacturers of analytical balances of the substitutional type provide accessories for hydrostatic weighing (as do the Gem Instruments Corporation). Also see the Westphal, Penfield and Hanneman balances under ***hydrostatic weighing*** in the dictionary section.

## Appendix B Colour Grading Standards for Polished Diamonds

Polished diamonds are visually graded for colour by inspecting them through the side of the pavilion against a neutral white background (i.e. in a folded white grading card or a grading tray).

**Table 1** Colour grading standards for polished diamonds

| *UK* | *German RAL Scan DN (0.5 carats upwards)* | *Scan DN (under 0.5 carats)* | *GIA* | *AGS* | *CIBJO* |
|---|---|---|---|---|---|
| Finest White | River | Rarest White | D | 0 | Exceptional White + |
| | | | E | 1 | Exceptional White |
| Fine White | Top Wesselton | Rare White | F | | Rare White + |
| | | | G | 2 | Rare White |
| White | Wesselton | White | H | 3 | White |
| Commercial White | Top Crystal | Slightly Tinted White | I | 4 | Slightly Tinted White |
| Top Silver Cape | Crystal | | J | 5 | |
| Silver Cape | Top Cape | Tinted White | K | | Tinted White |
| | | | L | 6 | |
| Light Cape | Cape | Slightly Yellowish | M | 7 | Tinted Colour |
| | | | N | | |
| Cape | Light Yellow | Yellowish | O | | |
| | | | P | 8 | |
| | | | Q | | |
| | | | R | 9–10 | |
| Dark Cape | Yellow | Yellow | S–Z | | |

Comparison colour grading is carried out in a 'north' light, or under a colour-corrected diamond grading lamp, which often incorporates a LW UV lamp to enable the stone to be checked for fluorescence (*Figure 7*). Blue fluorescence tends to make a

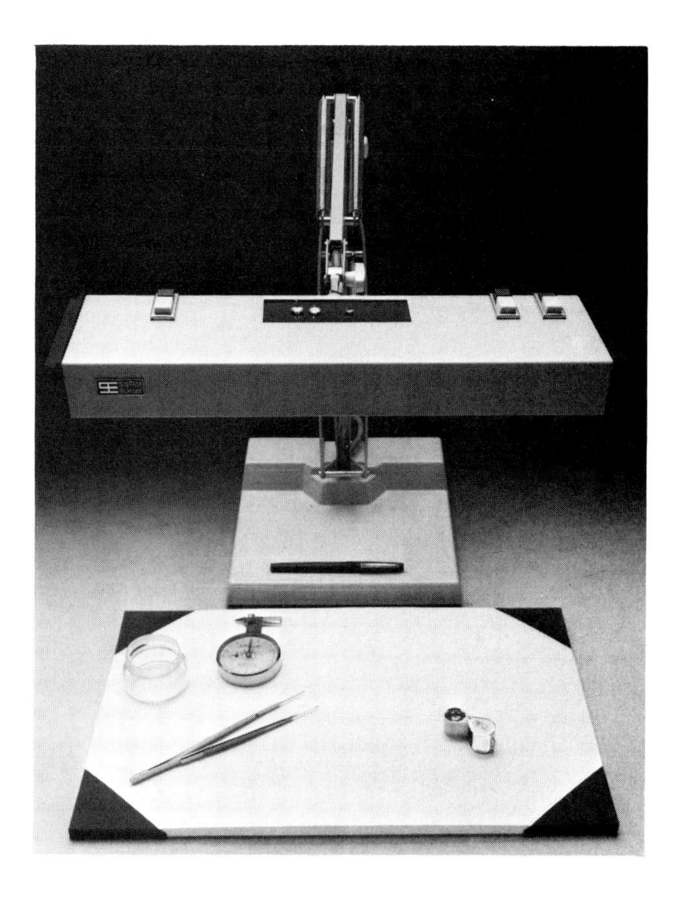

*Figure 7* A diamond grading lamp with a UV lamp window on top for checking fluorescence. (Eickhorst)

yellowish diamond appear whiter, and this is taken into account when grading strongly fluorescing stones. Master stones for comparison grading are selected to indicate the bottom limit of each grade. **Table 1** shows the relationship between the various national grading systems and the international CIBJO grades.

## Appendix C Clarity Grading Standards for Polished Diamonds

Clarity grading standards are based on the use of 10× magnification, although some systems which use microscope measuring graticules may use higher values with appropriate compensation. Clarity grading systems employing graticules normally incorporate 'weighting' factors to allow for the position of the flaw or inclusion within the stone, and to compensate for its opacity or transparency. **Table 2** shows the relationship between the various national grading systems and the international CIBJO grades. **Table 3** indicates the size and position of inclusions associated with the UK grades, **Table 4** indicates the CIBJO clarity grading standards.

**Table 2** Clarity grading standards for polished diamonds

| *UK* | *RAL* | *Scan DN* | *GIA* | *Belgium* | *CIBJO* |
|---|---|---|---|---|---|
| Flawless | IF | FL<br>IF | FL | IF | Loupe-<br>clean |
| VVS | VVS | VVSI 1<br>VVSI 2 | VVSI 1<br>VVSI 2 | VVS | VVS 1<br>VVS 2 |
| VS | VS | VSI 1<br>VSI 2 | VSI 1<br>VSI 2 | VS | VS 1<br>VS 2 |
| SI | SI | SI 1<br>SI 2 | SI 1<br>SI 2 | SI | SI |
| 1st PK | PK 1 | PK 1 | I 1 | | PI |
| 2nd PK | PK 2 | PK 2 | I 2 | | PII |
| 3rd PK | PK 3 | PK 3 | I 3 | | PIII |
| Spotted | | | | | |
| Heavily<br>Spotted | | | | | |
| Rejection | | | | | |

**Table 3** UK clarity grading standards (10× magnification)

| | |
|---|---|
| Flawless | Clean Stone |
| VVS | Very fine white or black spots, not central |
| VS | Fine white or black spots, not central |
| SI | Small inclusions, some central |
| 1st PK | Black or white spots, seen with difficulty, mainly central |
| 2nd PK<br>3rd PK | Several white or black spots, easily seen — can be central in 3rd PK |
| Spotted<br>Heavily Spotted<br>Rejection | Obvious large inclusions, cracks, etc. |

**Table 4** CIBJO clarity grading standards (10× magnification)

| | |
|---|---|
| Loupe-clean | A diamond is classified as loupe-clean if it is completely transparent and free from visible inclusions |
| VVS (VVS 1, VVS 2) | Very, very small inclusion(s) which are hard to find with 10× loupe |
| VS (VS 1, VS 2) | Very small inclusion(s) which can just be found with a 10× loupe |
| SI | Small inclusion(s), easy to find with a 10× loupe, but not seen with the naked eye through the crown facets |
| PI | Inclusion(s) immediately evident with a 10× loupe, but difficult to find with the naked eye through the crown facets. Not impairing the brilliancy |
| PII | Large and/or numerous inclusion(s), easily visible to the naked eye through the crown facets, and which slightly reduce the brilliance of the diamond |
| PIII | Large and/or numerous inclusion(s), very easily visible with the naked eye through the crown facets, and which reduce the brilliancy of the diamond |

Note: Sub-grades VVS 1, VVS 2, VS 1, VS 2 are used only for stones of 0.47 carats and larger.

## Appendix D Sorting Standards for Rough Gem Diamonds

1. **Colour classification for stones above 2 carats**
   Extra collection (top colour)
   Collection
   Extra Special
   Blue
   Fine
   White

2. **Colour classification for stones below 2 carats**
   Collection (top colour)
   1st Colour
   2nd Colour

3. **Shape categories**
   Stones (unbroken octahedra)
   Shapes (distorted but unbroken octahedra)
   Cleavages (broken crystals)
   Macles (twinned diamonds — usually triangular)
   Flats
   Note: under 2 carats, stones and shapes are called melée, and cleavages are called chips.

4. **Quality categories** (equivalent to clarity in polished stones)
   Over 2 carats, stones and shapes are divided into five qualities; cleavages, macles and flats are divided into four qualities. Under 2 carats, melée are divided into four qualities (finest, fine, dark, black); chips, macles and flats are divided into two qualities (fine and 'chips/macles/flats').

## Appendix E Stone Papers

Stone papers are manufactured in several sizes, the most popular being the No. 2 paper which, when folded, measures 50 × 100 mm, and can comfortably hold up to 50 stones in the one carat size range. Stone papers are usually supplied with an inner tissue lining to provide further protection for the contents, and these liners are sometimes coloured to provide an appropriate background for colourless or coloured gems. *Figure 8* gives the dimensions and folding sequence for making a No. 2 stone paper.

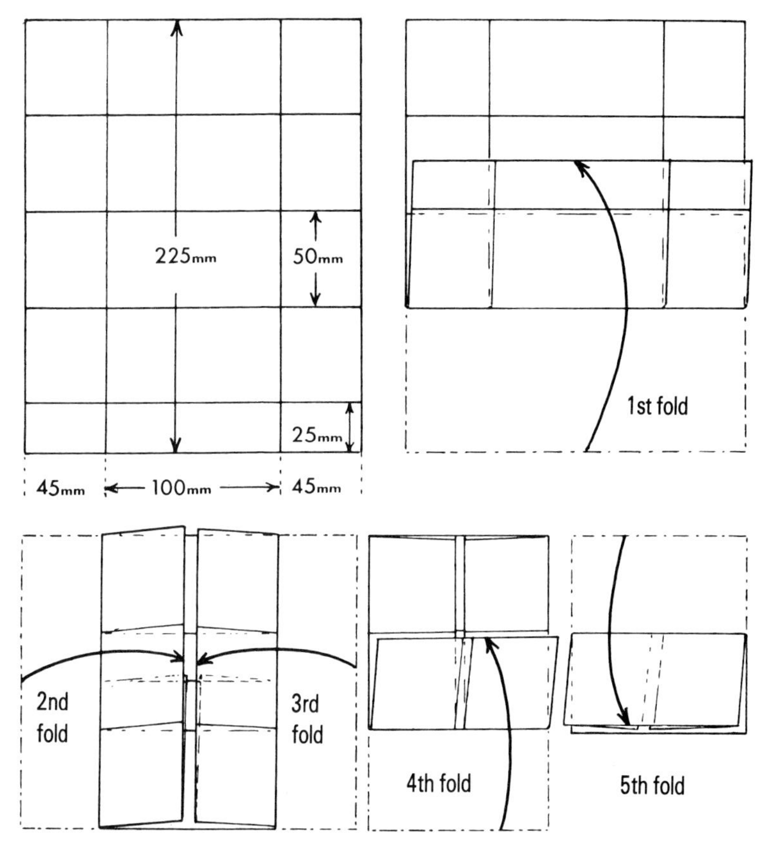


*Figure 8* Dimensions and folding sequence for making a No. 2 size stone paper.

## Appendix F Dispersion

The dispersion of white light into its spectral colours as it passes through a gemstone produces the multi-coloured flashes of light known as 'fire' when the gemstone or the light source is moved relative to the observer. This effect is seen most clearly in colourless gems, particularly where these have a high value of dispersion (e.g. diamond and some of the diamond simulants). The dispersion of a gemstone is measured as the difference between its refractive indices at the B and G Fraunhofer wavelengths (i.e. at 687 nm and 430.8 nm). **Table 5** lists the values for those principal gemstones whose dispersion is 0.02 and above.

**Table 5** Principle gemstones whose dispersion is 0.02 and above

| *Gemstone* | *Dispersion* | *Gemstone* | *Dispersion* |
|---|---|---|---|
| Almandine garnet | 0.027 | Peridot | 0.020 |
| Benitoite | 0.044 | Pyrope garnet | 0.022 |
| Cassiterite | 0.071 | Rutile | 0.280 |
| Cubic moissanite | 0.044 | Smithsonite | 0.031 † |
| Cubic zirconium oxide | 0.065 | Spessartite garnet | 0.027 |
| Demantoid garnet | 0.057 | Sphene | 0.051 |
| Diamond | 0.044 | Spinel | 0.020 |
| Dioptase | 0.036 † | Strontium titanate | 0.190 |
| Epidote | 0.030 | Yttralox | 0.039 |
| Flint glass | 0.040* | Yttrium aluminate | 0.028 |
| Gadolinium gallium garnet | 0.045 | Yttrium aluminium garnet | 0.028 |
| Hessonite garnet | 0.027 | Yttrium oxide | 0.050 |
| Kyanite | 0.020 | Zinc blende | 0.156 |
| Lithium niobate | 0.120 | Zircon | 0.039 |
| Lithium tantalate | 0.087 | | |

* Mean value.
† Maximum value.

## Appendix G Units of Measurement

### Weight

The standard international (SI) unit of weight is the kilogram (kg). The most frequently used sub-divisions are the gram and the milligram.

1 kilogram = 1000 grams
1 gram = 1000 milligrams
= 0.03527 ounce Avoir (1 ounce Avoir = 28.349 grams)
= 0.03215 ounce Troy (1 ounce Troy = 31.103 grams)

For gemstone weighing, the standard unit is the metric carat.

1 carat = 0.2 gram (1 gram = 5 carats)
= 0.007055 ounce Avoir (1 ounce Avoir = 141.747 carats)
= 0.006430 ounce Troy (1 ounce Troy = 155.517 carats)

For pearl weighing, the standard unit is the grain.

1 grain = 0.25 carats (1 carat = 4 grains)

*Note:* The weight of small rough diamonds is sometimes expressed in grains (e.g. a 1.0 carat stone may be called a 'four grainer').

Polished diamonds under 1.0 carat in weight are measured in points.

1 point = 0.01 carat (1 carat = 100 points)

**Length**

The standard international (SI) unit for the measurement of length is the metre (m). The most frequently used sub-divisions are the centimetre (cm), millimetre (mm), micrometre ($\mu$m), previously called 'micron') and nanometre (nm).

$$1 \text{ m} = 100 \text{ cm}$$
$$1 \text{ cm} = 10 \text{ mm} = 10^{-2} \text{ m}$$
$$1 \text{ mm} = 1000\ \mu\text{m} = 10^{-3} \text{ m}$$
$$1\ \mu\text{m} = 1000 \text{ nm} = 10^{-6} \text{ m}$$
$$1 \text{ nm} = 10^{-9} \text{ m}$$

**Wavelength**

The standard international (SI) unit for the measurement of light wavelengths is the nanometre (nm).

$1 \text{ nm} = 10^{-9} \text{ m}$ (one thousand-millionth of a metre)

1 nm = 10 Å (ångstrom units)

Light wavelengths are also sometimes given in microns ($\mu$m)

$$1\ \mu\text{m} = 1000 \text{ nm} = 10^{-6} \text{ m}$$

$$\text{Wavenumber} = \frac{10\,000\,000}{\text{wavelength in nm}}$$

**Temperature**

The standard international (SI) unit for temperature is the kelvin (K), and the degree Celsius (°C), both of which span equal temperature intervals. The kelvin is used mainly for thermodynamic work and represents an *absolute* temperature.

0 °C = 273.16 K

0 K = -273.16 °C (the temperature at which no more internal energy can be extracted from an object, and at which the volume of a gas is theoretically zero).

**Appendix H** Table of Elements

| *Element* | *Symbol* | *Atomic Number* | *Atomic Weight* | *Valency* | *Specific Gravity* |
|---|---|---|---|---|---|
| Actinium | Ac | 89 | 227.0 | — | — |
| Aluminium | Al | 13 | 26.97 | 3 | 2.6 |
| Americum | Am | 95 | 243.0** | — | — |
| Antimony | Sb | 51 | 121.76 | 3, 5 | 6.6 |
| Argon | A | 18 | 39.944 | 0 | — |
| Arsenic | As | 33 | 74.91 | 3, 5 | 5.72 |
| Astatine | At | 85 | 210.0** | — | — |
| Barium | Ba | 56 | 137.36 | 2 | 3.8 |
| Berkelium | Bk | 97 | 247.0** | — | — |
| Beryllium | Be | 4 | 9.02 | 2 | 1.83 |
| Bismuth | Bi | 83 | 209.0 | 3, 5 | 9.8 |
| Boron | B | 5 | 10.82 | 3 | 2.5 |
| Bromine | Br | 35 | 79.916 | 1 | 3.1 |
| Cadmium | Cd | 48 | 112.41 | 2 | 8.64 |
| Caesium | Cs | 55 | 132.91 | 1 | 1.87 |
| Calcium | Ca | 20 | 40.08 | 2 | 1.54 |
| Californium | Cf | 98 | 249.0** | — | — |
| Carbon | C | 6 | 12.01 | 4 | 1.9-2.3† |
| Cerium* | Ce | 58 | 140.13 | 3, 4 | 6.9 |
| Chlorine | Cl | 17 | 35.457 | 1 | — |
| Chromium | Cr | 24 | 52.01 | 3, 6 | 7.1 |
| Cobalt | Co | 27 | 58.94 | 2, 3 | 8.6 |
| Copper | Cu | 29 | 63.57 | 1, 2 | 8.93 |
| Curium | Cm | 96 | 248.0** | — | — |
| Dysprosium* | Dy | 66 | 162.46 | 3 | — |
| Einsteinium | Es | 99 | 254.0** | — | — |
| Erbium* | Er | 68 | 167.64 | 3 | 4.8 |
| Europium* | Eu | 63 | 152.0 | 3 | — |
| Fermium | Fm | 100 | 253.0** | — | — |
| Francium | Fr | 87 | 223.0** | — | — |
| Gadolinium* | Gd | 64 | 156.9 | 3 | 5.9 |
| Gallium | Ga | 31 | 69.72 | 3 | 5.95 |
| Germanium | Ge | 32 | 72.6 | 4 | 5.47 |
| Gold | Au | 79 | 197.2 | 1, 3 | 19.3 |
| Hafnium | Hf | 72 | 178.6 | — | — |
| Helium | He | 2 | 4.002 | 0 | — |
| Holium* | Ho | 67 | 163.5 | 3 | — |
| Hydrogen | H | 1 | 1.0078 | 1 | — |
| Indium | In | 49 | 114.76 | 3 | 7.3 |
| Iodine | I | 53 | 126.92 | 1 | 4.95 |
| Iridium | Ir | 77 | 193.1 | 4 | 22.4 |
| Iron | Fe | 26 | 55.84 | 2, 3 | 7.87 |
| Krypton | Kr | 36 | 83.7 | 0 | — |
| Lanthanum* | La | 57 | 138.92 | 3 | 6.12 |

**Appendix H** Table of Elements - *contd.*

| *Element* | *Symbol* | *Atomic Number* | *Atomic Weight* | *Valency* | *Specific Gravity* |
|---|---|---|---|---|---|
| Lawrencium | Lw | 103 | 257.0** | — | — |
| Lead | Pb | 82 | 208.0 | 2, 4 | 11.34 |
| Lithium | Li | 3 | 6.94 | 1 | 0.53 |
| Lutecium* | Lu | 71 | 175.0 | 3 | — |
| Magnesium | Mg | 12 | 24.32 | 2 | 1.74 |
| Manganese | Mn | 25 | 54.93 | 2, 3 | 7.4 |
| Mendelevium | Md | 101 | 256.0** | — | — |
| Mercury | Hg | 80 | 200.61 | 1, 2 | 13.59 |
| Molybdenum | Mo | 42 | 96.0 | 4, 6 | 10.0 |
| Neodymium* | Nd | 60 | 144.27 | 3 | 6.96 |
| Neon | Ne | 10 | 20.183 | 0 | — |
| Neptunium | Np | 93 | 237.0** | — | — |
| Nickel | Ni | 28 | 58.69 | 2, 3 | 8.8 |
| Niobium ‡ | Nb | 41 | 92.91 | 5 | 8.5 |
| Nitrogen | N | 7 | 14.008 | 3, 5 | — |
| Nobelium | No | 102 | 253.0** | — | — |
| Osmium | Os | 76 | 191.5 | 6 | 22.5 |
| Oxygen | O | 8 | 16.0 | 2 | — |
| Palladium | Pd | 46 | 106.7 | 2, 4 | 11.4 |
| Phosphorus | P | 15 | 31.02 | 3, 5 | 1.8†† |
| Platinum | Pt | 78 | 195.23 | 2, 4 | 21.4 |
| Plutonium | Pu | 94 | 242.0** | — | — |
| Polonium | Po | 84 | 210.0 | — | — |
| Potassium | K | 19 | 39.096 | 1 | 0.86 |
| Praseodymium* | Pr | 59 | 140.92 | 3 | 6.48 |
| Promethium* | Pm | 61 | 146.0** | — | — |
| Protactinium | Pa | 91 | 231.0 | — | — |
| Radium | Ra | 88 | 226.0 | 2 | — |
| Radon | Rn | 86 | 222.0 | — | — |
| Rhenium | Re | 75 | 186.31 | — | 21.2 |
| Rhodium | Rh | 45 | 102.91 | 3 | 12.44 |
| Rubidium | Rb | 37 | 85.48 | 1 | 1.53 |
| Ruthenium | Ru | 44 | 101.7 | 6, 8 | 12.3 |
| Samarium* | Sm | 62 | 150.43 | 3 | 7.8 |
| Scandium | Sc | 21 | 45.10 | 3 | — |
| Selenium | Se | 34 | 78.96 | 2 | 4.8 |
| Silicon | Si | 14 | 28.06 | 4 | 2.3 |
| Silver | Ag | 47 | 107.88 | 1 | 10.5 |
| Sodium | Na | 11 | 22.997 | 1 | 0.97 |
| Strontium | Sr | 38 | 87.63 | 2 | 2.54 |
| Sulphur | S | 16 | 32.06 | 2, 4 | 2.07 |
| Tantalum | Ta | 73 | 180.88 | 5 | 16.6 |
| Technetium | Tc | 43 | 97.88** | — | — |
| Tellurium | Te | 52 | 127.61 | 2 | 6.25 |

**Appendix H** Table of Elements - *contd.*

| *Element* | *Symbol* | *Atomic Number* | *Atomic Weight* | *Valency* | *Specific Gravity* |
|---|---|---|---|---|---|
| Terbium* | Tb | 65 | 159.2 | 3 | — |
| Thallium | Tl | 81 | 205.0 | 1 | 11.9 |
| Thorium | Th | 90 | 232.0 | 4 | 11.3 |
| Thulium* | Tm | 69 | 169.4 | 3 | — |
| Tin | Sn | 50 | 118.7 | 2, 4 | 7.28 |
| Titanium | Ti | 22 | 47.9 | 4 | 4.5 |
| Tungsten | W | 74 | 184.0 | 6 | 19.3 |
| Uranium | U | 92 | 238.0 | 4, 6 | 18.7 |
| Vanadium | V | 23 | 50.95 | 3, 5 | 6.0 |
| Xenon | Xe | 54 | 131.3 | 0 | — |
| Ytterbium* | Yb | 70 | 173.04 | 3 | 5.5 |
| Yttrium | Y | 39 | 88.92 | 3 | 3.8 |
| Zinc | Zn | 30 | 65.38 | 2 | 7.1 |
| Zirconium | Zr | 40 | 91.22 | 4 | 6.5 |

* One of the rare-earths in the lanthanum group.
** Isotope with the longest known half-life.
† Graphite
‡ Formerly called columbium (Cb)
†† Yellow (red = 2.2)

**Appendix I** Table of fluorescence of principal gemstones

| *Gemstone* | *LW UV* | *SW UV* | *X-rays* |
|---|---|---|---|
| Alexandrite | Red | Red | Red (faint) |
| Apatite (yellow) | Lilac | Lilac/pink | Pinkish-white, pinkish-yellow, mauve |
| Apatite (blue) | Blue | Blue | Faint pinkish-straw, faint blue |
| Cubic zirconium oxide (stabilized with $Y_2O_3$) | — | Greenish-yellow (faint) | Distinct whitish |
| Cubic zirconium oxide (stabilized with CaO) | — | Yellow (distinct) | Distinct whitish |
| Danburite | Sky-blue | Blue | Violet |
| Diamond (only 10–15% of diamonds luminesce under UV) | Blue*, green, yellow, red or pink | Same colours, but less frequent | White, yellow, blue (no phosphorescence) |
| Emerald (natural) | Red (some) | Red (some) | Red |
| Emerald (synthetic) | Red (strong) | Red (strong) | Red |

**Appendix I** Table of Fluorescent of Principal Gemstones – *contd.*

| *Gemstone* | *LW UV* | *SW UV* | *X-rays* |
|---|---|---|---|
| Fire opal | Brownish-red | — | — |
| Fluorspar | Violet (strong) | Violet (weak) | Blue, violet |
| GGG (gadolinium gallium garnet) | Pale Yellow (weak) | Orange | Lilac |
| Kunzite | Orange | — | Orange |
| Lapis lazuli | Orange spots and streaks | — | — |
| Massive grossular garnet | — | — | Orange |
| Opal (natural) | Random. White, bluish, brownish or greenish (weak), or no fluorescence** | | Green (some) |
| Opal (Gilson synthetic) | Random | Dusty-green | — |
| Paste | — | Pale blue or green | Green, blue (some) |
| Ruby (natural and synthetic) | Red (strong in synthetic) | Red (strong in synthetic) | Red (synthetic shows phosphorescence) |
| Sapphire (white, natural) | Orange | Orange | Crimson |
| Sapphire (white, synthetic) | — | Deep blue (weak) | Orange, violet (some) |
| Sapphire (yellow, natural from Sri Lanka) | Yellow | — | Orange |
| Sapphire (yellow synthetic) | — | — | Violet (some) |
| Sapphire (orange synthetic) | Red (strong) | Red | Red with phosphorescence |
| Sapphire (blue natural) | pink (few) | — | Red |
| Sapphire (blue synthetic) | — | Greenish-blue | Blue |
| Scapolite | Yellow | Pink | White, orange, green, violet |
| Scheelite | — | Blue | Blue |
| Spinel (green, yellow, synthetic) | Green (strong) when coloured by manganese | Green | Red (green spinel), green (yellow spinel) |
| Spinel (blue synthetic) | Red | — | Red, blue |
| Spinel (blue natural) | — | — | — |
| Spinel (white, synthetic) | — | Blue/white (strong) | Green, blue (some) |
| Spinel (red, pink) | Red (strong) | Red (strong) | Red |
| Strontium Titanate | — | — | — |
| Topaz | Yellow, orange | — | Orange (some), green, blue |
| YAG (yttrium aluminium garnet) | Yellow | — | Yellow |
| Zircon | Yellow | Yellow | Yellow, blue, violet |

* Faint yellow phosphorescence (when in association with blue UV fluorescence, this is diagnostic for diamond).

** All colours may show a persistent green phosphorescence.

## **Appendix J** Table of principal Fraunhofer lines

| *Fraunhofer line* | *Wavelength (nm)* | *Element* | |
|---|---|---|---|
| A | 762.8 (deep red) | Oxygen | in the Earth's atmosphere |
| B | 686.7 (red) | Oxygen | |
| C | 656.3 (orange) | Hydrogen | elements in the Sun's chromosphere |
| $D_1$ | 589.6 (yellow) | Sodium | |
| $D_2$ | 589.0 (yellow) | Sodium | |
| E | 527.0 (green) | Iron | |
| $b_1$ | 518.4 | Magnesium | |
| $b_2$ | 517.3 | Magnesium | |
| $b_3$ | 516.9 | Iron | |
| $b_4$ | 516.7 | Magnesium | |
| F | 486.1 (blue-green) | Hydrogen | |
| G | 430.8 (blue) | Calcium | |
| H | 396.8 (violet) | Calcium | |
| K | 395.3 (violet) | Calcium | |

*Note:* The twin sodium lines $D_1$, $D_2$ (with a mean wavelength of 589.3 nm) are used as the standard source when specifying gemstone refractive indices. Dispersion is measured as the difference in refractive index at the B and G wavelengths.

## Appendix K
Constants of Principal Gemstones
(in alphabetical order of gemstones)

| Gemstone | Crystal System | Approx. R.I. | D.R. | Dispersion | S.G. | H. |
|---|---|---|---|---|---|---|
| Alexandrite – see Chrysoberyl | | | | | | |
| Almandine (Garnet) | Cubic | 1.77–1.81 | – | 0.027 | 3.8–4.2 | 7.5 |
| Amazonite (Feldspar) | Triclinic | 1.53–1.54 | 0.008 | 0.012 | 2.56 | 6.0 |
| Amber | Amorphous | 1.54 | – | – | 1.05–1.10 | 2.5 |
| Andalusite | Orthorhombic | 1.63–1.64 | 0.01 | 0.016 | 3.18 | 7.5 |
| Andradite (Demantoid, Melanite, Topazolite-Garnet) | Cubic | 1.89 | – | 0.057 | 3.85 | 6.5 |
| Apatite | Hexagonal | 1.63–1.64 | 0.003 | 0.013 | 3.18–3.22 | 5.0 |
| Aquamarine – see Beryl | | | | | | |
| Aventurine (Feldspar) | Triclinic | 1.53–1.54 | 0.009 | – | 2.64 | 6.0 |
| Benitoite | Trigonal | 1.76–1.80 | 0.047 | 0.04 | 3.65–3.68 | 6.5 |
| Beryl (Aquamarine, Emerald, Goshenite, Heliodor) | Hexagonal | 1.57–1.58 | 0.006 | 0.014 | 2.71 | 7.5–8.0 |
| Bowenite | Monoclinic | 1.56 | * | – | 2.58 | 4.0 |
| Chalcedony | Trigonal | 1.53–1.54 | * | – | 2.58–2.64 | 6.5 |
| Chrysoberyl (Alexandrite, Cymophane) | Orthorhombic | 1.74–1.75 | 0.009 | 0.014 | 3.72 | 8.5 |
| Coral | Trigonal | – | * | – | 2.6–2.7 | 3.5 |
| Cordierite – see Iolite | | | | | | |
| Corundum (Ruby, Sapphire) | Trigonal | 1.76–1.77 | 0.008 | 0.018 | 4.0 | 9.0 |
| Cubic zirconium oxide | Cubic | 2.16–2.18 | – | 0.06 | 5.7–6.0 | 8.5 |
| Cymophane – see Chrysoberyl | | | | | | |
| Danburite | Orthorhombic | 1.63–1.64 | 0.006 | 0.016 | 3.0 | 7.0 |
| Demantoid – see Andradite | | | | | | |

| Gemstone | Crystal System | Approx. R.I. | D.R. | Dispersion | S.G. | H. |
|---|---|---|---|---|---|---|
| Diamond | Cubic | 2.42 | – | 0.044 | 3.52 | 10.0 |
| Dichroite – see Iolite | | | | | | |
| Emerald – see Beryl | | | | | | |
| Enstatite | Orthorhombic | 1.66–1.67 | 0.01 | – | 3.25–3.30 | 5.5 |
| Feldspar – see Amazonite, Moonstone, Oligoclase, Sunstone | | | | | | |
| Fluorspar | Cubic | 1.43 | – | 0.007 | 3.18 | 4.0 |
| Garnet - see Almandine, Andradite, Grossular, Pyrope, Spessartite, Uvarovite | | | | | | |
| GGG | Cubic | 1.97 | – | 0.045 | 7.05 | 6.0 |
| Goshenite – see Beryl | | | | | | |
| Grossular (Hessonite-Garnet) | Cubic | 1.74 | – | 0.027 | 3.65 | 6.5 |
| Haematite | Trigonal | 2.94–3.22 | 0.28 | – | 4.9–5.3 | 5.5–6.5 |
| Heliodor – see Beryl | | | | | | |
| Hessonite – see Grossular | | | | | | |
| Hiddenite – see Spodumene | | | | | | |
| Idocrase | Tetragonal | 1.70–1.72 | 0.005 | 0.019 | 3.32–3.42 | 6.5 |
| Iolite (Cordierite, Dichroite) | Orthorhombic | 1.54–1.55 | 0.008 | 0.017 | 2.57–2.61 | 7.5 |
| Ivory (dentine) | Organic | 1.54 | – | – | 1.7–2.0 | 2.0–3.0 |
| Ivory (vegetable) | Amorphous | 1.54 | – | – | 1.38–1.54 | 2.5 |
| Jadeite | Monoclinic | 1.65–1.67 | * | – | 3.3 | 7.0 |
| Jet | Amorphous | 1.66 | – | – | 1.3 | 3.5 |
| Kornerupine | Orthorhombic | 1.67–1.68 | 0.013 | 0.018 | 3.28–3.35 | 6.5 |
| Kunzite – see Spodumene | | | | | | |
| Lapis Lazuli | | 1.50 | – | – | 2.8 | 5.5 |
| Lithium Niobate | Trigonal | 2.21–2.30 | 0.09 | 0.120 | 4.64 | 5.5 |
| Malachite | Monoclinic | 1.66–1.91 | 0.25 | – | 3.8 | 4.0 |
| Melanite – see Andradite | | | | | | |
| Moldavite | Amorphous | 1.50 | – | – | 2.53 | 5.5 |

| Gemstone | Crystal System | Approx. R.I. | D.R. | Dispersion | S.G. | H. |
|---|---|---|---|---|---|---|
| Moonstone – see Orthoclase | | | | | | |
| Morganite (Beryl) | Hexagonal | 1.58–1.59 | 0.008 | 0.014 | 2.85 | 7.5–8.0 |
| Nephrite | Monoclinic | 1.61 | * | – | 3.0 | 6.0 |
| Obsidian | Amorphous | 1.50 | – | – | 2.4 | 5.0 |
| Oligoclase (Feldspar) | Triclinic | 1.53–1.54 | 0.007 | – | 2.64 | 6.0 |
| Opal | Amorphous | 1.45 | – | – | 2.1 | 6.0 |
| Orthoclase (Feldspar) | Monoclinic | 1.52–1.53 | 0.006 | – | 2.57 | 6.0 |
| Pearl | Orthorhombic | 1.52–1.66 | – | – | 2.71–2.74 | 3.5–4.0 |
| Peridot | Orthorhombic | 1.65–1.69 | 0.038 | 0.02 | 3.34 | 6.5 |
| Phenakite | Trigonal | 1.65–1.67 | 0.016 | 0.015 | 2.95–2.97 | 7.5 |
| Pyrite | Cubic | – | – | – | 4.84–5.10 | 6.5 |
| Pyrope (Garnet) | Cubic | 1.75–1.77 | – | 0.022 | 3.7–3.8 | 7.5 |
| Quartz | Trigonal | 1.54–1.55 | 0.009 | 0.013 | 2.65 | 7.0 |
| Rhodonite | Triclinic | 1.73–1.74 | 0.014 | – | 3.6–3.7 | 6.0 |
| Rhodochrosite | Trigonal | 1.60–1.82 | 0.22 | – | 3.5–3.6 | 4.0 |
| Ruby – see Corundum | | | | | | |
| Rutile | Tetragonal | 2.61–2.90 | 0.287 | 0.28 | 4.2–4.3 | 6.5 |
| Sapphire – see Corundum | | | | | | |
| Scapolite (blue) | Tetragonal | 1.54–1.55 | 0.009 | 0.017 | 2.60–2.71 | 6.0 |
| Scapolite (pink, yellow) | Tetragonal | 1.56–1.58 | 0.02 | 0.017 | 2.60–2.71 | 6.0 |
| Sinhalite | Orthorhombic | 1.67–1.71 | 0.038 | 0.018 | 3.48 | 6.5 |
| Smithsonite | Trigonal | 1.62–1.85 | 0.23 | – | 4.30 | 5.0 |
| Soapstone – see Steatite | | | | | | |
| Sodalite | Cubic | 1.48 | – | – | 2.28 | 5.5–6.0 |
| Spessartite (Garnet) | Cubic | 1.80 | – | 0.027 | 4.16 | 7.0 |
| Sphene – see Titanite | | | | | | |
| Spinel (natural) | Cubic | 1.717 | – | 0.020 | 3.60 | 8.0 |
| Spinel (synthetic) | Cubic | 1.727 | – | 0.020 | 3.64 | 8.0 |
| Spodumene (Hiddenite, Kunzite) | Monoclinic | 1.66–1.68 | 0.015 | 0.017 | 3.18 | 7.0 |
| Steatite (Soapstone) | Monoclinic | 1.54–1.59 | 0.05 | – | 2.5–2.8 | 1.0+ |

| Gemstone | Crystal System | Approx. R.I. | D.R. | Dispersion | S.G. | H. |
|---|---|---|---|---|---|---|
| Strontium Titanate | Cubic | 2.41 | – | 0.19 | 5.13 | 5.5 |
| Sunstone (Feldspar) | Triclinic | 1.53–1.54 | 0.009 | – | 2.64 | 6.0 |
| Tanzanite – see Zoisite | | | | | | |
| Titanite (Sphene) | Monoclinic | 1.89–2.02 | 0.13 | 0.051 | 3.53 | 5.5 |
| Topaz (white/blue) | Orthorhombic | 1.61–1.62 | 0.01 | 0.014 | 3.56 | 8.0 |
| Topaz (brown/yellow) | Orthorhombic | 1.63–1.64 | 0.008 | 0.014 | 3.53 | 8.0 |
| Topazolite – see Andradite | | | | | | |
| Tourmaline | Trigonal | 1.62–1.64 | 0.018 | 0.017 | 3.01–3.11 | 7.0 |
| Turquoise | Triclinic | 1.61–1.65 | * | – | 2.6–2.8 | 6.0 |
| Uvarovite (Garnet) | Cubic | 1.87 | – | – | 3.77 | 7.5 |
| YAG | Cubic | 1.83 | – | 0.028 | 4.58 | 8.5 |
| Zoisite (Tanzanite – blue Zoisite) | Orthorhombic | 1.69–1.70 | 0.009 | – | 3.35 | 6.5 |
| Zircon (normal) | Tetragonal | 1.93–1.99 | 0.058 | 0.039 | 4.68 | 7.25 |
| Zircon (low) | Amorphous | 1.78–1.84 | – | – | 3.9–4.1 | 6.0 |
| Zirconia – see Cubic Zirconium Oxide) | | | | | | |

* Crypto-crystalline

# A More Christlike Way
# A More Beautiful Faith

Bradley Jersak

Published by Plain Truth Ministries
Pasadena, CA | www.ptm.org

**Bible Translations**

***NTE:*** Default New Testament references are from N.T. Wright, *The New Testament for Everyone* [also titled *The Kingdom New Testament: A Contemporary Translation*] (SPCK, 2011).

***DBH:*** David Bentley Hart, *The New Testament: A Translation* (Yale, 2018).

***HB:*** Default Old Testament references are from Robert Alter, The Hebrew Bible: A Translation with Commentary (Norton, 2019).

**Emphases:** All emphases throughout the book are the author's, including those in Scripture texts and cited material, unless otherwise indicated.

Printed in the United States

**ISBN: 978-1-889973-33-3**

Library of Congress Control Number: 2019907431

Jersak, Bradley Mark, 1964 —
A More Christlike Way: A More Beautiful Faith / Bradley Jersak
1. Religion — Christianity — Theology

Cover Photo: Brian Zahnd / Subject: Peri Zahnd
Cover Design: Giselle (Gigi) Delgado www.thisisgigisworld.com

**CWRpress**

An imprint of Plain Truth Ministries

**For Rev. Peter J. Bartel**

*Your faithfulness*
*in bearing the wounds of the Jesus Way*
*planted Christ in me.*

**And for Brian and Peri Zahnd**

*We all wear the same thorny crown*
*Soul to soul, our shadows roll*
*And I'll be with you when the deal goes down.*

## Endorsements

Brad Jersak is an accomplished theologian, thoroughly grounded in Scripture and Patristics, but in *A More Christlike Way* he also writes from decades of pastoral experience. This is what makes his sequel to *A More Christlike God* so compelling. We have academic theologians and seasoned pastors, but it's rare to find both so beautifully combined in a single person. *A More Christlike Way* is a book for our time and place in North America, where so much of what is called Christianity has been hijacked to serve agendas that are decidedly unChristlike. *A More Christlike Way* sets forth a vision for following Jesus that is in keeping with the kind of faith that first turned the world upside down two thousand years ago.

**Brian Zahnd**
Lead Pastor, Word of Life Church, St. Joseph, MO
Author of *Postcards from Babylon*

Nobody has taught me more about the character of God than Brad Jersak. Together, *A More Christlike God* and *A More Christlike Way* are nothing less than the theological, pastoral foundation for a brewing revolution. This is the clear, bold, defining articulation of the Jesus path we desperately need. In this apocalyptic time, when so many people have become rightly disillusioned with religion that is anything but Christlike, this book is revelatory. If your faith has been unraveling or "deconstructing"—here is the new construction on the other side.

**Jonathan Martin**
Lead Pastor, The Table OKC, "Son of a Preacher Man" podcast
Author of *How to Survive a Shipwreck* & *Prototype*

In *A More Christlike Way,* Brad Jersak invites the weary, angry, cynical, struggling, deconstructing, numb, overwhelmed ones into a way of faith that cuts through triumphalistic, ego-driven, striving religiosity to resurrect resilient hope in a living, loving, and life-transforming God.

Jersak's voice rings with the honest authenticity of a disciple who walks out what he seeks to teach. This book is no silver bullet to a richer, more meaningful faith life. Jersak has traversed the hills and valleys of faith for too long to offer such an empty promise.

Rather, if you have reached the end of your best efforts; if after discarding the trappings of religion you find yourself empty; if you feel lost in the meaninglessness of it all and overwhelmed by the chaotic, violent mess of the world, then this book might just be the invitation you're seeking to step into a faith that embraces the paradox of liberation and surrender, sets mercy and compassion as its compass, and teaches the practices that allow us to live into a more Christlike way.

**Dr. Wendy VanderWal Gritter**
Executive Director, Generous Space Ministries
Author of *Generous Spaciousness: Responding to Gay Christians in the Church*

If a college course were named *A More Christlike God* I might see it as "Recovery of the Faith 101" and accordingly, *A More Christlike Way* would be "Recovery of the Faith 201." Dr. Jersak takes on the deviations of polytheistic Christianity which present us with gods "masquerading under the Christian brand." His embrace of Eastern Christianity provides a different lens to Western readers, giving a means to see how what is canonical and acceptable in some expressions of the faith can be challenged by a longer-standing version, which opens a door for us to ask essential questions of ourselves. Such questioning is critical to our wellbeing because we might otherwise surrender to a system that constricts, preventing us from becoming as beautiful as we should. Or we might just give up on the Spirit altogether, which is unnecessary because, as Brad writes, "many of our wounds are inflicted by systems and individuals that identify as 'Christian.'"

**Rev. Dr. David N. Moore, Jr.**
Lead Pastor, New Covenant Worship Center, Santa Barbara, CA
Activist, educator and ecumenical teacher
Author of *Making America Great Again*

Brad Jersak's new book, *A More Christlike Way,* is a refreshing breath of theological air! I've seen Brad preach. It was an encouraging, challenging and happy experience, so was the reading of this book.

**David Hayward**
The NakedPastor
Author of *Questions are the Answer*

The Cross means no one else needs to die to make the world right again, not one more person. Instead, we become human as God is human by joining God in his death for the sake of all, for the sake of the world God makes and loves. This life of dying as God dies is a journey the first Christians were called "The Way." Brad Jersak is here your Sherpa, a reliable guide who has seen Love in the face of Jesus Christ, a fellow traveler in the twists and turns of this foolishness that Christians call wisdom. Don't put this book back on the shelf, don't leave home without it. Put in your pack, keep it close, and may your walk with God flourish.

**Fr. Kenneth Tanner**
Pastor, Church of the Holy Redeemer, Rochester Hills, MI

Brad describes his own humanity by exposing his fails, his faults and his fractures. Yet through these self-same cracks the light of the restorative God of love shines through. The theology is thorough, and I love the dialogue with contemporary themes and topics. Brad bridges the distance from ancient wisdom to Instagram posts and Facebook activists. This demonstrates how the feminine voice of the Spirit's song is heard across the eras. He comes into his own as he dismantles the strain of violence in our societies and hearts. His voice echoes the voice of the (hu)man. Brad shows us by his life, and particularly the tender portrayals of family pain, a more Christlike way. I want to be 'woke' but I want love more, and Brad is a wonderful example of how to be awake to God's love and woke in God's world by "locking our gaze, not on our performance, but on Jesus."

**Azariah France-Williams**
Black British priest and storyteller
Author, *Chains Shall He Break* (Summer 2020)

Even though we know Jesus said, "I am the way . . . ," still many of us are confused on what that means. Is it a verb, a practice, a rhythm, a path? *A More Christlike Way* shows us it's all of the above and more than we can even imagine. Brad Jersak is the kind of loving guide you want on this journey to the center of what it means to know and follow Jesus.

**Scott Erickson**
Artist/Performer/Author
Author of *Prayer: Forty Days of Practice*

Brad Jersak's book is a challenge to anyone who would like to lead a life shaped by Christ. It's not easy. As Jersak points out, the "Jesus" many Christians seem to revere is far removed from the actual Jesus we encounter in the Gospels. The biblical Jesus eats meals with people whom the "upright" avoid, is a threat to no one's life, waves no national flags, reaches out with love to enemies, calls on his followers to live lives shaped by the double helix of love of God and love of neighbor, and prefers to die rather than kill.

**Jim Forest**
Peace Activist, Orthodox Peace Fellowship
Author of *Loving Our Enemies: Reflections on the Hardest Commandment*

*A More Christlike Way* is a timely, loving, intelligent, disarmingly honest and challenging look at how we can live as Christ-followers in the complexities of the twenty-first century.

What fuels this excellent treatment of learning to walk the *Jesus Way* is Dr. Brad Jersak's deep passion for objective, intuitive experiential truth and an even deeper love for people.

He is a profound thinker and brilliant scholar with the heart of a shepherd who cares deeply for people. Not so he might bask in their adulation to prop up his identity or because he has some power-driven agenda to proselytize others to his beliefs, he simply and genuinely cares for others. I know from personal experience that Brad actually does "love God and his neighbor," which has become quite a rarity in the spreading wasteland of North American religiosity. Don't let your familiarity with Jesus' words inoculate you to their power and truth, turning them into a phrase that upon hearing feels like someone just tossed a nickel on the counter for a cheap, plastic trinket.

In *A More Christlike Way*, Brad has shared a way forward for us to walk. I intend to walk with him in the *Way*.

**John MacMurray**
Director, Northwest School of Theology
Author of *A Spiritual Evolution*

With Grace, Brad has captured how we live and move and have our being in the circle dance of Love with Jesus, the incarnate one. For too long, the body of Christ has stood on the bridge of the Way proclaiming, "O Bridge, O Bridge. We love you, Bridge. We give our lives to this bridge. Bridge, you are our everything, our very breath," while failing to actually live the *Way*. All bridges are a connection between two points. In *A More Christlike Way*, Brad offers us the *Way* of Christ as a bridge—a bridge to Jesus' *Abba*, our *Abba*, and a bridge connecting us (humanity) to one another. Masterfully compelling us to turn toward Love, Brad encourages us with a strong prophetic warning to examine the ways in which we ourselves are complicit of pharisaical tendencies. However, he does not leave us without hope. If there was ever a time in history that we needed a guide, the time is now. If there was ever a time in history that we needed wise sages saturated in the ways of Love, that time is now. Brad Jersak, in *A More Christlike Way*, has delivered a gift to the Bride from Spirit steeped in *Abba's* love. May all who read it answer the invitation that lies within its pages. This is the way, may we sojourn together on the path.

**Felicia Murrell**
Copy Editor
Author, *Truth Encounters*

I loved Brad Jersak's book, *A More Christlike God: A More Beautiful Gospel*. I assigned it to students and shared it with people in our church community. It seemed counter-intuitive to speak about the weakness of God but this truth unlocked key concepts that made a great deal of sense.

In this new book, *A More Christlike Way: A More Beautiful Faith*, Brad may have done something even more valuable. With wit, with story, with sparkling insight, he has held our understanding of how to live close to the fire of Jesus' words and example. This affects everything, from political discourse to a way of being in the world that welcomes *all* others into an appreciation of their full humanity. I think it will be very difficult to read this material and come away unchanged.

**Peter Fitch** (D. Min.)
Professor of Religious Studies
St. Stephen's University

Any new book by Brad Jersak is a reason to celebrate, but this one is exceptionally remarkable if for no other reason than it offers real answers to difficult questions that all of us wrestle with. In *A More Christlike Way*, Jersak doesn't play it safe but tackles some of the most profound mysteries of faith and discipleship to Christ imaginable. Like, how do we love our enemies, how do we forgive injustice and how do we incarnate Christ in our own lives? The answers aren't easy, but they are honest, vulnerable and profound. If you're serious about following Jesus and putting his Sermon on the Mount into practice, this is a great place to start.

**Keith Giles**
Author of *Jesus Unbound*

In *A More Christlike Way*, Brad Jersak takes us on a journey of deep, often soul-searching, honesty. He confronts many of our twenty-first century western church assumptions, instead pointing us to the radical (root) realities of living the Jesus Way. This book is for all those who so hunger for a more authentic and abundant life in Christ that they are willing to leave the known in order to follow Him—no matter where He takes them.

**Steve Stewart**
President and Founder, Impact Nations

*A More Christlike Way* is an invaluable gift, and Brad Jersak is a trusted voice for anyone who's serious about taking up the cross of self-giving love, evading deceptive pseudo-ways and lazy othering, filling the void after deconstruction with a cruciform life, and transcending political spectrum dualism by instead, "tracing imperfectly Jesus' blood-stained tracks" on a path that leads to radical participation in God's rule on earth. Heed the time-tested wisdom in these pages . . . listen with ears to hear. Jersak entices us away from the temptation of partisan squabbles and knocks us off our ego-supported soapboxes from which we declare everything that we're against and instead invites us into a more beautiful life-giving alternative—*the Christlike Way*.

**Dr. Andrew P. Klager**
Director, Institute for Religion, Peace and Justice
Author/Editor of *From Suffering to Solidarity*

Brad is not always right, but he's always kind. The sort of wise-kindness that results from learning to receive who we truly are as a gift. This book is for all of us who need twelve-step programs, a warm community, honesty and healing. More than detoxing or deconstructing damaging religion, Brad wants to take you hiking through the fresh air and rough terrain of grace-filled discipleship to 'a more Christ-like God.' I love this brother and read everything he writes.

**Jarrod McKenna**
Larrikin activist trainer, pastor, writer
Host of the InVerse podcast
Founding CEO of CommonGrace.org.au

Brad Jersak's *A More Christlike Way* stands up there with books like Hauerwas and Willimon's classic *Resident Aliens*—painting an alternative picture of what following Jesus Christ might look like in this world. With his conversational style, Brad is able to lead his readers through the "either/or" false dichotomies that can often tempt and trap us. Instead, we see fresh possibilities open up. Rather than pointing fingers at enemies—real or imagined—this book invites us to take a deeper look into our own hearts, and to discover that a more Christlike God has already preceded us there.

Each chapter concludes with "Thoughts and Prayers," which I read as a kind of prophetic challenge—to those who are weary with trite lip-service in the face of pain and tragedy, and to others who have severed or compartmentalized contemplation and action. As the twentieth-century monk Elder Thaddeus of Vitovnica taught, "our thoughts determine our lives." *A More Christlike Way* reorients us to St. Paul's advice—"Do not be conformed to this world but be transformed by the renewal of your mind" (Rom. 12:2), and then offers concrete ways to practice that kind of radical faith. I'd highly recommend this book for personal or parish reflection.

**Fr. Matthew Francis**
Parish Priest, Holy Apostles Orthodox Church
Chilliwack, British Columbia

# Contents

## Part III - A More Beautiful Faith: Seven Facets

# Foreword
## Wm. Paul Young

My friend Jamie says that most people don't actually know what they believe but it is easy to tell; simply watch how a person lives their life. How easy is it to get lost in our own rhetoric and begin to believe that what we say is truly what we believe. Another friend, Baxter, calls this 'self-referential incoherence.' Do you want to know what you believe? Ask those closest to you; your kids, your spouse, your co-workers, your employees, your neighbors, your enemies. Perhaps it is time to stop talking and learn to listen and love. Words, as they say, are cheap, but love costs. Fyodor Dostoyevsky said that hell is simply the refusal to love.

Sadly, there is often a gaping emptiness between our cosmetic identification with Jesus and the penetration of our words into our daily life. Will word ever become flesh? How easy to spout religious platitudes and cliché, convincing ourselves that we really mean what we say.

By your fruit, by your fruit, by your fruit!!!!!

When others look at how we treat people, how we respond to those around and in front of us, what do they see?

Don't be looking for your culture to change when you won't. Stop whining about how the world is going to hell in a handbasket and you refuse to love your enemy, let alone your neighbor, let alone your spouse. Perhaps it is time for each of us to enter a post-Christian reformation in which we embrace and trust the person of Jesus rather than Christianity, rather than Moses, rather than civil religion. Please stop telling me about your commitment to Jesus and then also pledge allegiance to the violence of the law of Moses. Please don't tell me about your love for Jesus and the way of Jesus and then harangue 'those people' with holy prophetic tones and self-righteous indignation.

When Moses and Elijah slipped through the thin veil from the invisible reality into our earthly realm to visit with Jesus on the Mount of Transfiguration (remember this is not a parable, but a fact), Peter the disciple immediately wanted to start three churches. Three distinct denominations based on the Law, the Prophets and Jesus. God silences Peter by stating clearly, "This is my son (Jesus)! Hear Him!" Jesus the Messiah, the Christ, and His way, transcend all the Law, all the Prophets, all of Christianity and all of any other religious, political or economic way.

It is the Human Way, for Jesus is the complete human being. As a child, I thought, no assumed, that we were all human beings. Then I was told (or discovered) that human beings could be separated into colors, a vast array of colors. And as beautiful a spectrum as this was, it became evident that it was also useful. Suddenly, my white became smaller but rather than allowing it to blend into the joyful kaleidoscope of humanity, some thought it should stand out. By observing the world, I was educated that there is a hierarchy of value based on color and in my world the best color was White. It was the most valuable, most important. And so was Male, and so was American (or Canadian, or European). It became clear that almost everyone did this, categorizing value based on presentation. It didn't matter that I had no choice in picking my color, or gender, or social status. One buys a ticket for the lottery and some benefit and some don't. White became 'us' and everyone else on the spectrum of color was 'them,' and then even whites who thought different, acted different or lived different than our White became suspect, another box marked 'those people.' Over time, my White became even smaller as we continued to break down the unity of humanity into tinier and tinier bite-sized bits. Gender, ethnicity, social class and status, religious affiliation or not, job description, notoriety, . . . hundreds of categories that could each again be divided into sub-categories. How foolish to believe that color or gender or social standing or political affiliation or nation-state membership or class or vocation is that from which we derive our identity, rather than our simple but magnificent humanity.

It is the hunt for isolation, fueled by shame and fear, pushing us to climb into the highest turret we can find in order to get away from 'them.' And sitting in our high tower 'we' look down and judge 'them'—even if 'we' is just 'me.' When you sit alone, you have no need to deal with your own issues.

And then I stumbled into the Kingdom of God, Jesus and his *Way*, in which none of this mattered. Oh, our judgments are something to be acutely aware of, a contagion that can infect the mind, ravage the soul and break the heart, especially as it tends to shatter relationships. But the Kingdom of God is not a system or an enterprise. It is certainly not Christianity or any other humanly constructed system. It is a Person. It is Jesus, the Messiah, the Christ. To begin to be free from the destructive need to divide and conquer is to finally become a child again, or perhaps for the first time.

Paul the Apostle, in that clarion cry as he wrote a letter to the Galatians, "There is neither slave nor free man, there is neither male nor female; for you are all one in Christ Jesus" (Gal. 3:28, NASB).

It should come as no surprise that in the New Testament, the Greek word for Accuser (as in the great satan, the accuser of God and humanity) is *katagoro.* We derive our English word 'category' or 'categorize' from this word. To put someone or a group of persons in a box and label that box is to participate in evil, in accusation, in dehumanization.

Recently, I was speaking at St. Henry's Catholic Church in Nashville, a wonderful community intent on the Jesus Way. Most of us carry, as part of our baggage, the need to categorize and dehumanize. It gives us self-justification and comfort for our judgments. Shortly after I began, a friend handed me a phone and I held it up to the microphone so everyone there could engage in my conversation. It was Terry King, who has been on Unit 2 (death row) for thirty-five years after killing another young man when he was eighteen.

For half an hour, Terry shared about his journey, about the Jesus Way, and about the painful confrontation between him and God over exactly this same issue. Although he had confessed it, Terry never truly faced what he had done until he realized that even he sat in the seat of judgment. He had created a box and labeled it 'pedophiles on death row' and judged that at least he was better than them.

As I listened to Terry, I watched the room and could see boxes begin to disintegrate. "Killer on Death Row." A real conversation humanized not only Terry, but others including the pedophiles on death row.

One day, I was listening to four of our grandchildren talking. They were trying to figure out who got which part of their looks from which parent or grandparent.

"I think Elle got her nose from mom. Houston, you got your ears from Grandpa and Ivy, your mouth came from Dad. And Maisy, your eyes... you got them from Grandma." At its core, it was a conversation about belonging, about the connection of our common humanity. Everyone belonged, if you looked. It didn't occur to any of the children that just because Maisy was adopted from Uganda, she wasn't part of us. Just look at her eyes, beautiful and brown, just like Grandma.

The book you hold in your hands, or are listening to, is not an invitation to become a Christian. It is not trying to get you to join a team in some cosmic contest. If you already identify as a Christian, it is a summons to transcend your religious indoctrination and enter the Kingdom of Jesus, into Jesus Himself and His Way. This is the Way of someone who is fully human and fully alive. At the deepest and most sacred place of my longings, this is what I want. I want this Way to flow like a living river from within me and into all my relationships and encounters. I want people to watch my life and say, "He doesn't have to say a word. He is one of those *Jesus Way* people."

# Read this First!

I usually ignore demands to "READ THIS FIRST!" Is it laziness, defiance or my preference for learning things the hard way? Maybe I just hear ALL CAPS as a drill sergeant barking commands in my head. But when I fail to read directions, it often doesn't end well.

A READ THIS FIRST! caution is doubly important in the case of *A More Christlike Way*. The Jesus Way is already risky, given that it involves taking up a cross (whatever that might mean). But wrongly understood or approached, such a venture may also trigger shame, instigate perfectionism, induce cynicism or other unintended side effects. The following directions serve to avert unnecessary misunderstandings that divert us from our pursuit of the Jesus Way. So please: READ THIS FIRST!

## IT'S ABOUT A (HU)MAN

*A More Christlike God* (2015) was about God—the God revealed perfectly in Jesus Christ. I explored how Christ unveiled the divine nature as cruciform and kenotic. Essentially, I recounted the central dogma of the New Testament and Patristic Christianity: that the true God of triune Love is completely Christlike. We will review that material in chapter one below.

This sequel is also a book about Jesus Christ. In *A More Christlike Way*, I will lay out how Jesus Christ of Nazareth, in his fully human nature, forged the path for a new and true humanity. We'll call it the *Jesus Way*.

This is literally crucial. When I refer to the *Jesus Way*, I am describing the life and faith of a man—the Jesus of the four Gospels—whose earthly sojourn embodied complete surrender to and trust in the God he called his *Abba* (the Aramaic equivalent to Papa).

Knowing that our subject matter is "the man Christ Jesus" matters greatly because herein, I will make no grandiose claims for any church or any individual disciple, alive or departed, least of all myself. In fact, Christianity's infamy is that our way and our faith have not been very Christlike. Observers attempting to retrace the *Jesus Way* from the path walked by those who identify as Christian would become hopelessly lost. They would stumble over all manner of obstacles to our beautiful faith, including me. Jesus alone created the *Jesus Way* and walked it perfectly.

Each of the attributes I will use to describe the *Jesus Way*—for example, radical forgiveness, radical hospitality, radical inclusion—describe Jesus, not me and not the church.

Here's the problem—Jesus said, "Take up your cross and follow me," which is to say, "Imitate me." Largely, we don't. And the harder we try, the more we fail. Miserably. A rule of thumb: *the deeper our religious zeal, the further we stray from Christ*—just ask Saul of Tarsus! No, we don't become Christlike by willing ourselves into radical discipleship.

Whatever forays we do make along the *Jesus Way* occur by locking our gaze on Jesus, not on our performance.

> We must look ahead to Jesus. He is the one who carved out the path for faith, and he's the one who brought it to completion (Heb. 12:2).

When "the Word became flesh," God's unexpected total identification with humanity opened a road, a path, a *Way* for all of us. That *Way* is Jesus' path back to *Abba's* house, our return home to paradise. By the indwelling grace of triune Love, those who surrender to *Abba* as Jesus did are thus empowered to walk as he walked. As Paul said,

> I have been crucified with the Messiah. I am, however, alive—but it isn't me any longer; it's the Messiah who lives in me. And the life I do still live in the flesh, I live within the faithfulness of the son of God, who loved me and gave himself for me (Gal. 2:19b-20).

We live, we walk, we imitate the *Jesus Way* "within the faithfulness of the son of God." I love that. Whatever steps we take into a more Christlike faith occur because Christ lives in us and we (somehow) live in him—in the grace of today.

I cannot overstate this. This book could be—but must not be—mistaken for a manifesto. It is not a set of ideals we strive after or laws we live up to. Believe me; straining to achieve Christlikeness through self-will only leads to despondency (failure and disappointment) or to pride (zealotry and hypocrisy). The *Jesus Way* is surely a struggle, but one engaged not by striving, but by surrender.

*A More Christlike Way* calls us to *a more beautiful faith* as we focus on Christ and allow his life to fill and transform ours. Just as he showed us the perfect image of *Abba,* now Jesus of Nazareth shows us the perfect image of humanity. The miracle and the mystery is that in beholding his glory—his cruciform (i.e. cross-shaped) image—his glory incrementally transfigures us toward something closer to his image. Do you see that? His work and his *Way* is transformation—our part is trusting enough to follow him on the *Jesus Walk.*

## NAMES, PRONOUNS & CAPITALIZATION

In this book, I will occasionally write about "God" simply because that's the norm. At some point, "God" as a generic noun became a name we use—following the way New Testament Jewish authors who avoided using the divine Name directly. But the word "God" doesn't say enough. In fact, I heard one podcaster say, "God is the most promiscuously used word in our vocabularies today." By its vagueness, the word "God" may be emptied of its riches or loaded with idolatries. I'd like to practice more precision in our God-talk.

In the New Testament, "God" sometimes refers to the Trinity (Father, Son and Spirit) or the *LORD* (the unspeakable Name) but more often, God specifies the Father, especially on Jesus' lips. When referring to God the Father, I will mainly follow Jesus by using the name he revealed: *Abba* (equivalent to our *Papa*). I italicize *Abba* to remind myself that this is an Aramaic word, presumably Christ's first language. I will even take the liberty of swapping in *Abba* for Father when citing my default NT translation (Wright's *New Testament for Everyone*). When referring to the Trinity, I will occasionally experiment with *Trinity* or *Love* as a personal name for the one triune godhead. If I say, *"Trinity* loves you," I haven't mistakenly deleted "the"—I'm reminding readers that our God is both three-in-one and personal.

Pronouns for God are always tricky. When speaking of *Trinity,* I will use the "singular *they"* (to emphasize God's unity-in-trinity). When speaking of Christ, I'll call him "he" to match the Gospels, though his glorified humanity no doubt transcends "maleness." When speaking of *Abba,* I will retain the traditional "he" for Father, recognizing that God's parenthood is not gender-specific. So too, I like to use *"she"* for the Spirit (following the Hebrew feminine pronoun for Spirit), recognizing "she" indicates grammatical, not sexual, gender.

Speaking of the Holy Spirit, I will also refer to her as *Grace* (capitalized) because in the Eastern tradition, *Grace* is not merely "unmerited favor"—*Grace* is defined as "the uncreated energies of the Holy Spirit." That is, *Grace* is God experienced directly as the indwelling, transforming presence of the Holy Spirit.

Aside from my Trinitarian name preferences—*Abba, Christ* and *Grace*—I'll capitalize other words to emphasize the divine persons. For example, you'll see me capitalize *"Basis"* when I'm referring to *Abba* as the *"Source"* of our salvation. Or sometimes, you'll see *"Voice"* in the upper case when I'm talking about Christ speaking to our hearts. *"Voice"* is like *"Word"* here but perhaps more personalized to the individual being addressed. The upper case B or V in both cases is your hint that I'm talking about one of the Persons of the Trinity, or even all three when I write *"triune Love."*

## JESUS OR CHRIST

In the New Testament, *Jesus* (lit. *the LORD saves*) was our Lord's given name—the name by which the Gospel characters and writers knew and referred to him. *Christ* was the Greek word that means *anointed one*. It's the word the NT authors used to translate the Hebrew *messiah*, which likewise means anointed one. The *anointed one* was associated with God's anointed kings, inaugurated by the prophets with the oil of the Spirit. Eventually, *Messiah* and *Christ* designated the divinely anointed King whom *the LORD* would send to redeem Israel to reestablish the Kingdom of God. In their understanding, the Christ would be God's king on earth, but not necessarily divine or even if so, certainly subordinate to *the LORD*.

When Jesus of Nazareth was revealed as *the Christ*, at first this meant he was indeed king of the Jews, although not at all the warrior king their prophets seemed to anticipate. With his death and resurrection, the apostles realized (a) that Jesus was not only the *Messiah of Israel* but also (b) *Savior of the world*. Moreover, they believed this was not merely a human ruler or even a semi-divine king, but that he shared one divine identity with *the LORD!* Hence, *our Lord Jesus Christ*.

While John the Theologian (author of the Gospel and epistles) and the church Fathers insist that Jesus is the Christ and that Jesus Christ is one divine-human person, the name Jesus would gradually emphasize his human nature and earthly ministry, while the name Christ drew attention to Christ as our crucified, risen, ascended and glorified Lord and to his divine nature.

Because of this, just calling him Jesus became suspect of Arianism—a denial of Jesus' deity. But don't worry, when I use it, I'm merely following the Gospel writers and believe with them that Jesus was fully divine at all times. In modern times, it's become popular to refer to Christ in ways that I suspect leave behind his humanity. Not me. I'm with the apostle John *("Jesus is the Christ")* and the creed *("I believe in one Lord Jesus Christ")*. With those sensibilities in mind, if I use Jesus and Christ interchangeably it is to emphasize the unity of the one Person, not to distinguish his two natures.

### CHRISTIANS VS. CHRIST-FOLLOWERS

The term "Christian" has morphed such that now I think it's fair to call Christianity a "major world religion" with so much history and baggage that it's difficult to identify as "Christian" without first asking, "What do you mean by that word?" In this book, I'll use Christian generally to speak of that religious tradition. When such disparate characters as Donald Trump and Lady Gaga both identify as "Christian," we probably need to be more specific. While registering my concern with what the label now connotes, I can say that Christianity is the tradition from which I come.

More helpful, I think, is the term *"Christ-follower,"* which I'll use for those who follow (or intend to) the *Jesus Way* as lived and taught by Jesus Christ. By that definition, not all Christians are Christ-followers and not all Christ-followers are Christians. Gandhi was a Hindu, not a Christian. But given his devotion to following the *Jesus Way* of the Sermon on the Mount, he was arguably a Christ-follower. So too are many millions of Muslims today. This doesn't mean that Muslims and Christians agree. It's just that many have come to love and follow Jesus, their orthodoxy notwithstanding.

I hope I'm a Christ-follower, though I'll leave that for Christ to decide. I identify with the *Jesus Way* for sure. I just know that it's a journey and I've not yet arrived.

## THOUGHTS AND PRAYERS

"Thoughts and prayers" are often offered as comfort to victims in the immediate aftermath of a tragedy. Politicians and media outlets post "thoughts and prayers" via press conferences and social media after a devastating hurricane or the latest mass shooting.

As a euphemism for willful inaction, "thoughts and prayers" ring hollow and even blasphemous, worthy of derision in countless, equally useless internet memes. "Thoughts and prayers" are now associated with the powerless god whose people intend to do nothing when instead, they should be the first responders of a seamless connection between the Christlike God (who came down to help) and a Christlike faith (people who go out to help).

In this book, each chapter will conclude with "thoughts and prayers" as a sardonic warning against platitudes and as a sincere call to embark on and embody the *Jesus Way*. These summaries are written for personal study and should serve as guides to group book studies.

# Part I

# Christlike God, Christlike Way

# Chapter 1

# A MORE CHRISTLIKE GOD

## THE GOD WE WORSHIP

*"We inevitably become like the God we worship."*

So I claimed in my previous volume, *A More Christlike God.* I proposed that the image of God we hold in our hearts and minds is of great consequence because, for better or worse, we will inevitably mimic the character and actions we attribute to our "God."

I wrap "God" in quotation marks to distinguish God as God truly is from "God" as we conceive God: our image, ideas, interpretations or notions of God. And I say "for better or worse" because mimicking the God we imagine can be ultimately good or horrifically destructive, depending on who we believe we're worshiping. Ironically, whether through childhood indoctrination, traumatic life experiences, cultural trends or our own temperament, the "God" we emulate is often a projection of ourselves on a cosmic scale.

In *A More Christlike God,* I began by identifying some of the false images of God that people of all faiths, including Christians, commonly worship. To review a sampling, we may devote ourselves to:

- **A retributive God** we both fear and hate: a punishing judge, wicked stepparent, vengeful warlord or "mighty smiter."
- **A distant God** we both pine for and resent: an absentee landlord, long lost lover or deadbeat dad.
- **A compliant God** we hope to manipulate: our vending machine of blessings, a genie in the lantern or the fairy godmother who grants wishes for the right incantation.
- **The Santa hybrid** who is legalistic, distant and malleable all at once: "You better watch out! Santa Claus is coming to town!"

Such images of God are fabricated idols—made-up gods. As theologian David Bentley Hart points out, Christianity has not been immune to these distortions:

> The God in whom the majority of Christians throughout history have professed to believe often seems evil, at least judging by the dreadful things we eventually say about him… The God of retribution that has been proclaimed by so much of Christian knowledge is really not and cannot possibly be the God of self-outpouring love revealed in Christ. If God is the creator of all, he is the Savior of all without fail who brings to himself all he has made.
>
> (David Bentley Hart, "Is Everyone Saved? Universalism and the Nature of Persons," *University of South Carolina* (Nov. 16, 2018).

Hart's assertion is that Christianity, despite Christ's beautiful revelation of his *Abba*, has a history of devolving into worship of retributive, counter-Christian gods. Paul warns Timothy:

> The time is coming, you see, when people won't tolerate healthy teaching. Their ears will start to itch, and they will collect for themselves teachers who will tell them what they want to hear. They will turn away from listening to the truth and will go after myths instead. —2 Timothy 4:3-4

These desired myths are not about an all-merciful, cruciform Lord—the resentful flesh wants a pound of flesh and the mythical gods to match. And while our faux-deities are imaginary, they are far from benign. Idolatry is especially toxic when actualized in the lives of "true believers" who appoint themselves as agents of their idols in the real world. False images shape their acolytes' lives so profoundly that we may even infer the true nature of a god through its disciples' behavior, religious practices, moral code and ethical system. As Jesus said, "By their fruit you will know them" (Matt. 7:20).

## GOD IS LOVE, EMBODIED IN CHRIST

In *A More Christlike God,* I called readers to abandon these idols in favor of the one and only perfect image of our triune God: Jesus Christ. I argued my case from some key biblical texts. Among the most significant:

- Nobody has ever seen God. The only-begotten God, who is intimately close to the father—he has brought him to light.
  —John 1:18

- "Have I been with you for such a long time, Philip," replied Jesus, "and still you don't know me? Anyone who has seen me has seen the father! How can you say, 'Show us the father'?" —John 14:9
- He is the shining reflection of God's own glory, the precise expression of his own very being. —Hebrews 1:3
- He is the image of God, the invisible one, the firstborn of all creation ... In him, you see, all the full measure of divinity has taken up bodily residence. —Colossians 1:15; 2:9

Faith, reason and revelation tell me that *if* there is a God—where *"if"* expresses faith, rather than doubt or certitude—that God is infinite, eternal, triune Love. If you want to know what God (*Abba*) is like, look at Jesus. Jesus Christ showed us, in person, that God is Love. Period. Christ is the definitive image of triune Love: he is the Word of, from and about God's essential nature. The sacred texts that purport to reveal our *Abba* must finally align with the living Word—*Abba*'s self-revelation in the person of Jesus Christ. The four Scriptures above boldly assert that:

- Christ alone perfectly reveals who *Abba* is and what he does;
- Christ is the living image and final authoritative Word of, from and about God;
- Christ *is* himself fully God revealed as fully Love.

*Trinity—Abba, Son and Spirit (Grace)*—are co-eternal love (although I know Christians who deny it). But what is love? I hold to the Apostle John's conviction (1 Jn. 3:16) that if we want to see what divine Love looks like, we must zoom in on the Cross. Throughout his whole life, but especially on the Cross, Jesus shows us that triune Love is *cruciform* (cross-shaped) and *kenotic* (self-giving).

In other words, on the Cross, Christ revealed the holy Trinity in clearest focus as self-giving, radically forgiving, co-suffering love. That claim comprises the central thesis of *A More Christlike God.*

## CHRISTIAN POLYTHEISM

So far, so good. But unresolved problems linger—difficulties that gave rise to this sequel. First, it was risky business for early Christians to hold up Christ as the image of the one true God. Their gospel confession demanded a rejection of Rome's pantheon of pagan gods and the emperors' demand for worship. And that meant persecution. But at least the choice was straightforward: *Jesus is Lord* and Jupiter is not. *Jesus is Lord* and Diana is not. *Jesus is Lord* and Caesar is not.

But today, how are we to navigate the problem of polytheism (the belief in many gods) *within* Christianity? Let's say there's still a militaristic god of war, a patriotic god of nationalism, a puritan god of moralism, a partisan god of politics, an erotic god of promiscuity, a charismatic god of power, a prosperity god of consumerism, etc. Have these gods somehow survived and thrived, masquerading under the Christian brand? How might these gods inhabit and even direct the accredited Christian establishment? Do we see them lurking in the multitude of Christian sects, promising unwarranted immunity from the corruption of Christendom? All they needed to do was co-opt the name of Jesus. Talk about identity theft! Is it possible for the church to worship idols under a thin veneer of Christianese without even knowing it?

The second problem concerns how Christians can become libelous, defaming Christ through our own corruption and misbehavior. Christ had declared, "This is how everybody will know that you are my disciples, if you have love for each other" (John 13:35). Yes, early Christianity could be very messy and divisive. Remember the Corinthians? Yet Tertullian (155-240 AD) noted how bewildered pagans said of us, "See how they love one another!" Or even just, "See how they love!"

In other words, folks not only knew that *Abba* is love by looking at the person of Jesus. They knew that *Abba* is love (and that Christ is alive) by looking at Christians. Christians were the new and living testament to *Abba's* love revealed in Christ well before a collection of New Testament books were written, collected and circulated. How would people know what Trinity is like? An outrageous claim but there it is: look at Jesus' people and you will know John is right: "God is love."

## A CHRISTLIKE COMMUNITY

The Christlike God was revealed or embodied in a divine human—Jesus Christ—who gathered a community of disciples. They followed him on the Christlike way—*the Jesus Way.* At least that was their reputation.

And today? Allow me to preface some disillusionment with some gracious observations. Over the last fifteen years, I have visited hundreds of Christian communities across many nations and cultures. What did I find? Primarily, I witnessed the collective messiness of broken but loving people stumbling forward through this corrupt world into God's *Grace.* I have encountered hospitality and experienced the prayers of the poor in spirit. I felt their love for me and witnessed their care for one another. I saw this especially among faithful, long-suffering believers who offer healing hugs to the broken, bake casseroles for the grieving and knit blankets for the poor. Many of these people have remained within dysfunctional fellowships over a lifetime because they simply refuse to abandon the only family they know. I honor them for that.

I've also spent countless hours hearing tragic stories of those who love Jesus but repeatedly endured spiritual abuse and emotional trauma in abusive religious systems until they couldn't take it anymore and limped away, unable to stomach one more tainted spoonful. Whether the poison was unChristlike leadership or congregational mistreatment (because leaders get abused too), they were *done.* Surviving with their sanity demanded their exit. And I'm quite sure some left too late. I honor them.

Whether you've stayed in fellowship for love's sake or left for sanity's sake, I cannot write you off with the broad brush of condemnation so easily directed at "those Christians" or "the Church." I know better because, unlike the cynics, I've met you face-to-face—tens of thousands of you. And I truly like almost all of you.

Allow me to rephrase that. We aren't perfect. We may even be quite screwed up. If we're honest, as Christ's representatives, we set the bar extremely low. At least compared to Jesus, right?

Here's my point: if the world can never live up to Christ's example of true humanity—if they only lived up to *your* flawed example—that would be incredibly good news. The world would be profoundly more wonderful. John Lennon's song "Imagine" would practically be reality. Do I sound ridiculous? Hear me out:

If everyone in the world were just like *you,* I'm reasonably sure there would be no more war, no more murder, no more rape, no more child sex-trafficking, no more abductions or slavery, no more terrorism, no more mass shootings, no more Ponzi schemes bilking seniors, no more religious extremists beheading people. Imagine! That would be a great start. I'd almost settle for such a utopian paradise. Look at how much better you already make the world!

I know you stumble. Who doesn't? That doesn't make you a hypocrite. Hypocrites are *not* those who fail to perfectly walk the *Jesus Way*. Hypocrites are only those who pretend they do. That's not you, is it?

Even with a botched image of God, the above might hold true of you. And your family. And your friends. And *maybe* your faith community. For some readers, that may be stretching it, but my point is that even minimal participation in the *Jesus Way* would make the world a *lot* better. If Christianity, activated and empowered by *Grace*, collectively followed the *Jesus Way—only as well as you do*—the world would see and know that God is love!

## AN UNCHRISTLIKE MOVEMENT

Now for the severe mercy of hard news. Be not afraid—I'm not intent on bulldozing the faith. We're going to move through the dark valley of disillusionment and deconstruction to a sunrise of faith breathtaking in its beauty. But if you've ever experienced the gut-punch of disillusionment, let's first face it thoroughly and pass through the darkness together.

Sadly, catastrophically, the movement called "Christianity" is old enough and large enough to have adopted *unChristlike images* of God and transpose them into *unChristlike ways* of being in our world. If we're honest, we are no longer famous for communicating God's love, much less demonstrating it. Today, Christianity is frequently associated with *being against*—we're best known for being unkind, judgmental and condemning. To many of our critics, we're the very worst humanity has to offer.

Yes, from the beginning, followers of Christ have been unfairly accused and grossly misrepresented: the "accuser of our family" will "slander you and persecute you and say all kinds of wicked things about you falsely because of Christ!" When that is the case, "Celebrate and rejoice: there's a great reward for you in heaven. That's how they persecuted the prophets who went before you" (Matt. 5:11-12). Many attacks against Christianity are disingenuous, unvarnished slander. I don't intend to join "ol' slew foot" in bearing false witness against the family of God.

On the other hand, we urgently need to ask at what point does our disastrous reputation move beyond a propaganda smear into an authentic demand for repentance? We need to recognize that the Christian faith is not being rejected for all those terrible things we don't do (war, murder, rape, etc.) but for becoming an ugly entity voicing what we all do (whenever we're unkind, judgmental, condemning, controlling, etc.). If we have the maturity to wade past the false charges to humbly hear the valid grievances—laying aside defensiveness, denial and religious ego—we can start to reconstruct the broken paths of *A More Christlike Way.*

## THE BREAKING POINT

With those lengthy but essential caveats, I'll introduce you to a friend of mine. Jeff was a Christian. Our charismatic friends would say he was "prophetic," by which they meant he was gifted with unusual discernment. He never played the "God told me" card, but he seemed to know people's hearts and to know God's heart and had wise things to say about how the two connect.

Today, Jeff no longer identifies as a Christian. I wanted to understand why. His *why* is something I keep with me because he may have lost his faith but I doubt he's lost his gift. I believe he still sees to the heart of the matter and has a critical message for Christian leaders. As long as I presume to be a spokesman for Christian faith, I need this warning before my eyes:

> Christianity has sold its moral birthright for the porridge of political power, returning for a new bowl each election. The bill is due. For me, the breaking point came when I realized compassion for the poor had been sacrificed for party orthodoxy, empathy mocked, suspect. A new generation of Christians watch the kings of Evangelicalism set up idols in the temple, promising rain as the priests are slaughtered. It's ugly and blatant and craven and sad.
>
> I am no longer a Christian. But at its best the faith is a beacon

> and a haven for the wounded. At its worst, it is a cudgel in the hands of the power-hungry, just like any other totalizing belief. "March this way! God says you must."
>
> Faith, truth, love aside: pragmatic leaders must understand that all followers have their breaking point. Don't push your flock too far. Every sincere fundamentalist is just one shock, one sobering moment of late-night soul-searching from deciding it is *all* a lie. Reeds can bend to the wind, but oaks fall. Remember this when you decide how you will police the borders of your orthodoxy.
>
> *—Jeff E. (Facebook post)*

That was no bludgeon from the accuser. I sense in Jeff's words a sharp scalpel, devised to remove tumors from the body of Christ . . . if we'd willingly go under the knife of the Great Surgeon.

Some write off incisive messengers like Jeff as if he's the one having the "faith crisis." That's too easy for two reasons: first, the god he rejects is not the *Abba* of Jesus—it's little more than one of the religious idols I described earlier.

His apparent apostasy reminds me of the song *Dear God* by the band XTC. They ask God, "Did you make mankind after we made you? And the devil too!" The lyrical prayer concludes, "If there's one thing I don't believe in, it's you . . . dear God."

*Should we worry about Jeff?* I'm more worried about those who can't hear his truth. His journey recalls the insight of one of my heroines, the French philosopher-mystic Simone Weil: "There are two atheisms, of which one is a purification of our notion of God." Sounds about right.

More pressing, I believe, is a second cause to pause: *should I worry about me?* If I'm honest, I need not creep around looking for the offenders Jeff describes. I need only look inside. I am a Christian leader who knows all too well my own blunders into spiritual abuse. I live with the grief of knowing how I've wounded others' faith. I know the voice that says, "You're disqualified"—the bitter tears of Peter after denying Christ three times. I continue to serve one day at a time only by the *Grace* of God, the care of my mentors and the mercy of those who've forgiven me. No, this "spiritual father" cannot deflect Jeff's pointed charges.

The following indictment by my friend Jonathan Martin (a fellow minister who learned *How to Survive a Shipwreck)* may not apply to you. But he addresses my story for sure:

> I struggle to understand how, in this era, millennials are said to be the ones with the "faith crisis." If we hand our sons and daughters a faith exposed as misogynistic, racist, unconcerned about creation and the poor, they aren't wrong to leave it. We give sons and daughters a serpent instead of a fish, a stone instead of bread. They leave—we say it's due to "cultural relativism." Sons and daughters leave—we say, "they just don't honor spiritual authority." If we loved like fathers and mothers, we'd be honored as such.
>
> To quote Paul, "You have not many fathers." That's why many people leave the Church—they can't find spiritual fathers and mothers there. Sons and daughters of the church know they don't have fathers:
>
> - When authority reacts to them like wounded peers, rather than grieved parents;
> - When authority would rather defend their egos than hear the cries of their own;
> - When they come home to find the prodigal Father's unconditional embrace replaced with a lecture;
> - When authorities insist they listen to them, rather than listening themselves.
>
> *—Jonathan Martin (Instagram post)*

## DO YOU LOVE ME?

Guilty as charged. So, what's to be done? Part of me is inclined to wallow in regret for my past and in fear of my future, to dig a deep hole and crawl into it. I may still do that one day. But when I listen to God, to my wife and those who know me best, I hear a different message. I hear Jesus' words to Peter on the beach, "Do you love me? Then feed my sheep." He calls us to think about the greatest good we can possibly imagine, to give ourselves to that good, and to serve that good just for this day.

As I ponder my wins and losses, my virtues and vices, my life message to date can been distilled to this truth: God has shown me relentless mercy through Christ and the loving care of Christlike people (Christian or not). That love compels me to pay it forward as a flawed but grateful emissary of the *Jesus Way*. May Christ use this work to serve that end.

## THOUGHTS

1. What false images of God have you observed in the world? In other religions? Within Christianity? Within yourself? How has God begun to deconstruct that false image and restore the true image *(a Christlike God)*? What remnants of an unChristlike image persist in your perspective? How goes your faith renovation?

2. How has Christ shown you that God is love? How does Jesus demonstrate this in the Gospels? Are there key stories in the Gospels that highlight this for you? How has Christ shown you that God is love in your experience? Are there key moments in your life that illustrate this?

3. Simone Weil speaks of two kinds of atheism. One is about purging our vision of God of toxic elements, such as vengeance and violence, in favor of a more Christlike image. But an atheism also exists that turns from God yet retains the idols. Have you witnessed this? How might secularized belief systems still embody the toxic elements of a god they no longer accept? How might a *Christlike God* challenge toxic atheism?

## PRAYERS

*Lord Jesus Christ, Word and Image of divine Love, I welcome your cleansing Grace to continue healing me of un-Christlike images that worm through my mind and work in my life. Restore in me a healthy vision of the cruciform God who you revealed.*

# Chapter 2

# TRENDING: #DECONSTRUCTION

I have placed my hope in the revelation of Jesus Christ: that the *Abba* he disclosed is the God of triune Love—lover and redeemer of all humankind. I pray this beautiful gospel will again become the dominant message of Christianity, our good news to the world. Given our spiritual investment in diversions and regressions, moving forward as individuals and communities will require a serious course of what is popularly called "deconstruction."

The term is a favorite among "nones" and "dones" who have flown the coop of the unChristlike god and its institutions. *Deconstruction* is especially used, overused and misused by "ex-vangelicals" who found the emergency exit door out of fundamentalist homes and churches, under the frowning glare of their movement's retributive deity. I regularly encounter a new kind of testimony—counter-conversion stories that start with, "When I went through my *deconstruction* . . ." In other words, deconstruction is not so much undertaken (something I plan) as it is undergone (something that happens to me). Many a spiritual refugee has discovered that for faith of any kind to be retained, they must first pass through the valley of disillusionment and deconstruction.

Deconstruction is a metaphor that evokes images of jack-hammers, dynamite and building demolition. After all, don't you need to clear the decrepit ruins of a condemned building before you can build a new structure where it once stood? On the other hand, I'm not the first to point out that the metaphor seems quite violent. The destructive tone of deconstruction expresses well the anger one feels when they realize they've been duped by religious doctrines and controlling leaders into life-long spiritual bondage and abuse. The lament quite rightly carries an edge to it—an impulse to raze the whole structure to the ground is understandable.

Then again, what is the "structure" we're deconstructing? It's not actually somewhere *out there*—unless you're assassinating pastors, setting fire to cathedrals or actively dismantling institutions. Quixotic rants against something so vague as 'the Church' in fact serve to deconstruct very little. No, when we speak of *our* deconstruction, the edifice we're dismantling is first of all internal—structures within one's own soul or faith. For that reason, I'm disinclined to the havoc and carnage inherent in the dynamite/bulldozer picture. I believe the metaphors we use shape our approach, so we ought to weigh carefully the symbols that best fit our situation.

In this chapter, I will offer alternative word-pictures and the reasons for a gentler approach to the necessary process. But first, let's briefly deconstruct the pop-misuse of *deconstruction.*

## "NOT WHAT YOU THINK IT MEANS!"

As Inigo Montoya famously said to Vizzini (in *The Princess Bride*), *"I do not think it means what you think it means!"* The following analysis of *deconstruction* comes via a dear friend and Anglican scholar, Sean Davidson. I'm citing and paraphrasing him freely, but these are his ideas. He says,

> *I'm pretty sure one thing deconstruction does* not *mean is a cynical, angry interlude on the way to militant progressivism.*
>
> At least it wouldn't have meant that for Jacques Derrida, the French philosopher who coined the term. Deconstruction, for Derrida, isn't about manning the barricades. It's about learning to *slow down*, to *attend closely* to the way we use language. It is to *be mindful* about how we discuss and practice truth and meaning.
>
> This has important implications for theology. If you pay close attention to Derrida, he doesn't try to disprove truth claims—nor does he try to prove them. He remains open to truth and meaning. The point of deconstruction is to unmask *claims* to truth that pretend to stand on their own, independent of conditions and contexts.
>
> The pop version of "deconstruction" fails to appreciate these dynamics in its own discourse. For many post-Evangelicals, deconstruction tends to be practiced as an intermediary stage of doubt and cynicism in the service of militant progressivism. That

form of deconstruction is a *construction* that Derrida himself would have deconstructed.

I know there have been very real abuses in the church. I've lived through enough of them to have my own struggles and misgivings. What troubles me is the strident reactionary and rationalistic spirit as recourse. I can understand that to an extent, given the experience of abuse. But not as a concerted strategy for moving forward in faith, hope and love. There's too much about this spirit that seems fueled by the very thing it's supposing to resist.

Derrida's original practice provides a much-needed corrective—*it not only helps to critique institutionalized problems, but also reactionary solutions.* It forces us to consider genuine alternatives that are less about ideological tactics and posturing and more about participation in the gospel.

What strikes me in Sean's critique is the nearly irresistible temptation of arrogance in so much deconstruction. Still stinging from our most recent delusion, we're too quick to congratulate ourselves for being "woke" and too credulous of the new bandwagon we uncritically board—as if fresh certitude constitutes arrival and enlightenment. I find it *most* disturbing and shameful when I notice it in myself, unsure that I can escape it even in these pages. See—now I'm actually deconstructing!

Can deconstruction leave you agnostic? Sure it can. But it helps if we are mindful that the object of our deconstruction is not Truth or Christ or the gospel per se, but rather, my own constructed ways of thinking and talking about God.

If the picture-language of deconstruction itself needs deconstruction, I'd like to suggest a sampling of alternatives for consideration. You can determine for yourself which pictures resonate most, but I hope they also serve as invitations to healthier ways of transitioning.

## ART RESTORATION

In a blogpost titled "Deconstruction or Restoration" (4-20-16), Brian Zahnd suggested that the imagery of art restoration might serve us better.

He imagines the faith as an ancient icon of Christ, covered in centuries of grime, dirt and soot. A restoration expert is commissioned to restore the icon's original vibrancy. Among the artist's tools, you wouldn't expect to find dynamite. You don't restore a priceless masterpiece by blowing it up. Brian applies the analogy to our faith:

> In our passion to rescue Christian faith from its myriad of distortions, we are not like the Taliban blowing up the Buddhas of Bamiyan, but like the artists who restored Michelangelo's vandalized *Pietá*.
>
> In rethinking Christianity, we must always keep in mind that we are handling something enormously precious—faith in Christ. It's precisely because faith in Christ is so precious that we are committed to the difficult task of restoring it to its original beauty. But we cannot use cheap cynicism and crude mockery in this delicate task. We go about it patiently, reverently, gently, always showing deep respect for the Great Tradition that has sustained Christian faith and practice for two thousand years.

## *Ecce Homo* (Behold the Man)

I can't improve on Brian's illustration, but it does recall a comical instance, a disastrous attempt at art restoration. Readers may have heard of the failed efforts of a certain Cecilia Giménez, who gave her best shot at restoring a Spanish fresco of Christ—the now infamous *Ecce Homo* (from Pilate's words, "Behold the man") in the Sanctuary of Mercy church in Borja, Spain. Painted circa 1930 by Elías García Martínez, the deteriorating mural depicted a forlorn Jesus, wearing his crown of thorns. Giménez, an elderly amateur artist, botched the intervention so badly that mockers have dubbed the painting *Ecce Mono* ("Behold the monkey"). The moral of the story might be, if your faith needs a facelift, beware of who you let do the makeover.

## *Salvator Mundi* (Savior of the World)

In contrast to *Ecce Homo*, we have another famous Jesus artwork, the *Salvator Mundi* (Savior of the world) by Leonardo da Vinci. Passed from one collector to another, disappearing for fifty and one hundred years at a time, so marred by touch ups and lacquer, the masterpiece became unrecognizable. Both its beauty and pedigree were buried in grime and history. It once sold at auction for just £45.

But over the course of a three-year restoration, Dianne Dwyer Modestini, a world-class "conservator" (an expert in art repair and preservation), worked through the layers of gaudy accretions to recover the *Salvator's* original brilliance and true identity. The time invested was not merely about stripping away what didn't belong, but "extracting the precious from the worthless" (Jer. 15:19).

Upon completion, the *Salvator Mundi* went back to auction, this time for over $450 million—the world record for a work of art.

In reality, there is no work of art as precious as the living *Salvator Mundi*—our Lord Jesus Christ—and his gospel of cruciform love. It is tragic that through misuse, mishandling and gaudy touch-ups, the glory of the originary Christian faith becomes nearly unrecognizable. In our darkest hours, it has been difficult to identify the Master with what has become of his handiwork.

But the solution is not this new wave of *iconoclasm*—the frenzied destruction of the sacred, whether religiously or ideologically motivated. Will hasty carpet knives and corrosive turpentine restore what's beneath the centuries of botched religiosity? No, what we need today are expert conservators who believe in the beauty of the gospel and who recognize that your faith is priceless. We can trust those who perceive and preserve the eyes, the smile, the hands of the Savior peeking out through whatever grime has despoiled the faith. The masterpiece of Christ is still there for those who realize its value.

## LIFESTYLE NETWORK

> "The latter glory of this house shall be greater than the former," says the LORD of hosts. "And in this place, I will give peace," declares the LORD of hosts. —Haggai 2:9

Maybe you're not an art aficionado. Like my wife Eden, you might prefer winding down from a long day with the Lifestyle Network, bingeing on home renovation series and extreme makeovers.

## Home Renovation

The principle of home reno shows is similar to art restoration. Our favorites involve restoring heritage homes to their former glory—especially when the contractors discover solid hardwood floors beneath ratty shag carpet or yellowed linoleum. Instead of barging through with a sledgehammer, the real experts preserve the integrity of the original structure. They peel back layers of wallpaper, pulling out asbestos insulation and cleanse the homes of black mold.

By the end of each episode, what looked like a dilapidated haunted house becomes what it once was—an exquisite Southern Gothic mansion in Savannah, Georgia. I must confess the sin of covetousness by the closing scene.

Did you know God is into home renovations? Years after Solomon's temple in Jerusalem was destroyed by the Babylonians, it was rebuilt by Zerubbabel, refurbished by Herod, then burned and flattened again by Rome. Haggai had prophesied a temple of far greater glory, but his prediction was never fulfilled with limestone blocks construction. God's glorious new temple is built of living stones—people of faith—who together are God's refurbished house.

The house might look worse for wear—even beyond repair. Shall we abandon it? Or destroy it and burn it to the ground? Do we prefer exile in a strange land? Or will we hear Haggai's call to rebuild and renovate? I wonder what would it look like in our time?

## Extreme Makeover

Likewise, with makeover shows, the program focuses on taking someone who feels ugly through a process that draws out their true beauty. We're not just talking about someday potential. Everyone is beautiful when appropriately adorned. The hairstylist, the wardrobe designers and make-up artists go to work.

The makeover experts know their best results come, not by covering up their clients' features, but by accentuating the gifts God has given them. Hair is shaped to highlight face shape, make-up is applied to draw out the eyes and mouth, clothing is fitted to accentuate the curves. Often, less is better and the only real ugliness is how someone's appearance is neglected, deliberately hidden or buried in cultural clichés. That affects their posture, bearing and confidence.

I don't like to admit it, but I've shed a few tears during the final shots where the person breaks down before the mirror, finally seeing something of their true self radiating back at them.

You see my point. Art restoration, home renovation and extreme makeovers are all just modern metaphors that say more than, "Don't throw the baby out with the bathwater." They say, rather, "Yes, bathe the baby! Then scoop up the baby from the bath, dry and powder her, diaper and dress her, put ribbons in her hair and take her out. It's time to show her off to the world . . . and hang on! Do that for yourself too (sans diapers). And for Grandma as well!"

There shines generations of living beauty for which "deconstruction" is an inadequate and even destructive metaphor. As we test run alternatives, which works best for you? More to come . . .

## UNTIL DEATH DO US PART

### Without Spot or Wrinkle

I'd like to propose my own metaphor for spiritual renewal—a heart-warming illustration that comes from the biblical record, ancient hymnody and my own family. Both the Bible and the liturgies of the early church frequently compare God or Christ to a bridegroom and his people to a bride. Song of Solomon describes the bride's beauty and the glory of her wedding day. The prophets Isaiah, Ezekiel and Hosea lament her unfaithfulness. When the people of God rebel, they are compared to an unfaithful wife who has *"stained her garments."* By contrast, redemption in Christ is said to *cleanse* the Bride [and her dress] of every stain and ultimately present her to himself at the great wedding feast of the Lamb "without spot or wrinkle." When you think about the beauty and expense of a wedding gown, if the dress somehow gets stained or wrinkled, how does one best restore it?

When my firstborn son got engaged a few years back, Colette, my daughter-to-be, began the quest for a vintage dress. To her great joy, she found a gorgeous ivory, silk satin wedding dress—sewn in the 1930s. The size seemed right, so she ordered it and sure enough, it fit perfectly without any alterations. It was a beautiful work of art. Naturally, the dress had aged for about eighty years and came with wrinkles and stains.

What to do? Deconstruction? No. You don't use scissors to cut stains out or flames to burn away wrinkles. Removing the stains was important, but that was secondary to preserving the exquisite fabric. Thankfully, "I know a guy" who shares these values. *Yong's Tailoring* advertises "Expert Dry Cleaners" on his marquee signage, and rightfully so. Mr. Yong invested the time and meticulous care required to restore the dress to its former glory—drawing out the stains without overusing products that could have ruined Colette's treasure.

While waiting for the couple to pick it up, the dry cleaner proudly displayed the wedding gown at the front of the shop for other customers to see. Folks who came in would *ooh* and *aah* at the dress, hanging there "without spot or wrinkle." But then, Colette put on the dress, and to me, she looked like a princess. Elegant and radiant.

See how replacing the metaphor from deconstruction to restoration shifts our focus from the more aggressive tone of tearing down to cleansing and renewal? Like Colette's dress, your faith is a precious gift, a treasure more likely inherited than fabricated, passed down over many centuries. Those centuries bring with it a history of corruption and abuse but have also increased its value.

The gospel of Jesus Christ is not something you or I contrived or conceived. You didn't sew this dress; you received it. It is the "faith once delivered" by Christ through his apostles to the church. That gospel is like a priceless wedding dress or vintage diamond ring—however tarnished, it's a treasure worth conserving.

For that reason, I find restorative language more hopeful and helpful than deconstruction. Maybe that's because it better reflects the nature of *Abba,* whose heart is "the restoration of all things" (Acts 3:21).

I'll speak frankly now. I've watched dear friends deconstruct their faith so completely that they not only moved on from toxic religion—they abandoned Christ as husband as well, as if they'd never given themselves to him. They ditched their ugly retributive theology, but then discarded the gospel too, proving right their accusers who cried "slippery slope." If their exodus from Christianity results in greater love and freedom, the detox might be worth it. But how is it that so many make the transition without the transformation? If we retain the very self-righteous and hateful posture that drove us from un-Christlike religion in the first place, what exactly have we deconstructed?

And so, Derrida counsels us, "Slow down. Critique your language, your tone, your metaphors. Keep close watch for your own hidden premises and power plays." Ephraim of Syria prayed, "O Lord and King, grant me to see my own transgressions, and not to judge my brother"—difficult, but loving correction need not condemn the erring other. Fix your eyes on Jesus, who authored our faith to begin with and who alone can ultimately perfect it. Yes, learn to let things go, but leave the sledgehammer in the shed. Debate the demerits of unChristlike doctrine and practice but please, avoid pelting his bride with hammers of condemnation.

## Tailor-Made Faith

Another metaphor related to our family wedding comes via fitting the groom (my son Stephen) for his suit. Stephen is a professional hospital improvement analyst. His expertise includes seeing inefficient and dysfunctional systems and how these negatively impact the care with which the hospital serves the needs of its patients. A bad system affects people's lives. But when a system isn't working, he knows you don't just tear everything down and start from scratch without any standards. Nor can you apply a one-size-fits-all approach, since every solution needs to be tailor-made. And there's the beginning of a metaphor he regularly uses in the field: the tailor-made suit.

When Stephen went shopping for his wedding suit, he couldn't simply walk into a men's shop to buy something off the rack. He's 6 feet, 8 inches tall, with broad shoulders, a slender frame and impossible inseam. One size does not fit all. The suit needed to be tailor-made. On the other hand, *tailor-made isn't custom-made,* which would mean designing and creating from scratch. Custom-made suits are far more expensive and the tailors in men's shops aren't expert designers. Tailors begin with a pattern—a standard—and adjust for a perfect fit, appropriate fabric and preferred color.

Let's transpose this principle to faith engineering. When we see how corrupt the structures and systems of Christianity can get, right down to morbid conceptions of God, the temptation is to trash the whole project and make up our own version . . . from scratch. To break free from the suffocating control of religious leaders, doctrines or texts, we might set aside all previous standards for truth or patterns of practice. Then we cobble together a home-made garment from our own sewing kit and fabric scrap box. To use Stephen's language, "People start making sh*t up."

When it comes to self-made religion, believe me—it shows. I see the rush from religious hierarchy into spiritual anarchy. I also read history: those pages are bloody. The path of spiritual progress is not fleeing the Royal Priesthood of all believers (interdependent communities) to become one's own Pope (independent wildcards). I haven't decided which is worse: when the lone rangers stop using Scripture as their pattern for faith or when they use it to cut and paste, mix and match their own gospel. How do rogue teachers reinvent bad religion?

By leaving behind the pattern established by the apostles and fathers who gathered the New Testament and designed the creeds. Their custom-made confessions recycle the old errors again and again. Others, less inventive, gravitate to self-made gurus who offer more exotic fabrications than what they've left behind.

The basic lesson is this: when it comes to faith, don't shop at a one-size-fits-all warehouse and don't approach it as a do-it-yourself project. Or if you do, at least name it after yourself, rather than attaching Christ's brand to your amateur fashion line.

What is the pattern from which faith is tailor-made for our era, our region and our needs? The Bible and the church that compiled it identify the pattern as Christ himself—the revelation of God as cruciform love. Christ perfectly revealed the nature of the divine Groom, and by his human nature also became the prototype for God's cruciform Bride. Said another way, Christ patterned *the Jesus Way* for us to follow.

## DETOX & REHAB

Any of the above metaphors may work as models of *reformation*. *RE-forming* our faith is about *restoring* and *restory-ing* our faith back to its primary beauty. But to be fair, some folks have been too brutalized with toxic religion and spiritual abuse to remain where they are. There may be "no room in the inn" for their doubts and questions or their grievances with abusive authority and corrupt systems.

I'm not talking about disgruntled grumblers who exited the church because the pastor was too conservative or too liberal for them, or because the music was the wrong style or volume. Sure, many do leave because they are easily triggered by trivialities or lack the social grace to get along with others. I've been privy to many "church failed me" tales that can be boiled down to, "I didn't get my way."

I'm not referring to them—that crew will need to bottom out on whatever in them draws their finger to the self-sabotage button. No, I'm thinking about those who really have been trashed in one faith community after another—dehumanized by the theology, demoralized by the moralizing or minimized to the margins. They're wrung out like dishcloths in the church kitchen or ground down as toothless cogs in the big wheel. Some were gifted, put on a pedestal for a time, then had the stool kicked out from under them. Whatever it was, they NEEDED to leave. And they finally did. Possibly too late.

They don't need another *deconstruction.* The church has already demolished them badly enough. For those beaten and broken in the very place that was meant to be a hostel and hospital, the metaphor I like is a two-stage "dietary detox cleanse" or "addictions detox and rehab."

When someone has languished with toxins in their system for a long duration, whether through bad diet or substance abuse, the first step to healing is a short-term intervention detox. With detox diets, the initial stage aims to eliminate the toxins from your body—typically beginning with a fast. From there you reintroduce select foods, such as fruit and veggies. Some detox diets may use special herbs, teas and supplements. In more extreme cases, you might resort to an unpleasant colon cleanse or enema.

Dietary detoxes can be painful, smelly and messy as the body pushes out years of accumulated poison. Some people report gross body odors and frankly, I decided not to research the side-effects further. But once complete, the goal is to reintroduce a more nutritious diet and better eating practices.

The same two-step analogy works with addiction recovery programs. The addict begins with detox, supplemented with medication to lessen the side-effects of withdrawal. Withdrawal can be excruciating—cravings, the shakes, cramps and heavy sweats are common symptoms of the detox phase when coming off drugs.

After the detox stage (e.g. one or two weeks), the addict may go into a series of recovery houses for the rehabilitation stage (from twenty-eight days to a year). There, they live in a community where they can work a twelve-step program (such as A.A. or N.A.) and pursue therapy that addresses the underlying issues behind their addiction. Their addiction is not treated as a moral failure, but as a diseased and mistaken way to medicate one's deeper suffering, whether it's childhood trauma, self-will, control issues, etc.

Whenever religion is toxic and/or addictive, freedom may begin with a significant detox period, where separation from the whole Christian culture is necessary for any faith to survive long-term. The first stages of religious detox can include disorientation, cravings and panic attacks. One of my friends, a life-long churchgoer and professional worship leader, found she *needed* to get away from the church scene. Upon leaving, she initially experienced panic attacks, a racing heart and hyperventilation every Sunday morning. She wasn't merely missing church—she was in serious withdrawal and something ugly from her religious experience was *leaving* her.

How long must a religious detox go on? As long as it takes. Churchgoing friends worry that they've "backslidden" (trigger word!)—they suffer their own anxiety issues about winning them back. Believe me, you're not doing them any favors.

That said, detox is not meant to last a lifetime. Fasting from faith and isolating from family eventually leads to starvation. At some point, we all need to move on from religious detox into faith rehab. What will that look like? That's not my call. Your faith is as unique as your body. Your needs are different than mine. I wouldn't want you to return to a toxic faith environment, nor do I advise becoming a spiritual anorexic.

Hopefully, the Holy Spirit will lead you into life-giving, faith-nourishing relationships where faith is expressed as love, where Jesus is the focus and where loving God and loving others is the bottom line.

## "EX-VANGELICAL" DECONSTRUCTION

I'm not alone in noticing millions of "Ex vangelical" deconstructors making their exodus from rigid religiosity into long-overdue freedom. I'm specifying that stream of Christianity because those are my people. But it's not only them. Brick-and-mortar churches of all types are shrinking or shutting as cradle Catholics, Protestants and Orthodox head for the exit. For many, it's like shucking off a straitjacket and finally feeling what it's like to dance as children, barefoot in spacious fields of lush grass and wildflowers. Are they "backsliding" or are they growing up and waking up?

I'm among those who try to keep track of where that dance leads. Some of my "none" and "done" Evangelicals buddies have found their way into liberal churches or progressive movements. Others gravitate to contemplative streams or 'high church' traditions. Others leave the institutional church but continue to (or finally begin to) love Christ wholeheartedly and integrate apostolic faith and prophetic action into postmodern culture. They find or create entirely new forms where faith can flourish.

That said, I will confess to losing some sleep over another phenomenon: a great number of the Ex-vangelical friends I grew up with have traveled from strict conservatism *through* progressivism *into* agnosticism and atheism. Coupled with that trajectory, I see an obvious general move from community (however dysfunctional the herd) toward increased segregation, alienation and spiritual loneliness.

That's their journey—it is what it is. I apologize for worrying. It's not very Christlike. The question that niggles at me in the night is this: must our flight from Christian fundamentalism inevitably dead-end in a denial of Christ and spell an end to faith-based belonging? Is loss of faith and family unavoidable?

For those who see the slippery slope, but want to stick with Jesus, yet know they can never return to Evangelicalism, what can we say?

Here's my triage-speed diagnosis:

1. *Ex-vangelicals lose their faith* when they identify the poison of Christian fundamentalism with Jesus himself. If the exclusivity of conservatism is identified with the uniqueness of Christ (not the same

thing!), freedom from the former seems to necessitate discarding the latter. It need not.

2. *Ex-vangelicals lose their focus* when they make deconstruction the sacred point. Instead of restoring and preserving the beauty of the gospel masterpiece, a deconstruction bias moves beyond ditching retributive theology (e.g. penal substitution, eternal conscious torment, Old Testament violence) to abandoning fealty to Christ and a family connection with other Christ-followers.

3. *Ex-vangelicals let go of faithfulness* when they confuse or replace the *Jesus Way* with any -ism as our base-line ideology (theologically and politically). For example, progressivism promotes a necessary revolution of thought and action . . . but when the revolutionary untethers from Christ and the *Jesus Way*, what is left to conserve?

Everything must burn, including Christianity itself. After all, the church has been notorious for propping up the establishment, entrenching patriarchy and oppressing the marginalized. That's no caricature. But watch: when it's delinked from the *Jesus Way*, progressive *iconoclasm* (destruction of sacred images, literally or metaphorically) becomes absolute and violent—the new Puritanism. Compassion is reserved for the victimized in-crowd (until they go off-script). Cruelty is permitted when directed at the patriarchy or any religious institution with its own history of cruelty.

The *Jesus Way* is not about dethroning the cruel and enthroning a new regime of cruelty. Christ calls us to renounce every cruel throne altogether. His throne was a Cross and his reign is humble and *kenotic*. So are his real followers.

4. *Ex-vangelicals become agnostics or atheists* when they no longer hold to Christ's unique revelation of *Abba* and the centrality of his cruciform life, death and resurrection.

Unless we know Christ as a living person who rescued us from darkness and transformed us by *Grace*, he becomes as disposable as any other imaginary childhood friend. If Jesus is only ever a fairy-story we hear as children or a belief system into which we were indoctrinated, the shelf-life of faith inevitably expires and sours in our mouths. Christ is a Reality whom we encounter along the *Jesus Way*. It's worth thinking about how that happens for each of us.

5. *Ex-vangelicals lose their sense of faith family* when they unhook from diverse relationships where Christ is the rallying point and opt instead for the ever-fragmenting quest for homogeneity (sameness). The seeds of this fragmentation were sown in religious sectarianism and have simply been secularized. We inherited the Protestant impulse to split and split and split again. Throw in individualism and you end up alone.

This is observable: Ex-vangelicals who leave a fellowship broader than their own convictions or culture, choosing instead to gather only in fraternities of identity sameness, where conformity is the litmus test of truth, will continue to *atomize* and end up bouncing between social network groups—some even imagine trolling competing factions is "doing justice." Sigh. I know—it's incredibly difficult to change course on that toboggan. I'm suggesting there's a *Jesus Way* option that's both free and life-giving—and far less lonesome.

## FIRST STRIDES

In chapter 1, we reviewed the basics of *A More Christlike God:* that despite the toxic counterfeits and broken human conceptions, the *Abba* of triune Love is revealed perfectly in Jesus Christ. We also recognized that when distorted images of God are expressed in ugly versions of faith, those stung by its barbs experience the wounds of disillusionment.

In this chapter, we have explored a powerful trend, popularly dubbed "deconstruction." I suggested that the impulse for deconstruction is necessary for spiritual survival, but that the metaphor is itself fraught with violent undertones. I offered a series of alternatives that I believe supply an emotionally healthier path for those in transition.

I would remind readers that any illustration can either clarify or obscure the truth, so I want to close with two important takeaways to remind you of the main lesson and acknowledge its constraints.

First, *remember the big picture*. Deconstruction is a violent metaphor that invokes, evokes and provokes imagery and acts of tearing, smashing and blowing up. I've argued that if the real object and focus of restoration is one's own heart and one's own faith or if it's the "faith once delivered" (the gospel itself)—not just some external person, system or institution we hate—then more Christlike *means* and *metaphors* for our recovery and restoration are required.

Second, these *illustrations are limited* to this assumption: there is something there worth finding and saving. Yes, there is a heart and faith and gospel worth discovering and preserving. But you won't necessarily find it everywhere. Some artwork is just counterfeit right to the canvas. Some homes are rotted out right to the foundations. Some recovery programs and diet programs are pure snake oil. And sometimes, we're diving in the wrong waters altogether.

So too, there exist today (as in New Testament times) teachers, churches and ministries that claim to represent Christ but who Paul describes as "false." Christ calls some seasoned servants to confront and refute them. Unfortunately, there's also a proliferation of accusers out there, self-appointed "watchmen" as wolfish as the "false teachers" they claim to expose. What to do? If you're "in deconstruction" mode, your first order of business is probably just to move on. I hope this chapter has affirmed that what you *don't* need to deconstruct or leave behind is Jesus Christ. Even when we've been burned—*because we've been burned*—our best hope is to ask Christ to show us the *Jesus Way* and invite *Grace* to lead us there.

In the following chapter, we will take our first tentative strides into the major theme of this book: the *Jesus Way*.

## THOUGHTS

1. Have you experienced a deconstruction of your old belief systems? What aspects of your religious background needed to go? What essential elements of your faith survived? What was letting go like for you?

2. What have you found most difficult about deconstruction? Did you undergo tumult in your faith? Did you experience resistance or exclusion from your clan or camp? Where did you find support as you transitioned from one faith to the next? What advice would you give others as they pass through similar changes?

3. Do you find any of these gentler metaphors helpful? Are you drawn to any particular picture? Why? Do other metaphors ring more true to your experience?

## PRAYERS

*Lord Jesus Christ, Master Artist of God's image in us, restore your masterpiece with Grace and care. Bridegroom of your beloved bride, cleanse our garments of the stains of un-Christlikeness, without spot or wrinkle. Renew and restore our souls to Christlike faith.*

# Chapter 3
# THE JESUS WAY

## IN FATHER'S FOOTSTEPS

When I was a child, I walked a lot. I walked to school, walked downtown, walked to the beach, walked through oak forests and across fields—even across the lake when it was frozen. As a small-town prairie boy, much of my walking led me along paths of mud and ice, or across fields of snow. Deep snow.

*Pet peeve:* stuff in my boots—stuff like pebbles or water or snow.

*Solution:* walking in my father's footsteps. This suggests a parable:

Whether trekking through mud or snow, I learned that my dad's footprints compacted the trail. If I just traced his steps, I wouldn't sink and best of all, my feet would stay dry. But if I didn't take care, one misstep onto untrodden ground and I would suddenly sink all the way to my crotch. I would exhaust myself struggling until dad pulled me out and set my way back onto his path.

Now this is important: when my dad cautioned me to follow his tracks, he was not giving me a law that, if broken, would require punishment. It was entirely about a caring dad helping me along. "This way, son. Follow me." When I strayed or slipped, my dad was not angry; he never stopped loving me. I was still his son.

So it is with *Abba.* When Scripture describes *two ways* and *two walks, Abba* was not setting conditions for his love. To read these texts as law rather than love is a projection of our own legalism (or unhealed fear of legalism). Rather, the *two-way* counsel found in the Psalms and Proverbs, the Gospels and epistles are expressions of *Abba's* parental love. *Abba* sent Jesus to be the one human who would mark out and walk the *Way of life* perfectly. Then Jesus calls us to follow in his footsteps because he cares and wants to help us 'keep our feet dry.'

Scripture often contrasts two types of paths or *'ways'—where* we walk. It also distinguishes two *'ways'* of walking—*how* we walk. To summarize the two ways, a brief Bible survey is in order.

## WHERE WE WALK

**1. God's way vs false ways**

In the Psalms, David prays, "Show me your ways, O LORD; teach me your paths. Guide me in your truth and teach me, for you are God my Savior, and my hope is in you all day long" (Ps. 25:4-5).

God's way is set against the false ways (Ps. 119:104), the ways of the other gods (Mic. 4:5) or doing things our own way (Isa. 50:10-11, Jer. 10:23).

**2. The sure way vs the slippery way**

We find that by sticking to God's way, our feet will not slip (Psalm 17:5). Even when traversing "the high places," God makes our footsteps as sure as a mountain goat (Ps. 18:33). God's heart is to lead us through dangerous ground onto level paths (Ps. 27:11).

**3. The straight way vs the crooked way**

In the New Testament, Peter contrasts following the "straight way" of God with those who wander off onto crooked paths (2 Pet. 2:15). The contrast is between faithfulness to God's direction vis-a-vis rebellion and the corruption of "crooks."

**4. The narrow way vs the broad way**

Sometimes, God's way is pictured as a broad highway, away from the treacherous back roads where muggers and wild beasts lurk (Isaiah 35:8-9). According to Isaiah, the redeemed walk on this "highway of holiness" while "fools" avoid it at their peril.

But Jesus reversed the analogy, speaking of the "broad road" as the wrong way:

> "So whatever you want people to do to you, do just that to them. Yes; this is what the law and the prophets are all about. Go in by the narrow gate. The gate that leads to destruction, you see, is nice and wide, and the road going there has plenty of room. Lots of people go that way." —Matthew 7:12-13

I regularly hear this passage interpreted as though Jesus were saying that in the end, very few will "be saved and go to heaven." That's not what Christ is referring to at all. Read it again. Regardless of our faith profession or final destiny, our Lord is summarizing his takeaway from the Law and the Prophets—he's describing *the Jesus Way* in this life in terms of the famous "Golden Rule."

He laments that most people—even most Christians—opt out of the *Way* that leads to life and instead, face the tragic self-destructive results of following the violent mob on the broad path (see also Ps. 1:6).

**5. The way of life vs the way of death**

So, practically speaking, *the Jesus Way* truly leads to life, which includes human flourishing now and eternal life beyond (see also Jer. 21:8).

Remember my opening analogy: this is not an ultimatum from a volatile God but the wise counsel of a caring Father.

"Look," he says, "if you walk this way, you won't sink. But if you walk that way, you could slip and fall to your death. Please, walk *this way.* Follow *my way.* It's the *way of life!*"

## HOW WE WALK

The Bible tells us where to walk, but also *how to walk.*

**1. Walking in the light vs walking in the dark**

First, we are called to "walk in the Light, just as he is in the light" (1 Jn. 1:7). The Light, of course, is Christ himself, illuminating the path of life.

The prophets foretell Christ our lamp, lighting up the path for us:

> "I will lead the blind by a way they do not know, in paths they do not know I will guide them. I will make darkness into light before them and rugged places into plains." —Isaiah 42:16

Yes, Christ is the lamp in whose light we walk, now and for eternity.

> And the city has no need of sun or moon to shine on it, for the glory of God gives it light, and its lamp is the lamb. The nations will walk in its light . . . —Revelation 21:23-24

**2. Walking in the Spirit vs walking in the flesh**

The apostle Paul speaks to *how* we walk. He urges us to "walk by the Spirit" (Gal. 5:16, Rom. 8:1), to "keep in step with the Spirit" (Gal. 5:25), and contrasts this to "walking in the flesh," which he associates with the cravings of our old selves.

Following the lead of the Spirit means no longer white-knuckling external laws. Rather, we're living by the internal law of Spirit (love). How so? God says to Ezekiel,

> "I will give you a new heart and put a new spirit in you; I will remove from you your heart of stone and give you a heart of flesh. And I will put my Spirit in you and move you to follow my decrees and be careful to keep my laws."—Ezekiel 36:26-27

But wait, I thought it wasn't about obeying commands or keeping laws? That depends. Certainly *not* if we are asking, "What must I do to be saved?" And surely *not* if obeying commands is about law-keeping under threat of punishment. Then what does it mean?

### 3. Walking in the *Jesus Way* of Love

John the Beloved distilled *the Jesus Way* to this: "And this is love: that we walk in obedience to his commands. As you have heard from the beginning, his command is that you walk in love" (2 Jn. 1:6, NIV).

By the end of the first century, the *Didache,* a very early Christian catechism/manual, summarized *the Jesus Way* as *walking in love.* It opens this way, recalling the words of Christ:

> There are *two ways,* one of life and one of death, but a great difference between the two ways. The *way of life,* then, is this:
>
> First, you shall love God who made you; second, love your neighbor as yourself, and do not do to another what you would not want done to you. The teaching is this: Bless those who curse you, pray for your enemies, and fast for those who persecute you. For what reward is there for loving those who love you? Do not the Gentiles do that? But love those who hate you, and you shall not have an enemy... If someone strikes your right cheek, turn to him the other also, and you shall be perfect. If someone forces you to go one mile, go with him two. If someone takes your cloak, give him also your coat. If someone takes from you what is yours, ask it not back, for indeed you are not able. Give to everyone who asks you and ask it not back; for the Father wills that to all should be given of our own blessings (free gifts).

See how difficult *walking in love* can become? It sounds impossible—like "take up your cross." Exactly. But Jesus meant it—walking in his footsteps of love is a real way of life. In his own words, "This is my command: love one another, in the same way that I loved you" (Jn. 15:12).

A "command"? Yes. A tall order, yes, but it is, after all, the *Jesus Way.* Would you rather hack your own trail through the jungle of life with a machete of self-effort? No thanks. Rather, to walk the *Jesus Way* is to follow the Christ—the divine human—by the *Grace* of *Abba* through the power of the Spirit. The *Jesus Walk* is a faith pilgrimage in the company and in the strength of triune Love. As the carol says, "their law is love and their gospel is peace." Yes, sign me up for that, please.

## THE WAY OF THE CROSS

On second thought... "Love each other as Christ loved us"? Give me a moment, please... But Christ laid down his life for us. Is John saying...? Apparently, he is. Read that back to me:

> "This is my command: love one another, in the same way that I loved you. No one has a love greater than this, to lay down your life for your friends." —John 15:12-13

I get it now: the *Jesus Way* conjoins the *way of love* with the *way of the Cross.* The *Jesus Walk* is the Way of sacrificial love—*cruciform* (cross-like love) and *kenotic* (self-giving love), just like him.

But the Cross? That's supposed to be a done deal. Why does Christ say, "If any of you want to come after me, you must say No to yourselves, and pick up your cross every day, and follow me" (Luke 9:23)? Are Christians called to be crucified? Literally, hardly ever. Okay, we talk about "dying to self," which means something like letting go of self-centeredness and ego. But it's more than that.

I believe Christ intends the cruciform love of *Abba* revealed through him to *become flesh* in those who follow him on the *Jesus Way.* Remember, *cruciform* love refers to God's self-giving, radically forgiving, co-suffering love. Those who've read *A More Christlike God* or articles I've posted about the Cross will recognize that three-fold refrain. It is typically how I summarize the nature and way of triune Love.

But now we add to that this truth: Christ-followers who truly follow—who walk the *Jesus Way*—will also manifest his love in our lives, "on the ground," so to speak. Christ claimed his disciples would be known and recognized by this love (Jn. 13:35). They are identified with Christ as they exhibit his cruciform love in this world.

Note: the popular catchphrase "identity in Christ" is not merely the disembodied *truth* of our being boldly *asserted* in self-important "I am" statements ("I am perfect," "I am holy," "I am the righteousness of God," etc.). "Righteousness" is not a dissociated identity. Jesus repeatedly insists that our identity in him be expressed in the *Way* of our being, humbly *demonstrated* when his *Grace*-energized life lifts us up just as he was lifted up—to *give* ourselves unselfishly, to *forgive* others supernaturally and to *co-suffer* with others according to Christ's compassion and empathy.

Pause. Am I setting up love as a new law? No! Jesus did that. He said, "I'm giving you a new commandment, and it's this: love one another! Just as I have loved you, so you must love one another" (Jn. 13:34). It was the one commandment he gave his disciples at the Last Supper.

But fear not—this is not "love legalism." By the *Grace* (transforming energies) of the indwelling Spirit, love becomes a law of nature—our *new* nature. We must not reduce this to an abstract righteousness declared in some hypothetical heavenly verdict. The love-righteousness of Christ-in-us must and will "show up" as the *way we walk—the Jesus Walk.*

## THE WAY OF LOVE

John, the apostle of love, is utterly insistent on this point. His logic is unequivocal: first, God is love because that love did not hunker down in God's heart in the comfort of Paradise. Triune Love is a divine verb Who entered space-time history through the Incarnation. Divine Love necessarily appears and acts or it is not love at all. That act of love is Jesus Christ—the eternal Word enfleshed as perfect, cruciform Love.

John the Beloved extrapolates: divine Love—Christ in us—is only real when it actualizes—when it appears and acts in the tangible world of our relationships. Love shows up or it isn't love. John leaves no room for a heaven/earth, heart/hand, feeling/action dualism. As my firstborn once said to his youngest brother, "At some level, you are what you do." Your identity and your walk—your faith and your love—are indivisible.

At the same time, John is no naïve perfectionist who believes we've already arrived. John knows this is a *way*, a walk, a journey. The "finished work" of the Cross has not finished working on me. For John and for Christ, the *Jesus Way* is a path we're walking one day at a time in fits and starts, stumbles and recoveries. Perhaps at best we're staggering forward, but as we imperfectly hear and follow—*imitate*—Christ's faithful footfalls, life is the venue where we're learning to love.

According to John, those who live this way—*the Jesus Way of love*—know God. Here he is verbatim:

> "Beloved, let us love one another, because love is from God, and *all who love are fathered by God and know God.* The one who does not love has not known God, because God is love." —1 John 4:7-8

The next verse doesn't start with "but" or "if." No caveats or flinching. John sets aside the question of whether we identify ourselves as Christians or not. He doesn't care who we presume to include as "saved" or exclude as "lost." For John, *those who love know God. Those who do not love, do not.* Period. To be blunt—and John is very blunt—you may be a confessing "Christian," but without love, you don't know God, because God is Love. Confessions and claims to the contrary are lies.

He says, "If someone says, 'I love God', but hates their brother or sister, *that person is a liar.* Someone who doesn't love a brother or sister whom they have seen, *how can they love God, whom they haven't seen?"* (1 Jn. 4:20).

Why so harsh, John? Practically condemning! Probably because we need some sharp rhetoric whenever the name of Christ gets co-opted and associated with unChristlike ways. It's as if John foresaw our day, when Christian faithfulness is frequently associated more with *being against* rather than *standing with*, self-righteousness rather than humility, condemnation rather than compassion, and hate rather than love.

John must have been up against the same serious missteps that plague Christianity on a grand scale today. For John, any so-called "faithfulness" that divorces love and truth or love and faith is a blasphemous perversion and proof that we simply don't know God.

Conversely, John is entirely generous to those who live in the *Light* and on the *Way* of Love. For John, *anyone who loves knows God*—anyone? Anyone who loves!

## ETERNAL LIFE

Furthermore, *knowing God is eternal life.* John records Jesus' words in his Gospel, *"Now this is eternal life: that they know you,* the only true God, and Jesus Christ, whom you have sent" (Jn. 17:3, NIV).

So for John, eternal life is *knowing* God and Jesus Christ, whom he sent. What does *"know"* mean here?

Does eternal life/knowing God come by *believing* in Christ? Yes, according to John 3:16. Those who *believe* in God's one and only Son have eternal life. But then again, even the demons "believe" and shudder (Jas. 2:19).

Is eternal life/knowing God a matter of *confessing* faith in Christ? Yes, according to Romans 10:9—". . . if you profess with your mouth that Jesus is Lord and believe in your heart that God raised him from the dead, you will be saved." But then again, Jesus warns that not all who profess, "Lord, Lord" enter the kingdom of heaven (Matt. 7:21).

Does our salvation require or at least include a *faith* response? It surely does, according to Ephesians 3:8: "You have been saved by grace, through faith! This doesn't happen on your own initiative; it's God's gift." And what does a faith response look like? Just belief? Just words? Just obedience? Paul tells us:

". . . the only thing that counts is faith expressing itself through love" (Gal. 5:6, NIV). Faith without love is worthless (1 Cor. 13:2), for faith is our love response to *Grace* and love is how *Grace* is expressed through us.

Note: *Grace* is another name for the Holy Spirit, just as Word is another name for Jesus Christ. The transforming *Grace* who lives in us bears the fruit of love. In fact, all of *Grace's* gifts and fruit are expressions of love.

## *HOW* IS FAITH EXPRESSED BY LOVE?

To summarize so far: eternal life is knowing God, which means a faith response expressed as love. That sounds like the Great Commandment and its twin:

> Jesus said, "You shall love the Lord your God with all your heart and with all your soul and with all your reason. This is the great and first commandment. The second is like it: You shall love your neighbor as yourself. All the Law and the prophets depend upon these two commandments." —Matthew 22:37-40 (DBH)

When Jesus says the second commandment is *like* the first, I don't believe he means it is *similar to but less than* the first. Rather, love of neighbor is the *likeness* or *visible image* of our otherwise invisible love for God. To love your neighbor is to love God. To love your neighbor is faith in God—faith in God expressed as love for neighbor. Why? Because your neighbor bears the image of God—icons (lit.) of the invisible God.

Who inherits eternal life? Those who love the Lord their God (via their neighbor) with all their heart, soul, mind and strength. Love has always been God's prescribed way of expressing living faith.

Next question: *How* is faith expressed by love? Through worship, prayer and Bible study? By assembling to focus on Christ and his mission? Those are good faith practices, for sure—important for spiritual health. But they are not "the only thing that matters." For Christ, as for Paul and for John,

- Salvation starts with God's love for us—God's amazing *Grace,* expressed as the cruciform love of Christ for the world.
- *Grace* summons and empowers our response: *faith in Christ is love for God demonstrated by love for each other.*
- *"Master, what must I do to inherit eternal life?"* Jesus said, *"Love the Lord your God"*—how?
- *Love of God / Faith in Christ are expressed by cruciform love of neighbor.*

According to John (and John's Jesus), only those who love their brothers, sisters, neighbors and enemies can claim to love God, know God and believe in God. Boiled down, faith in God looks like loving his children, while failure to love disproves our claims to faith in the God who is love.

That's where John is coming from. Love is *not* a good works alternative to faith in Christ. John, following his Master, insists that love is the only reliable expression of Christ in us, *Grace* in us, faith in us.

This is why Christ is not wrong (is he?) when he portrays our treatment of the poor, hungry, naked, sick and imprisoned as the criteria for the final judgment (Matt. 25). "What you did for the least of these brothers and sisters of mine, you did for me." It's not good works instead of faith in Jesus. Rather, love-works ARE faith in Jesus, because response to others (especially those who most need mercy) IS response to God. They are evidence that *Grace* is at work in us, *even when we don't know it!*

## ON WHAT BASIS?

With all this talk of *the Jesus Way* of love, I'm compelled to insist that our own capacity to love is not what has saved, is saving or will save us. What is the basis of our faith? John said it, "We love, because he [Love] *first* loved us" (1 Jn. 4:19).

Our love, such as it is, is evidence of *Abba's Grace*—a sign of willing participation in *Abba's* love initiative. *Grace*—the Spirit of divine Love—precedes, exceeds and propels God's transforming love in us. How else are we assured of *Abba's* saving *Grace* within us except that it spills out through our lives? Then we know Trinity is at work—not by signs and wonders, but by evidential love. Even while our love is immature, narrow and glitchy, it signals to and draws from the limitless spring of our divine Lover.

Further, to recognize the love of Christ at work in others who are not like us is *not* a compromise to pluralism (the idea that all paths lead to God). Rather, it is a testimony that *Grace* is everywhere present, "poured out on all people" (Acts 2:17)—initiating, igniting and eclipsing right belief, right behavior and even right love.

Let's reinforce John's theology of love with an easy review quiz:

- Who forged and founded the *Jesus Way of Love?* Whose love always comes prior to ours and prompts love to grow in us?
- Of what does the *Jesus Way* consist? Is it a matter of professing right doctrine? Joining the right club? Or is the *Jesus Way* a life of living faith that mirrors the love of Christ?
- What does *the Jesus Way* of living faith look like in practice according to Jesus? According to John?
- Do those who walk *the Jesus Way* save themselves? Who does?
- On what *basis* does Christ save those on *the Jesus Way?* Their

> beliefs? Their goodness? Their faith? Their love? Or is the *basis* found elsewhere?

"On what basis?" is a very strong phrase. The *Basis* of our faith is not our faith. Yes, *Basis* with a capital B, as in our Rock, our Foundation. The *Basis* of our faith is the *Abba*-love of the triune God. The *Basis* of our faith is the self-giving, cruciform Son whom *Abba* sent. The *Basis* of our faith is *Grace* alone, the fountain of divine Love that springs up from within (Jn. 4:14) to eternal life. *Abba,* Word and *Grace* (Father, Son and Spirit)—infinite triune Love—call us, fill us and lead us on their *Way of Life and Love.*

Ironically, "grace alone" traditions are not immune from reverting to "response alone" salvation (e.g. I'm "saved" by my sinner's prayer, my confession of faith, my baptism, etc.) while simultaneously recoiling from the *Jesus Way of love* as "works" that undermine *Grace.*

## *ABBA'S* LOVE

The *Basis* of our faith is *Abba's unfailing love.* Of course our response matters, but our faith is not the *Basis* of our faith! The *Basis* of our faith, of our response and of our love is *Abba's* lovingkindness and divine initiative. *Abba's Love* paved the *Jesus Way* for us to walk. Apostles such as John and Paul had clear ideas about what constitutes a good response, but they don't imagine our good response saves us. *Abba's* love, revealed in Christ, saves us by *Grace*—there's Trinity!

Since the Reformation, Protestants have asked rhetorically, "Does the goodness of man measure up to the perfect righteousness of God?" That question is a non-starter. Of course it doesn't. The question we should have been asking is, "Does *Abba* ever abandon his children?"

Of course he doesn't! Only on *that* Foundation—*Abba's unfailing love*—do we begin to understand *sola gratia* (grace alone). *Grace* (the transforming love of the Holy Spirit) proceeds from *Abba's* heart of love.

In the name of "none is righteous," even grace-alone religion often forgets it is *Grace* alone—not our right doctrine of grace alone—that reconciled us to *Abba's* house. When we glimpse *Abba's* amazing *Grace,* revealed in Christ's selfless love, we are taken by its expansiveness and beauty. We see that it rests not in our response, but in *Abba's* refusal to disown any of his children.

On the *Basis* of *Abba's love,* Christ transforms our hearts, inducing trust in him and love for others. Why? Because to behold his cruciform love is to become like him in this world (1 Jn. 4:17). Inspired by his sacrifice of *Grace,* we're drawn to willingly follow *the Jesus Way* of unselfish love. *He does this in us.* Our surrender to Christ's call is evidence that our hearts have been joined to his—proof that *Grace* is transforming us from the inside out. James 2:22 describes this love as the synergy (working together) of faith and works. We might go further to describe love as God's heart and ours working as one because in Christ, God and humanity are united forever.

Our response to the *Basis*—to *Abba's love*—does not cause, earn or secure *Abba's love.* It is the natural exhale of those who've inhaled the resuscitating love of our *Abba.* This is the testimony of both John and James. If we witness the exhalation of Love's Breath from someone, we can know they must have inhaled *Abba's* loving *Breath,* whether they could name it or not. For there is nowhere and no one on whom the *Breath of God's Spirit—Grace*—is not blowing.

Okay, I called this a *natural exhale,* but then we need to stop holding our breath, right? That's surrender. And we do need to breathe, right? That's participation—whether unconsciously or deliberately. Even breathing takes effort when life knocks the wind out of you. That's struggle—laying down resentment, apologizing and/or forgiving are obvious examples. Even then, we don't produce the breath of *Grace.* We receive it and we release it. On our difficult days, it might feel like we're gasping one breath at a time. In the best case, we synchronize our breathing to the divine Breath—the Breath of Love. Isaac the Syrian once said, "The person who lives in love reaps the fruit of life from God, and while yet in this world, even now *breathes the air* of the resurrection."

Paul's metaphor for synchronizing with *Grace is,* "keep in step with the Spirit" (Eph. 5:16, NIV). Christ conveys the same idea as an imperative of imitation: "Be like your *Abba* in heaven."

The *Jesus Way* is not about hapless striving to be what we aren't. He's not saying *pretend.* It's about becoming who we are by *Grace:* actualizing *Christ's* life in us and growing into recognizable children of our *Abba.* It's both a reality (Christ living in us—Gal. 2:20) and a process (Christ formed in us—Gal. 4:19) so that we both are and we become by *Grace* what Christ is by nature: children of God.

Here's Gregory of Nyssa, from his *Great Catechism:*

> Now the physically born child shares his parents' nature. If you have been born of God and have become his child, *then let your way of life testify to the presence of God within you. Make it clear who your Father is.* For the very attributes by which we recognize God are the very marks by which a child of his reveals his relationship with God. "God is goodness and there is no unrighteousness in Him." 'The Lord is gracious to all . . . He loves His enemies." "He is merciful and forgives transgressions." These and many other characteristics revealed by the Scripture are what make a godly life (*Oratio Catechetica,* 40).

## SUMMING UP

In this chapter, I've laid out the *Jesus Way* theme by surveying those Scriptures that use the road, path or *Way* as a metaphor for how we live our lives. There are slippery, foolish, destructive *ways* to avoid. And there's the *Way* pioneered by Jesus Christ—the *Christlike Way.* Jesus both walked and is the *Way of Life* and the *Way of Love.* The *Jesus Walk* of self-giving love and surrender is the *Way of the Cross* that led all the way to Golgotha. On that Cross, Christ revealed the *Basis* for our salvation: *Abba's* relentless, redemptive, reconciling love for the whole world.

And now Christ calls us to take up our cross and follow him—that is, to respond to his love by receiving and expressing his love. That's why love is the evidence of living faith and the way we recognize *Abba's* children. None but Christ managed this perfectly. How are we expected to? By embarking on the *Jesus Walk* in the same indwelling, transforming and empowering *Grace* that filled Jesus: the Holy Spirit of Love.

Later, in Part III, I will expand on eight radicals (literally "roots") of the *Christlike Way.* Before we get there, we need to be fully awake to the *unChristlike counterfeits* that make for an ugly gospel and an ugly faith. Pseudo-ways abound but I will sample just four of the biggies that confront us every day.

## THOUGHTS

1. Much of Scripture contrasts the two ways. Read Psalm 1 as an example. Can you see how Christ fulfilled Psalm 1 in his life? Can you see how the Pharisees may have imagined Christ violated Psalm 1? What lenses do we need to avoid using 'two ways' texts legalistically?

2. Meditate on the two trees of the Garden of Eden. How do they represent the two ways discussed in this chapter? How might we find ourselves eating from the "Tree of the Knowledge of Good and Evil"? How does "The Tree of Life" symbolize the Cross?

3. How does the apostle Paul integrate faith and love in his ministry and letters? How do his epistles embrace the commandment to love without falling into legalism? Hint: on what *Basis* does he call us to love?

## PRAYERS

*Because of this, I am kneeling down before the father, the one who gives the name of 'family' to every family that there is, in heaven and on earth. My prayer is this: that he will lay out all the riches of his glory to give you strength and power, through his spirit, in your inner being; that the king may make his home in your hearts, through faith; that love may be your root, your firm foundation; and that you may be strong enough (with all God's holy ones) to grasp the breadth and length and height and depth, and to know the king's love—though actually it's so deep that nobody can really know it! So may God fill you with all his fullness.* —Ephesians 3:14-19

# Part II

# Ugly Gospel, Ugly Faith: Four UnChristlike Ways

# Introduction: "Sorry, Not Sorry"

"Faithful are the wounds of a friend;
but the kisses of an enemy are deceitful."
—Proverbs 27:6

### "NOW WHO'S GOING TO HATE US?"

It's inevitable. Whenever I write on provocative themes, my wife Eden will half-jokingly ask, "Now who's going to hate us?" She asks because whether I'm retrieving ancient wisdom, exploring new territory or questioning problematic assumptions, I'm bound to step on a toe, push a button or trigger a sensitivity. I also know from experience that trying to play it safe has never alleviated that risk. Not in the slightest. And so I write what I care deeply about—I critique ideas and practices that I see as harmful. Sometimes my criticisms sting. But if I put my foot in my mouth, I hope you'll know I'm not trying to be hurtful. I'm looking for a better way. Or as they say in meme world, "Sorry, not sorry."

We're all in need of redemption from delusional *ideas* of "god." We also need freedom from the unChristlike *ways* that trickle down from those images. Just as we need to be cleansed of noxious notions of *who* God is—so too, we need deliverance from belief systems and faith practices that infect movements, shatter fellowships and injure souls. In this chapter, I'll unmask four fraudulent faiths—a mere sampling of the endless chorus that would lure us off the *Way*:

- Moralism – puritanical religion
- Partisan Amoralism – politicized faith
- Retributive Factionalism – culture wars ideology
- Nationalism and Civil Religion – clan and country creed

Big words. But fear not, all will become clear. I will explain.

My personal and shared experiences with trauma and addiction have convinced me that some wounds are so deep and some crimes so grievous that Christ alone can heal them and in fact, our darkness is the very place where we find him . . . or rather, where the Good Shepherd finds us.

The hard truth is that many of our wounds are inflicted by systems and individuals that identify as "Christian." An understandable impulse to flee toxic Christian environments arises. In cases of spiritual abuse (versus chronic discontent), survival instincts kick in that may also be the voice of the Spirit saying, "Flee!"

But if we hope to see our deepest wounds healed and our strongest hungers sated, I don't believe we can simply move on from Christ himself. I have no faith that any ideology (conservative, progressive, liberal, etc.) can meet the challenges of twenty-first century humanity. In the end, social and political ideologies are just prettied-up or dumbed-down secular religions. The litmus test for gauging any religious or ideological claim is how well they address the brokenness of the human condition. Redemption boils down to Christ or nothing. But what if our wounds were inflicted in his name?

Those who've truly experienced Christ will testify: he is not a religious fairy story, or one among many great teachers or spiritual avatars. I'm not talking about signing up for a religious club or signing off on a Christian creed. Faith is neither mental nor sentimental assent to an idea or belief system. Christ is known through authentic encounters that generate trust. I won't presume to prescribe what constitutes an encounter. I only know from my experience that when I met Christ in my abyss, where nothing and no one else could reach me, there was no "moving on" from Jesus. That's why I grieve for those who walk away from Christ. Hadn't they met him? Or had their religion offered them a disposable substitute? The woman at the well, the woman caught in adultery, even the one who denied him three times couldn't do it. They'd sooner be martyred—and were. Maybe this is where Judas Iscariot had it right: for him, it was Christ or nothing.

I hope you know him. Or that you'll somehow meet him on the *Way*. I hope you'll despair of endless knockoffs and impotent counterfeits. I pray you'll discover him in your deepest place of need. Now that would be a gospel story!

So now, let's commence with deconstructing these unpleasantries. Then we can truly "move on"—on to the *Way* of the Christlike God who calls cruciform people to follow him on his *Christlike Way*.

# Counterfeit 1

## MORALISM: When Morality Becomes Heresy

Just as Christless religion composes false images of God, so also it constructs false faiths—counterfeits to the *Jesus Way*. Readers are no doubt familiar with terms for classic religious perils such as legalism, ritualism and spiritual abuse. Much ink has been spilled elsewhere. I want to begin by defining and addressing a more slippery beast that seeks to divert us from the *Jesus Way*—namely, *moralism.*

Perhaps you haven't heard that term before or know what it includes. The first I heard of it was just prior to my first appearance on national television in Canada, circa 2004. Knowing I would primarily be addressing fellow Evangelicals, I asked one of my mentors, Vladika Lazar Puhalo, "If you had the opportunity to address the Evangelical church as a movement, what is the one thing you would say?"

He responded without any hesitation:

*"I would tell them, 'Your moralism is killing you.'"*

I didn't immediately understand what he meant. I had probably conflated moralism with legalism. I figured it had to do with obsessing over moral measuring sticks and using those sticks to beat Christ's flock rather than following the *Jesus Way* of Life or being led and empowered by the Holy Spirit. I knew Vladika wasn't rejecting *morality* as such. To clarify, I asked him, "What is the difference between Christlike morality and religious moralism?" Here was his answer:

> *Morality* is a condition of the heart, not conformity with the law. To become moral one must undergo a transformation of the inner person into the realization of Christ's moral imperatives (namely, love). No deed has any moral value unless it proceeds from the heart and is motivated by love. Otherwise, it is mere compliance.

> *Moralism* demands obedience to laws that may themselves be arbitrary and ideological, often feigning compassion, but with an underlying absolutism that cannot yield when proved wrong or contrary to reality.
>
> *Moralism* relies on fear. Fear worked a little better in the middle ages through superstition. Today, fear (and especially fear of death) only encourages us to grab at everything we can get in this life—it has the opposite effect. *Morality* requires a motivation other than law (fear of punishment), compulsion or fear. *Love alone is the ultimate motivator.*

In others words, *true morality* works from the inside out as Christ wins our hearts and transforms us by love, for love, to love. *True morality* is nothing less than the fruit of the Spirit, transfiguring us from glory to glory into the image of Jesus Christ. *Moralism,* by contrast, is externally imposed conformity to a set of rules or laws—*even good laws.*

With *moralism,* conformity is promoted as proof of faithfulness to whatever the dominant religion or ideology demands of you. Failure to conform is deemed *immoral* and *heretical*—grounds for derision or expulsion.

*True morality* is motivated by a new heart and empowered by indwelling love. *Moralism* is repressed behavior, manipulated by external pressures and demanded by those who wield the power.

## MORALISM AS HERESY

Vladika was making a radical claim. Morality itself can become a heresy. How so? When living within moral hedges becomes a substitute for what he calls "your life in Christ" or "living faith."

You know moralism has displaced your life in Christ when living faith is reduced to a system of correct behavior and moral merit badges instead of a dynamic relationship with the indwelling Holy Spirit. We don't acquire the presence of the Holy Spirit by accumulating moral merit badges.

The fruit of moralism is not authentic holiness. The great holiness movements of history may have started with real repentance and a "great awakening." It's possible. But historically, almost immediately, we see evidence of self-righteousness, pride and condemnation—so alien to the fruit of the Holy Spirit described in the New Testament. The moment we identify ourselves or our movement as the litmus test for morality, we consign everyone who breaks our social mores to the dung heap.

I was once given a stern warning by a staunch moralist on social media. He rebuked me by citing his favorite celebrity pastor, "Yes, God wears a velvet glove, but never forget that inside that glove is an iron fist."

No! *Abba's* hand is love through and through, even in his most severe mercy. Paul, like Hosea before him, was convinced that it's "the kindness of God that leads to repentance." More to the point, Christ demonstrated and taught that perfect holiness—for God and for us—consists only in perfect love. Righteousness is not mere taboo avoidance, but the genuine faith of unselfish (cruciform) love.

*Morality* itself is not the problem—but our morality must be rooted in and motivated by love. Human ethical systems come and go and vary according to one's culture, era or region. Required behavior in one territory may be a grievous sin in another. One camp's standard of righteousness may be a sure sign you're a pagan in the next. Religious culture may load meaning ("good" or "bad") into acts that have no foundation in love or faith—or those foundations crumbled at some point.

Keeping the law may preserve a society for a time, but it certainly never saves it. It didn't save the Pharisees; not even when they kept its commandments to the letter. Indeed, their *moralism* led them to reject God when he came in the flesh. Their self-righteousness crushed those they deemed "immoral," pushing them deeper into the darkness. Thus, their moralism stood as the height of unrighteousness. Do you see how dangerous an obsession with morality can be?

As Abraham was justified *by faith* (centuries prior to the reception of the Torah), so Christ fulfilled all righteousness by the "perfect law of love." Our struggle is not about defining and conforming to moralistic perfection nor is it an abstract imputed righteousness that changes nothing. Rather, we are being transformed by *Grace* into the image of Christ, whose love radiates from transfigured hearts in real life (Phil. 3:14, 2 Cor. 3:18).

## DEAD MAN'S BONES

Fr. Stephen Freeman is a discerning teacher who has helped me see exactly what's wrong with *moralism*. He echoes Christ's critique of moralism for a new era:

> The moral life, if rightly understood, cannot be measured by outward actions. The Pharisees in the New Testament were morally pure, in an outward sense, but, inwardly, were "full of dead men's bones." When morality is measured by dead bones, it is still nothing more than death. However, the path that marks the authentic Christian life should be nothing less than "new life," a "new creation." This is a work of grace that is the result of Christ "working within us to will and to do of His good pleasure" (Phil. 2:13).
>
> (Stephen Freeman, "Existential Despair and Moral Futility," *Glory to God for All Things*—blogs.ancientfaith.com).

So far, so good. Nothing new that any Bible-believing Christian wouldn't recognize from the Gospels and affirm. But then Freeman begins to meddle.

> What passes for a "moral life" in our culture is little more than the *successful internalization of middle-class behavior.* "I'm doing ok," we think. It is quite common for those who are "doing ok," to feel generally secure and superior to those who fail to do so. In earlier modern centuries, this modest morality was sufficient to earn someone the title of "Christian." *It meant nothing more than being a gentleman.*

Should well-behaved, middle-class gentlemen who fit the status quo become the measure of Christian morality? Perhaps their "morality" is nothing more than the fruit of carefully satisfying the status quo. If we are too naive to question how any status quo is formed and have no suspicions about how they are maintained, Freeman suggests raising an eyebrow at the myth of a self-made man:

> It is necessary, I think, to see the emptiness of our efforts (moral futility). Just as we cannot make ourselves to live, neither do we make ourselves better persons. An improved corpse is still a corpse.

> Our repentance is born out of the revelation of our emptiness and the futility of life apart from God . . . This is the work of God who hears our cries and works within us, doing what He alone can do, just as He alone gives us the life we live and breathe at every moment.

## TWO TREES IN THE GARDEN

I find it helpful to use the two trees in Eden as a metaphor to distinguish between living faith and moralism (religious or secular). *Moralism* arises when we seek to become divine by eating the fruit of the forbidden tree: the knowledge of good and evil and conformity to its code. *Living faith,* by contrast, partakes of eternal life at the tree of life (i.e. the Cross of Christ).

In the Garden of Eden, we see the life-and-death difference between the two trees. On my cul-de-sac in Canadian suburbia, it's not so obvious. Did I live today by faith in God's *Grace* and dependence on the Son of God . . . or was I just being the good neighbor everyone expects me to be? Be good, yes, please. But don't mistake that as capital for eternal life.

The two trees can look very similar, but consider:

*Moralism* is idealistic. First it says, "Come, eat of the knowledge of good and evil, and you will be like God." But when we eat, the ideal bites back: "You *must not* sin—but you *have* sinned. Shame on you! What will God think? Go, hide your face in shame!"

*Living faith,* in contrast, is realistic. Christ says, "All have sinned—of course you have! I'm not surprised or appalled. No need to hide! Come to the tree of life and freely partake of its healing fruit!"

Thus, *moralism* is intimately connected to that first tree—to law, judgment, shame and death. But *living faith* is rooted in the life of Christ—the cruciform image of divine Love. What is our "life in Christ"? Christ's transforming love for us. In the words of my colleague Greg Albrecht,

> Timid souls who are religious slaves live in fear, afraid that they may break a law and thus displease the Master, while the *Grace* of God is like the wind of the Holy Spirit, free to blow where it wills, filling sails of faith and propelling God's children boldly into new frontiers.

## THE MARKET FOR MORALISM

Since moralism is so shaming and punitive, you would think the market for it would have dried up long ago, especially in the hedonistic West. But no. It continues to thrive, and I see no signs of it ebbing away any time soon. Why not? How is it that even the younger generations flock to booming mega-churches to binge and purge on moralism?

I can think of four reasons from the hip:

**1. Moralism offers black-and-white certitude in a world of anxious grays.**

I've read that today's young people are the most anxious generation in history. If so, in addition to factors such as stimuli bombardment, a paralyzing overload of options and social media drama, they also flail about in a sea of moral ambiguity at ever younger ages. *Moralism* perceives the neuroses of living with "fifty shades of gray" and offers clarity—the knowledge of good and evil.

"Just tell me what to do!"

"Okay, we will." [But it will cost you].

**2. Moralism serves as false penance in a world without confession.**

The Evangelical rejection of private Catholic confessionals or Protestant liturgical absolution left a vacuum. To whom could you share your secret sins? From whom could you hear that you're forgiven? Accountability partners were laughably impotent—notorious for legalism and unreliable with confidentiality. What were they to do without an outlet?

One local pastor was describing the popularity of the current "hottest church in the city," where the preacher berates members weekly for their depravity: "You are disgusting. You have no idea how disgusting you are before God!"

Why, I asked, would they return for a beating every Sunday when I know for a fact that through the week, they continue to live like the rest of Vancouver's pagans? My pastor friend suggested that the verbal abuse serves as a pseudo-penance in lieu of confession or absolution. Attendees are cleansed of last week's immorality and licensed for the coming week's escapades by the haranguer's *moralistic outrage*. Rinse and repeat.

The reprimands are violent, but also cathartic . . . Self-flagellation for the suburbs.

**3. Self-loathing fuels entitlement and scapegoating.**

*Moralism* instills in its victims a deep sense of self-loathing, so it would make good sense to flee from it. But some can't or won't because failed moralism offers us the gift of entitlement. The fruit of failed moralism is self-loathing. Self-loathing triggers self-pity, which establishes our identity as victims. Victimhood, even self-inflicted, is a hot commodity because it sponsors a sense of entitlement. Then we project our self-hatred outward onto others—blaming and scapegoating—and ultimately, entitlement is our license for more immorality.

It's a self-centered and circular system, both for individuals and entire movements, which leads us to our fourth point.

**4. Moralism works just as well in Christless ideologies that thrive on retribution.**

*Moralism* is generally identified with religious legalism and conservative fundamentalism, but it's not restricted within those boundaries. *Moralism* is just as happy (and cruel) in vehemently anti-faith ideologies, so long as there's a "thou shalt" script to be followed and enforced by a movement's Sanhedrin and its mob—whether right or left, conservative or progressive, hierarchical or anarchist, Christian or atheist. It doesn't matter. What matters is those who don't adhere to the rules face swift retribution.

In the next two chapters, we'll see how this works in what I'm calling "partisan amoralism" (the political side) and "spectrum factionalism" (the ideological side). Both are profoundly moralistic *and* simultaneously immoral because they are rooted in the world system, united in opposition to Christ just as surely as Pilate and Caiaphas ever were.

## REJECTING MORALISM: NEITHER IMMORAL NOR AMORAL

Please understand that to reject *moralism* is not to adopt *immorality* (bad morals) or *amoralism* (absence of morals). I'm not advocating living beyond good and evil (that's Nietzsche), but rather, living from the Tree of

Life as branches grafted into Christ himself. In real life—*this* life—*Grace* (the Holy Spirit) internalizes and empowers the love-morality of Christ's life and teachings within those who orient themselves to self-giving love. When we discover that the moralistic counterfeits are bankrupt, the solution is *not* an exemption from or evacuation of goodness from our character. "May it never be," says Paul—his eyes rolling at the ludicrous notion. Rather, authentic *Grace* transforms us into Christ-followers in practice—bearing the fruit of love that grows on the Tree of Life.

## THOUGHTS

1. This chapter contrasts *true morality* with *moralism.* How would you describe the difference? Where have you witnessed true morality in action? Where have you experienced moralism and its effects?

2. We also distinguished between *moralism* and *living faith.* How do they get conflated in a child of faith? How do they infect a fellowship or movement? Can you recall times when Christ faced off with moralism in the gospels? What steps lead us from *moralism* back to *living faith?*

3. Review the ways in which our twenty-first century popular church culture still attracts adherents to *moralism?* How is it that *moralism* survives even in post-Christian contexts? Can you think of examples? What payoffs still attract you to *moralism?* Could you imagine being completely ready to let it go? If you did, do you think you would become immoral? Why or why not?

## PRAYERS

*Lord Jesus Christ, author of living faith and transformer of hearts, free us from the tyranny of moralism and establish the true morality of love as our Way of Life. Lead us from the enticements of the tree of Law to the tree of Life.*

# Counterfeit 2

# PARTISAN AMORALISM: When Politics Trump Morality

"The Devil makes many disciples by preaching against sin."
—Thomas Merton

When we separate Jesus from his ideas for an alternative social structure, we inevitably succumb to the temptation to harness Jesus to our ideas—thus conferring upon our human political ideas an assumed divine endorsement. With little awareness of what we are doing, we find ourselves in collusion with the principalities and powers to keep the world in lockstep with the ancient choreography of violence, war and death. We do this mostly unconsciously, but we do it. I've done it. And the result is that we reduce Jesus to being the Savior who guarantees our reservation in heaven while using him to endorse our own ideas about how to run the world. *This feeds into a nationalized narrative of the gospel and leads to a state-owned Jesus.*
—Brian Zahnd, *Farewell to Mars*

## PARTISAN AMORALISM DEFINED

**Partisan amoralism:** (1) When any national government, political party or ideological faction co-opts the Christian brand and replaces Christ's moral and ethical content with its own, remaking the faith in their own image. (2) When one's ethical center does not derive from Christ but from the talking heads who parrot the ever-shifting platform of one's political party.

In the preceding section, I recounted how fifteen years ago, my friend Vladika Lazar's greatest concern for my fellow Evangelicals was, "Your moralism is killing you." More recently I asked him, "Would your answer be different today?"

He replied, "Yes, Evangelicalism—and Christianity at large—has entered a new and more dangerous period: *"partisan amoralism."* I hadn't heard the phrase before and asked him to describe what he meant.

> Christian morality has now completely bowed the knee to political partisan policy. Christians today (not only Evangelicals and not only Americans) often identify more deeply with their government's policies or their political party's platform than with Christ on moral and ethical issues.

In other words, he sees contemporary Christians locating themselves less in the Gospels than on the left-right political or social spectrum. Thus, we become subservient to the groupthink dictates of the culture wars and its powerful "us-them" binary. *Partisan politics* and *spectrum ideology* would swallow the church whole. In truth, they are new religions masquerading beneath a thin mask of "Christianese" lingo and symbols.

I'm not talking about Christians with conservative or liberal leanings. I'm referring to those who redefine Christianity itself and rewrite the "politics of Jesus" according to their party handbook. This trend becomes especially obvious when a political party reverses its own policies and the church follows suit—as if Jesus had changed his mind with them.

Whenever one's political partisan allegiance leads Christians to reject Christ's central moral teachings—the *Jesus Way*—we are witnessing a counterfeit way and the fall of the church. I will explain each component of this allegation in the following pages.

## PARTISAN ALLEGIANCE (IDOLATRY)

Several words require very careful definition. I ask readers to bear *my* use of these words in mind, rather than swapping in other meanings that I don't intend.

The word *"partisan,"* as I use it, refers to *identification* with a political party or social ideology, in competition and at enmity with other camps in today's us-them, left-right hostilities. This is more than saying, "I voted for so-and-so" in the last election. I'm not discounting the hard choices involved in casting a ballot or entering public service in a broken democracy. After all, God sprinkles salt and light everywhere in the world.

Partisan allegiance as I define it is far more problematic than political engagement—it is to graft oneself onto an ideological identity, such as "*I AM* a conservative/progressive/liberal."

And yes, it is frequently also political: "*I AM* Republican/Democrat/Independent" (in America) or "*I AM* a Liberal/Progressive Conservative/NDP/Green" (in Canada), etc.

This compulsion to *identify* is especially powerful when it comes to the left-right political/social spectrum. I propose that *the spectrum itself is an idolatrous lie* that we have uncritically adopted—a matrix in which we're enslaved to "the world"—i.e. the world system at enmity with the kingdom of Christ:

> Do not love the *world*, or the things that are in the *world*. If anyone loves the *world*, the father's love is not in them. Everything in the *world*, you see—the greedy desire of the flesh, the greedy desire of the eyes, the pride of life—none of this is from the father. It is from the *world*. The *world* is passing away, with all its greedy desires. But anyone who does God's will abides forever. —1 John 2:15-17

John is not just talking about avoiding covetousness for material property—he's assessing a system that, however it claims to adopt "Christian values," hates the *Jesus Way* (1 Jn. 3:13; 4:1-4) and means to supplant it.

Nor is he advocating a "moderate" or "centrist" solution. The matrix comprises and enfolds the entire continuum.

Why? Because to be "partisan"—to "*I AM*"—to *identify* with spectrum ideology—is a question of *allegiance* to the party line or an ideological script. Partisans are *followers* of the party—*members* of a body other than Christ's. We are partisan when the party platform or policies *determine* (a euphemism for *dictate*) what we support and more critically, what we imagine to be "Christian."

Partisanism obviously plagues religious sectarianism, whether across or within faiths. For example, adherents of the major religious worldviews claim, "*I AM* Christian, Muslim, Hindu, Buddhist, Atheist," etc. Within faiths, we are also partisan about our denomination: "*I AM* Protestant, Evangelical, Charismatic, Catholic, Orthodox" or "*I am* Baptist, Pentecostal, Lutheran, Methodist, UCC, Mennonite," etc. These distinctions aren't necessarily evil in themselves, insofar as they locate us on our journey. But as factious labels used to identify the other as "enemy," we know well how rancid and violent they can become.

But in our era, my concern is not with naming our faith affiliation. The lethal issue I'm flagging is the poison of subordination of one's faith to political ideology. That's not stating the crisis strongly enough. To be *partisan* is to *co-opt and redefine* one's faith and morality in service of political ideology such that we imagine they are one and the same. So, the party not only trumps one's faith convictions—it recreates them in its own image and demands our fealty. Then effectively—in real life—the party *is* my faith. Left or Right is my *religion. I AM what I identify as* and ultimately, *"I AM* just following orders."

The repetition of *I AM* statements above are a creepy parody of Christ's *I AM* statements in John's Gospel. That's my point. Partisanism (as I've defined it) is in idolatrous competition with the first and last *I AM* claim to Lordship—loyalty to Christ alone. Baptismal identification with Christ and initiation in his kingdom challenges every other card-carrying membership we hold. When the two are at odds, if our party loyalty requires me to disobey or ignore Christ—or worse, to reinvent and rebrand Christ into the party's golden calf, elephant or donkey—then Paul's pointed charge to "come out from among them" is poignant and urgent.

And that is what I mean by "partisan."

## AMORALITY

The adjective *"amoral"* is normally defined as lacking moral sense or being unconcerned with whether one's actions are right or wrong. Thus, the phrase *"partisan amoralism"* means something like "my country, my party, my clan, right or wrong." It is loyalty to one's movement or ideology regardless of moral *compromise*—where compromise is code for using *immoral* means to justify political ends.

In Christian context, *partisan amoralism* puts one's ideological loyalties ahead of Christ's moral injunctions and ethical teachings. In short, it ignores, denies and betrays what Christ taught his disciples concerning good and evil, right and wrong, justice and injustice—demanding that we turn a blind eye and deaf tongue to party immorality.

You know you're battling the partisan matrix when you cite Christ on an issue of justice, mercy, morality or ethics and the first reaction is to be dismissed with a political label in the name of setting aside Christ's explicit commandments. My friend Wendy Francisco says it well:

> This is like the world Jesus entered—a world totally out of touch with God. Everything is politics. Politics is no longer a framework of civil function, it is our flesh and our breath and the glasses we see through all day long. Our standard of judgment. Our measure of righteousness.
>
> It is our god. It's not for me. It was not just evangelicalism that I left, but a dead mechanism that shapes evangelicalism and many other large movements. I left a fallen framework of humanity.
>
> I am interested in confronting the enemy in me. Forcing a moral agenda is the great evil that allows us to avert our eyes from our own hearts. Both sides are exchanging love for law and we are seeing sanity leave us.
>
> Do I want the red pill or the blue pill? How about no pill. I want something older, something deeper.

## PARTISAN OR PROPHETIC?

Understand that the *partisan way* is a counterfeit way that attempts to silence the prophetic voices (i.e. those who speak the *Truth* to power) and seduce the herd into groupthink and complicity with injustice. The partisan way doesn't allow the church to speak either *for* justice or *against* injustice because when Christ, the disruptive voice of resistance to death, challenges any of the popular scripts—and he always will—the partisans will accuse you of politicizing.

So, what will the church's role be—which voice will Christ's followers assume? Will we be cheerleading chaplains who echo the desires of the state or its parties? Or will we give voice to the gospel's subversive message?

This is a life-and-death problem because no matter where you are on the damned spectrum, the partisan belief in redemptive violence is convinced that *someone* must die for the world (or your world) to be made right. Who dies? Anyone we demonize as a threat to our personal freedom or national security.

Christ's seamless ethic of life ("and that more abundantly") for *all* finds nowhere to lay its head in that system. Oppose death-dealing of any kind and you'll be pigeonholed into the matrix and silenced by some "other" on the spectrum. But whether we're talking about the death penalty, abortion or terrorism, my friend Ken Tanner likes to insist, "The Cross of Christ means no one else needs to die to make the world right."

Christ must have our first allegiance and no party's manifesto takes priority over the gospel. To lapse into *partisan amoralism* by identifying party politics as the "Christian" position is, frankly, defection from the *Jesus Way*. We may argue our opinions, but when we bring Jesus' name into it, we'd better make our case from a sustained engagement with his actual words in the four Gospels.

## THOUGHTS

1. I've suggested we can engage in political processes (like voting) and even enter public service without compromising fealty to the *Jesus Way*. *Partisan amoralism* denies or redefines the *Jesus Way*. How might you stay the course when you see your party manifesting unChristlike ethics?

2. I've included peacemaking and care for the poor as Christlike Ways that get slotted into spectrum politics—put in their place, so to speak. Can you think of other elements of Christ's message of public faith that get co-opted and politicized by the spectrum for party means? How about unChristlike ways that get labeled "Christian" and pervert the gospel?

3. Colonialism, Capitalism and Marxism, democracy and monarchy—even anarchy—have all claimed and even assumed Christ for their agendas. It's been disastrous. We might think the *Jesus Way* solution is an apolitical, privatized faith. That doesn't sound like the Sermon on the Mount (as we'll see). Is there a "Politics of Jesus"—a public faith that transcends our polarized spectrum?

## PRAYERS

*Lord Jesus Christ, King over all kings, please guard my heart and mind from party religion. Open my eyes to the counterfeit ways they preach in your name. Grant me the gift of faithfulness to your way amidst the bombardment of political propaganda. Grant me the courage to follow your Way when popular culture calls me away from the Narrow Way of cruciform love.*

# Counterfeit 3

# RETRIBUTIVE FACTIONALISM: Are You on the Spectrum?

"Identity is only as helpful as it is descriptive."
—Stephen Jersak via Dominic Jersak

A huge diversity and polarization exists in our world. The world has become more insular, closing ranks around the many forms of identity. Many take sides irrationally and when some fact or new data contradicts the worldview that defines and confines them, that information is rejected and recast to fit the indoctrination so that "their side" is always right.
—Greg Albrecht

## SPECTRUM FACTIONALISM

The previous section focused on the heresy of altering or redefining Christian morality according to party policy—when faith crawls beneath the sheets with partisan politics. Related to *partisan amoralism,* we need to expand on a phrase I used earlier: *"spectrum factionalism."*

I am more familiar with the term *tribalism* but was admonished by friends to consider its problematic and complex use historically, especially as a colonialist reference to indigenous people groups. Credit where it's due: Sean Davidson and Glenn Runnalls suggested *factionalism* as a more sensitive and accurate alternative, defined this way:

> **Factionalism** involves aggressively partisan and schismatic behavior across the socio-political spectrum. One effect is an especially puritanical form of *othering.* That is, we treat people in our own camp as healthy and sane and others as a contagion.

Yes, that says it exactly. Indeed, that definition covers eight of the infractions in Paul's list of "the works of the flesh" in Gal. 5:20-21: hostilities, strife, jealousy, bursts of rage, selfish ambition, factiousness, divisions and envy. That's *factionalism.*

Paul also warns readers that "those who practice such things will not inherit the kingdom of God." I don't think he means "they won't go to heaven when they die." He's listing ways we stray from the straight path, the *Jesus Way* that leads to God's kingdom of peace and justice on earth as in heaven. No ideological faction will fulfill its promise of utopia for all—they are always fixated on *us first.*

Now, let's press harder against binary mindsets, casting a net wider than political membership to include any of the social movements that occupy today's cultural battlefields. Here's an indisputable fact: intrinsic to the constructs of left-right, liberal-conservative, populist-establishment, etc. is an *us-them assumption of division and exclusion.*

The us-them "othering" mindset has proven impotent in creating a just society or achieving a greater common good. *Othering* refers to the ways we classify individuals or groups as "them" so we can exclude them from belonging or marginalize their voices.

The whole ideological spectrum is an *othering* structure. It relies on demonizing the other, often in the name of opposing (and self-centered) notions of "freedom"—a euphemism for power-grabbing self-will. To some degree, all of us are immersed in that adversarial matrix of *spectrum factionalism.* Politically, socially, theologically—we live and move and have our being whenever we cubbyhole ourselves and the other into opposing camps.

It's unlikely I can write about this without doing so myself. I can only confess and lament my complicity. As part of the problem, I insist that seeking justice or real freedom *anywhere* along the culture wars spectrum(s) is inviolable. Why? I'll say it again: the spectrum itself is a lie—the "spirit of this world." It's the über modern algorithm (even literally) in which we're all trapped into polarizing groupthink and exclusion of the other.

The twin problems of human self-will and injustice are not solved on any *us-them* spectrum. Nor can they be resolved if we switch sides while failing to change spirits. We just end up handcuffed to the other side of the same chain-link fence of division. Ernest Hemingway saw it long ago:

> Being against evil doesn't make you good. Tonight, I was against it and then I was evil myself. I could feel it coming just like a tide.

> . . . I just want to destroy *them.* But when you start taking pleasure in it you are awfully close to the thing you're fighting.

The *Jesus Way* calls us and frees us from the fence into an alternative reality, "a kingdom not of this world," governed by another King, another rule (love) and another gospel (peace).

That's why I contend that the spectrum itself and any allegiance to it is "the world" system that the apostle John rejects. It is ultimately devoted to hatred of the other (1 Jn. 2:15-17). That sense of *world* (in contrast to the world God loves in Jn. 3:16) hates Christ and his *Way* of peace and reconciliation (Jn. 15:18).

## IF I'M "WOKE" BUT HAVE NOT LOVE: SIAMESE TWEETING FISH

On June 12, 2016, an assault-rifle toting homophobe massacred forty-nine people and wounded fifty-three others in a gay nightclub in Orlando, Florida. At the time, it was the deadliest mass shooting by an individual in American history.

I worried that amid our rightful grief and anger, uncontrolled outrage might play into the hands of far-right extremists. I unwisely posted this comment on social media:

"Let us guard our hearts from outrage, because outrage makes us vulnerable to the outrageous."

I was sincere but stupid. Even though I validated anger against injustice, joined in the grief for lives lost and affirmed calls to concrete life-saving changes, the damage was done. An offended activist/critic (self-identifying as an "angry, queer atheist") latched onto the statement as ammo with which to attack me. Hoping to de-escalate the offense and make amends, I confirmed his critique, issued an apology and suggested (wrongly) that the greater power behind his own activism might be love rather than anger. (He denied it. And who was I to say?). I affirmed his work as a volunteer in safe-houses for transgender teens at risk. And I offered my social media platform to promote donations to a safe-house of his choice.

His response was immediate: "You misunderstand me. My goal is to create a world in which your grandchildren are embarrassed of you."

His answer was exactly what I had been worried about—that our outrage toward this heinous crime would devolve into hateful and venomous resolve.

Hurt and angry, I replied [bad idea!], "Your tone is so fundamentalist—it reminds me of Jerry Falwell, Sr." Now I was *outraged* (there it is!) at his hatred and self-righteousness in the name of justice. I both blocked him and mirrored his attitude. We were Siamese fighting fish trapped in the same tiny bowl of hostility. He was *not* "woke." And apparently, in that heated "us-them" moment, neither was I.

We cannot claim to be "woke" and have not love. That's not doing justice, loving mercy or walking humbly. At least his -ism doesn't require that. My faith does. Whose was the greater sin?

The whole incident blindsided me because I had grown accustomed to taking shots from the fundamentalist "conservatives"—to the point of bored detachment. But this felt like a below-the-belt blow. Why? Probably because I had imagined myself as an ally. I was forgetful of how the spectrum works and how it treats missteps.

Do you understand? It's not just angry atheists who oppose Christ. The cruel Christian is no less an enemy of the *Jesus Way*. When our wounds and anger—very much real—become excuses for unChristlike means to securing justice, we've fallen into factiousness. As James says, "The wrath of man does not produce the righteousness of God . . . Peacemakers who sow peace sow a harvest of justice."

If self-giving love gives way to self-will, if advocacy morphs into open derision, if Christ's requirements around forgiveness don't extend to the hated other, then cruelty will ultimately be easier (and more destructive). One can leave religion without ever becoming free in Christ.

## PECKING ORDER

The spectrum is relentless . . . and not only with cruelty to the "other side." Somehow, by design, any faction eventually turns on their own—it's cruel and ugly and inevitable.

On another occasion, I witnessed the social media lynching of a pastor after he posted an inclusive but apparently problematic tweet—nowhere near as insensitive as mine. I'm sure I even "liked" and "retweeted" it. At first, some thoughtful critics engaged in respectful pushback. I honor such men and women. I like to say their resistance is *not* futile—it's fertile and fruitful. Respectful engagement is an inclusive and productive act.

But by day's end, the manure hit the fan and character assassination commenced. No holds barred. That week, David Hayward (a.k.a. "The NakedPastor") private messaged me. He's a fellow "Ex-vangelical" and a cartoon critic of unChristlike religion. Here was his commentary:

> Hey Brad:
>
> Next time you're over, we should hang out.
>
> I'm feeling sorry for our friend these days.
>
> I think what he tweeted was honest but unfortunate.
>
> Here's the thing though: it's impossible to develop, grow and arrive in public and online. You are crucified until you are perfect. Which of course never can happen because, well, you get crucified before you get perfect.
>
> I'm saddened by some people who I worked alongside online for justice that I am so familiar with. I got crucified for some mistakes I made. And no matter how much I grew through that, and no matter how much I apologized, and no matter that I even corrected the mistakes, it was never enough for some.
>
> I critique things. I know. But I admire people who take the critiques and change something that's terribly wrong.
>
> That's what I did when I got critiqued.
>
> But it didn't seem to matter.
>
> There are some critics who believe that once you're an asshole you're always an asshole, no matter what you do.
>
> To me, they are mean-spirited and lazy people who deeply delight in watching others suffer, and they especially love the praise they get from others who laud them for their valiant efforts to make the world a perfect place by crucifying anybody they can find who doesn't meet their standards.
>
> It's exhausting, sad and disappointing.
>
> You know, I raised chickens many years ago. I always had to watch the chicks when they first came. If one had even the slightest blemish, say, on one of their feet, they had to be separated or they'd

be pecked to death. Even then, they would never be integrated in. They usually died. Hence the phrase "pecking order."

This is what I see online. People delight in making and watching a progressive Christian bite the dirt because he isn't perfect, his theology doesn't match theirs, and his church policies aren't fully developed yet . . . as I'm sure they will be one day if he's given the chance.

It's ugly.

I agree with David. It's as Tim Minchin wrote in his song *15 Minutes,*

> I am scared to write anything
> that might upset my own tribe,
> but never mind, 'cause in the future,
> everyone will have their 15 minutes of shame.

For all his talent, I'm not a Minchin fan—I generally find him to be a cynic and mocker of faith, but give the devil his due, he knows where factionalism goes:

> 15 minutes of shame, where they are unforgivable,
> irredeemable, inexcusable scum,
> fit only to be strung up in the village square,
> I will see you there.

My son Justice sees this all too well. He posted the following ardent exhortation on his Instagram feed—flexing his independence. You'll see I've been influenced by him:

> We need to break free from this new form of violent group-think. I see society weaponizing shame as an instrument of control, place hyper peer pressure on each other to conform blindly to whatever the current popular belief, stance or opinion is.
>
> We have simply swapped one toxic system for another and it has pushed society into a deeper state of anxiety and close-mindedness. I spit in the face of this toxic system. I'm leaving the matrix forever and taking back my freedom of individuality.

## TRANSCENDING THE MATRIX: BOB & CAROL

What if instead of goose-stepping to the ugly faux-faith of factionalism, we committed to the *Jesus Way* alternative that transcends the spectrum path and remains rooted in Christ?

I was treated to a beautiful example of escape from the matrix by two diverse friends. The story is more vivid if you remember my conservative background, where ominous Christian trigger terms were uttered in *whispers.*

Bob and Carol were fellow students in a university module where I teach. Before the course, I imagine Carol being a tad nervous. After all, the university in question has a *Christian* core and the students in the program normally identify as Christian.

Yes, Carol is a Christian, too—one of the most mature Christ-followers I know. So why be nervous? You see, Carol is also a *lesbian.* And you know how "Christians" can be. Perhaps she had to wrestle through how sincere our welcome would feel in a classroom of mixed faith cultures.

But the university is also *inclusive,* fully embracing of anyone, regardless of race, gender, sexuality or social standing . . . including lesbians, a word we don't need to whisper.

Prior to the course, Bob was likewise nervous. After all, this was an *inclusive* university. He knew that gay students are welcome. But Bob is a straight, white male—he feels secure about that. Bob isn't so sure about homosexuality. He's a conservative pastor (the sane, moderate type). More specifically, word has it he may also be a *Republican.* He too needed assurance that he'd be welcome. You know how "inclusive" people can be.

But the university welcomed him. We are, remember, an *inclusive* school, fully embracing of anyone, regardless of religious affiliation or even political leanings . . . including Republicans.

The prevailing perception of Christianity today is that Christians are judgmental and unkind. But by welcoming both Bob and Carol, the school was practicing the *heart* of Christlike faith in terms of the *Jesus Way.*

In this increasingly polarized political and cultural era, we hope to be a refuge of intentional hospitality and inclusion. We want people to feel free to be themselves, faithful to their own journey. Consequently, we are an affirming, inclusive community that values and embraces *all* who want to join our community and journey with us.

Now Bob and Carol sat together in class for two weeks—side by side. They obviously differ. Both regard their differences as faithful Christ-following. They both like and love each other—and they say so often.

The loudest voices would demand Carol and Bob to join their culture wars' us/them construct. Choose a side and bash the other! But what if the fault-line dividing the whole population into one of two camps is a farce? What if MOST people are like Bob and Carol, able to differ and love and coexist *together*? What if spectrum aggression does not describe the general population? What if the 10% or 5% fundie extremes at each end of the spectrum are mirroring each other from their little camps , campaigning to recruit the Bobs and Carols from the spacious common ground of mutual respect into the hatefulness of unChristlike and uncivil wars?

Or maybe Bob and Carol truly are rare. Are they groundbreakers and peacemakers in an insane culture? Well, then they are models of God's alternative society, sharing one mind (a la Phil. 2)—and their one mind is not agreement on *theologoumena* (doctrinal opinions). One mind, as defined by Paul, is that we share in the *kenotic* humility of Christ that comes from orienting all our various perspectives toward the Cruciform God of self-giving love. To *behold* that is to *become* that in some degree. Bob and Carol modeled it beautifully.

Their friendship works because while Bob is conservative, he's not a fundamentalist. And while Carol is gay, she's not an ideologue. Bob never calls her an abomination and Carol never calls him a homophobe. Their embrace of each other may even run them into trouble with those who expect them to be exclusive and hateful of the other. But their *Jesus Walk* means they don't even think that way. Bob doesn't reject and condemn Carol's sexuality—that would not be faithfulness. He listens to her carefully as they share meals and study together. Carol doesn't ridicule or silence Bob's conservatism—that would not be faithfulness. She shares her story patiently, from the heart. They've both transcended the culture wars' factionalism and its destructive *othering*. Instead, they enjoy their shared union in Christ.

Their journey into relationship couldn't have been easy for either of them. But surrendering to the *Jesus Way* is a lot lighter yoke than the burden of judgment and resentment. And what do you know? They discovered that they are spiritual siblings, born, not of sameness or willfulness, but by the Spirit of *Grace* that makes them family.

## RENEW YOUR MIND

I'll say it again: the left-right matrix is itself the partisan, factionalist delusion. Reject it altogether—renew your mind. Don't worry about the "other side." Worry that you still believe in sides and practice othering, because as long as we do, we're still ensnared. Wiggle free first and then help your brother out.

*Partisan amoralism* and *spectrum factionalism* are counterfeits—they betray *the Jesus Way*. And when our party line or faction ideology is cross-branded with Jesus, we take the Lord's name in vain—as if our ideology is God's image in this world or our talking points represent Christ's kingdom.

## THOUGHTS

1. The issue in this chapter is not the existence of distinct people groups or faith convictions, etc. Christ is, after all, Lord of "every tribe, tongue and nation." The great variety of cultures and convictions is ultimately enriching. The warning is against idolizing our clan, crowd or camp as superior—turning it into a contentious faction. Instead, we can be grateful for our cultural and spiritual inheritance. For example, I would identify as a Christ-follower with Anabaptist and Orthodox convictions. I'm also a Canadian boy of prairie extraction. My friend Joe Beach would certainly identify strongly as a Denver Broncos, Tom Wright and Bob Dylan fan. Who are "your people"?

2. The problem occurs in factionalism with any *-ism* that identifies "the other" as an enemy to be excluded or silenced. What groups were you indoctrinated to "demonize" as a child? Do you still struggle to see "the other" as a brother or sister? Did you learn to regard certain races, faith groups or political persuasions as enemies to be feared or hated? Be honest. Was it the Commies? Or the Catholics? How about Muslims? Oh, I know!

It's the Yankees, right? Can you recognize "them" on sight with a glance? What marks them as "other"? Complexion? Mannerisms? Dress code?

3. Ponder how Christ has dismantled the wall of "us-them," "in-out" separation. What does that look like? How might Christ accomplish this unity without destroying the beauty of diversity? Hint: what is the glory and wealth of the nations that the kings of the earth will bring into the New Jerusalem (Rev. 21:26)? Could this be about our cultural uniqueness, gathered together as a diverse offering of worship?

## PRAYERS

*Lord and King of every tribe, tongue and nation, grant me a spirit of humility and charity, that I would view others different than me through your eyes. Empower me to hold and cherish difference. Cleanse me of the idolatry of factionalism and the sins of othering and exclusion. Free me from the tyranny of the spectrum so that I can embrace everyone as they are, just as you have.*

# Counterfeit 4

# NATIONALISM & CIVIL RELIGION

Evangelicals have sliced up a religion explicitly built by Jesus to be unified—anti-factional. They have turned to idols—including their blasphemous belief in America as God's chosen country. They have embraced wealth and nationalism as core goods, two ideas utterly anathema to Christ.

—Andrew Sullivan, "America's New Religions"

"When you don't have a real God, your nation and your politics, of course, become your god."

—Richard Rohr

We'll finally round out our sampling of the major current counterfeits to the *Jesus Way* with a look at *nationalism* and *civil religion*—"we" because I've recruited a bit of help, as you'll see shortly.

## NATIONALISM DEFINED

***Nationalism*** and ***civil religion*** are sometimes related, but they're not identical. Sometimes, we use the word *nationalism* to describe *patriotism* toward a specific country. For example, in his landmark manifesto, *Postcards from Babylon,* Brian Zahnd critiques "American Nationalism" as a counterfeit to the *Jesus Way.* He identifies its glaring trifecta of patriotism, civil religion and empire. In my view, he nails it.

I'm going to come at *nationalism* along slightly different lines: i.e. when *nationalism* idolizes races or people groups rather than specific nation-states.

A clarifying example was Adolf Hitler's "German nationalism." When Hitler wrote *Mein Kampf,* his nationalist obsession was the reunification of the German people and what he saw as their right to an ever expanding

*Fatherland*—German-controlled territory large enough to meet their agricultural and industrial needs. He wanted to gather the German *Volk* (folk) or *nation*, scattered post-World War One by the Treaty of Versailles across the countries of Germany, Austria and parts of France and Czechoslovakia. To him, justice meant regathering his people and regaining their territory as a cohesive unity—an empire of destiny with global appetites and heavily religious overtones. National Socialism (Nazism) included a poisonous recipe of pseudo-Christianity, German mythology and the occult. To the Germans crushed after "the Great War" (1914–18), *der Fuhrer's* Messianic promises stirred *German nationalist* blood.

Hitler also recognized that Jews are not merely a religious faith—they are in fact a people group—a *nation*. He reasoned that the German and Jewish *nations* couldn't share one homeland or control one state and its apparatuses (government, courts and press). His perception that the Jews flourished in positions of influence and power fueled his deep resentment toward them and desire to be rid of them. Hence, his plan for the expulsion or eradication of the Jews from what he regarded as German territory. Today, we call this agenda "ethnic cleansing."

How tragic and ironic that in March 2019, Prime Minister Benjamin Netanyahu declared that Israel "is the national state, not of all its citizens, but only of the Jewish people."

Those who balked were charged with anti-Semitism. Jewish opponents who rejected "Bibi's" domestic policies as apartheid were dismissed as "self-hating Jews." I personally believe in Israel's right to exist as a secure and peaceful state. But is the Prime Minister's policy of nationalism impervious to critique? What of Judaism's great prophetic tradition of justice?

I raise the country-nation distinction because of the overt resurgence of *nationalism* today—especially among Christians. We need to be clear that *nationalism* is *not* simply love for one's country. Rather, it is the belief that one's people group has first dibs on a territory, state power and civil rights, regardless of whether they or other people groups were the first occupants or have been citizens for generations.

Further, as with Nazi doctrine, today's *pop-nationalism* inherently regards other people groups as threats to be feared, hated and expelled.

Since *nationalism* is first about race rather than country, it becomes implicitly racist toward visible minorities, paranoid of their presence and resistant to their influence. Thus, appeals to *nationalism* are not primarily about love for one's country. Across Europe and North America, they are "dog-whistles" (i.e. subtly aimed political messages intended for the in-group) for *white nationalism.* And of course, whenever white nationalism bares its ugly fangs, its counterparts across the races are energized.

Again, *nationalism* in this sense is not just patriotism—it is specifically about racial subordination. If you didn't know this, you're probably not a *nationalist* (thank God), no matter how much you love your country. Not that we must ignore or hate our own people—I love my Czech, Scottish and Canadian heritage. The *-ism* in *nationalism* comes when I believe my national identity makes me superior and anyone else second-rate and subservient.

In the case of America, *nationalism* is diametrically opposed to Thomas Jefferson's statement, "We hold these truths to be self-evident, that *all men are created equal,* that they are endowed by their Creator with certain unalienable Rights, that among these are Life, Liberty and the pursuit of Happiness." I realize that Jefferson's *"all men"* were once implicitly limited to white male landowners. Black slaves, American natives, Hispanic occupants and women of all races didn't count. But to the degree we're past that (we're not), his words, at least, described an *anti-nationalist* vision.

Some, in Europe and North America, have labeled themselves *Christian nationalists*—as if Christians of European heritage have a God-given birthright to govern the land and rule the world. That's not just a bad idea—it's a tried and true catastrophe that has nothing to do with the *Jesus Way.*

So here it is. *Nationalism* competes for the *Jesus Way.* When Paul said, "In Christ there is neither Jew nor Greek," he wasn't referring to the state-territories called Israel and Greece. He was claiming Christ's Lordship envelops all *people groups*—every race, color and culture—where none shall dominate, oppress or exclude another.

## IMPERIAL BEASTS

*Nationalism* is monstrous but the Bible also refers to other "beasts" that we've historically called "empires." Imperial beasts come in various forms.

The Bible describes these beasts in Daniel 7 and again in Revelation 13. Historically, they included Assyria, Babylon, Persia, Greece and Rome. These were expansive empires—military industrial complexes—in which city-states had evolved into empires, demanding total allegiance equivalent to religious devotion. Empires in those days were usually autocracies with kings or emperors who enjoyed divine status and required worship along with their pantheon of pagan gods.

The empire itself would also become a sacred idea greater than any one king—a political deity that survives and transcends the passing of one monarch to the next. For a nation-state to rise to empire status, it must be infused with sacred significance such that we become willing to sacrifice our children as fodder for its vision.

Such were the biblical beasts. Eventually, in the West, the Holy Roman Empire gave way to competing colonial powers who raced to plant their flag across every square inch of the world. Great Britain, France, Portugal and Spain were powerful beasts for a time.

All of these, whether monarchies or democracies, were colonizing empires that also claimed to be *Christian theocracies.*

*Theocracy* is a form of government where the ruling powers presume to reign in the name of the God or religion they worship. Israel was a theocracy of Yahweh, whether under judges, kings or in exile. The Holy Roman Empire was a hybrid monarchy and Christian theocracy. Today, Iran is a hybrid of Islamic theocracy and modern democracy. *Theocracies* by definition claim to hold high a specific religion, its god and its Holy Books. Thus, the clergy of a theocracy holds great political power, at least in principle.

I worry about Christians who campaign to elect enough Christian politicians to make America—history's most powerful empire—a *theocracy.* That's a terrifying thought. Imagine a Christian Taliban securing the Supreme Court and legislating their moralism—*theonomy*—Christian *sharia.* But America is *not* a *theocracy,* and I pray it never will be. Neither were France or Russia after their revolutions. The Enlightenment revolutions that overthrew the monarchy also overthrew *theocracy.* They formally divorced state and church.

Still, a nation-state or empire can reject *theocracy,* claim separation of church and state, and yet still be religious. We call this phenomenon *civil religion.*

## CIVIL RELIGION DEFINED

*Civil religion,* first described by Jean-Jacques Rousseau in *The Social Contract* (1762), takes the next step (chronologically) beyond theocracy by imagining it leaves religion behind. Civil religion is a public profession of faith that inseminates its politics with its founders' philosophies and values, then prescribes doctrines, rites and rituals for its citizens. Rather than marrying an institutional religion, such as Islam or Christianity (thus castrating clergy power), it claims separation from established religion while itself becoming a religion.

*American civil religion* is widely accepted as a reality by both patriots and detractors. Others vehemently deny it or are in denial of it. Others acknowledge that America has become a civil religion but actively resist it.

I am not an American. I cannot speak for America. And while my principle audience happens to be American, I am not America's judge nor its prophet. Nor are hardly any who claim to be—I know this because of their *partisan amoralism* and *spectrum factionalism. See above!*

Before I go on, let me be clear: what follows should not be heard as a "hate your country" rant. The *Jesus Way* doesn't require us to hate our people or be ungrateful for the land in which we live. But can there be any question that he calls us to undivided allegiance to his kingdom? Christ's gospel, "Repent, for the kingdom of God is at hand," comes with an implicit exhortation to turn from all counterfeit ways and pervading idolatries, including *nationalism* and *civil religion.*

Perhaps as an observer with some credentials in political philosophy, I could ask: do the following analogies have any merit as markers of civil religion? And if so, do you see it as problematic?

## IS AMERICA A RELIGION?

If America had a *confession of faith,* it might be the Pledge of Allegiance. Its primary *images* (using that term advisedly) could be "Old Glory," Lady Liberty and its *standard,* the American Eagle. If America has *solemn rites* and *rituals,* they include "presenting colors" during a range of *sacred ceremonies.* Events such as inaugurations, the national prayer breakfast and burial rituals for Armed Forces personnel are religiously choreographed services. *Sacred relics* might include the Statue of Liberty and the Liberty Bell, but the *deification* of Old Glory stands out strongest. If someone violates one of the many *commandments* (the Flag Code) for its proper use and display, the misuse is counted by some as *sacrilege.* Can national flags become *idols* we worship?

*A good test:* would you die for the flag? Would you kill for it? What does honor of burial in a flag represent? It means we've made the *ultimate sacrifice* in service of our nation. Is that a bad thing? I don't think so. But is it a religious act? And in that case, which religion?

*Another test:* what if a pastor dares to remove *the Stars and Stripes* from his church stage or hangs it below the "Christian flag" on their church flag pole? Just watch. I've seen it become a national news item! Disrespect the flag and you may feel the wrath worthy of a traitor—civil religion's equivalent to a *heretic.* Conversely, others deem their right to burn the flag as an equally sacred first amendment right!

How about *Scriptures?* If America is a religion, it would have canonical texts, right? How about the Declaration of Independence, the Constitution and especially certain of its Amendments? Do other inspired writings or speeches come to mind? There have been some epic oratories, from Lincoln's Gettysburg Address to MLK's "I Have a Dream" speech.

So too, an extended *hymnography* abounds, including multiple national anthems (*The Star-Spangled Banner, America the Beautiful, My Country Tis of Thee, God Bless America*) and a few runners-up, old and new (*This Land Is Your Land, The Battle Hymn of the Republic* and *God Bless the U.S.A.*).

And *dogmas?* Not all Americans agree with the doctrines of the "Manifest Destiny" and "American Exceptionalism," but those who do, do so religiously. America's highest moral value ("freedom") is enshrined in *mottos* and *slogans* such as "The American Dream," "Life, liberty and pursuit of happiness," and "Give me liberty or give me death."

The United States' highest *holy day*—Independence Day—celebrates America's liberation from the tyranny of the British Empire. Establishing independence came at great cost, which leads us to America's *saints and martyrs*—its great presidents, generals, activists and those in the military who've *sacrificed* their lives in battle.

Some heroes sit like gods in their "temples" (e.g. the Washington Monument and Lincoln Memorial). A striking example is the "Apotheosis of Washington" in the dome of the Capitol Building, in which America's first president ascends with the angels to *become a god* among the gods (that's what *apotheosis* means) after the pattern of the ancient Greek and Roman pantheons.

## IN GOD WE TRUST–WHICH GOD?

Upon reflection, a case can be made. America appears to be both an empire and a civil religion, at least by analogy. *Next question:* Is that religion also Christian? When we read "In God we trust" on the currency, is the God in question our Lord Jesus Christ? That's an ongoing debate.

The difficulty is that the religion of America and the faith we call Christianity are not identical, and yet they've been blended. Sometimes, they overlap and at other times, they compete. When the President says, "And may God bless these United States of America," some hear an invocation to the God revealed in Jesus and rejoice that they still live in a "Christian nation."

Others point out that many of the founding fathers did not identify with classical Christianity. They were avowed *Deists* who believed in "Nature's God" or Providence. *Deism's* Creator/clockmaker is impersonal and does not interact with the universe. That "God" leaves its operation entirely to natural law and human reason, similar to Freemasonry's "Great Architect."

*Deism* is not apostolic Christianity—it's what "religious atheists" called themselves back then. They saw Christianity as superstitious and unenlightened. Among the *Deist* fathers were John Quincy Adams, Ethan Allen, Benjamin Franklin, Thomas Jefferson and James Madison. Thomas Paine and possibly George Washington were also *Deists*. It's complex because a "Christian/Deist" syncretism was common among respectable eighteenth century churchgoers taken with the "Age of Reason" or "Enlightenment," despite also citing the Apostle's Creed weekly (with fingers crossed).

Later, during America's "Second Great Awakening" (early nineteenth century), *Deism* would largely be overtaken by Evangelical Revivalism. If America was ever a "Christian nation," it occurred then . . . or did American *civil religion* adopt and co-opt the trappings of Christian faith? Is that an unfair line of inquiry—an impossible question?

This is not to pick on America. It's just the best test case because (1) without falling into *theocracy,* it managed to become a *civil religion* and (2) claimed to be Christian while maintaining separation of church and state.

My friend Derek Vreeland (an America pastor and author) offers these four conclusions in a *Missio* article titled "Four things you need to know about American Civil Religion":

> 1. *American civil religion* is not altogether a bad thing. Civil religion offers shared values and certain practices or rituals that reinforce American values.
>
> 2. The God of *American civil religion* is not the God and Father of our Lord Jesus.
>
> 3. *American civil religion* serves the interests of America, not the church.
>
> 4. *American civil religion* is a false hope for salvation.

This last point shouldn't need reinforcing, but then again . . . what should we make of this popular statement? "Only two people have ever died for you: Jesus Christ and the American G. I. One died for your soul, the other for your freedom." That's a remarkable description of the Civil Religion-Christian hybrid!

Again, the *Jesus Way* doesn't require us to hate our nation—but the kingdom of Christ holds first claim to our allegiance. And "kingdom" is a political metaphor that calls us away from the counterfeit ways and pervading idolatries of *nationalism* and *civil religion.*

## THOUGHTS

In whichever country you now live, the same questions apply:

1. How does my nation-state embrace or reject the *Jesus Way?*

2. How has my nation-state replaced the *Jesus Way* with its own way?

3. How has my nation-state masqueraded as the *Jesus Way?*

4. How does my nation-state demand that I knowingly depart from the *Jesus Way?*

5. How does my nation-state subtly divert me unknowingly from living the *Jesus Way?*

## PRAYERS

*Lord Jesus Christ, King of kings, I pledge allegiance to you as I did on the day of my baptism. Grant that I might be a peaceable exile in the land where you've planted me, serving its people as Daniel did in Babylon or Joseph in Egypt. Deliver me from evil and embolden me to stand firm and faithful against every seduction of the empire and any temptation to respond violently to it. Grant Grace that I would forever seek first your kingdom and righteousness so that whatever heat I face would be for you alone.*

# Part III

# A More Beautiful Faith: Seven Facets

# Introduction: "THE RADICALS"

Thank God we've passed through that Valley of Unsavory Counterfeits. I confess that unlike the Psalmist, I do sometimes fear evil, the comforting rod and staff of the Good Shepherd notwithstanding. It's not that I fear death—it's the maiming by one thousand ideological paper cuts (or tweets) that leaves me jittery. I do it to myself, don't I? Call it the "provocateur anointing." Never mind. Now we're leaving the Land of Shades and about to pass into the bright sunrise of the Risen Christ, his *Way* and his more beautiful path.

I'm going to unpack just seven facets of the *Christlike Way*—remember, each facet reflects the *Way* as Jesus walked it. I make no claims to competence in the *Jesus Walk* for myself or for his church. The focus is on Jesus' *Way* of being divinely human—how he lived as the true human faithful to his *Abba* and full of *Grace*.

That said, the One who forged the *Way* has in fact beckoned us to follow, tracing imperfectly Jesus' blood-stained tracks. We set aside every puritanical idealism, march out of the world's box canyons and opt instead to stagger forward in the company of fellow stumblers, counting on *Grace*. She's our wise and faithful guide, committed to keeping us roughly on course to the degree we heed her Voice.

And what a course it is! Joyful . . . but it's perilous at times too. Ever-challenging the bucking ego—but also moving beyond description, especially when we glimpse Christ himself unveiled in the life of faithful sisters and brothers. It's as if this "*Grace*-thing" is doing her work.

## "RADICAL"

*A linguistic note:* the word "radical" has been misapplied to political extremism (e.g. the "radical" left) and watered down to a cliché for enthusiasm (e.g. "That rollercoaster was radical!"). Nevertheless, I risk using it in the remaining chapter titles to recall the word's richer origins.

*Radical* has to do with "roots." The sixteenth century Anabaptists were called the *Radicals* because they were committed to returning to the *roots* of Christian faith found in the Gospels, and especially the words and example of Jesus Christ. The inquisitors who tortured them accused them of demonic possession because they memorized and cited chapter after chapter of the Gospels during their interrogations. *Radical!* Authentic Christ-followers have always been the real radicals, returning to the taproot of their faith in the life and words of Jesus. I attempt that same retrieval of our Gospel roots in the following seven chapters.

I also understand *radical* in the sense that the *Jesus Way* is a dramatic alternative to status quo religion. After all, the *Cruciform Way* did pass through Gethsemane and Golgotha. The *Jesus Walk* calls us to a life dependent on *Grace*—it asks us to exceed ourselves, our comfort zones, our controlled environments and our controlling systems. Christ-followers are *radical* to the degree that we follow the *Radical One* who spoke truth to power, peace to storms and life to death—and asks us to do so too. *"You'll do even greater works than these because I'm going to the Father!"* (John 14:12).

Most of all, Christ's *radical love* compelled him to lay down his life for the world, and he leaves that same vocation of radical self-giving love with us. Will I follow to the end? I'm not so sure. The question is, will you? No pressure! You know how resolutions go. Still, *Jesus Christ is our Radical and together, we'll take a first step.*

So, let's launch into this section, for "He is the one who carved out the path for faith, and he's the one who brought it to completion" (Heb. 12:2). It's time we look at the diamond's first facet: Christ's *radical self-giving.*

# Facet 1

# "He set aside privilege" RADICAL SELF-GIVING

***Privilege*—definition:** a special right, advantage or immunity granted, assumed or available only to a specific person or group of people.

In our era, privilege has become a pejorative buzzword. You can use privilege in one of three ways, only one of which leads to life.

- You can *exploit privilege* for yourself to marginalize others and maintain your hold on power at their expense and to their disadvantage. Privilege climbs over those bent double to gain the advantage of sitting atop the heap, blind to and immune from the troubles suffered by the "least of these" because of socio-economic disparity.
- You can *weaponize "privilege"* as *ad hominem* ammo with which to assault those who won't follow your ideological script. Used as a dismissive generalization, it turns would-be allies and advocates into adversaries to be torn down and silenced. In the world of social media, "privilege" is a dog whistle for trolls. Those who blow it even believe they're doing justice.
- But you can also *employ privilege* in solidarity with those who are disadvantaged, serve their needs, make space for their voices and create opportunities for them to flourish. This use of privilege is the first of seven facets of the *Jesus Way* we'll explore in the remainder of this book. Yet as we'll see, Christ not only used privilege—he willingly *set aside privilege* in his *kenotic* descent into extreme humility.

### THE GREAT DESCENT

Privilege is real and it is risky. Since it can be used or misused, we need a model for living and dealing with it. I've inherited advantages that require divine wisdom, not enslavement to perpetual guilt. Rather than surfing the fickle waves of momentary cultural trends, I'm choosing to pay closer attention to Christ who, through the Incarnation, (i) used privilege, (ii) set aside privilege, and then (iii) assumed real disadvantage. I'll explain briefly, then posit the symbols of one of Jesus' prophetic mimes to illustrate his "great descent."

Philippians 2, the beloved Christ hymn, says,

*[Christ], though in God's form, did not*
*Regard his equality with God*
*As something he ought to exploit.*

*Instead, he emptied himself,*
*And received the form of a slave,*
*Being born in the likeness of humans.*

*And then, having human appearance,*
*He humbled himself, and became*
*Obedient even to death,*

*Yes, even the death of the cross.*
*And so God has greatly exalted him,*
*And to him in his favor has given*

*The name which is over all names:*
*That now at the name of Jesus*
*Every knee within heaven shall bow—*

*On earth, too, and under the earth;*
*And every tongue shall confess*
*That Jesus, Messiah, is Lord,*
*To the glory of God, the father.*

—Philippians 2:6-11

In this beautiful anthem of the Servant-King, we see how Christ related to privilege—the greatest privilege of all: his co-eternal deity and co-equal status within the Trinity. Now let's watch what he does with it.

## 1. HE EMPLOYED PRIVILEGE

First, I have no doubt that as Son of God, Christ enjoyed the inherited privilege of equality with his *Abba*. The inherent privilege as heir of God's universal kingdom did not make him bad. It was not something to feel guilty about. He didn't despise who he was or the great advantage of his majesty.

But neither did he regard privilege as something to exploit for himself. He saw that the privileges of his sonship were to be employed to serve others, rescue the afflicted and raise up humanity with and in himself. Christ would embrace and unite himself to us. Intrinsic to that union is an exchange of our poverty for his riches, our predicament for his prosperity (see 2 Cor. 8:9). Ironically, to *employ privilege* first meant *setting it aside*. This is the downward mobility of the kingdom of God!

## 2. HE SET ASIDE PRIVILEGE

In the Philippians hymn, N.T. Wright translates the word *kenosis* as "emptied himself" (Phil. 2:7, NTE). That's accurate and can be helpful. However, "emptied" also becomes problematic when we start asking what was emptied from Christ or out of Christ. In the Incarnation, while Christ assumed a fully human nature, he in no way ceased to be fully God at any time. Fully God. As in, nothing of his deity was diminished. In what sense, then, can Paul say Christ *emptied* himself?

My quick answer is that the text doesn't say "something" was emptied from Christ. What is emptied, says the hymn, is not a "what"—it's a "who"—it is Christ himself. Jesus Christ is emptied into the world as self-giving, servant Love. And this does not make him less than God. Indeed, his *kenosis* reveals the very nature of God.

Theologically, I'm happy with that. I wonder how we might see it as a *Jesus Way* to be followed (as Paul suggests in the four verses preceding the hymn).

During a grad studies discussion, one of my students, Deanna Fillion—a community youth worker based in Yellowknife—suggested that we understand and translate Christ's *kenosis*—"he emptied himself"—as *setting aside privilege.*

*Privilege* is a sensitive word these days and bears identifying. Oxford defines privilege as a special right, advantage or immunity granted or available only to a particular person or group. When it comes to privilege, let's take sex and race as examples.

While I don't like to imagine myself as racist or misogynist, the truth is that I don't live and breathe the experience of how power exerts itself on women or people of color. I'm oblivious to the advantages intrinsic to my sex or color in my culture. That blind spot is what we mean by privilege.

In systems of privilege, sexism and racism are more than fear and hatred of other sexes or races. That's just prejudice. Sexism and racism are prejudice plus power, which is why misogyny and racism can be unilateral and even unconscious.

My friend, Azariah France-Williams explains how he has experienced racism:

> When one feels sewn into a corner from which you cannot easily escape; when you look up and see a white child being lovingly taught how to thread a needle, seemingly unaware of your screams. Or when you feel looked upon as a cute child in costume in a nursery or kindergarten, watching the grownups through the window who dictate the terms of your existence, your play is parody.

I don't think like that. I am unable to think like that. I have no adequate point of reference for Azariah's experience. That's my point. That's privilege. Lord, have mercy.

If anyone has been accused of privilege, it's God. "You don't understand! You don't know what it's like! You're God! You're all-powerful!" And this is exactly what Christ, in the Incarnation, by *kenosis,* sets to debunking.

*Christ set aside divine privilege,* not his divine nature. That is, he truly and fully "humbled himself." To take on human "likeness" doesn't mean Christ became *similar* to us. Rather, he identified with us so thoroughly that he *became* us and *like us in every way* (Heb. 2:17), including all that we suffer—exempt from and immune to *nothing* intrinsic to the human condition.

*Not even death.*

Christ is not "unable to sympathize with our weaknesses, but one who has been tempted [tested] in every way, just as we are . . ." (Heb. 4:15).

In setting aside divine privilege (perhaps "the form of majesty")—truly letting go—Christ came to know by direct experience all the realities of growth, submission and obedience, just as he learned what it is to suffer and die with no recourse to Daddy's platinum card. Why did he do this? The author of Hebrews explains that Christ's agenda was to fully and authentically empathize with us—to identify with humanity so completely that his divine life would mysteriously heal and transform us. He plumbed the depths of the human condition and raised us up with himself.

## 3. HE ASSUMED REAL DISADVANTAGE

When the Virgin squatted to give birth, the infant who emerged came without a silver spoon in his mouth. Yes, the divine nature—infinite Love—continued to reside in the Son of God—but as the son of Mary, the reality of Christ's humanity was uncompromised by divine privilege or what we might call "majesty."

Any privilege Jesus of Nazareth enjoyed as a Jew or a male or freeborn was offset by the scandal of his birth (in Bethlehem), his refugee status (in Egypt) and his blue-collar upbringing (in Nazareth). He also endured the troubles of an oppressed race under imperial occupation. When cultural privileges connected to his trade, his sex or his faith were in play, Christ made use of it as an ally of the poor, healer of the sick and friend and advocate of the "sinner."

In the end, he went beyond using or willingly setting aside privilege—divine or human—to complete submission, beyond exemption, to the unfeigned disadvantage of every victim who has been falsely maligned, unjustly incarcerated and wrongly executed. He endured the pitiable fate of every cross-bound insurgent and hell-bound heretic.

## 4. EVEN DEATH ON A CROSS

The great descent didn't appear to end well. Not in this life. There would be no eleventh hour intervention. By the end, Christ would not (and some argue *could not,* if his *kenosis* was real) call a myriad of angelic special ops for extraction. Completion of the *kenotic* descent required his mockers to stumble onto the truth: he saved others but could not save himself. Nor did his Father. Not from the Cross, at any rate. If Jesus could have reversed course, he would not have experienced the true weakness that saves us from powerlessness. It would have been a sham, pseudo-incarnation. Like countless others before and since, Christ's vindication counted on the faithfulness of his *Abba,* awaiting post-mortem justice. But what justice that was!

In loving us to the bottom, Christ was raised and exalted. We need to know that following the *Jesus Way* includes a call to set aside privilege and the *Jesus Walk* involves a Cross. But the final word is not a tomb. Not for Jesus. Not for the martyrs. And not for you.

Those who exploit their privilege, who desperately cling to it or use it to bludgeon others will, in the end, suffer loss. Those who lay it aside will follow the *Jesus Way* to the Cross, through the Cross, beyond the tomb and into the vindication of the one Voice that finally matters. "The way down is the way up."

While the hymn is a beautiful opportunity for worship, Paul sees it as a call: think like this, live like this, be like this. He says,

> That way, nobody will be able to fault you, and you'll be pure and spotless children of God in the middle of a twisted and depraved generation. You are to shine among them like lights in the world, clinging to the word of life. That's what I will be proud of on the day of the Messiah. It will prove that I didn't run a useless race, or work to no purpose.
>
> Yes: even if I am to be *poured out* like a drink-offering on the sacrifice and service of your faith, I shall celebrate, and celebrate jointly with you all.
>
> —Philippians 2:15-17

We are given the Christ hymn as an example of setting aside privilege. And we have Paul's example of self-giving service. Just as Christ is emptied into the world as humble Love, so Paul is "poured out like a drink offering" in collaboration with the sacrificial love of his Philippian loved ones.

## THE GRAND PANTOMIME

In addition to the soaring Philippians hymn, Christ's great descent is portrayed in John 13 via the grand pantomime of his Paschal foot-washing.

Let us peek in on this intimate scene together, viewing it through *kenotic* lenses.

The Gospel says, Jesus knew that *"his hour* had come" (Jn. 13:1, DBH).

At the wedding in Cana, Christ had said to his mother, *"My hour* has not yet arrived" (John 2:4). But with that first sign, transforming water to wine, the clock begins to tick toward *the hour.*

Now, the night before his death, he knows *his hour has come* (John 17:1).

What "hour"? The *hour* of his death. The *hour* of his crucifixion.

More than that, *the hour* has come for Christ to be "lifted up" (Jn. 12:32-34), enthroned and glorified by his Father on the Cross.

Now, at supper, the bell of *that hour* is already beginning to chime.

John continues, "He had always loved his own people in the world; now he loved them right through to the end" (Jn. 13:1).

Now, he loves his own—those who have taken up their cross and willingly followed him on the *Way* thus far. He also loves those who had not received him—they too are *his own.* He even loves the one in the Upper Room who would deny and betray him.

He loves them all—in this moment and right to the end.

*To the end—the telos,* a word that speaks of completion and fulfillment.

The same word he will speak from the Cross tomorrow.

## "IT IS FINISHED"

*"It is finished."* Completed, fulfilled, accomplished.

What is fulfilled and accomplished? His mission of love, for his own, for us all. John Behr (in *Becoming Human)* even suggests (following St. Maximos the Confessor) that in Christ's Passion, *Abba* at last finalizes the creation of humanity begun in Genesis chapter 1—Christ becomes the first complete and true image of God!

Now, Christ signifies that mission, his whole life trajectory, through an intimate and touching prophetic act. Holy Week has already been charged with such acts, infused with great and terrible meaning:

His anointing with spikenard for burial.
His triumphal entry on the colt of a donkey.
His upheaval of the corrupt temple money tables.
His cursing of the fig tree.

But this footwashing drama—full of radical love and extreme humility—is a tender and beautiful summary of Christ's entire mission of love. It is a pantomime that recalls and recapitulates the whole Incarnation journey.

Foot-washing illustrates Jesus' love—it foreshadows his readiness to die for his friends and for us. And it prefigures his cruciform glorification.

I believe Jesus knew what he was doing, or perhaps he was so intuitive it all just flowed unconsciously. Either way, John saw it. He noticed. Watch for the seven signs:

*Jesus knew that the father had given everything into his hands (vs. 3):*

Here, *Abba* has granted his Son all authority to his mission of love (cf. 17:2).

*So he got up from the supper-table:*

The Son arises from his seat at the Father's right hand in glory.

*Took off his clothes:*

Without ceasing to be fully divine, Christ lays aside his glory, lays aside divine privilege. "He emptied himself."

*Wrapped a towel around himself:*

The divine assumes humanity, revealing the humility of true divinity. When the Word becomes flesh, he takes up the human condition and embraces the form of a humble servant.

*He poured water into a bowl:*

The divine Word pours the living water, the spring of his life out into the world.

*And began to wash the disciples' feet, and to wipe them with the towel he was wrapped in:*

He washes us clean of the stains of sin, the ashes of sorrow, and the dust of death.

*He put on his clothes:*

Ascending to the Cross, he is crowned, enthroned, glorified and revealed as the Son of God. Having laid down his life, he takes it up again (Jn. 10:18), resurrected and ascended to the heavens,

*And sat down again:*

At the Father's right hand, from where he rules as "Pantocrator"—

i.e. ruler of the universe—by means of his unfailing mercy.

As with the Christ hymn of Philippians, we may be tempted to make worship the whole point. Yet, I believe we only truly worship when we join Christ on the *Jesus Way* of humility, service and self-emptying love. What does Jesus think about that? His personal takeaway is that his act calls for imitation. After this drama of redemption, he says to them, "Do you understand what I have done for you?"

Do we? This is *kenotic* love par excellence. That Christ left his throne, set aside privilege, stooped down from heaven, humbled himself even to death to wash clean humanity.

"Do you understand what I have done for you?" Probably not. Probably no more than they did.

He continues, "You call me 'teacher' and 'master,' and you're right. That's what I am. Well, then: if I, as your master and teacher, washed your feet just now, you should wash each other's feet. I've given you a pattern, so that you can do things in the same way that I did to you" (Jn. 13:12-14).

Understand it or not, the day some traditions call Maundy Thursday comes with a command: a new commandment. Pay it forward. Or, in Jesus' words,

"Love one another. Just as I have loved you, you also are to love one another. Everyone will know by this that you are my disciples—if you have love for one another" (Jn. 13:34-35).

Christianity is not so much about working up my faith, but about imitating Jesus' faithfulness in voluntarily setting aside privilege and taking up the towel of self-giving love. By *Grace,* let us imitate Christ in his *kenotic* love—the *Way* and *Walk* by which we are identified as his disciples.

Tragically, that's not what Christians are known for these days. Usually we are known, fairly or not, by what we're against, how we judge and who we exclude. We're more easily recognized by our embrace of the counterfeits that have seduced us onto fraudulent ways.

What then are we to do?

Let us allow Christ to wash our feet of all that is against love so that even the world would say, "How beautiful are the feet of those who bring good news."

Let us allow his blood to purge our hearts of all malice, resentment and bitterness. Let us allow him to love us "to the end" that his love would fill our hearts, our eyes, our arms and our hands.

Let us count on *Abba's* amazing *Grace* through whom we become imitators of Jesus' faithfulness, letting go of ego, setting aside privilege and expressing his love one for another.

## THOUGHTS

1. The fact that you can read this book indicates privilege—the literacy behind your reading, the funds behind holding a book in your hands and even the freedom to do so—all indicate privilege. What other privileges do you normally enjoy and assume without giving it a second thought? Take a moment to list and express gratitude for them.

2. Think of others who don't share in the privileges you enjoy. Are you aware of ways that your experience of privilege might be at their expense? Is your enjoyment contingent on a sacrifice they make, willingly or not? Rectifying this inequity is one aspect of "doing justice, loving mercy and walking humbly with your God." How might you use privilege, set aside privilege or adopt disadvantage as Christ did? What acts of self-giving love could you enact that would raise up others?

3. Imagine sitting at the Last Supper, allowing Jesus to wash your feet. Is this as awkward and as hard to receive for you as it was for Peter? What do you think is being challenged in our ego when we resist such *Grace?* How might we "let go and let God" as grateful recipients of his cleansing? Is there something you need to let him wash away today?

## PRAYERS

*Humble Servant-King, today I open my heart and even my feet to your cleansing touch. Wash away my pride. Cleanse every stain of ill-gotten or misused privilege and make me a Christlike steward of all the gifts I've been given. Empower me to be disempowered and to know the joy of self-giving love.*

# Facet 2

# "Space for all" RADICAL HOSPITALITY

"The *Jesus Way* makes space for all at God's table;
it enfolds all people as those whom God loves."
—Greg Albrecht

"It's easy to call people out. It's harder to call them in.
But confession is a helpful start."
—Jarrod McKenna

### THE PHARISEE & THE PUBLICAN

To some who were confident of their own righteousness and looked down on everyone else, Jesus told this parable:

> "Two men," he said, "went up to the Temple to pray. One was a Pharisee, the other was a tax-collector. The Pharisee stood and prayed in this way to himself: 'God, I thank you that I am not like the other people—greedy, unjust, immoral, or even like this tax-collector. I fast twice in the week; I give tithes of all that I get.'
>
> "But the tax-collector stood a long way off, and didn't even want to raise his eyes to heaven. He beat his breast and said, 'God, be merciful to me, sinner that I am.' Let me tell you, he was the one who went back to his house vindicated by God, not the other. Don't you see? People who exalt themselves will be humbled, and people who humble themselves will be exalted." —Luke 18:10-14

Oh, those Pharisees. Dastardly Pharisees.
Thank God that I'm not like those Pharisees!
See what I did there?

To thank God that I'm not like the Pharisee is to miss Jesus' point—this very act is to become the Pharisee! Just like the self-righteous, pious Pharisee of the parable, we are prone to fall into the same self-congratulating presumption by identifying ourselves with the publican, glaring back down our noses at the Pharisees. We despise them to prop ourselves up, practicing exclusion and reserving only our place at the table—just like the Pharisees.

Christ told this parable, not merely to "call out" the Pharisees for their hubris, but to "call them in" to the Father's table. He has no desire to see anyone—including them—wallow outside in the cold night of religiosity. And neither should we. If we imagine we're better than they are, we become exactly what we hate—it's ironic.

Self-righteously condemning someone for being self-righteous and condemning is like being intolerant in the name of tolerance. Get it? The *Jesus Way* modeled here is not merely a condemnation of religious pride and self-righteousness. It was Christ's heartfelt appeal to the prideful—his *radical invitation* to the feast that the humble were already eating. "Humble pie" need not be the dessert of humiliation. Humility is the featured *hors d'oeuvres* at *Abba's* banquet.

Over coffee, my old hiking partner and PhD supervisor, Ron Dart reflected on the parable with me, walking me a bit further into Christ's intent:

> The parable of the Pharisee and Publican praying in the temple illustrates the perennial nature of "the Pharisee spirit." I am the parabolic "Pharisee" when I hold myself *above* versus participating *with* the imperfect. The Pharisee takes a superior attitude to the other and stands aloof from engagement with the messy world of people and processes, whether ecclesial or political.
>
> The Publican admits his imperfection and recognizes his need for mercy. The point of the parable is not to beat ourselves up but to maintain a stance of humility—our existential recognition in thought, word and deed of our need. Ironically, that contrition enables us to participate in the messy world as agents of the mercy we've received.
>
> The more deadly position is that of the Pharisee. We are in a real dilemma because inevitably, we need to distinguish right from wrong, better from worse. These critical reflections tempt us to become judgmental. It's a double-edged sword because we need

moral reformers who present legitimate valuations. Either we face that inevitable risk or we opt for a naive relativism with no moral vision.

Christ knows we must constantly evaluate our choices and our environment, including others. His counsel: start with the beam in your own eye. I'm as imperfect as anyone. I'm one of those I critique. The three-fold *kyrie eleison* ("Lord, have mercy") takes us into the Trinitarian Heart of mercy. The stance of humility—of acknowledging our complicity—enables us to patiently welcome the other and participate with the imperfect as servants.

## INVITE THEM—GO BRING THEM—COMPEL THEM

### The Parable of the Great Banquet

Christ's vision of *Abba's* kingdom as an open banquet comprised a good number of his parables and aphorisms. The *radical* invitation is featured in the "Parable of the Great Supper," where I've noticed an escalating compulsion in the invitations of *Grace.*

> Jesus said, "Once a man made a great dinner, and invited lots of guests. When the time for the meal arrived, he sent his servant to say to the guests, 'Come now—everything's ready!'
>
> But the whole pack of them began to make excuses. The first said, 'I've just bought a field, and I really have to go and see it. Please accept my apologies.'
>
> Another one said, 'I've just bought five yoke of oxen, and I've got to go and test them out—please accept my apologies.'
>
> And another one said, 'I've just got married, so naturally I can't come.'
>
> So the servant went back and told his master all this. The householder was cross, and said to his servant, 'Go out quickly into the streets and lanes of the town and bring in here the poor, the crippled, the lame and the blind.'
>
> 'All right, Master,' said the servant, 'I've done that—but there's still room.'
>
> 'Well then,' said the master to the servant, 'go out into the roads

> and hedgerows and make them come in, so that my house may be full! Let me tell you this: none of those people who were invited will get to taste my dinner.'" —Luke 14:16-24

## Authentic Invitation, Free Response, Escalating Compulsion

Prior to and aside from the horrific notion that God pre-selects some to eternal life and others to everlasting damnation, historic Christianity held high God's desire that *everyone* is invited and that all would *freely* respond to his *Grace.*

> "The spirit and the bride say, 'Come!' And let anyone who hears say, 'Come!' Let the thirsty come; let anyone who wants the water of life take it freely." —Revelation 22:17

God's invitation is authentically universal ("whoever desires") and wholly uncoerced ("take freely").

With that freedom firmly in mind, what are we to make of the Parable of the Great Banquet where Jesus describes an escalating use of pressure in the invitation?

**Group 1** At first, the Man/Master (God) **invites** *"many"* to his banquet—he announces that *"all things are now ready."* But the RSVPs are not coming in as hoped. Jesus labels these responses "excuses." They are meant to sound absurd. Who takes out a mortgage on a property, sight unseen or buys five oxen before test-driving them? And who gets married but doesn't think the invitation includes their spouse as the "plus-one" to bring along? Jesus wants us to know this first group are not merely busy—their polite excuses communicate real rejection.

**Group 2** The second invitation is not to the general "many," but to a second group: "the poor, the maimed, the lame and the blind." It sounds like more than an invitation. There's a greater urgency—"Go out quickly to the streets and lanes of the city." And the Servant (singular, for God the Father is sending Christ himself) is to **bring** them. Why is that? First, notice that this group includes the impoverished and those who suffer disabilities. They need someone to bring them. Willingness may not be their issue—mobility is.

And from where? Why are the poor and disabled in the streets and lanes? In the context of his culture, Jesus clues us in—these are likely lower-caste, infirmed beggars. In any case, something more than an invitation is required. Even if they willingly respond, they still need someone—a care-giver or Good Samaritan if you will—to pick them up and bring them in.

**Group 3** But even then, some place settings remain vacant. The Master tells the servant to go out *further*—beyond the lanes and city streets to the highways and hedges. But it's more than geographic. The implication is that the Servant should go further out into the *margins* of society. The preachers and commentators of yesteryear saw in this third campaign a call to the "sinners"—those who never got invitations because they were excluded by sin—society's dregs, the perverted and the treacherous. The social untouchables that the Gospels exemplified by "tax collectors and prostitutes." And these, the Master says, must be **compelled**.

## *Anankazo*—to Compel

But wait—isn't a free-will response of utmost importance? And isn't "compelling" sort of like forcing? Traditionally, *anankazo,* the Greek verb here, did carry the force of necessitate, compel, constrain, drive to—even force, sometimes with threats. But the best New Testament Greek Lexicon (*BAGD*), also considers the context of the word for weaker nuances: *strongly urging, attempting to persuade or entreaty.* That makes most sense here—the Servant doesn't arrest, cuff and drag these folks to the banquet by force. He didn't do that to the excuse-makers. Then, why the need to *compel* this group?

Have you ever tried to *persuade* someone who is reluctant to *freely* respond to an invitation? Without using force on them, you might find yourself pleading: "You should really come. Please! *You know you want to!*"

Why hadn't this level of compulsion been used on the first group? *Because they didn't want to come.* They were free to come but made up reasons not to. In this latter group, the very opposite is true. These folks would dearly *love to come,* but because of years of socio-religious exclusion, they've lost hope and need to be convinced—*freed, in fact*—to receive God's welcome. Their sense of "I can't" had been imposed on them by others.

But even their broken lifestyles betray a deep hunger for belonging, or the need to dull that hunger by illicit means. To them, the invitation might seem too good to be true. *Compel them!* says the Master—*make them an offer they can't refuse!* And so the Servant does—not by arm-twisting but through a message of compelling love. Thus compelled, they not only come freely, they probably come running!

This parable reflects Christ's move from the religious in-crowd to the social pariahs. I believe it also touches on the Temple establishment's rejection of Christ and ultimately, the inclusion of the Gentiles into the Church. But that is a conversation for another time.

How does this compelling *Grace* look today? The economically wealthy and/or the religious elite may presume upon God's blessing but find Jesus' actual invitation distasteful, especially when it means caring for the perpetually poor or the chronically disabled—or worse, having to rub shoulders with society's "riff-raff" and their crazy-making dramas. Don't ever doubt that we live in a caste-system, but understand that Jesus is most often found schmoozing with the "wrong crowd."

## Compelled Invitations Today

I've known both sides of that table. I can testify to my own experience of gospel compulsion—not Calvinism's irresistible grace, but the Spirit's compelling persuasion. I regularly see it come in two ways:

1. Through servants of *Abba* who plead with me to receive Christ's forgiveness and the kindness of *Grace,* especially when I'm convinced that I'm worthless and disqualified—when I believe the accuser and participate in self-rejection. You may know that voice, too. When we buy into the lie of our exclusion and find ourselves stuck, we need faithful friends to *invite* and *compel* us to join in the gospel banquet. As the Mumford and Sons song goes,

*It seems that all my bridges have been burned,*
*but you say, "That's exactly how this grace thing works."*
*It's not the long walk home that will change this heart,*
*but the welcome I receive with every start.*

2. The *compelling* invitation can also take another, more perilous path.

That happens when my resistance to *Grace* and my stubborn self-will lead to consequences so painful that I *will not* surrender until I bottom out. If at that point I surrender, my own failures *compel* me to return from the pigpen to the Father's house.

As Star Wars' Yoda says, "The greatest teacher, failure is." Maybe, but while trials do *compel* a decision for repentance, it *only* ever happens when our self-will is broken and in a moment of clarity, we offer our *willing* response. In other words, to summarize this parable and *Grace's* escalating invitation, the Master's instruction to the Servant Jesus, *"Compel them to come" is not a violation of my freedom, but a heightened opportunity for it.* The only question for us is *when* we'd like to say our willing "yes" to the *Grace* of God.

## NO HOPE FOR SOME?

The end of the parable begs a further question. What of Jesus' ominous closing line: *"Let me tell you this: none of those people who were invited will get to taste my dinner."*

Ouch! Not one of them? Ever? Those who first rejected the invitation have no hope whatsoever. Or so it sounds.

But given Jesus' free use of all/nothing, always/never hyperbole, we need to bear in mind other texts, such as:

> "Even so, however, *quite a few of the rulers did believe in him.* But, because of the Pharisees, they didn't declare their faith, for fear of being put out of the synagogue." —John 12:42

Does their waffling disqualify them? Perhaps. But wait! After Pentecost there are more:

> "The word of God increased, and the number of disciples in Jerusalem grew by leaps and bounds. This included *a large crowd of priests* who became obedient to the faith." —Acts 6:7

Did these second-chance conversions stick? Are they exceptions to Jesus' 'rule'? Consider that Paul was initially in the violent anti-Jesus camp. He certainly came around:

> Circumcised? On the eighth day. Race? Israelite.

> Tribe? Benjamin. Descent? Hebrew through and through.
> Torah-observance? A Pharisee. Zealous? I persecuted the church!
> Official status under the law? Blameless.
> Does that sound as though my account was well in credit? Well, maybe; but whatever I had written in on the profit side, I calculated it instead as a loss—because of the Messiah." —Philippians 3:5-7

In view of these responses, how do we hear the Master's words: *"None of these men who were invited will taste my supper"?* Do the facts finally contradict Jesus'? (I don't think so.) Are the Master's words confined only to the characters in the story? (I don't think so.) Is it simply a matter of Jesus' love of hyperbole—a way to intensify the rhetorical effect for his listeners? (Perhaps, but not *simply* so.)

## PAUL: CASE STUDY IN CHANGING CREWS

Proposal: God honors the wishes of those who decline his invitation—he doesn't force anyone who refuses to enter God's kingdom. God doesn't constrain anyone who says "No" to following Christ (see Luke 14:25-24).

The Psalmist once promised that God would grant us the desires of our heart. Sounds great but that's also a dire warning—take care with your desires. That's why we're taught to guard our hearts.

*Read this part twice, please:* So, those in group one (the decliners) who *DON'T WANT to come* will never experience eternal life in Jesus Christ . . . *unless and until they abandon their first response.*

The good news from Paul's life is that no one needs to be stuck in group one permanently—self-exclusion need not be the last word. *Anyone and everyone can leave that crew at any time*—perhaps even at the final judgment when "every eye shall see him" and "every knee shall bow."

On the Road to Damascus, Paul is struck blind by his vision of Christ and he must be brought to Ananias of Damascus, where Paul ultimately says his free "Yes" to God's amazing *Grace.* As a *blind man being brought* to the banquet of *Grace,* Paul now finds himself part of group two in the parable. As a member of group one, he would never taste of the banquet, but when circumstances changed, so could he.

We might also see Paul falling into group three of the parable. The

Servant (Jesus) goes out to confront Saul of Tarsus on a "highway" and "*compels* him" to join the gospel banquet. When he finds Saul, Christ describes him as an ox "kicking against the pricks" (KJV) of his own stubbornness and misplaced religious zeal. In that moment, Saul bottoms out on his self-defeating behavior—he's *freed* to exit group one, *freely* confesses Christ as Lord and is soon baptized *freely* into the faith.

Thus, Saul of Tarsus becomes our case-study, demonstrating the Master's authentic invitation, our free response, but also how Jesus the Servant visits us with an escalating persuasive *Grace.* And this, I believe, has been the story of many of us. As long as we didn't want to come in, we couldn't. But thanks be to God, life circumstances (and especially our failures) made us ready for *Grace* to come calling. And then it did, and his name was Jesus.

As the Great Fisher of humanity declared,

> "And when I've been lifted up from the earth, I will *draw* [*helkyso*—drag, draw, pull—as with a fishing net!] *all people* to myself."
> —John 12:32

The Pharisee and the Publican, the resistant and the eager—the Cross is God's compelling *radical* RSVP.

> *Lord and Master, thank you for your invitation to the gospel feast. Thank you for sending your Servant Jesus to find me and to compel me to come. In gratitude, I offer my free Yes to your Grace. Amen.*

## THE PRODIGAL SON(S)

The subtitle speaks of the "prodigal sons" (Lk. 15:11-32) in the plural advisedly. In some ways, these brothers are as different as Cain and Abel, Isaac and Ishmael or Jacob and Esau. But they also have a lot in common. Both receive their inheritance when the Father divides it between them (vs. 12). Both brothers alienate themselves, "slaving" in their respective fields—the field of riotous rebellion and the field of resentful obedience. Neither enjoys the warmth and intimacy of the Father's house (vss. 15, 29). Both young men are lost—but remember, the Father never thinks of them as anything less than beloved sons. The open door of *radical invitation* never shuts on either of the boys.

He loves both, grieves for both, and in the end, welcomes both. He runs to the younger son "while he is still a long way off" (vs. 20). And he goes out to the field to plead with the older, resentful brother (vs. 28).

As the Father excludes *no one* in the story, Christ excludes *no one* with whom he shared the parable. Both *Abba* and Son are celebrating the lost being found and pleading for the elders to join in their joy. There's not a hint of condemnation for either the younger brother or older brother, for the publicans or the Pharisees. Both groups were "*all* gathering around to hear Jesus" (Luke 15:1). *All* were welcome.

Jesus ate dinner in both Simon the Pharisee's home (Luke 7:36-49) and Zacchaeus the tax collector's house (Luke 19:1-10). They received him differently, but he honored both with his presence, nonetheless. And while it's extremely hard for us, maybe we could too.

## CONFESSIONS OF A PHARISEE

Do you feel more at home with the squeaky-clean folks of good reputation? Or with those on the messy margins? Do you rub shoulders more easily with the up-and-comer or the down-and-outer? Do you relate better to the religious elder or the rebellious sibling? Either way, how might we make space for all those who feel most "other" to us?

After years of ministry at the margins, I find it easier to "let my hair down" with the messy—people with disabilities, addictions or in poverty. I feel comfortable because I'm used to meeting Christ in them. Their social faux pas, painful relapses or hygiene issues don't trigger me. I can be myself around them.

Sadly, I also like being seen in their company because it makes me seem noble, hip and "woke" (hipster lingo for socially aware) to my peers. "Woke" people are admired. "Woke" is the new "righteous." Voila! "Woke" is the new Pharisee.

So, as I'm strutting out my faith, my tattoos and my craft beer, I find my heart cold toward those I judge as more "religious" or "righty-tighty" than me. And there, I've done it again.

I can imagine myself as spiritual but not religious—so proud of my "freedom in Christ" and my "pure grace" religion: but if I'm self-righteous and condescending toward "those Pharisees," I'm still enslaved to the religious impulse. I may have switched sides, but I'm still possessed by the same fundamentalist spirit. And it's not the Spirit of Jesus.

How will this play out? Well, now I'm tempted to resentment toward those "woke folk" who claim to be progressive but are terrifying in their capacity to exclude or devour allies who step out of line. Believe me; I've witnessed it. I don't want to be at their table or make space for them at mine. And there, I've done it again.

But where do we find Jesus? Again, at a prominent Pharisee's table. What does Jesus say?

> When you give a luncheon or dinner, do not invite your friends, your brothers or relatives, or your rich neighbors; if you do, they may invite you back and so you will be repaid. But when you give a banquet, invite the poor, the crippled, the lame, the blind, and you will be blessed. Although they cannot repay you, you will be repaid at the resurrection of the righteous. —Luke 14:12-14

I could just take Jesus literally. Invite the poor, the crippled, the lame, the blind. No problem. After all, Eden and I served in a community where they were our central focus. But I know better. For who is so spiritually poor, blind, crippled and lame (in my eyes) as the last group I turned away from? I can have a warm conversation with a sex addict or a Muslim Imam, no problem. But a tea-totaling, "straight-edge" Southern Baptist? If not, who's the Pharisee? Lord, is it I? It is.

Whenever I pronounce "Ichabod" (lit. the glory has departed) on someone else—the Evangelicals of my childhood, for example—I am on trial, not them. My rejection of anyone I've excluded makes me the goat under judgment in Matthew 25, because what I do to anyone (if they're as sick with religion as I claim), I am still doing to Christ. *"Brad, Brad, why do you persecute me?"*

When I think about how rotten with religion the church can be, do I hope she dies or do I hope she recovers? Do I call her *out* or call her *in?* If reconciliation were possible, would I be open to it? Do I thank God I'm not like her, or can I see how I'm exactly like her? She is yet another measure of my transformation towards love.

## ESAU'S KISS

There's this tender moment between brothers in the story of Jacob and Esau. After years of estrangement, the younger brother (Jacob) must face Esau, whose inheritance he had stolen. What will happen?

> [Jacob] bowed down to the ground seven times as he approached his brother. But Esau ran to meet Jacob and embraced him; he threw his arms around his neck and kissed him. And they wept. —Genesis 33:3-4

When Christ composed the parable of the prodigal son, he borrowed the very same phrase to describe the Father's run, embrace and kiss. Using that phrase in his parable not only shows us the scandalous *Grace* of God the Father—Christ was also exhorting estranged spiritual siblings to that same grace and reconciliation for their younger, wilder and more wayward brothers.

## LLOYD EVANGELICAL

Today, it helps me to think of my dad, Lloyd Jersak. Since he met Christ as a teen, he's been a faithful, "soul-winning" Baptist, boldly proclaiming the gospel as he sees it to all who will listen.

He excludes no one, calling in everyone from urine-soaked vagrants to obnoxious fundies to a wider vision of God's mercy.

He's old—over eighty. Forgetful, too. He's famous for locking his keys in the car. Doesn't hear well. He labors along on bad knees. He's survived a heart attack, valve replacement and three bouts of kidney cancer.

Lloyd also loves playing *Amazing Grace* on his baritone—sometimes while driving gravel roads, other times for Hutterite farmers in the fields on their coffee break, and again to street-people on skid row. He took it on himself to lace up his skates and organize a town-wide prayer/skate night in support of Humboldt, Saskatchewan after their junior hockey team lost sixteen lives in a tragic bus crash.

Lloyd's an Evangelical. His virtues, vices and maladies may be symbolic of all Evangelicals.

I love him. I hope he lives. And I'm way more grateful to be like him than not. Where I'm not, I don't pray, "Thank God," but "Lord, have mercy on me." He can eat at my table any time. He always welcomes me to his. So, there may be hope for this old Pharisee (me) yet.

Love is so hard to do. But turning from love (othering), leaving the table (alienation) or closing the table (isolation) are not the solution, much less a foundation for a life or a movement. No *ism* is founded on a turn to love. But the great and abiding movements were rooted and established in love.

And yes, love has healthy boundaries. Love means I must sometimes get away to detox. But detox that doesn't lead to rehab and recovery is an alienating prison of loneliness.

Sometimes love wisely says we cannot and should not re-enter toxic relationships or communities. You may need to move on. But you're not destined to be all alone.

When seeking out new relationships or entering a new community, ask yourself: do they manifest the *radical hospitality* of *Abba?* Are they marked by their turn to love? Or do they find their coherence in exclusion and a shared turning away from love? It matters because you will inevitably experience one of the two in due course. I'm deeply grateful for my encounters with those who've included me in God's *invitation.*

## ISAIAH'S "HO!"

When I was part of the twenty-year project called Fresh Wind Christian Fellowship, we experienced God's open arms and radical invitation through those on the margins who became the pillars of the church. They included people with disabilities in full-time care (one-third of our community), children, prodigals coming home (often addicts) and the poor. As pillars, they taught us what is truly important in God's kingdom:

- Love is God's nature and *Abba's* first commandment. The residents suffering physical and mental challenges didn't care about position or performance. Their first concern was, "Will you love me and may I love you?"
- Little children taught us that one does not even enter the kingdom of God without childlike trust in God's loving care.
- Those with addictions taught us that fresh mercy is available every day.

- The poor taught us what it is to be rich in faith (James 2:5).
- All together—the disabled, the children, the addicts and the poor—comprised God's beautiful, open table where *all* were invited, *all* were welcome to taste and see that God is good and merciful and a lover of humanity.

In that context, we often sat at the feet of Jesus as he discipled us through these friends of his—our guides along the *Jesus Way*. One of my mentors in that journey was Bobby, a fellow who loved to oversee the service from his wheelchair, parked in easy eyeshot of those leading the service.

Bobby doesn't speak. He communicates only through whistles, laughs and shrieks. But he does know one word, and he bellows it loudly as a sign of approval. At any given moment in the service, he would shout, *"HO!"* And when he did, others throughout the congregation delighted to echo back to him, *"HO!"* to his exceeding joy.

One morning as Bobby shouted, *"HO!"* the words of the prophet Isaiah blasted through my mind:

> *HO!* Everyone who thirsts, *come* to the waters
> And you who have no money, *come* buy and eat.
> Yes, *come*, buy wine and milk, without money and without price.
> Why do you spend money for what is not bread,
> And your wages for what does not satisfy?
> Listen carefully to Me, and eat what is good
> And let your soul delight itself in abundance.
> Incline your ear, and come to Me.
> Hear, and your soul shall live;
> And I will make an everlasting covenant with you—
> The sure mercies of David.
> —Isaiah 55:1-3

Through both Bobby and Isaiah (each filled by the same Holy Spirit), God makes his enthusiastic invitation to the free and open *agape* feast of his eternal covenant with Jesus Christ, the Son of David.

After that, whenever Bobby shouted *"HO!"* we were all reminded of God's *radical* hospitality.

## THOUGHTS

1. Have you ever suffered exclusion by an in-group? How did you feel? How did you act? In retrospect, where was *Abba* in that moment? How did *Abba* see you? What would *Abba* say to you there?

2. Are there people who you struggle to include at your table? How does *Abba* see them? If Christ invited them to the banquet, what would you do? Would you need to let go of some prejudice or resentment? Is there a reason why you couldn't do that now?

3. The Psalmist says, "You prepare a table before me in the presence of my enemies." Can you picture that?

## PRAYERS

*Lord of the feast, thank you for your radical invitation. Thanks for including me. Please show me how to include others.*

# Facet 3

## "He broke the wall" RADICAL UNITY

With sorrow, we recognize the grievous fact that factionalism and partisanship have infected Christianity with institutional rancor and division—i.e. schism and denominationalism. It's sad and embarrassing and cause for disillusionment. The fractured body of Christ stands—or rather, hunches—as a testimony to our brokenness and defiance to the *Jesus Way* of love.

Christ's intention was for a community of *radical unity* established in our fellowship with him and each other. In Christ, apartheid of every type is to crumble before the Cross. What saith the Scriptures? Please, don't skim through the following passages. Instead, line by line, ask how seriously you take them—where and when do you see them happen? Meditate on how you might experience them as true in your relationships.

### John 17:20-23

> I pray also for those who will believe in me through their message, *that all of them may be one,* Father, just as you are in me and I am in you. May they also be in us so that the world may believe that you have sent me. I have given them the glory that you gave me, *that they may be one as we are one*— I in them and you in me—so that they may be *brought to complete unity.* Then the world will know that you sent me and have loved them even as you have loved me.

### Ephesians 2:14-22

> For *he himself is our peace, who has made the two groups one and has destroyed the barrier, the dividing wall of hostility,* by setting aside in his flesh the law with its commands and regulations. *His purpose was to create in himself one new humanity* out of the two, thus making peace, and in one body to *reconcile both of them to*

*God through the cross, by which he put to death their hostility.* He came and preached peace to you who were far away and peace to those who were near. For through him we both have access to the Father by one Spirit.

Consequently, you are no longer foreigners and strangers, but fellow citizens with God's people and also members of his household, built on the foundation of the apostles and prophets, with Christ Jesus himself as the chief cornerstone. *In him, the whole building is joined together* and rises to become a holy temple in the Lord. And in him, you too are *being built together* to become a dwelling in which God lives by his Spirit.

### 1 John 4

Beloved, let us love one another, because love comes from God. Everyone who loves has been born of God and knows God. Whoever does not love does not know God, because God is love ... If anyone says, "I love God," but hates his brother, he is a liar. For anyone who does not love his brother, whom he has seen, cannot love God, whom he has not seen. And we have this commandment from Him: *Whoever loves God must love his brother as well.*

## ONENESS IS LOVE, NOT UNIFORMITY

When it comes to Christ's desire, prayer and command for the unity of love between Christian brothers and sisters, he could not possibly have made his will any clearer. To love *Abba* is to love *Abba's* family. Not as an abstraction but as real people in real communities of faith. To love *Abba* is to love *Abba* in them.

We also know that those who identify as Christian come in all shapes and sizes, cultures and convictions. Uniformity is neither possible nor desirable. The unity or oneness that Christ prayed for is not about compliance to uniform faith forms or identical worship practices—even in the first century.

Their unity was from first to last in their love for one another, rooted in their love for Christ and his love for them. These days, we call this a "centered set" faith, where we identify a common focal point—the person of Jesus Christ—and gather around him. This contrasts with what we call a "bounded set," where instead of the common center, we obsess about boundaries of who is in (always 'us') and who is out (always 'them').

These boundaries of fellowship feature distinctive doctrines or practices whereby we decide who we cannot "abide with" in love. And let's be honest, if you refuse to abide, you have turned from love. There's no such thing as an abstracted unity of some disembodied universal church. Bottom line, can you break bread together around the person of Jesus Christ?

But what if we differ? IF? *When* we inevitably differ, maturity looks like putting love ahead of your differences. It's called being a spiritual grown-up. Our theological opponents have real lives, families, needs and hardships that require a listening ear, an empathetic heart and helping hands. How will we know this without sharing our stories and mingling our tears? And how will you be vulnerable enough to share stories if you can't or won't break bread together? And where better to break bread than in the presence of Jesus Christ? It probably means surrendering enough of our arrogance and egoism to have adult hearts, willing to gather in the name of Love Incarnate.

## TO *BE CHRISTIAN* IS TO OPEN OURSELVES TO LOVE

To be Christian is to turn toward *all* in love—to open our hearts to the other and to see and name the other as brother or sister. We share a common humanity with everyone on the planet—that obligates us to be loving neighbors. Wait a second. Is it really love if it's an "obligation" or a commandment? Jesus thought so. How about this: what if our common gratitude for the *Grace* of *Abba* revealed in Christ causes us to embrace anyone who seeks to follow him—no matter how differently they might understand what following Jesus means?

### So-called "False Unity"

I will say it again: *to be Christian is to turn toward love.* Whenever we turn *from* love, we turn *from* God. And according to John the Beloved, when we turn from love, we cease to know God and cut ourselves off from eternal life. It's okay to let that sting a bit. Jesus' best friend said it, not me. But thank God, although we turn away from *Abba's* love, his love never fails. This has nothing to do with going to heaven or hell when we die. It is about whether we're living in the Father's house or sulking in the field as the older brother.

I hear a well-rehearsed script at work in Christendom that claims overlooking our theological and ecclesial differences to gather around the Lord's Table is "false unity." Make no mistake (I hate that phrase): this is nothing but a sophisticated cliché for Junior High-level religious snobbery. No, it's worse than that. It is an inherited script in direct defiance to the explicit desires, prayers and commands of Jesus Christ.

To turn from love in the name of avoiding "false fellowship" is a deliberate act of disobedience to the red letter Voice of John 17. I've noticed those who can recite the cold lines of their divisive script fail to mention John 17, nor do they seem to be familiar with it.

## So-called "False Prophet" of Ecumenism

A similar myth persists that claims any act of "ecumenism" (having fellowship with Christians across the theological aisle) is to fall prey to the Antichrist. The idea is that some forthcoming Antichrist (the beast of Rev. 13) will establish one world government in partnership with a False Prophet, who will organize one world religion. The accusation is that all ecumenical movements and interfaith gatherings serve that end. In other words, unity with other believers (as Christ commanded) is loyalty to the Antichrist. Thus, allegiance to Christ requires disfellowshipping other believers!

Both scripts call good evil and evil good. They are equally false when practiced by individuals or denominations, not least when any group claims to be the "one true Church" to the exclusion of others.

And I need to say this to such groups: I'm guilty. I don't always like you. I don't really desire fellowship with you. I don't want to love you. And so I pray, Lord Jesus Christ, have mercy on me, a sinner. Soften my heart, turn it toward love, deliver me from the evil one! How can I reject schismatics and sectarians when ALL Christians are indictable of the first heresy—*turning from love*? And what is repentance but humbly *turning toward love.* Are we even willing?

### Every "Wall of Partition"

Any hope we have for Christian unity began on Good Friday when Christ shattered the temple's "wall of partition." We recall how Christ's wounded body tore the veil that excluded us from the holy of holies, making peace with God. But we also need to become familiar with the text in Ephesians, where Christ's broken body also broke the wall of separation that partitioned Jews and Gentiles. Spiritual apartheid ended that day and the two people became one new humanity.

According to Paul, the divine demolition of that temple wall marked the symbolic destruction of every humanly-erected religious barrier: Jews and Greeks, Scythians and Barbarians, males and females, slaves and freemen (Gal. 3:28; Col. 3:11). I hope we're not so obtuse as to suppose this sampling marks the limits of a comprehensive list. No. *Every* us-them division across the Christian spectrum came down *in his body on the tree.* When we rehang the holy drapes and rebuild the religious walls, we are resisting Christ's ministry of reconciliation—we are saying "No" to the work of the Cross.

How tragic then that I should encounter a Christian prayer meeting of "national intercessors" gathering to denounce the Canadian Charter of Rights and Freedoms. With fiery zeal, they reviled the document as "the charter of wrongs" because it included this line: "without discrimination based on race, national or ethnic origin, color, religion, sex, age or mental or physical disability." While a secular government happened to align itself with values akin to our discrimination-free gospel, some who identified with Christ's Name "prayed against" the charter's inclusive commitment and politicized faith to establish a pro-barrier political lobby.

## WE ARE LEGION: SCHISMATIC AND SECTARIAN

I had a vision—a spinoff of Christ's encounter with the Gadarene demoniac recounted in Mark 5. I saw our Lord Jesus Christ get in a fishing boat and cross Galilee. He sailed to our shores to visit us. He didn't land in Gadara or Decapolis—our region is called Denomination. But for a few rags, we're naked. We're mobile, but we're scarred by scores of abrasions—self-inflicted. We're observably insane, but we come running because it's Jesus.

Jesus then asks our name and we intend to say, "I'm Baptist" or "I'm Mennonite" or "I'm dispensational" or "I'm charismatic" or "I'm Orthodox" (all labels I've personally worn—assume your own). But that's not what comes out of our mouth. With a hoarse croak, we blurt, "We are Legion."

Isn't it true? Is there any entity so possessed and fragmented by schismatic and sectarian spirits as the Church for whom Christ implored his Father, "That they would be one"? What did we think would happen when we traded love for one another with lashing one another?

But we couldn't help ourselves. We are powerless over this addiction. We turned from love again and again until the house Christ built is a rubble of tens of thousands of broken bricks. Where do we even start? Mergers? Agreements? Treaties? No.

It begins with Christ delivering us from the evil of turning from love.

We return to unity by living our amends one turn to love at a time, whenever the choice confronts us.

## RADICAL UNITY!

Do I see evidence of the radical unity for which Christ died? Not long ago, I would have said, "Not even close." I might have hoped beyond hope that *radical* repentance could one day lead to *minimal* unity. I've long dreamed that the *Jesus Way* would move us to start somewhere. But what's the first step? John gives us one simple, painful, beautiful practice: *"Whoever loves God must love his brother as well."*

Then something terrible and something beautiful happened. The terrible occurred when a gunman open-fired in a Mosque in Christchurch, New Zealand, slaughtering scores of defenseless worshipers during their prayer time. Families were torn apart by death—men and women, seniors and children were murdered. Blood flowed into the streets. Trauma and despair and wailing rocked the world as images of their defiled sacred space went viral. It was a waking nightmare.

And yet, in that abyss of grief when it looked like evil had prevailed, a miracle occurred. Words of kindness and solidarity flowed in from across that city and from around the globe.

Jewish organizations voiced their concern—offering condolences and condemning the vicious act. The Jewish Agency and NZ Jewish Council announced that Synagogues would cancel their Shabbat services as an act of solidarity with the bereaved. The Holocaust Centre in New Zealand declared, "It is our responsibility to care for, respect and protect everyone and we all have the right to feel as safe in a place of worship as we do in our own homes." An American Jewish advocacy group recalled, "After the Pittsburgh shooting, Muslim communities showed up for us, protecting us at vigils, actions, and Shabbat prayers. We must do the same for them."

Christians joined in this show of co-suffering love, then Sikhs and Hindus as well. Representing the *Jesus Way,* my Christ-following peace-building friend, Mercy Aiken, spoke out in a blog post:

> *The sin of Islamophobia can never atone for the sin of anti-Semitism.*
>
> We need to stop falling prey to this idea that there must inevitably be some sort of war and murderous hatred between the children who call Abraham their father.
>
> I pray that true Christian peacemakers will arise with open hearts towards the gorgeous God-given humanity of the others—and for the sake of Christ (our beautiful Christ), become ministers of reconciliation and a gospel that is actually good news for the world rather than ministers of hateful conspiracy theories. How does anyone even breathe in that tight, dark little world?
>
> That compressed little stunted version of Christianity will someday merely be a chapter or book in some future generation's analysis of the ways Christianity failed in this generation.
>
> I am not saying that Christianity is an utter failure in this generation. I have full and glorious confidence in Jesus Christ and his righteous and peaceable kingdom. And for those who are wondering, neither am I laying the blame for all the problems at the feet of the Christian world. However, Jesus taught us to take the log out of our own eye first, before looking at everyone else. I wish everyone would take this approach.
>
> I dedicate this statement, with honor and respect, to various pastor friends of mine who are taking their congregations to visit mosques, sending words of condolence and support to them. I also dedicate it with honor and respect to the Jewish congregations in

New Zealand and elsewhere who are standing mourning with their Muslim brothers and sisters—and finally to my dear Muslim brothers and sisters who have taught me so much about love and friendship.

Lord, teach us the way of love, for love never fails. Teach us to dwell in the broadness of Your heart. Amen.

The response of good-faith Muslims was so different from the Jihadist death-dealers who terrorize the world. Safi Kaska, a Muslim friend of Mercy's and translator of the Koran, wrote the following exhortation to his fellow Muslims:

My official response to all acts of terrorism and violence. This is my choice and it doesn't have to be yours:

ُفـاَخَأ يِّنِإ َكَلُتْقَأل َكْيَلِإ َيِدَي ٍطِساَبِب ْاَنَأ اَم يِنَلُتْقَتِل َكَدَي ّيَلِإ َتطَسَب نِئَل}
(28 ةدئاملا) {َنيِمَلاَعْلا ّبَر َهّللا

*Even if you try to kill me, I will not try to kill you. I fear God, the Lord of all the worlds* (5:28).

The proper response to attacks on Islam and Muslims should begin with the following:

1) to respond for the sake of God and seeking his approval, not for the sake of revenge.

2) to respond with the intention to guide others to the ways of goodness, mercy and love. Too often, some Muslims respond to hateful attacks with more hatred, which only continues the cycle of vengeance. Rather, we must intend by our responses to guide and benefit the very people who launched the attacks in the first place.

Eternity with God is not here on earth but in the hereafter. He is the ultimate judge of our deeds.

On Safi's seventy-fifth birthday, just about a week after the attack, he posted this resolution:

A new year of my life is just starting.
I resolve to live in a meaningful way.
I will trust God and allow him to lead.
I will keep my mind open for new ideas.

I will be a teacher/learner.
I will serve humbly.
I will not judge others.
I will forgive freely.
I will work for peace and try to be a bridge builder.

Safi then followed up with this message on Twitter:

> Wisdom from my life experience: "'Love the Lord your God with all your heart and with all your soul and with all your mind.' This is the first and greatest commandment. And the second is like it: 'Love your neighbor as yourself.' All the Law and the Prophets hang on these two commandments." —Jesus of Nazareth

I would note that the name Safi means "pure, sincere friend." Indeed. For my own response, I posted the following:

> In co-suffering love, I join our Muslim neighbors in their prayers tonight as they mourn the New Zealand tragedy:
>
> In the name of God, the Merciful-to-all, the Mercy Giver:
> Praise be to God, the Lord of the Worlds,
> The Merciful-to-all, the Mercy Giver,
> Master of the Day of Judgment.
> It is You we worship, and it is You we seek for help.
> Guide us to the straight path,
> The path of those whom You have blessed, with whom
> You are not angry and have not gone astray.

The momentum for this radical unity expanded far beyond the petty boundaries of factional Christendom. Our common humanity and our neighborly love across diverse faiths has not been deterred by subsequent attacks in Africa or in Israel. I've come to believe that no event in history has done more than the New Zealand massacre to rally the children of Abraham—Muslims, Jews and Christians—together in radical unity against religious hatred. I suspect one reason for this tipping point was that peace-loving New Zealand was itself a victim—and that her government's response was such an outpouring of beautifully Christlike radical unity.

As I wrote this paragraph, citizens of New Zealand gathered four-deep in concentric circles around the major Mosque in Wellington so that prayers could be offered in peace, surrounded by love.

Peace, love and radical unity—in Christchurch.

In Christchurch.

In Christ's church. That's my prayer.

Last word goes to my colleague at St. Stephen's University, Peter Fitch:

> A lifetime of following Jesus led us to fall in love with his life of justice, beauty and compassion, so we could easily embrace all people from any ideology who embrace those values.

## THOUGHTS

1. *"Blessed are the peacemakers."* Blessed are the *bridge-builders.* Can you think of Christ-followers who believe and worship differently than you? Are you able to speak to each other? Are you able to hear each other? What assumptions or prejudices make it most awkward or difficult? What practices help you better hold the differences with respect and appreciation?

2. What excuses have you heard to promote segregation and disunity? How might you respond to those voices? How might your confession of complicity be a first step toward calling others to the table of fellowship?

3. *Challenge:* Would you take the first step to reach out? Could you visit believers of a different persuasion than you? Would you invite them to your family table? What questions would you ask them to aid your understanding of their faith?

## PRAYERS

*Sorry, Lord. We, your people—your family, knew what you wanted. We knew the new commandment you gave your disciples and read your prayer to* Abba *for unity.*

*We're sorry, Lord. We have turned from Love. Sometimes we spiritualized our hardness of heart and called it "faithfulness"—as if you would reckon it as righteousness.*

*All-wise Potter, you know what needs to happen to your ruined pot. You're not one to discard broken things—we ask that with your skilled hands you would refashion us in love on the wheel of Grace.*

# Facet 4

# "Take up your cross" RADICAL RECOVERY

In this section, we move from faith as trust further into faith as discipleship—what I've already been calling the *Jesus Walk*. In this chapter, we will begin with a discussion of Christ's *Sermon on the Mount* as the core of Jesus' teaching or what we might call, "the *Way of the Cross*." The Sermon's *Way* or *Walk* establishes Christ's transforming *Grace* as the spiritual and ethical foundation for our formation throughout this section of the book. It's not to be mistaken for an "application section"—rather, we're diving into Christ's program for our transfiguration into blessed peacebuilders, recreated into the pattern of the cruciform One.

Specifically, the Sermon on the Mount demonstrates that the demands of the *Jesus Way* are deeper than efforts to obey a series of stricter commandments on enemy love. The Sermon takes us on a journey of inner transformation, described as "taking up a Cross and following" in the *Jesus Way*. We will see how Jesus' core teaching transposes his death and resurrection into our lives as daily discipleship. Peacebuilding apart from this transformation devolves into angry activism and violent peacemaking. Christ, on the other hand, goes to work on the very structures of our hearts. This chapter explores that truth.

## TAKE UP YOUR CROSS AND FOLLOW ME

More than any other prophet, teacher or preacher, Jesus Christ is what Walter Brueggemann calls *"a Voice from Elsewhere"*... the ultimate foreign prophet. A voice from another land, another kingdom, another realm.

Matthew 5-7 introduces that Voice. It's Christ's inaugural Sermon, his life message and his catechetical teaching for those who follow him.

We can leave it to others to unpack *what it says*. Many have. I especially commend to you the ancient works of St Gregory of Nyssa and St John Chrysostom. And in our days, we have modern classics, such as Dietrich

Bonhoeffer's *Cost of Discipleship,* Dallas Willard's *Divine Conspiracy,* Eberhard Arnold's devotional, *Salt and Light* and Jim Forest's *Ladder of the Beatitudes.* By all means load up your library—but don't forget to read the Sermon itself!

My task in this chapter is not so much commentary as it is to cover the following ground

1. **What the Sermon *is*.**
   That is, what are these words meant to be?
   What has its message become for Christianity?
   What is its message for the world?
2. **What the Sermon *does*.**
   That is, how does it function?
   Not just, "What is Jesus saying?"
   But, "What is Jesus doing? What is he up to?"
3. **And the Sermon's *scandalous claims***
   From the outset, we'll see the Sermon's claims on the disciple, on the church and on humanity.

## WHAT IS THE SERMON ON THE MOUNT?

> The cross is laid on every Christian. The first Christ-suffering which every man must experience is the call to abandon the attachments of this world. It is that dying of the old man which is the result of his encounter with Christ. As we embark upon discipleship we surrender ourselves to Christ in union with his death—we give over our lives to death. Thus it begins; the cross is not the terrible end to an otherwise god-fearing and happy life, but it meets us at the beginning of our communion with Christ. *When Christ calls a man, he bids him come and die.*
>
> — Dietrich Bonhoeffer, *The Cost of Discipleship,* 99.

*What is the Sermon on the Mount?*

It's the core of Christ's teaching. Certainly in the New Testament, the Sermon on the Mount is our introduction to the words, the message and preaching of Jesus. In this Sermon we find the very core of Jesus' teaching.

This message is *Jesus' interpretation of the Law.* The Rabbi Jesus takes us into the deeper meaning, the heart-meaning of the whole law.

This is *Jesus' distillation of the Prophets.* The prophet Jesus stands at the zenith and climax of the Hebrew prophetic tradition, the prophet like Moses, Elisha, David and Isaiah . . . fulfilling in himself what they foresaw.

These chapters represent *the peak of the entire biblical tradition,* Jewish *and* Christian. The Living Word stands as king of Mount Zion and the whole of the Judeo-Christian revelation.

In fact, the Sermon on the Mount is *the pinnacle of all prophetic religious traditions.* I love this account of Mahatma Gandhi, the Hindu peacebuilder who committed himself to reading the Sermon on the Mount once every day and to obeying Jesus' call to follow (i.e. obey) his *Way* explicitly.

> When Lord Irwin, the British Viceroy to India asked Gandhi what he thought would solve the problems between Great Britain and India, Gandhi picked up a Bible and opened it to the fifth chapter of Matthew and said: "When your country and mine shall get together on the teachings laid down by Christ in this Sermon on the Mount, we shall have solved the problems not only of our countries but those of the whole world" (citing Frank E. Eden in *Treasury of Christian Faith*).

Jesus not only speaks as *high priest* of the church, or as *prophet above all prophets,* but he also speaks as the *creator* of humanity, the *prototype* of humanity (in whose image Adam was created) and the *telos* of humanity (the first human to be fully glorified). Thus, in the Sermon, Christ is not merely telling us how to be *Christian* or how to be *spiritual,* but how to become *human.* In that sense, the Sermon on the Mount is the *premier humanist document!*

*What is the Sermon on the Mount?*

As received by communities, the Sermon has been called:

- the *constitution* of the Kingdom of God.
- Christ's *manifesto* for God's alternative society.
- the *new culture* of the Second Adam.
- Christ's vision for just and merciful world.
- the inauguration of the Cruciform Reformation.

As received by individuals, it has been described as

- the *ethical backbone* of our new life in Christ.
- Christ's *recovery program* for the ego in bondage.
- the *cruciform Way* or *the Way of the Cross.*
- Christ's *death and resurrection* lived daily.

Earlier, we discussed the popularity of the language of deconstruction. We don't know the half of it—not until we've *undergone* the Sermon's narrow way, the "Cross-way."

*What is the Sermon on the Mount?*

It is a *Way.* A specific, practical, commanded *Way* to live and *Way* to life. It is the *Jesus* Way.

To be a disciple of Christ is to follow Christ on his *Way.* Hence, *Christ-followers.* To *be a Christ-follower* is to *Walk* with Jesus in your real life at school, at home, at work, at leisure . . . on *his Path.*

The *Jesus Way* is the way Jesus empowers us to live and be. It's a bidding, a summons to follow. The *Way* to be neighbors, brothers and sisters, spouses and parents, to be citizens who have real enemies. It's the *Way* to be faithful to God and to our own humanity.

*When Jesus says, "Take up your Cross daily and follow me," what does he mean? What does that look like?*

The Sermon on the Mount is Jesus' answer. My friend Wm. Paul Young reminds me that Jesus' call to take up your cross is not to say that Jesus crucifies you or that *Abba* makes crosses. *Abba* is not cruel and Jesus did not fashion crosses in Joseph's workshop. No, it is *we* humans who fashion crosses. We get cruel, we become mockers, we throw stones and pound nails.

Humans tortured and crucified Jesus. *Abba* didn't. For Jesus, taking up his cross describes his self-giving, radically forgiving, co-suffering love response. In a Q&A session with Wm. Paul Young, he explained,

> God, by submitting to our torture device, destroyed its power and transforms our torture device into an icon and monument of *Grace* that is so precious to us that we would wear it on our rings and around our necks. We are wearing the sign and symbol of human brokenness that has been redeemed by a God who

submitted to it. That means that there is nothing you can bring to the table that is so dark and broken that God cannot climb into and transform it into an icon and monument of *Grace*. We are surrounded by a community of people who give testimony that the redeeming Genius has climbed into our brokenness and is transforming us into icons and monuments of *Grace*—to the praise and the glory of God the Father, Son and Holy Spirit.

(Wm. Paul Young, 01-26-19)

To take up our cross as Jesus did—to follow the cruciform *Way* in his steps—describes the *Grace*-filled life that willingly faces into and passes through the darkness (within or without) and by *Grace*, transforms that darkness into light. Such *Grace* alone has the power to transform even the perpetrators of darkness into children of the Light.

This is what it means to be a Christ-follower on the *Jesus Walk*.

## THE BEATITUDES

A few words of review on the opening section—*the Beatitudes*—because they form the foundation of the rest of the Sermon. At this point, I'd like to share a translation of the Beatitudes by Ron S. Dart (my mentor, PhD supervisor and hiking guide). He begins this way:

### "The divine life"

That's a new take. Ron points out that the Greek term *makarios* signifies more than merely *blessed* or *happy* or what the late Robert Schuller called "the Be-Happy-Attitudes." The Hebrew word we translate "blessed" (from Psalm 1:1 for example) may carry the connotation "happy" or simply "blessed." And that *may* be all Jesus means. But the Greek term *makarios*, from classical Greek, is more loaded. It had been used in Hellenistic Greek to denote "the life of the gods." Imagine what that meant in terms of the violent and hedonistic stories of the Greek or Roman pantheon. The divine life was all about power plays, sexual exploits, wars and gluttonous revelry.

But now Christ speaks and completely overturns every such notion, revealing that the *Divine Way* is marked by humility, purity and peace. It is the upside down *Way* of the truly *divine life*. Or as the apostle Peter says, this is what it is to be "partakers of the divine nature" (2 Pet. 1:4). A bold statement to be sure—a privilege afforded those who join the dance of the Trinity, as Richard Rohr likes to call it. With *makarios* under our belts, here is Ron's translation of Matthew 5:3-12.

> The Divine Life is for those who die to the demands of the ego. Such people will inhabit the Kingdom of Heaven.
>
> The Divine Life is for those who have lived through tragedy and suffering. Such people will be comforted at a deep level.
>
> The Divine Life is for those who bring their passions under control for goodness. It is such people that will inherit the earth.
>
> The Divine Life is for those who hunger and thirst for justice. Such people will be fed to the full.
>
> The Divine Life is offered to those who are gracious and merciful. Such people will be treated in a merciful and gracious manner.
>
> The Divine Life is offered to those whose Home is clean on the Inside. Such people will know the very presence of God and see His face.
>
> The Divine Life is offered to those who are Makers and Creators of Peace. Such people will be called the children of God.
>
> The Divine Life is known by those who are persecuted for seeking Justice. Such people will know what it means to live in the Kingdom of Heaven.
>
> The Divine Life is known by those who are mistreated and misunderstood in their passion for justice. They will inherit the Kingdom of Heaven. The prophets were treated this way in the past.

## LITERAL, MORAL OR SPIRITUAL

In his instant classic, *The Divine Conspiracy*, Dallas Willard saw in the Beatitudes a list of the losers, the lowly, and the broken. Jesus assures them and assures *us* that God's kingdom is available *even to the losers.* That is, Willard saw the first half of each Beatitude as a negative to be overcome. Poverty will be turned to wealth, mourning to comfort, meekness to greatness, persecution to vindication, etc.

Influenced by the Fathers, by Ron Dart and others, I believe the

Beatitudes go *way* beyond that. The first line of each Beatitude is not just an "in spite of" statement. That might be a valid *literal reading.*

Nor are they merely a new list of commandments to be obeyed, though some have treated them as such given some obvious parallels of the Sermon to the giving of the tablets at Mount Sinai. That might be a valid *moral reading.*

But to truly ascend the Mountain of the Beatitudes, we must perceive the *spiritual reading*—by which we mean "how the Beatitudes point to Christ."

In the Beatitudes, we behold *the glorified, transfigured life of Christ and his Way of the Cross.* The Christ of the Beatitudes surprises us with a "beatific vision" of the true nature of *God in Christ* and the nature of *humanity* (the true self) *in Christ.* In the first half of each Beatitude, Christ unveils the surprising glory of the divine human—his own life (and death). In himself, Christ reveals:

- the *kenosis* of letting go—the bankrupted ego;
- the gentle yieldedness of meekness that renounces selfishness and my rights over others,
- the capacity to mourn with the broken rather than obsessing over fixing and patching;
- the mercy that has bid "good riddance" to dominance and coercion;
- the hunger and thirst for true justice in the Amos, Micah and Isaiah prophetic tradition;
- the purity of heart baptized in water and blood without demanding vengeance.

Then, in the second half of each Beatitude, we recognize Christ's promises are not *someday* hopes (at least not entirely) of an entirely *not yet* kingdom. Each of the promised blessings touch on our access *now* to the kingdom of heaven—what John calls the *eternal life* of knowing *Abba* and his Son (Jn. 17:2-3). Each blessing describes our participation in the resurrection life of Christ—the life of the age to come as it breaks into our lives now.

## TRINITARIAN LIFE

As recipients of the divine life or participants in the divine nature, we enjoy the fellowship of *Abba,* Christ and *Grace*—we're included in the life of the Trinity. The Beatitudes reveal particulars of each Person of the Trinity and our life with them.

### The Beatitudes, Jesus and our life with Jesus

Pope Benedict XVI said, "The Beatitudes are a veiled autobiography of the life and character of Jesus Christ."

This is the message Christ *lived*—these words became flesh through his life among us. He practiced what he preached here in his life, death and resurrection. The Beatitudes take the Death and Resurrection of Jesus and they transpose it (think musically) into the life of daily discipleship. This corresponds to Paul's understanding:

> I have been crucified with the Messiah. I am, however, alive-but it isn't me any longer, it's the Messiah who lives in me. And the life I do still live in the flesh, I live within the faithfulness of the son of God, who loved me and gave himself for me.
> – Galatians 2:20

For Paul, his life in Christ refracted the life of Christ. His trials and triumphs reflected his fellowship with Christ in his suffering and his resurrection:

> This means knowing him, knowing the power of his resurrection, and knowing the partnership of his sufferings. It means sharing the form and pattern of his death, so that somehow I may arrive at the final resurrection from the dead. —Philippians 3:10

What Paul makes explicit (however mysterious), Jesus had already made implicit in the Beatitudes.

In the Beatitudes, each "blessed" describes the company of the crucified—the poor in spirit, the mourning, the meek, the merciful, those hungry for justice, the pure in heart and those peacebuilders who endure persecution.

All these traits are gathered up in the first Beatitude, where poverty of spirit indicates our crucifixion with Christ to the demands, dictates and cravings of the lost and deluded ego. By *Grace,* the poor in spirit leave the house of lies we called home and embark on the *Jesus Way* of *kenosis.* Like Christ, we "let go" of attachments, "empty" ourselves of egoism and "set aside" the slavery impulses of grasping and clinging.

Thus, we turn from selfishness to self-giving participation in Christ's *"they shall be"* promises—Christ's comfort, his mercy and righteousness, his pure vision and his ministry of reconciliation. Each Beatitude shows us our inheritance: the fullness of Christ's resurrection life poured into the emptied cup of self.

## The Beatitudes, *Grace* and our life in the Spirit

Earlier, I alluded to parallels between God giving Moses the stone tablets on Mount Sinai and Christ's Sermon on the "Mount of Beatitudes." The parallel is most notable for its contrasts:

- Christ is *not* the new Moses, receiving the new Law from the LORD. Rather, Christ is identified as the LORD, delivering the New Covenant to his disciples.
- Christ's Beatitudes and Moses' Laws are not direct equivalents. Christ sees himself fulfilling the Law (Matt. 5:17-19). John later contrasts the Law that came from Moses with *grace* and *truth* that came from Christ (Jn. 1:17).

Whether you read Paul's statement that "Christ is *the end* of the Law" (Rom. 10:14) as negation or fulfillment, this much is certain: the Beatitudes are *not* a moralistic "to do" list we cannot obey or should ignore. Rather, they are *Jesus' version of the fruit of the Spirit and signs of the Spirit-filled life.*

When Christ says, "unless your righteousness is superior to that of the scribes and Pharisees, you will never get into the kingdom of heaven" (Matt. 5:20), he is *not* saying that we need to be stricter legalists than the Sanhedrin. But neither is he saying that the demands of righteousness are too extreme to obey them and we must not even try—as if living in *Grace* exempts us from living righteously. Paul never said, "The unrighteous live by faith." But how do the righteous live?

Righteousness is not simply *imputed* to us by our amazing faith. True righteousness is *lived* by Christ's Spirit—the Spirit of transforming *Grace. Grace* indwells to empower and bears fruit in real life. That fruit-bearing

*Grace* life looks like something. It looks like the Beatitudes:

- The Beatitudes are Jesus' sign (evidence) of those who have been baptized and filled by his Spirit.
- The Beatitudes are the Holy Spirit's work of transformation and sanctification in action and in practice.
- The Beatitudes are divine virtues, impossible to attain by fleshly effort but a very real description of what the Holy Spirit produces in those who "abide in the vine" of Jesus Christ (Jn. 15:4-5).
- The Beatitudes describe those who are being transfigured into the image of Christ by the *Grace of the Holy Spirit.*

As Paul sees so clearly:

> Now the Lord is the *Spirit*; and where the *Spirit* of the Lord *is*, there *is* liberty. But we all, with unveiled face, beholding as in a mirror the glory of the Lord, are being transformed into the same image from glory to glory, just as by the Spirit of the Lord.
> —2 Corinthians 3:16-18

This is the life that *drinks* from the well of the Spirit. These are the *springs* of the Spirit that gush from within. This is what it is to *walk* in the Spirit.

*Grace* is fashioning new creatures. This is ultimately what Jesus means by "theirs is the kingdom of heaven"—and what Paul calls *glorification.*

But *glorification* isn't quite what we expected. Christ surprises us: glorification is *not* the nobility, honor and triumph of the heroes of Greek mythology or even Old Testament history.

Rather, *glorification* by the Holy Spirit is humility, meekness and mercy. *Glorification* turns worldly power on its head with a force more powerful: self-giving, cruciform servant-love.

## The Beatitudes, *Abba* and our life with *Abba*

The Beatitudes show us what it is to be "perfected" by *Abba.*

In the Sermon, Jesus picks up the Levitical phrase, "Be holy as I am holy," and reworks it to say, "Be perfect as your heavenly *Abba* is perfect" (Matt. 5:48). He's not talking about perfectionism. The word for "perfect" here is *telos*—come to your *telos* (full maturity). The whole Sermon is a finger pointing to *Abba's* love, made resident by the Spirit in human nature and manifest in Christ and his followers. The Fathers go so far as to say that we will become by *Grace* what Christ is by nature—a doctrine they called *theosis, divinization* or *deification.* These words are unfamiliar and even shocking to modern ears, but they were foundational terms coined to summarize the convictions of two great apostles concerning the miracle of our *Grace* transformation:

> **Paul:** "And all of us, without any veil on our faces, gaze at the glory of the Lord as in a mirror, and so are being *changed* [literally "transfigured!"] *into the same image (Christ!), from glory to glory . . ."*
> —2 Corinthians 3:18

> **Peter:** ". . . he has given us his precious and wonderful promises, and the purpose of all this is so that you may . . . *become partakers of the divine nature."* —2 Peter 1:4

The Beatitudes show how *Abba's* life brings humanity to its fullest bloom and ripest fruit: the very image of Christ is being formed in us!

In Luke's Sermon on the Plain, Jesus surprises us with what holiness and maturity look like in the divine life. He says, "Be *merciful* as your heavenly *Abba* is merciful" (Lk. 6:36). The holiness of *Abba* perfected in us turns out to be Christlike mercy!

What is it to be "perfect" or complete and mature as children of *Abba*? What does that look like? Like this:

The Beatitudes. The Sermon on the Mount.
The Cruciform Way.

*Abba's* heart is *reflected perfectly* by Jesus Christ, *described perfectly* in the Beatitudes and *prescribed perfectly* in the Sermon on the Mount. The Sermon shows us what *Abba* is like, it shows us what Christ is like, and it shows us what *Abba's* children are like—and how they get there.

So, that's a sound bite responding to the question, "What is the Sermon on the Mount?"

I don't know whether we should feel hungry and thirsty or if we should be in shock and awe. But if nothing else, we need to know what Jesus said here. I need to know it in my heart. I need to eat it, drink it, breathe it, sweat it, ooze it. Or if it is the *Jesus Walk,* how about, "I need to walk it"? This brings us to the Sermon's *function*—from what it *is* to what it *does.*

## WHAT THE SERMON *DOES*

I can tell you what it does. It pushes my buttons! If you are willing to let Christ sow these words into your heart—if you *really* hear them and put them into practice—this message will first plow the soil of your heart and then plant new seeds of life.

Christ's words will empty you and then they will fill you.

They will deconstruct and reconstruct you—they will renovate, restore and refurbish you.

They will purge you of all the dross that is "not of love's kind," purifying the gold of your true self. They will cleanse the diamond of your heart of the tarnish so that every facet shines with the light of Christ.

If we'll surrender to these words of Jesus, they will not return void. They will accomplish what they purposed to do from the start.

These words of Christ are simple but not easy. Love your enemies, forgive your debtors, trust *Abba* daily—such words are a litmus test of the heart. They are a diagnostic tool that roots out every hint of rebellion and toxic religion. These words of Christ are intended to lay out your heart, to tenderize it, to salt it and season it, and throw it on the barbecue. To be a living sacrifice (a la Rom. 12:1) is *not* about punishment. It's about becoming the aroma of *Grace* that smells like the good news of Jesus' love.

There's this saying in the barbecue world: tense cows make tough meat. That's a good description of me. To get me from tough to tender requires a process. For Christ-followers across the centuries, Christ's Sermon on the Mount has been the slow-cooker or smoker of choice. An alcoholic friend of mine told me that he sees the Sermon as the original program of recovery from humankind's deepest and oldest addiction: self-will.

By "self-will," my friend does not mean to negate either the self (the gift of our personhood) or our will (our capacity for willing love). Rather, he's awoken to the truth that the "autonomous will" ("My will be done!") is a delusion, since in Christ "we live and move and have our being."

He reads these words of Christ every day as part of his twenty-five-year plus sobriety. He says he's not a Christian. I'd say he's a Christ-follower—if hearing and following mean anything. And they do.

## BOILED DOWN

I would make the case that the whole life and teachings of Christ are encapsulated in the Sermon on the Mount. And the Sermon on the Mount is boiled down in the Beatitudes. And all the Beatitudes are summarized in the first one: "Blessed are the poor in Spirit" or in other words, "Not my will, but thine be done."

*What does the Sermon on the Mount do?*

The Sermon is a call and means to discredit, disown and detach from the old Adam (the ego, the false self, the wicked conscience, our inner demons).

It's a living word, a two-edged sword.

Before you're done, IF we hear Jesus aright, these words will bankrupt our ego. It will challenge the self-defeating messages of self-centeredness, self-hatred, self-pity.

The sermon invites us to drink Jesus' new cup, a bloody cup, a covenant cup of other-centered, self-giving love.

*What does the Sermon on the Mount do?*

The sermon systematically dismantles that old self, the false self, the Adam and Eve self, making room for the new self, the Christ-life, the new heart of Jesus in you.

As we play out the whole Sermon, virtually every practice—giving away cloak and tunic, forgiving and blessing enemies, cutting off hands, letting go of stuff, faithfulness to spouse, and all manner of sacrificial love—all of these are consistent deliberate acts with a far deeper agenda than a social ethic or upgraded activism.

While they *are* that . . . what I see is that the Sermon is the *Jesus Walk* that thoroughly strips the ego of all its attachments, cravings, lusts, pride, impressiveness, independence, etc. The *Jesus Walk* impoverishes the ego, starves our cravings, and finally, detaches us from the craver itself. Indeed, "I am crucified with Christ."

The Sermon uses my perceived external enemies to defeat my real inner enemy. This is the genius of *Grace* and her severity, for the Fire of Love is not about leaving us half-baked. She relentlessly opposes all our resistance to Love, but because she IS Love, She awaits willing surrender rather than violating our will. She never gives up, but we set the pace. We decide when we've bottomed out on slavery to Self.

*What does the Sermon on the Mount do?*

The Sermon is the *Jesus Way* to become poor in spirit *and* the fruit of being poor in spirit.

It's brilliant. Every handle, every bit of leverage that the flesh could grasp is loosed from it systematically. Where our tight-fisted hearts surrender—when we open to "let go and let God"—we're infused with the *Grace* of the resurrection life. Christ is formed in us.

The Sermon followed—lived out—is the *Jesus Walk*. Those who "take up their cross" not only *believe* the *Jesus truth*. By God's empowering *Grace*, Christ-followers trust and embrace and follow the *Jesus Walk* in practice.

Becoming *a* Christian (taking the label) is quite easy. You just jump through whatever hoops of identification your brand requires. The biblical way to identify was baptism upon confession of faith. Modern Evangelicals reduced it to an event of faith expressed as "sinner's prayer." Easy.

*Becoming Christian* (becoming Christlike) is more difficult. As a *Way of faith*, Christ describes the *Walk* as continuous (i.e. following) and ongoing (i.e. daily). Not so easy because it's the *Cross*-way, a *narrow* way, and the *only* way to life.

Christians *believe* in Jesus as a Person but Christ-followers (Christian or not) also *trust* his words, follow his program and practice his prescription for a new world.

*What does the Sermon on the Mount do?*

It saves me from believing that I am the center of the universe. It assures me that the world does not revolve and orbit around me.

It saves me from believing I am God or that I need to be God. It saves me from having to manage everyone else's joys, sorrows and choices.

It exposes my inability to manage others.

It exposes my inability to manage myself.

It exposes my inability to manage God.

It IS step one of my recovery.

For me, it began when Beatitude #1 showed me the painful truth that I really do still think I am Lord and that everyone and everything, even God, should be my servant. It walked me through the narrow door to the Kingdom where Jesus is Lord and it is *not* about *I, me, mine* or about *my* will and *my* freedom and *my* rights.

I thought *my* freedom was the highest moral imperative. The Sermon says Christ's love of God, neighbor, stranger and enemy is our guiding star.

I thought, like Alice in Wonderland, "I MAKE the path."

Christ says, "I AM the path."

I thought, "I am free! I shape my destiny."

Christ said, "Follow me. Listen to my words. Do what I say. Then you'll be free.'

But I so much wanted to be god. To be independent, self-sufficient, in control. The *Grace* of the Sermon exposed that in me. And then it stripped it from me and starved it out of me (as much as I let it, in fits and starts, a day at a time). And then it re-clothed me. And re-fed me. Or at least it will.

Odd: Christ's Sermon has to convince us to stop clinging and grasping at the forbidden fruit—my demand to be god—so that we open our hearts to *Grace* who makes us divine humans. *Grace* alone imbues us with divine poverty and mourning, divine humility and hunger, divine peace, forgiveness and patience.

That's what *Grace* does. That's what the Sermon does.

## THE CRAZY SCANDAL

The crazy scandal of this Sermon is whether we will not only *believe in Jesus*—but whether we will actually *believe Jesus.* Do we trust him enough to obey his words? Did he even expect us to *obey*? Did he actually mean for us to hear and heed his invitation, "Take up your cross and *follow* me?"

Some have strayed so far as to boast of their faith in Jesus by *not* obeying him! Unfortunately, in their noble battle against works-righteousness, the Reformers found a way for Christians to take Jesus' core message, his call to discipleship, his beautiful *Jesus Way*... and to cleverly disarm it of its power to move us from forgiveness into freedom.

Here is the demonic logic that obscures and ultimately silences the voice of Jesus. Beware it's familiar and convincing:

*Myth 1:* Christ is giving us a version of the Law even MORE strict and extreme than the religion of the Scribes and Pharisees.

*Myth 2:* Christ knows that you cannot keep it, that it is not practical or possible.

*Myth 3:* Christ's excessive demands will drive you to despair until you admit there's no way you can do this.

*Myth 4:* Thus, Christ's strategy was to overwhelm you with the Law he alone could keep. At that point, you will be forced to die to your own efforts and cast yourself upon the gospel of grace alone.

*Myth 5:* Rather than trying to obey Jesus, you will simply have to put your faith in him, trusting that he obeyed for you (instead of you).

*Myth 6:* Christian faith is that Jesus has done it all, so you don't have to. Counting on his obedience alone is the only thing that saves you.

*Myth 7:* In other words, believing in Jesus as your Lord and Savior means that you are *not* able to and *not* even supposed to obey him.

*Myth 8:* You are saved by grace, not by works, so *do not* try to follow Jesus by obeying this Sermon. In fact, if you determine to obey the Sermon, you are repudiating grace and trampling the gospel underfoot!

I may sound like I'm making this up, but consider the following quotes that represent nearly every commentary in that tradition (cited in Clarence Baummann, *The Sermon on the Mount: The Modern Quest for Its Meaning*):

> *Eduard Thurneysen:* "Not only are we unable to do what Jesus said, but we are not even invited to do what Jesus did. For those who nevertheless seek to follow Jesus is only a curse and despair. What matters is not our obedience but that of Christ who did everything 'for' us" (page 275).

> *Bonhoeffer's critical restatement of Luther:* "We are still sinners 'even in the best life,' so let the Christian live like the rest of the world, let him model himself on the world's standards in every sphere of life and not presumptuously aspire to live a different life under grace from his old life under sin. That was the heresy of the enthusiasts, the Anabaptists, and their kind. Let the Christian not attempt to erect a new religion of the letter by endeavoring to live a life of obedience to the commandments of Jesus Christ!" (page 180).

Bonhoeffer rightly calls this "cheap grace," not because he forgot that grace is free, but because he's seen a pseudo-grace that cannot heal a heart or transform a life. Thankfully, we don't need to adjudicate a theological debate between Luther and Bonhoeffer. We just need to read the Sermon! It's as if Jesus anticipated how slippery the ego gets when it senses a threat to its autonomy. Here's his answer:

> "Not everyone who says to me, "Master, Master" will enter the kingdom of heaven; only people *who do the will* of my *Abba* in heaven." —Matt. 7:21
>
> "Therefore everyone who *hears these words* of mine *and puts them into practice* is like a wise man who built his house on the rock. The rain came down, the streams rose, and the winds blew and beat against that house; yet it did not fall, because it had its foundation on the rock.
>
> But everyone who *hears these words* of mine and *does not put them into practice* is like a foolish man who built his house on sand. The rain came down, the streams rose, and the winds blew and beat against that house, and it fell with a great crash."
> —Matt. 7:24-27

To summarize so far:

- What is the Sermon on the Mount?
  *It's the Jesus Way of the cross.*
- What does the Sermon do?
  *It's the Way that Grace transforms us.*
- What is the crazy scandal?
  *Take up your cross and follow. Or don't.*

## THE WORK OF SURRENDER

In the culture of addiction recovery, we've discovered a paradox rooted within the gospel itself—in fact, it's there in the Sermon on the Mount. The paradox is this: *Grace alone transforms* but willing surrender is required. We're not saved by works, but there's some work involved on our part—it's the ongoing struggle to surrender, let go and keep letting go.

An elderly man once challenged me: "Brad, your greatest struggle is that you struggle." We struggle against *Grace* rather than surrendering to it. Or we could say that coming to surrender is a struggle?

And that's what addicts mean by "working the program." It means being still before *Abba*—resisting the urge to bolt—as *Grace* does her work. Giving in to *Grace* is a struggle. In my case, that struggle has many complex fronts. I'll say more later concerning my struggle with the violence in my heart and accompanying vengeance fantasies. However, I've chosen to bring that up now to illustrate one way that Christ teaches us to "work the program" prescribed in his Sermon: namely, *the Lord's Prayer.*

Some of my friends struggle to pray the Lord's Prayer because they think it sounds "old covenant"—specifically when Jesus says we should ask for a forgiveness that we've already been given at the Cross. They point out that the Sermon predates the Cross. I point out that the written Gospel in which we find the Sermon does not. A full generation after the Cross, Matthew teaches his community to pray this prayer and to ask for the forgiveness that's already theirs.

Why would we do that? Why ask for a gift already given? Because our participation in the "finished work" involves appropriating the gift already given. We ask, not so that *Abba* will forgive us, but because our hiding parts and tormented consciences need to let *Grace* into all our dark closets with the good news of what's been done.

Asking for forgiveness is an act of surrender to *Grace.* Christ teaches us to do that because it's far more effective than burying our shame in a theology of denial. Some take this so far as to deny their sin and even deny there's such a thing as sin. Does that work? Would their parents, spouses or children concur?

### "WORKING THE PRAYER" IN VIOLENT TIMES

Well, it doesn't work for me or our violent times. At home, abroad . . . violence has brought us to the point of exhaustion, hopelessness and/or numbness. I see no reprieve in sight and I have every reason to expect further escalation. I find myself in daily need of prayers that guard my heart and mind from both despair of the violence around us and the vengeance fantasies of my own repressed rage.

In that context, I have begun to pray the Lord's Prayer daily in a focused way with some new (to me) understanding about Christ's strategy in ordering the phrases in series as he does. Here is the section that seems super-relevant to my surrender to *Grace*-transformation right now:

## "Forgive us our trespasses as we forgive those who trespass against us"

This phrase calls me to forgive the sins of my enemies. And if we want to be a little technical, at least with *ye olde English,* I think particularly of "trespassing sins."

I remember wandering the gravel back roads of Manitoba, occasionally seeing signs that said, "Trespassers will be prosecuted," or a few hours further south, they might read, "Trespassers will be shot."

The word *trespasses* suggests the violation of boundaries by intruders. It can include anything from military incursions and occupation to a rash of local home invasions to the pettiness of feeling someone push my buttons with an intrusive word or look or social media comment. *Trespasses* are about boundary-breaking. My boundaries. Jesus knows how trespassers threaten us, offend us, tempt us to react.

And so he instructs us, "When(ever) you pray, pray this: "Forgive *us*..." See what he does there? He makes us own the sin of trespassing, as if somehow we should look in the mirror first. Later in the Sermon, Christ warns us sternly (but humorously):

> "Don't judge people, and you won't be judged yourself. You'll be judged, you see, by the judgment you use to judge others. You'll be measured by the measuring-rod you use to measure others. Why do you stare at the splinter in your neighbor's eye, but ignore the plank in your own? How can you say to your neighbor, 'Here, let me get that splinter out of your eye,' when you've got the plank in your own? You're just play-acting! First take the plank out of your own eye, and then you'll see clearly enough to take the splinter out of your neighbor's eye." —Matthew 5:1-5

What is Jesus up to? He's not talking about "getting God to forgive you." He's guiding us toward forgiving others by reminding us that we've been forgiven. He's not about making us beg for forgiveness. He's telling us to check for beams in our own eye before condemning others (who *Abba's* already forgiven).

How have I crossed boundaries? How have I offended the other with my words or actions? How have I participated in trespassing on others' property? How has my citizenship made me complicit in boundary-breaking on a historical or international scale? Who are those in the world right now who continue to live with the harm I've done to them, either personally or as part of my nation's sins?

Having pondered that, I can then move to those who've trespassed against me. How many have truly harmed me? Who has actually invaded my space, my home, my nation? In my own case, that list is always shorter and less extreme. Oh dear. It seems my own offenses don't have a leg to stand on! I am disqualified from judging others for that which I am clearly also guilty. I cannot live in the land of *Grace* while relegating those I hate (yes, hate) to the land of retribution and retaliation . . . I can't even ask God for his vengeance on them when I'm pleading to avoid it myself.

So we come to the Cross and pray, "God, forgive them as I want to be forgiven. Correct them as I want to be corrected. Have the same mercy on them as I want for myself." IF I can remember that the work of forgiveness is already finished for me, will I presume to withhold it from those who offend me?

But Jesus doesn't just move on to a new topic in the next phrase:

### "Lead us not into temptation"

We can, of course, pray generally for deliverance from all temptations. And we can apply this request more specifically to the list of temptations we most frequently battle as individuals. But more precisely, the prayer connects forgiveness of others with a request for help with temptation. In these violent times, we pray for deliverance from the evil we're tempted to perpetrate on our trespassers.

When someone trespasses on our lives, what temptations do we face? Almost universally, our temptation is to respond with either eye-for-an-eye retribution (and call it "justice") or seventy-times-seven retaliation (we call it "eradication"). Jesus knows this. He saw it in his own community, province and nation. The trespassers (Rome's occupying forces) had trampled on all that was sacred to his people. Most especially their freedom. When an overwhelming military force enters your land, crushes your troops, imprisons and humiliates your young men, the overwhelming temptation is to strike back and to feel righteous in doing so. Retaliation thus becomes sacred. This was the temptation of Jesus' disciples. A few had even been freedom fighters (or insurgents, depending on your perspective) of his day.

Jesus warns them: that is the broad (or popular way) that leads to destruction. Don't do it. Pray that God would cleanse your heart of malice and release you from resentment. Ask him to lead you away from the tempting options for vengeance and violence, even in the hidden harbors of your mind and heart. If you don't give *Grace* access to your temptations, you can get drawn into retaliating to "restore honor." We can become so consumed with a sinful response that we become the very evil we abhor. Which brings us to the next phrase:

### "But deliver us from evil (or 'the evil one')"

When we know we are forgiven and have therefore forgiven our trespassers, when we have been led out of the temptation of retribution and retaliation, Christ encourages to ask *Abba* to rescue us from evil (including becoming evil ourselves) and the evil one (whether that means some spiritual evil or even human enemy).

As the apostles, the early church and our spiritual family in war-torn nations have discovered, this prayer does *not* ensure we'll be delivered from all trespassers, persecutors or even martyrdom. Rather, in the face of such threats (because for most of us, that's all they ever are), the real evil we're praying against is the temptation to embrace the evil that would overtake our hearts. We need to pray fervently that we would not *become* the evil one we thought it our duty to attack. When in our fear, grief and frustration, we abandon the *Jesus Way* and choose to answer trespasses with trespasses, the "evil one" has already trespassed our minds and occupied our own hearts . . . even in the comfort of the quietest and most peaceful cul-de-sac. In these violent times, I find myself coming to these three phrases again and again: forgive as I forgive my trespassers, lead me out of the tempting reactions of retribution and retaliation. And please deliver me from becoming the evil I want to overcome.

That's just one example of how we might "work the program" of surrender to *Grace*. By "hearing these words of mine and putting them into practice," Christ does his transforming work.

## THOUGHTS

1. Have you made yourself familiar with the Sermon on the Mount? I suggest reading it all, out loud, in one sitting. As you do, highlight the phrases that you find most troubling or triggering. After reading, return to those highlighted sections. Ask yourself, what it is that's bothering me? Is it an interpretation issue? Or could Christ be provoking something in your ego with an agenda to healing you of it?

2. How might the Sermon work as a program of recovery in your life? What do you think *Grace* is longing to heal or transform in your character as you "hear these words and put them into practice"?

3. Have you memorized the Lord's Prayer at some point? Why not schedule a daily reminder of the prayer on your smartphone? Could you pray the prayer with attention and expectancy? If *Abba* wills his kingdom to come on earth as it is in heaven *through you*, how might you participate in answering your own prayer? Better: how might *Grace* bring the kingdom through Christ who lives in you?

## PRAYERS

*Our Father in heaven, may your name be honored*
*may your kingdom come, may your will be done*
*as in heaven, so on earth.*
*Give us today the bread we need now;*
*and forgive us the things we owe,*
*as we too have forgiven what was owed to us.*
*Don't bring us into the great trial,*
*but rescue us from evil.*

# Facet 5

# "Confessions of a violent SOB" RADICAL PEACEMAKING, RADICAL FORGIVENESS

**QUESTION:**

How do you respond to people who object that we are imposing our own ideology of peace onto the Bible rather than letting the Bible speak for itself? Some ask, "When you 'unwrath God,' aren't you cherry-picking according to our own wishes for what you wish the text had said rather than submitting to what it actually says?"

**RESPONSE:**

I hear this objection regularly, sometimes even weekly. I've been asked to respond often enough that a standard answer has begun to unfold.

**1. First, we must acknowledge the real problem of bias when coming to the text.**

We must indeed be mindful as to how our prejudices impact our reading and interpretation of the Scriptures. Wearing cultural or personal lenses is normal and unavoidable. In fact, the great danger is in failing to see how personal backstories and temperaments impact *everyone's* reading of the text. To believe that we can set aside all bias and have a purely objective experience of the Bible is a delusion. Imagining we can be so objective IS a highly subjective position of the modernist Evangelicalism in which I was trained. So, the first order of business is to embrace this objection as a real possibility and do our very best to analyze what filters our eyes, ears and mind are creating.

**2. Second, in my case, I insist that my bias is not toward peacemaking but toward violence.**

I don't *naturally* come to the text hoping for the peaceful, non-wrathful God who sets forgiveness at the center of the gospel. I have a history of violence, violent fantasies and the desire for a violent God. This begins when I think historically and globally about tyrants such as Nero, Hitler, Stalin or Mao. Part of me wishes God had revealed himself as wrathful toward such men *before* they slaughtered millions upon millions of people. I object to God's reluctance to do so. The fact that "they'll get theirs" in the next life is of no help to those interred in death camps or to the survivors of history's holocausts. If God is as wrathful as the opponents of peace theology believe, then he is utterly impotent and indiscriminate in carrying out his supposed vengeance. With David, my heart cries out, "Then why do the wicked prosper?"

The objection only gets stronger as it becomes more personal and closer to home. My wife and I have prayed for countless victims of sexual assault and/or childhood molestation. They always ask, "Where was God when I cried out to him then?" Whatever answer God reveals in that vulnerable moment, we know this: he was not there striking down the wicked to prevent the abuse. In MOST cases, the offenders have never experienced justice in this world, either by the wrath of human courts or by the violence of God. This angers me. I want God to commence with his wrath and if he won't, I would and have volunteered to be his agent. As if I would get off Scot free!? Lord, have mercy!

And this is precisely where the gospel of Jesus Christ, the Prince of Peace and nonviolent Lamb, confronts me. Rather than affirming what I hope the Bible would say, it brings me to the heart of the gospel and sternly summons me to repentance and conversion, revealing my spiritual peril whenever I nurture and yes, take pleasure in the violence of my heart. As a childhood victim of bullying, my propensity is to look for a God who will satisfy *my* wrath against *my* enemies. Thus, the Sermon on the Mount is of very little comfort to those egoistic desires.

So, if I wish to impose some worldly ideology or fleshly ideology onto the text, it is not toward peacemaking, but toward wrath. I'm a violent S.O.B. When I come to the Cross, this is precisely what needs to be crucified in me. This is what, "Take up your cross and follow me" demands of me. Whatever gentleness or kindness has emerged in my life is either the fruit of weakness and defeat before injustice or it's the transforming *Grace* of the gospel, and maybe both. In either case, I know I didn't generate it.

**3. The solution to cherry-picking preferred Bible verses is the anchor of the Cross.**

Returning to the question of unavoidable personal bias, we overcome these only by adopting a Christ-centered template for interpretation. We note our own temperament and wishes, but then return to the Incarnation of Jesus Christ for the definitive exegesis of God's true nature of Triune Love. Christ becomes our gospel, our canon and our hermeneutic through his life, teachings and most especially his death and resurrection. The apex of the Gospels comes at the cross —that cruciform revelation becomes the corrective and clarifying lens for our skewed vision, not only for the whole of Scripture but even when reading Christ's own teachings.

I mention the latter because some of Jesus' own parables and predictions appear to be quite violent. In his parables, God (is it God?) is sometimes depicted as the master or king who comes in wrath. But the final word from Christ—the Living Word who IS what God says of himself—reveals the punchline to all these parables on the Cross. We see God in the flesh crucified. We see him renouncing the way of wrath as a solution to evil and living his message of enemy-love. He does not smite his enemies or visit them with retribution. He treads the last mile to Golgotha as the Lamb to be slain. He not only dies without retaliating but completely pardons the sins of those who connived to murder him—as they do it! The Cross then becomes our clearest vision of the nature of God.

The Cross reveals God unwrathed—nonviolent, self-giving, radically forgiving, co-suffering love. And this—impossibly, amazingly—is how he overcomes evil with good. God in Christ draws all the evil, all the sin, all the violence and the resulting suffering into himself. And the Light of his love overcomes the darkness so that from that moment, "It is finished" also means "It begins!" What begins? *"Behold, I am making all things new!"*

**P. S. A Humbling Summons to Repent:**

To these three lines of response, I will add an addendum. To those who cannot track with me through to the gospel of peace, but insist that Christ's teaching and example for nonviolence are naïve and unpractical for today,

I return to the question of bias and ask, "What is it in your temperament, your backstory or your culture that *needs* to read retribution back into Scripture after Christ expunged it? Whatever that might be, whatever desire for violent wrath you might be imposing on God, I would call you to repentance."

On this, I don't speak from the lofty place of arrival, but as a sinner dependent on daily mercy to be cleansed of vengeance. If I give this kind of pushback, it may be because I'm getting impatient and grumpy. And it can sound arrogant if I communicate a sense of awakening that critics have failed to achieve. It sounds condescending to say that *we* must patiently wait for *them* to grow up. That's a real risk, and itself can be a manifestation of ungodly zeal.

That said, the truth is that the *Way* of peace IS known by revelation. Christ says, "The pure in heart see God" and, as a result, become "blessed peacemakers"—children who walk in the footprints of Papa. Rarely do we receive that revelation in a magical Damascus Road ecstasy. Normally, repentance comes through an encounter with the disconcerting gospel of forgiveness and the testimony of its witnesses (Rev. 12:11).

The question then is whether peacemaking in a particular situation means (a) remaining patient and silent or (b) giving voice and issuing an invitation. Will speaking up sabotage someone's journey through my own misplaced zeal? Or will remaining silent consign them to bumbling forward on the broad and violent way that leads to destruction?

This calls for the *Grace* of the Holy Spirit. And so we pray, "Lord have mercy," because, thank God, he is.

## NAIVETY OF VIOLENCE

A dear friend of mine was fostering a "problem child" in his early teens. He knew he couldn't control how the lad in his care acted outside the home or what type of trouble he'd get into by antagonizing the wrong crowd. But my friend wanted him to know that at least in his house, the boy would be loved, cared for and protected—and he told him so:

"I want you to know that regardless of what happens out there, once you're here, you're safe. I promise you: if anyone comes after you through that front door, they'll be exiting through the living room window."

I don't fault my friend for the dramatic, rhetorical way he communicated his care. The message given and received was his commitment to making their home a bastion of stability and belonging. The boy need not fear because this home was his safe-house. And for whatever reason, he wanted me to know what he had said. Perhaps he perceived in my commitment to nonviolence a naïve idealism. My response may have surprised him.

"The problem with your plan is you're not thinking it all the way through," I said. "You're not working through to the aftermath. Exiting through the window isn't the end of the story. Violence begets escalating violence. That's kind of naïve, don't you think?"

He stared back at me with a puzzled, expectant expression. I continued.

"Your problem," I said, "is *not* that you're too violent. Your imagination is limited because you're not evil enough. You don't anticipate the people you're manhandling to be nastier than you. As if they'll just conclude, 'I guess that's the end of that. Oh well.' No, that's not how it works. Your heroic fantasy needs to include the escalation factor. Do you want to hear how it plays out?"

He seemed willing, so I continued. "After you throw this wicked person out of your house through the big glass pane of your bay window, you'll need to pay for a new window. And he'll need to go to the hospital for stitches. I'm assuming you're imagining a *he*, right? Or would you throw an angry girl through the plate glass, too? Either way, that's when you'll be charged with assault and/or get embroiled in a lawsuit. Or maybe your enemy doesn't charge you. Maybe the bad guy doesn't go to the cops, because he's evil, remember? If he weren't evil, you wouldn't have needed to use violence in your fantasy. You wouldn't be the hero if they weren't evil. So, fine, they're evil. And what would the "evil one" do next? Let me tell you. He'll go get two or three or ten of his evil friends. You don't know when they're coming, but they will come. It will be at night, when you don't expect it and you're fast asleep. They'll quietly block all the doors. They'll soak the perimeter of the house with gasoline and they'll burn the house down with you and your family in it."

My friend's eyes were wide with disbelief, horrified at the violence of my vision.

"At least that's what I would do," I added. "If I were evil, that is. But if I, a naïve pacifist, can imagine such awful payback from the top of my head, what would the evil man dream up as he licks his wounds?"

## WHAT'S MOST REAL?

I e-mailed Andrew Klager, director of the *Institute for Religion, Peace and Justice* and asked how he handles the naivety card. He responded with a gut-check for reality:

> Those who say *Jesus Way* of nonviolence and peacemaking are naïve and unrealistic reveal what they think is most real. The kingdoms of this world are more real to them than the kingdom of God.
>
> Violence never creates peace, only a lull. It defeats or exhausts your opponents without dealing with the conditions that first created the violence. Defeating the other only puts us in the position of power (e.g. the Treaty of Versailles). We become the belligerent who exacerbates the problem. The pseudo-peace only buys time for the defeated to reload. The next war becomes inevitable. Violence doesn't work—killing only enrages the clan and escalation comes next. The next retribution must always be one step higher. It's a naïve non-solution.
>
> Compassion and kindness, by contrast, have real potential to tap into and draw out the true self of our would-be enemies. Compassion and kindness are more effective than bullets and bombs because they awaken what is more real than this life. However twisted, we are still humans created in the image of God. Peacebuilding is effective in awakening the kingdom of God in this world because it IS more real.

I agree. If only we believed in the kingdom of Christ enough to resource it with the people-power and finances we're willing to flush away on violence. The motivation to retaliate after a drone strike wipes out your village is very high. But who wants to attack the sponsors of your own water treatment plant or hospital? No one—not if they want to maintain the popular support of those enjoying better health.

## CONFESSIONS OF A HATER

Here's where we might draw on the common advice of three quite different voices: Jesus Christ, Martin Luther King Jr., Friedrich Nietzsche (of all people) and U2:

> "Satan cannot drive out Satan."
>
> —Jesus of Nazareth

> The ultimate weakness of violence is that it is a descending spiral, begetting the very thing it seeks to destroy. Instead of diminishing evil, it multiplies it. Through violence, you may murder the liar, but you cannot murder the lie, nor establish the truth. Through violence, you may murder the hater, but you do not murder hate. In fact, violence merely increases hate. So it goes. Returning violence for violence multiplies violence, adding deeper darkness to a night already devoid of stars. Darkness cannot drive out darkness: Only light can do that. Hate cannot drive out hate: Only love can do that.
>
> —Martin Luther King, Jr.

> "Beware that, when fighting monsters, you yourself do not become a monster . . . for when you gaze long into the abyss. The abyss gazes also into you."
>
> —Friedrich Nietzsche

> They say that what you mock
> Will surely overtake you
> And you become a monster
> So the monster will not break you
>
> —U2

I must confess, I lied to my friend. My vengeance fantasy wasn't from the hip. And my commitment to peacemaking isn't the natural expression of naivety or a pacifist temperament. Whatever kindness I've acquired has come through either carnal despair or spiritual transformation. It requires telling you a slice of my story.

I deal with the demon of violent vengeance fantasies. They began through a childhood of bullying, fist fights, retaliation and escalation.

The beatings I've taken and given weren't all that bloody, never heroic and not worth retelling. When I could avoid fighting, I did. I used whatever tools I could find to de-escalate threats, from clowning to scapegoating to becoming a bully myself. For years, I experienced the constant anxiety of hyper-vigilance. The vengeance fantasies I spawned to cope with fear and powerlessness were rooted early and very deep. I dreamed of broken glass and blood and flames and death.

I wasn't naïve. I know the fear of punching someone too hard or worrying I hadn't hit them hard enough. I knew by experience that victory over the bully would just invite his bigger brothers and their friends to hunt you down. And then what? Beat them and you face the drunk dad. Eliminate him and then what? Generations of blood-feud. Violence always begets new levels of violence—if the escalation didn't rebound on me, it would be paid down as cruelty to the bully's own children. I saw all this and had the foresight to cut out before I ever got to the "big boss level."

Still, I was convinced of the morality of violence for self-defense and was finally hooked into thinking violence "works" when I kicked my way out of an attempted sexual assault by three young men. I didn't have rape prevention knowledge or the tools to bring Jesus into that situation, so I resorted to the one thing I knew. Just remember that violent resistance always feeds brutality in wicked men, whether the rapist or the dictator. I'd now suggest more effective, less risky ways for which training is available (cf. Walter Wink, *Engaging the Powers).*

When I grew up, I eventually became a peace-lover and had my own family. Horribly, for all our prayers, training and interventions, my boys still got it worse than I ever did—especially our youngest. He was victimized by taunting, bullying and swarming homophobia long before he ever came out as queer. He was once cornered in a boys' room by half-a-dozen guys—one wielded a knife. Domo reasoned his way out of that one—but did not escape at least one violent mugging and a sexual assault.

Years of these relentless experiences sowed into him anxiety disorder, self-loathing and suicidal ideations. His violent fantasies were self-directed. Sometimes, he carried them out. We're grateful he's learning to manage the stress and has even redeemed those dark years into a calling to serve disadvantaged and disabled children in our community. I could not be a prouder dad. Life gave him a cross—he picked it up and became the kindest person I know.

As for me, I frequently felt rage toward his tormentors and powerless against his demons. I lost a lot of sleep over these injustices. I know my own darkness of chronic worry and bottled-up outrage. I know the exhaustion of navigating violence and the sin of indulging its fantasies. I sometimes still see broken glass, blood and fire at night. I still pray the imprecatory Psalms. A naïve peacenik I am not. I am still in need of transformation.

This is my confession. The confession of a violent SOB.

And my two-stage conversion.

## FIRST CONVERSION

My first conversion from violence to the *Jesus Way* concerned militarism. Like many little boys, I grew up hearing stories of soldiers in the family and the wars in which they fought. A sniper, a hero, a deserter, a war bride. My people.

I saved my own little coins to buy my first G.I. Joe when I was seven. *Blam! Blam! Blam!* I got my first war book when I was eight—a biography of the world's last five-star General, Omar Nelson Bradley (who I fancied I'd been named after).

I collected Sgt. Rock and General Lee comic books and gloried in their exploits. I created my own comic strip—Sarge Stogie (samples on request). His motto was, "Over here, ya ugly moron!" as he peppered Nazis with his machine gun. By grade eight, I had read every Leon Uris novel in print—*Mila 18, Battle Cry, Exodus, Trinity, The Haj,* etc. Uris was especially pro-Zionist, which suited my dispensational triumphalism just fine. (He was awful at endings.) I built model battle ships and fighter jets. And I dove into the news of military battles involving Israel. I cheered for the "good guys" through the Yom Kippur War, hoping it would escalate into Armageddon and trigger the rapture.

One day, I was playing war loudly with my toy soldiers, mowing them down mercilessly with a pillowcase, then doing triage and sending those who landed face-down back into battle for the next obliteration.

*"Ka boom! Ka pow!"*

My mother interrupted, trying to explain that we don't love war or glorify killing. She spoke of the gruesome injuries that continued to torment veterans still confined to nearby Deer Lodge Hospital. I remember feeling ashamed, but I continued to play—more soberly for sure—convinced war was necessary for the good guys to stop the bad guys, be they Nazis or Commies.

This conviction carried on through my Bible college and seminary years. Ironically, the first church to call me was my wife's Mennonite Church. Ah, the Mennonites.

Flashback: I'm an eight-year-old Baptist who loved the military miracles of the Old Testament. And it dawns on me, our town had two Mennonite churches. How is it that they had escaped the genocide of Gideon? Hadn't he slain them all? (See Judges 6 for all the gore).

"Midianites," my Sunday School teacher corrected. "He slaughtered the Midianites—not the Mennonites."

Ah ha! Well, that's okay then. Close call.

I knew the Mennonites were pacifists (in theory). But by the time they recruited me, I knew all the best "just-war theory" counterpoints to their position. I wasn't sure I wanted the job. I wanted to teach Bible in a college, not become a pastor. I agreed to go through the motions of the interviews but resolved to stand firm in my opposition to "the peace position." I did so—belligerently—then also had the gall to emulate Gideon by "setting out a fleece" (see Judges 6:36-40). That's an old idiom for testing God's will—in my case, secretly demanding a 95% congregational affirmation if I was to agree to go. Wisely, both the senior pastor and the conference minister (sort of a bishop) both recommended that the congregation reject my candidacy. The vote came back: 96% affirmative. Ugh.

Bethel Mennonite Church (Aldergrove, BC) hired me, and I began my ministry as a militarist Mennonite. I even got in a fight with a little gang of drunk teens vandalizing the church one night, proudly taking a beer bottle to the side of my head for my folly. Some of the youth group were with me as back-up. Sheer idiocy. The congregation's response was mixed.

I heard their best arguments for nonviolence many times. It had no impact on me because mine was a closed system with a family military history and national pride in Canada's heroism at the battles of Vimy

Ridge (WWI, 1917), the Battle of Dieppe (WWII, 1942) and so on.

Several years in, my resistance had not budged. I was entrenched in my worldview and the congregation mostly left me to it. Some even "saw my point." But then came a series of five events in rapid succession:

1. **Oma Redekop**, one of the senior members of our church, approached me after I preached a sermon that glorified militarism. She was a tiny lady, normally meek and mild. But with her thick German accent, she confronted me sternly, saying, "I was a girl in Germany in 1945—we lived in a civilian city. The Allies fire-bombed our city three days *after* we surrendered. Don't tell me there are *'good guys'* in war."

2. **Ron Dart:** I heard Ron Dart for the first time (a university prof who became a mentor and my Ph.D. supervisor) when he delivered a lecture to a group of pastors, titled "The Banality of Evil" (riffing off Hannah Arendt's article assessing the Adolf Eichmann trial). He outlined specific arms deals behind the scenes of the popular and supposedly benign Abbotsford Air Show. These included weapons sales by Canadian companies to the Saudis, who regularly used them to persecute Christian groups residing in Saudi Arabia.

Wait, I thought we were the *"good guys"?*

3. **Haiti, late 1992:** My wife Eden and I witnessed political violence first hand (under false pretenses) against a Mennonite relief worker. He was hog-tied, beaten with rods and only released when others risked their lives to free him. He survived but with permanent injuries.

The coup-led dictator of Haiti and his generals in charge had been trained in torture at Georgia's "School of the Americas" (closed in 2017, happily). Self-defense? The military used terror to defend capitalist business interests against the threat of a seven dollar per day minimum wage proposal. *"Good guys"?* As far as I could tell, the good guys were the fearless priests of the nonviolent resistance.

4. **Somalia, 1993:** Canadian peacekeepers of the Airborne regiment stationed as peacekeepers brutally beat to death a teenager who had tried to loot their camp. Peacekeepers? I thought we were the *"good guys"!*

5. **Apocalypse Now?** I was watching Francis Ford Coppola's Vietnam

War movie, *Apocalypse Now?* for the third time during this same period—with Oma Redekop's rebuke still ringing in my ears.

As I watched a graphic scene portraying the massacre of an unarmed family in their fishing boat, her words echoed in my head. *"Good guys?"*

Previously, I'd watched the movie dispassionately for entertainment. This time, I was traumatized. But it's just fiction, right? *Don't fool yourself,* I realized. *This is how war works.* I'll recount the moment in the form of a letter I later sent to Martin Sheen, the lead actor, devout Christ-follower and peace activist:

> Dear Mr. Sheen,
>
> Today I came across some fantastic quotes by you on taking Jesus' teachings on nonviolence seriously. I thought it might encourage you to know your role in bringing me to these same convictions in the early 90s.
>
> As a young minister, I was invited to serve in a Mennonite Church, but I did not buy into their message of nonviolence. I always found some theological loophole that made sense to me and could rationalize certain expressions of violence in the usual ways. So even though I was surrounded by that culture and the voices that called for love, prayers and forgiveness of enemies, they could not turn my stiff neck.
>
> Then one day, during my third viewing of *Apocalypse Now,* I saw "the puppy in the basket" scene and felt a switch flip in my heart and mind. In the space of a moment, I completely renounced the way of violence as a solution and for the first time, could see and embrace the Jesus Way.
>
> Since then, I pastored for twenty years and now teach the Gospels in a theological college. I teach my students what you taught me through your powerful medium and throughout your career. I cannot say thank you enough.
>
> Many lenses in our culture distort reality badly. But you offered me lenses that clarify. I'm so very grateful,
>
> Dr. Brad Jersak

Mr. Sheen kindly responded in a hand-written card:

Dear Dr. Jersak,

Many thanks for your very kind and thoughtful letter which was given to me by our friend Ben Eisner last evening.

I must say that over the years since *Apocalypse Now* was released there have been an equal number of young men who told me that they joined the Army because of the film as there were who avoided the Army because of it. (Go figure).

But you are the first person who has ever told me that they had found the 'Jesus Way' because of that film! What an extraordinary insight! And revelation!

Thank you again for your letter and I hope this response reaches you . . .

God bless,
Sincerely,
Martin Sheen

As I said, a switch flipped. All my previous arguments seemed devoid of reality and compassion. However airtight I thought them, they were coldly unChristlike. In that moment, they were also fragile. I had heard all the best arguments for active peacebuilding and nonviolent ways to overcome evil . . . but I had never *seen* them. Since that moment, I cannot unsee them. They *are* the *Jesus Way*. And as Martin Sheen said, the *Jesus Way* prescribed by the Prince of Peace is a *revelation*. We'll examine this more shortly when we examine the inspired teachings of Jesus, Paul, Peter and John. But not yet. Now for my *second conversion*—one closer to home. I'm talking about how Jesus is saving me from the violence of my own heart. This leads me to a second, more personal conversion: love of "haters."

## "LOVE YOUR ENEMIES"

### "Back off, haters!"

So says "Miranda," the internet comedy persona, whose "Miranda Sings" viral videos generate a barrage of tongue-in-cheek comment wars. She's one of the online celebrities who have popularized the term "haters" to describe a real phenomenon in cyber-world. "Haters" are those who stalk and "troll" public figures (mainly online), hoping to draw a reaction from their celebrity targets and so attain a moment of pseudo-infamy. Miranda's satirical engagement with (mainly) pretend haters parodies the infectious "trending" of virtual bitterness, malice and libel whereby anyone can say anything about anyone, however harmful, without having to face consequences. The haters' accusations, including outright lies, become part of the permanent public record thanks to the power of web browsers. Google anyone of note and you'll find their haters on the front page, regardless of the veracity of the attacks.

Inane first-world problems? Hardly. I know an upstanding businessman who was falsely accused by a vengeful hater through an opportunistic reporter. Defenseless against libel because the headlines were worded as a suggestive question ("Where's the money?"), the online version of the paper caught the attention of his regulating board. They launched a long and expensive investigation and found the businessman—whose integrity had been untarnished for decades—had *not* broken any laws. He was nevertheless asked to surrender his license, lost his public reputation and after years of legal costs, had to sell his dream home.

Victimized and discredited by groundless slander, he can testify to the truth of James' epistle, which says,

> The tongue is a little member but boasts great things. See how small a fire it takes to set a large forest ablaze! And the tongue *is* a fire. The tongue is a world of injustice, with its place established right there among our members. It defiles the whole body; it sets the wheel of nature ablaze and is itself set ablaze by hell. —James 3:5

These verbal brush fires are that much more devastating when unleashed and amplified globally and permanently over the Internet.

Sadly, the most vicious haters are those who incite violence and terror in the name of Christless religion. I need not sicken you with heinous examples; that's not my point. You've likely already been flooded with email "forwards" of fear-filled, alarmist vitriol—often, ironically, in the name of Jesus. And here's the hard truth: that won't change. Sorry, Miranda—haters, by nature, don't back off. In their obsessive jealousy and insatiable ego needs, resistance only energizes them.

Certainly our heroes of the faith had haters. Serious haters! Worse than cyber-bullying or lawsuits, we know that "some were tortured . . . some faced jeers and flogging, and even chains and imprisonment. They were put to death by stoning; they were sawed in two; they were killed by the sword" (Heb. 11:35-37, NIV). And of course, the great Hero of our faith, Jesus Christ, faced the wrath of his haters as he was mocked, beaten, scourged and crucified. Indeed, the author of Hebrews was right: "the world was not worthy of them" (vs. 38).

Nor has this changed. Lethal religious hate-crimes abound, whether it's "Christians" literally lynching a homosexual teen or the brutal martyrdom of Coptic Christians by Islamists in Libya. An end is *not* in sight.

If violent haters are truly incorrigible, and if faithfulness to the gospel engenders hatred, how shall the faithful live?

### "Love your haters"

Of course, we know very well Christ's straightforward response. I feel the urge to respond to my own haters and "trolls" in kind, infected with my own bitterness, malice and vengeance—all very justifiable in my mind. Ironically, the majority of my detractors are supposedly "brothers in Christ," which makes my reciprocal hatred all the more embarrassing. But Jesus intrudes: "Love your haters!" Remember his words in the Sermon on the Mount?

> "You heard that it was said, 'Love your neighbor and hate your enemy.' But I tell you: love your enemies. Pray for people who persecute you. That way, you'll be children of your father in heaven. After all, he makes his sun rise on bad and good alike, and sends rain both on the upright and on the unjust." —Matthew 5:43-45

Elizabeth Gilbert wrote a bestseller titled *Eat, Pray, Love.* In Jesus' special rendition focused on haters, it's *Love, Bless, Do Good, Pray.* And why? Because this *Grace*, this generosity, this indiscriminate goodness is the very reflection of our *Abba* in heaven.

Religions of all stripes claim, "If you're good, God will reward you. If you're bad, God will punish you. If you experience blessing, it's because you earned it. If you're faced with calamity, it's because you deserved it."

This is exactly what my religious flesh would like to dole out on those I deem evil, hateful and offensive.

When my son Justice was little, he instinctually inverted the Golden Rule. He would hit his little brother and say, "He hit me, so I'm just treating him the way he wants to be treated!"

But Christ says, "No, that's not actually how it works. Your *Abba* is gracious, generous and good to *all*, whether they've been 'naughty or nice.' It's not about earning or deserving. It's about an *Abba* whose *Grace*-nature has been freely replicated in us, so that we are energized by Love to walk step-in-step with him.

The apostle Paul was once a notorious Christ-hater, a sanctioned assassin with a religious "license to kill." But after his fateful confrontation with a blinding Light, his conversion was in great measure a turn from religious hatred. He didn't merely change sides to become a Christian Jew-killing machine . . . he changed hearts, from hater to lover. He follows the *Jesus Way* when he says,

> Bless those who persecute you; bless them, don't curse them. Never repay anyone evil for evil; think through what will seem good to everyone who is watching. No: "If your enemy is hungry, feed him; if he is thirsty, give him a drink. If you do this, you will pile up burning coals on his head." Don't let evil conquer you. Rather, conquer evil with good. —Romans 12:14, 17, 20-21.

We know this. But far too often, we just don't like it. We cling to our notions of what is unforgivable, hold on to our resentment like the "Onion Lady" of Dostoevsky fame. It's the story of a bitter old woman whose guardian angel pleads for her soul, based on the only noble deed of her wretched life: she once shared an onion.

In this tale, God graciously allows the angel to pull her out of the fires of hell by that lone onion—her one good deed. But when others in hell see her rising, they grab her feet and begin to rise with her. She will have none of it! "Mine!" she cries, kicking them loose. They plummet back into the flames. And at that point, the onion breaks and she falls away with them. The parable is not about earning our salvation with a good deed. It's about the difficulty of letting go and the disastrous consequences when we don't.

## THE FRUIT AND TEST OF ENEMY LOVE

In my own faith journey, I have come to hold these truths in tension:

- When Jesus says, "Love your enemies," he actually wants me to obey him. He is not merely making the point that I can't do it. Jesus himself gave us a series of injunctions about love and, like it or not, called them "commandments." If *obeying* Jesus sounds too religious to us, we likely haven't read the Gospels, heard his words, or met him in person.
- Obeying Jesus is not a renunciation of *Grace.* It is the fruit of *Grace*—what Dietrich Bonhoeffer called *the Cost of Discipleship.* Jesus called us to "follow" and defined this as *hearing* his words and *doing* them.
- Nevertheless, trying to obey Jesus' commands through *self-effort* and *will power* is pointless and impossible. That is a regression from the *Grace* of Christ. In fact, the call to "enemy-love" is the quintessential test of whether I'm living under the law (the flesh) or living in *Grace* (the Spirit). How so? Because I simply *can't* love my enemies in the flesh. Unlike a thousand other virtues, this one can't be faked—at least not for any length of time. Indeed, apart from *Grace,* we don't even want to.
- Obeying Jesus in the impossible demands of enemy-love involves my willing surrender to and participation in the empowering *Grace* I've already been given. I have all the *Grace* I need to do it . . . but willingness? Hmm. Enemy-love is not accomplished by self-effort but is a real struggle because it involves death of the old self (the *hater* in me). Painfully, this is "death on the installment plan" because it happens through one opportunity for *Grace* after another. "Opportunity for *Grace*" is code for "people I despise," if I'm being completely honest with myself.

So, here's my dilemma: I want this. I want to love my enemies. And I'm not there yet. Now that you know the violent soil of my heart, you can imagine my resistance and the darkness from which I need to be rescued.

Honestly, I would love to learn how to cooperate with Christ in loving my enemies as he does, for several reasons:

First, I really do have enemies—people who believe God has called them to ruin me and have told me so. If I don't learn to love them, what will my default mode be? Bitterness and resentment will eat me up. As the saying goes, that's like drinking poison hoping it will kill the other person.

Second, I want to love my enemies because I think that's on the front burner of my own discipleship. That is, I think enemy-love is "in my face" again these days precisely because *Grace* wants to give me (and you) a special gift of freedom—especially freedom from fear! It's already on the table. And if that's true, bring it on! (but gently, please).

Third, I want to love my enemies because frankly, the truths I'm learning (hopefully) and teaching require every ounce of discernment I can acquire. I define "discernment" as *Grace*-given wisdom and reliable spiritual sensitivity. What does discernment have to do with enemy-love? After reading about the life of St. Silouan, a twentieth century monk from Mount Athos, I've concluded the following (with due credit to Silouan):

How can you know whether you are walking in truth or living a delusion? How can you discern if you are enlightened by God or deceived by the devil? There are two easy and completely reliable tests: humility and enemy-love. *Grace* produces humility and love of enemies. It just does.

If I am an arrogant ass who treats his enemies harshly, no amount of religious striving can change that. My hubris only magnifies my hate and baptizes it in self-righteousness. That's what makes enemy-love such a good litmus test for the truth.

## "YOU SHALL OBTAIN MERCY"

If so, how do I get there? I *don't* get there on the same hamster wheel that already failed me for fifty years. Instead, my second conversion—love of haters—requires lots of third-party help. I need *Grace*-filled people further along than I am in the struggle—seasoned sages who embody the *Jesus Walk,* willing to tuck me under their wings for a time. Personally, I found some older men with silver beards, tender hearts and the wisdom to speak peace to my turmoil. I also discovered two men of peace who demonstrate unusual *Grace* in this area: a priest and an activist.

I attended a weekend retreat with Fr. Michael Gillis, who shared his wisdom on the Sermon on the Mount, focusing on the Beatitudes. I left rich with some precious gems. I will share just one.

He spoke about ascending the Mount with Jesus (Matt. 5:1), a symbolic detail pointing to the fleshly, soulish and spiritual readings of the Beatitudes. Fr. Michael led us to the higher sense that the Spirit of Jesus wants to reveal—a mystery to be unveiled. For example:

Jesus said, "Blessed are the merciful, for they shall obtain mercy." Think about showing mercy to the poor beggar, the broken addict or most of all, one's sworn enemy. The "lowest" or fleshly way to read this Beatitude is as a social law. Like, "if you are merciful, your enemy will be merciful back to you." Maybe. Sometimes.

There's also a second "soulish" way to read it: "If you are merciful, God will be merciful to you." At best, this elevates the law of sowing and reaping from horizontal to vertical. *If* you're merciful, *then* God will respond in proportion to the mercy you showed others. Sounds good, but that reading is at odds with what we read later in the chapter about *Abba's* kindness and mercy to *all*, whether or not they are merciful.

So we ascend further to a "spiritual" reading, where Jesus sits and teaches his disciples. "Blessed are the merciful."

I hear the Voice of *Grace* say, "Oh, Brad, you aren't merciful yet—certainly not to your haters. It's not yet engrained in your character—mercy is not yet *who you are.* But I've given you the *Grace* to participate in *Abba's* transforming mercy. You could begin by becoming an agent of *Abba's Grace*, one act of mercy at a time. Freely you've received it, now freely give it away. *Abba* in his mercy pardons and forgives, so pay it forward. Receive *Abba's* kindness and give it away. You might not *feel* merciful yet; but as you share *Abba's* little *mercies* one day at a time, lo and behold, one day you find that you have *become* a mercy-bearer. It *is* who you are. You didn't generate it . . . you received it; you *obtained* that mercy-trait of Christ as a Beatitude *from* Christ."

To summarize, we receive by *Grace* what we could never muster on our own: *Abba's* mercy for our debtors. And we *become* mercy in our nature as we freely distribute the mercies we receive from *Abba.* The reality of our *Grace*-transformation is revealed most thoroughly by the mercy we show our enemies.

**Problem:** Christ did this perfectly. I'm not there. Not even close. I needed a *Way* to "hear these words of mine and put them into practice."

## THE ACTIVIST

As I continued to follow Christ in enemy-love , I made a pilgrimage to the Netherlands where I tracked down peace activist and director of the Orthodox Peace Fellowship, Jim Forest. For his fascinating background, you might do an internet search of Jim Forest and "the Milwaukee fourteen."

By the time I saw Jim, I was so stirred by the damage my haters were doing to my reputation and our family income that I suffered a resurgence of my childhood vengeance fantasies. It wasn't bad when I was fully awake, but if I woke up in the night, I'd fall into obsessing over the losses and my desire for payback.

I pulled out my notebook and asked outright, "Jim, how do I love my enemies? Help me!"

**Jim:** Love of enemies starts with prayer.

It starts with a prayer of *confession*: confession of my hate, of my fear, of my dread. Confession that I would not be sad if they die. That I find it difficult to care about them.

It comes with an *openness to serve* God. Is it our heart to serve God? What if serving God includes extending the kindness of God to them? Doesn't serving God also include asking what you can do, how you can be part of their salvation journey?

**Brad:** When Jesus tells us to love our enemies, what do we mean by "love"? Who is included in "enemies"?

**Jim:** We need to define our terms carefully.

For example, "Love" of this kind is not merely a sentimental feeling of warmth and affection. It includes a way to pray and a way to live in relation to our enemies, the *Way* Christ taught and lived.

"Enemy" is a term that came from the Latin word, *enimicus*. Literally, a "non-friend." That is, someone I wouldn't want as a friend; someone whose well-being is of disinterest to me. Or somebody where there's ill will between us.

**Brad:** Where did love of enemies start for you?

**Jim:** During the Cold War era, I thought, how can we love our enemies if we don't even know them? So I began to make trips to Moscow to connect with the Russian believers there. This was very difficult because we had to cut through red tape and negotiate our way through the KGB. But eventually, even Gorbachev came to some of these meetings. Once we'd met our "enemies," we could begin to talk to them, pray for them and love them. We were also able to meet and worship with our brothers and sisters in Christ in the Soviet Union.

**Brad:** And I guess you've experienced some ill will throughout your life as a peace activist.

**Jim:** Definitely. Including others in the peace movement who disagreed with some of my positions and did great harm by accusing me of being in the CIA. And of course, what could be more impossible to disprove?

**Brad:** So when you pray for your enemies, what do you pray?

**Jim:** Nancy and I created a name list of our enemies, and we present their names to God every night. We offer their names to God without instructing him what to do or trying to manipulate the outcome. We simply pray, "Lord, have mercy."

**Brad:** And how does living with enemies work?

**Jim:** We consider how best to contribute to their salvation [journey] or at the least, we don't want to become an obstacle to it.

**Brad:** Some folks think love of enemies is no more than a modern revulsion against violence—a trendy thing Madonna and Lady Gaga are into for the sake of liberal tolerance. But what I'm trying to grasp is the deeper well of Christ's own teachings.

Surely this is at the heart of the gospel.

**Jim:** Of course, and so we must immerse ourselves in the Gospels, where Jesus Christ teaches us to love our enemies. But if you can't understand what Jesus *said*, then watch what he *does*.

Remember: his last healing miracle was to heal the wound of a policeman, a servant of the High Priest, who had come to harm him.

Remember the total body count of all those who Jesus killed in his entire life and ministry. Zero.

**Brad:** But we resist this because we feel victimized and therefore justified in our hatred. And to be fair, we also don't want to collaborate with or enable evil.

**Jim:** Yes. So, St. Paul says, *"Do good to them."* James says it's like putting burning coals on their heads. Why? Just to torment them? No, remember Isaiah 6? The burning coal purified Isaiah's lips. So too, loving our enemies applies the burning coals that can purify their souls.

**Brad:** When I think of hatred (and especially hating my haters), it's such a contagious virus. I become the hater. Especially troublesome for me, since the time I was being bullied as a child, are vengeance fantasies. When someone is mean to me, it's not that I think I'm especially violent, but in my powerlessness, there they are. What can we do about vengeance fantasies?

**Jim:** I've experienced this too. When I was overwhelmed by fantasies, I was so frightened of myself. I mean, what if I acted on them? So I went to a priest and I confessed how I was feeling. He completely surprised me by giving them a blessing.

**Brad:** He gave your vengeance fantasies a blessing?!

**Jim:** Yes! He said to me, "Don't be ashamed. They are one way you experience who you are at this moment."

And he made me laugh out loud at my fantasies. How ironic that a peacemaker would have them!

**Brad:** What about my own haters? How do I love them? Can you give me some practical pointers?

**Jim:** Sure. 1. Remember what Mark Twain said. Anger is an acid which destroys the container that holds it.

2. When doors are locked for you because of them, look for other doors.

3. Look at their providential role in your faith journey, how they are saving you from pride and arrogance that your friends would be unable and even unwilling to crucify.

**Brad:** That's true, they have certainly pushed me to clarify and purify my own understanding and presentation of the gospel.

**Jim:** Good! And remember to read the lives of the saints, specifically the martyrs. Remember their example—how they responded to hate with courage and Christlike love.

**Brad:** When I read about them, I feel like I'm whining.

**Jim:** Whine away; but remember what others have endured and how they forgave. Then your trials will not seem as big a deal in the big scheme of things. Remember, they are only monumental in the universe of Self.

Read them and see their boldness and lack of fear, even their humor. St. Lawrence, first deacon of Rome, was fried to death on a grill. He said, "You can turn me over. I'm done on this side."

Jim sent me on my way with this prayer composed by St. Nikolai Velimirovic, a twentieth century Serbian bishop. He resisted Nazism and was eventually taken to Dachau. In this prayer, he focuses on prayer for his personal enemies. In praying with him, we may be more able to act justly rather than rashly and let go of our hatred and bloodlust.

## PRAYER FOR ONE'S ENEMIES
## by St. Nikolai Velimirovic

*Bless my enemies, O Lord. Even I bless them and do not curse them.*

Enemies have driven me into your embrace more than friends have. Friends have bound me to earth, enemies have loosed me from earth and have demolished all my aspirations in the world. Enemies have made me a stranger in worldly realms and an extraneous inhabitant of the world. Just as a hunted animal found its safe shelter, so have I, persecuted by enemies, found the safest sanctuary, having ensconced myself beneath Your tabernacle, where neither friends nor enemies can slay my soul.

*Bless my enemies, O Lord. Even I bless them and do not curse them.*

They, rather than I, have confessed my sins before the world. They have punished me, whenever I have hesitated to punish myself. They have tormented me, whenever I have tried to flee torments. They have scolded me, whenever I have flattered myself. They have spat upon me, whenever I have filled myself with arrogance.

*Bless my enemies, O Lord. Even I bless them and do not curse them.*

Whenever I have made myself wise, they have called me foolish. Whenever I have made myself mighty, they have mocked me as though I were a dwarf. Whenever I have wanted to lead people, they have shoved me into the background.

Whenever I have rushed to enrich myself, they have prevented me with an iron hand. Whenever I thought that I would sleep peacefully, they have wakened me from sleep. Whenever I have tried to build a home for a long and tranquil life, they have demolished it and driven me out. Truly, the enemies have cut me loose from the world and have stretched out my hands to the hem of Your garment.

*Bless my enemies, O Lord. Even I bless them and do not curse them.*

Bless them and multiply them; multiply them and make them even more bitterly against me: so that my fleeing to you may have no return; so that all hope in men may be scattered like cobwebs; so that absolute serenity may begin to reign in my soul; so that my heart may become the grave of my two evil twins: arrogance and anger; so that I might amass all my treasure in heaven; Ah, so that I may for once be freed from self-deception, which has entangled me in the dreadful web of illusory life.

My enemies have taught me to know what hardly anyone knows, that a person has no enemies in the world except himself. One hates his enemies only when he fails to realize that they are not enemies, but cruel friends. It is truly difficult for me to say who has done me more good and who has done me more evil in the world: friends or enemies.

*Therefore bless, O Lord, both my friends and my enemies.*

A slave curses his enemies, for he does not understand. But a son blesses them, for he understands. For a son knows that his enemies cannot touch his life. Therefore he freely steps among them and prays to God for them.

*Bless my enemies, O Lord. Even I bless them and do not curse them.*

## KILL OR DO NOTHING?

Both Jim Forest and Nikolai Velimirovic showed me *a more Christlike Way* to deal with the violence out there and the violence in me. Their response does not resonate with pride or bravado. They expose vengeance as impotent and naïve. They seem free of fear, and their actions are ordered by Love.

By contrast, somehow among Christians who think they're being practical, there is a heart-hardening binary that says the only options are "kill or sit by and do nothing." They do not believe in the power of prayer and ignore the effectiveness of peace-building as if prayer and peace-building are impotent and passive non-responses to evil. As if the *Jesus Way* were idle and ineffective. This is the voice of the enemy—a lie from the pit from which "the destroyer" comes to wreak havoc.

The beautiful reality is that the *Jesus Way*, as Paul preached and practiced it, is never passive or idle. It seeks to "overcome evil with good." While retributive "Christians" may poo-poo Christ's direct commands as dangerously naïve, the truth is that the *Jesus Way* of enemy love is the only alternative to escalating violence. His *Ways* are creative and effective. For those with the willingness to look more deeply at the *Jesus Way* of creative nonviolence, I leave you with the example of my friend, Jarrod McKenna, a peacemaking activist from Australia who courageously advocates for refugees in detention on Manus Island. He says,

> It's hard to kill you if you have gone out and built their home. It's harder to kill you if you have helped them with their kids. It's hard to kill you if you have put them through a program that is helping them gain meaningful employment.
>
> If you want ISIS to win, keep vilifying and stereotyping all Muslims. Keep perpetuating this violence against Muslims. That kind of hatred just helps radicalize disenchanted youth. We need to love our Muslim neighbors.

Amen. Whether we're Christian or Atheist, Muslim or Buddhist, Hindu or whatever, if the name of the game is retribution, the fruit will always, always be escalation, violence and destruction. Jarrod's specific challenge to Christians concerned with Islam is that we have two options: (1) fear, hatred and retribution leading to violence and self-destruction, or (2) the *Jesus Way* of enemy-love. We aren't answering to *Abba* for their crimes. We're responsible for our response—will it be cruciform or wrathful? Forgiving or vengeful? In the case of retributive Christianity, we just swapped out the Nazis and Communists as enemies and replaced them with Islamists. I wonder: is Christ up to loving them too? What would that look like? What Christlike *good* would overcome their evil? It better be something more effective and morally superior to more death-dealing and escalation. That will take the creative genius of the Holy Spirit. I believe she's up to it—after all, we are talking about the infinite and all-powerful God of triune Love.

## FROM PRACTICE TO SURRENDER

In this chapter, I've confessed the violence in my heart and brought it into the presence of Christ. By laying bare the vengeance impulse at the throne of *Grace,* I did not experience *Abba* as surprised, disgusted or punitive.

*Abba* looked beneath the malice and repressed rage to show me the hurt, grief and anger of little Bradley who needs healing and transformation.

*Radical peacemaking* in the *Jesus Way* happens as *Abba* offers us new ways to see, sends messengers to help us, and trains us to follow him in enemy-love. *Grace* summons us to the *Jesus Way* of sharing and praying *Abba's* many mercies, even for our enemies.

I've become more and more confident that when Christ said, "Love, bless and pray for your enemies," *Grace* could permeate and shift me from prayers through gritted teeth to supplication for my heart and from the heart.

I know. These practices can simply become the new legalism. The ego makes sure of it. But the solution to legalism has never been abstaining from following the *Jesus Way,* giving up on prayer or failing to be merciful. Rather, for me, the *Jesus Walk* involves the next step of transformation: *radical surrender.*

## THOUGHTS

1. One needn't feel animosity toward anyone to have enemies. Nor does our discomfort or denial about having enemies change the fact that sometimes people see us as enemies and take up enmity toward us.

I've found it far easier to love my enemies and pray for them when I became willing to label them (initially) as such. The moment I add them to my "enemy list," I know exactly what Christ wants me to do: "Love, bless, do good and pray."

If you compiled an enemy list *by name,* who would you find there? How does leaving them off the list absolve you of walking the *Jesus Way* on their behalf? God doesn't need the names—he knows them—but we seem to in order to break through denial about our grudge-keeping.

2. When I developed my enemy list, I sensed the Lord asking me to include all those who I feel had done me harm or intend to harm me in some way. I was only to pray, "Lord, have mercy" for each enemy by name until my obsession with their injustices had lifted. In other words, praying for them was the *Jesus Way* of freeing me from my own obsession and their ongoing effects on me.

Are there those who've so wronged you that you've internalized them by obsession? Would you like to be free of the chains that bind you to your enemies? Why not free yourself by praying "Lord have mercy" for them by name each time you start to obsess over them?

3. At first, I wasn't sure I wanted to "let go" of my enemies. Holding them in my courtroom of judgment gave me a twisted sense of satisfaction and superiority. I know: gross, right? Then I sensed *Abba* asking me to compile another list: all those I had hurt or harmed from childhood on, especially those who might still feel the pain of my offenses, those who've forgiven me and those who can never forgive me.

I was prompted to lay this list before Christ *first,* and to pray "Lord have mercy" for each of them by name *first.* After that, I could pray through the list of my offenders. Sadly, the list of those I'd harmed was far longer. By the time I'd prayed through their names, I had no desire to hang onto the offenses of others. The pedestal of my resentment had been knocked out from under me. This served two functions: to humble me . . . but also to begin the painful prayer therapy of healing my own long-term shame by bathing it in a daily sitz bath of mercy.

Would you dare try that exercise? Have you ever hurt or harmed anyone? Did they forgive you? Do you still need to experience *Abba's* mercy for those offenses? Why not let him have them?

## PRAYERS

*Lord Jesus Christ, have mercy on me.*

*I pray for those I've hurt and harmed, those I've offended and caused turmoil. Those who've forgiven me and those who have not. Lord, have mercy on them (by name).*

*I pray for those who've hurt and harmed me, those who've offended me and caused me turmoil. Those I've forgiven and those I cannot seem to forgive. Lord, have mercy on them (by name).*

*I thank you for your superabundant mercy. Bathe me in mercy that the stains of shame would no longer cling to me. Tell me again about Grace to quiet the accuser and my own tormenting conscience. Grant me the freedom and peace of knowing "It is finished."*

# Facet 6

# "Rest for the weary" RADICAL SURRENDER

## WHAT WEARIES YOU?

I left the previous chapter with some *Grace*-empowered practices of *radical peacebuilding and forgiveness,* including inviting (daily) *Abba's* mercy upon those we've harmed and those who've harmed us until we're freed from obsessing over them. Apart from the transforming *Grace* of the Holy Spirit, even the disciplines of cruciform enemy-love may become ego-centric striving—although it's the toughest of all spiritual virtues to counterfeit.

In this chapter, we advance another step on the *Jesus Walk* of spiritual recovery—the counterpoint and antidote to religious self-will and humanist self-help: *radical surrender.*

Caveat: *surrender* does not make *Abba* love us. *Surrender* falls *into Abba's* love for us. Nor can we will ourselves to surrender—self-will and surrender are opposites—very much at odds. Rather, surrender to *Abba's Way* is a work of *Grace.* In fact, this pattern was established long ago in Gethsemane when, having assumed a human will, Christ heals the human will by surrendering his will to *Abba.* "Not my will but thine" becomes for humanity the great undoing of Adam's rebellion. Christ's vicarious willing surrender to his *Abba* is ground zero of my own healing and surrender.

Even as we bottom out on *Our Ways,* Christ is at work, healing us of pride, defiance and rebellion (willfulness) and restoring us to the *Christlike Ways* of humility, willingness and submission.

In the last chapter, I unearthed the driving emotions beneath my struggles with vengeance and violence: hurt, grief and anger. These are authentic human emotions rooted in real events. We can't strive our way out of them, nor does repression free us from them. I will use this part of my story to illustrate the role and necessity of *surrender* to experiencing *Abba's* healing love and freedom.

## WHAT WEARIES ME

Hurt and grief weary me. Anger, hatred and violence weary me. Fear and worry weary me. Slavery to myself and my addictions weary me. The list goes on. The sleep deprivation, digestive problems and migraines worsen the problem and create new health issues. So do the religious platitudes and worldly-wise prescriptions echoing in my head, "If you would just . . ."

I get it. It's my fault. I'm not a victim. I'm a whiner.

I want to retire, to sleep, to depart.

I'm weary.

Maybe you are, too. Don't add my burden to yours—and I have no intention of telling you what you have to do or guarantee that my ways work for anyone but me. I do intend, however, to share an aspect of the *Christlike Way* that has granted some reprieve to me and some of my friends.

I've titled this chapter, "Rest for the Weary" (that's me) with the subtitle, "Radical Surrender" (that's where I found some rest).

Back in the day, during a heavy bout of weariness, I faced the revivalist pressure (both Evangelical and Charismatic) to "press in for a breakthrough." It became obvious to me that we had been trying to will ourselves back to joy by pulling ourselves up by the bootstraps of triumphalist declarations. But I felt like giving up. Then a possibility occurred to me. Resignation and surrender aren't all that different. It's much easier to make the lateral move from "giving up" to "giving in" than trying to dig my way out of the snowy pit. Instead of psyching myself out of despair, I could despair of myself, resign from my burned-out soul strength and give up on religious self-effort and hype of calls to "rise up, people of God!" Instead of giving up on life or giving in to despondency, I could surrender to God. If only I could figure out what that meant in practice.

What came to mind was the old George Bev Shea hymn we'd sing at the end of Billy Graham crusades: "Just as I am, without one plea." What if I came to Christ empty-handed and open-hearted and just laid down?

That's a dangerous thought because striving and striding involve a certain momentum. What if you lose the momentum? What if you lay down and can't get up again? Some people go through the motions for a long time before they finally crash. Others just crash, as I would in 2008, and discover that laying down is easier once you find you're already laid out. Then surrender ceases to be a dreadful prospect and sounds more like freedom from mental and emotional slavery. It's much easier to let go when you dearly want to. But getting there involuntarily is messy and can be harmful to others. It can be fatal to a marriage, to a career, to one's health or all of the above.

"Rock bottom," as the recovery community calls it, does not have to mean "as low as you can go." It doesn't require unemployment or divorce or a stroke. You can bottom out at whatever moment you choose to surrender. No pressure, but I recommend weariness as a sign that it's time to "let go and let God."

## I MENTIONED 2008 **#$@?!!!

That was a bad year. Or was it?

My friend Robin asked, "What if the worst thing that ever happened to you is the best thing that ever happened to you?"

I had been pastoring for twenty years. I was into the tenth year of our exciting little church plant, Fresh Wind, where we had seen a beautiful influx of newcomers. They filled the high school cafeteria where we met with oodles of joy. With great regularity, you'd see people with disabilities, little children, recovering addicts, ex-cons and the city's poor celebrating Christ together, sharing potluck meals, praying for each other and even dancing. It was surreal and heavenly.

But starting in January 2008, we began to see one tragedy pile on top of the next for over a year. There were strokes and cancer deaths, overdoses and suicides, then an abduction, a murder and an in-house leadership scandal. Folks were grieving and leaving, and I felt the pressure to hold it together. Hey, who was I kidding? I was a management addict self-medicating my insanity with a love-addiction, which is to say I suffered an insatiable craving for affection to soothe my self-loathing and self-pity.

My physical, emotional, mental and marital health were coming apart. I wasn't just weary—I was seriously unraveling.

By the time my doctor assessed me in September, I had recorded thirty-five significant traumas. When he told me straight-up, "You need to resign," I could only feel relief to have his permission. Even after that, things only got worse before they got better. I was doing more harm than good, to myself and to others. I'm so sorry for that.

I began meeting with a counselor, a spiritual director and a twelve-step recovery sponsor. A decade later, I still make monthly visits to Steve, my spiritual director, and I attend regular twelve-step meetings when I'm not traveling.

My main takeaway from my collapse and from my healing team's input is this: the *Jesus Way* requires *radical surrender.* Here is what surrender meant for me:

***1. I admitted I was powerless over my addictions and that my life had become unmanageable.***

I had to surrender the delusion that I could will myself back to health. I couldn't. My dysfunctions were bigger than self-help, religious or otherwise. Once you've unraveled and realize you're unable to function normally, admitting this seems a lot easier. I had finally come to see that "I can't."

***2. I came to believe a power greater than me could restore me to sanity.***

It's not that I needed to believe there is a God. I needed to surrender notions of God that made him my servant or my genie or my sugar daddy. Letting go of my vending machine God, I had to start from scratch with the truly difficult question: is God good? Even if he let me crash? Can I trust a God who consents to crushing human affliction?

I could not *make* myself believe this. But somehow, by the *Grace* of *Abba* and with the help of my healing team and fellow addicts, *I came to believe it.*

***3. I made a decision to turn my life and my will over to the care of God.***

Having surrendered those delusions about myself (my Messiah complex) and about God (the mighty fixer), I became willing to surrender myself to the care (not the control—God isn't a controller) of a loving, caring, forgiving God. I became willing to surrender to *Abba's* Love—never more than a day at a time. My friend, author Wm. Paul Young calls this "living in the *Grace* of today." Sometimes not a day—just an hour, a moment or a decision at a time. When I do surrender, weariness lifts. When I don't . . . ugh. See, it's not a one-time deal. Living in and from *Grace* is not an event—it's a lifetime lifestyle. It's the *Jesus Way*.

I'll let readers decide if these three steps apply to anyone but me. You can also explore the remaining nine steps of recovery elsewhere, such as A.A.'s *Big Book* or Richard Rohr's *Breathing Under Water*.

But at this point, I want to explain how my crash required completely renovating my prayer life. Let's turn to the *Jesus Prayer*.

## THE PRAYER OF SURRENDER

*"Lord Jesus Christ, Son of God, have mercy on me a sinner."*
—the Jesus Prayer

Most Christ-followers in the Protestant West are unfamiliar with "the Jesus Prayer," or mistake it for "the Lord's Prayer" (or "Our Father"). I'd like to teach it to you because of its role in restoring me, saving my prayer life and guarding my heart from imagining I can manage God and the universe. That's a story in itself.

When I first discovered the painful truth that *Trinity consents* to both the beauty and the tragedy of natural law and human choices, I lost my prayer life for six months. My prayers had been reduced to futile attempts at managing the world and other people. I called it "intercession" but I was basically trying to manipulate God into being my personal fixer. When that failed, I lost prayer altogether. Why pray if it doesn't "work"?

Certain contemplative sources (especially Thomas Merton, Henri Nouwen, Thomas Keating, Richard Foster, etc.) were of great help at first. They taught a form of prayer where I could wait on God in quietness, assured of his loving gaze and just breathe. They relieved me of the pressure of striving. I could finally rest from trying to save the world.

But then a popular contemplative motto, "Prayer doesn't change things; it only changes you," began to annoy me. The slogan sounded so faithless to me—so foreign to Christ's teachings on prayer and faith. I'd been so burned by Christless religion that I wasn't about to opt for Christless spirituality. Christ's instructions on prayer include faith, trust and expectancy. And yet my faith had dead-ended. I had to start from scratch.

## PRAYER FROM SCRATCH

The phenomenon of prayer has raised questions for me since I was a little boy. Is anyone listening? Does God hear me? Why pray if God already knows? How specific must I be? Is prayer bargaining with God? Can we change God's mind? How long must I pray and what words and terms should I use? Is there one and only one way to pray? I asked these questions while I was still learning to read.

I have an entire tightly-packed shelf of books devoted only to prayer. Books about prayer are, after all, an excellent alternative to (diversion from) prayer. But that's not where I learned to pray anyway. I learned from my mother. Mom taught me to worry and she taught me to pray . . . often at the same time. Eventually, her lessons opened my eyes to some truths and some errors about how I prayed.

For example, my Mom served at a Bible camp one summer. I was there too. An alarm was raised when the cook's child—just a toddler—found and drank poisonous cleaning fluid. This young child was rushed away in an ambulance, his life hanging in the balance. The whole camp gathered to pray. I remember Mom "praying up a storm"—with passion and tears, faith and desperation, citing Bible promises and pouring her heart out.

I found this kind of prayer stressful and exhausting. At the time, such prayers seemed like striving and cajoling and tons of effort to get God to do something I wasn't sure he'd do. Was my mother asking God to save the child, or were the quality of her prayers responsible for saving the child? I saw the pressure on her and on God.

As for me, I was overwhelmed by the pain of a suffering child and needed an out. Intending to pray "God's will be done," I simply retreated behind the shield of cold-hearted fatalism. *Whatever will be will be.* I didn't truly surrender the child to God; I abandoned him to fate. When the child's life was spared, maybe God had heard and answered. Maybe my Mom's prayers had helped. I know mine didn't.

This story illustrates two ditches into which people of prayer frequently slip. I've learned a lot of good lessons about prayer from both the charismatic and contemplative schools of faith, but I've also experienced their unhealthy extremes.

## EXPECTANT FAITH

Charismatic Christians are known for their emphasis on Christ's calls for expectant faith in the Gospels. He commends faith wherever he finds it (Matt. 8:5-13). We may disagree about what Jesus meant, but he did make very bold claims and demands for faith. For example, even the "faith teachers" are barely this audacious.

> "Whatever you ask in prayer, you'll get it, if you believe." —Matthew 21:22

> "I'm telling you the truth: if anyone says to this mountain, 'Be off with you—get yourself thrown into the sea,' if they have no doubt in their heart, but believe that what they say will happen, it will be done for them. That's why I'm telling you, everything that you request in prayer, everything you ask God for, believe that you receive it, and it will happen for you." —Mark 11:23-24

In these texts, "faith" has something to do with believing God is a loving Father who cares about us and is active in our lives. Faith isn't about psyching ourselves up into a state of mind ("faith in faith") but rather, looking with *expectancy* to the kindness of our heavenly *Abba.* Jesus encourages us to present our needs to *Abba,* rather than stubbornly asserting our self-sufficiency. However that works (We. Don't. Know.), we do know this: Jesus commands us to *ask, seek and knock.* Christ himself claims that askers receive, seekers find, and knocking opens doors (Matt. 7:7). That is a challenge for me, especially knowing I don't always receive my requests and I'm chronically averse to disappointment.

Yes, my "inner charismatic" reminds me of Jesus' call to faith. Sadly, my prayers of faith betray my desire for control. Faith may morph into revving up emotions, lapsing into denial, asserting my own will, demanding God keep his promises, and ultimately blaming unanswered prayer on someone's lack of faith. My track-record is that Christlike expectancy gives way to self-will. And *self-will is not faith,* no matter how one spiritualizes it.

## SELF-WILL IS NOT "AUTHORITY"

I was praying for a child who was dying after a lengthy, losing battle with a terminal disease. Now he was enduring his final, pain-wracked last days in hospice.

I dearly loved this little guy and was not prepared to give up just yet. I had witnessed more than one deathbed healing before. Desperate for a healing, I stepped into a popular pattern of charismatic prayer. Instead of *asking* God for healing, I began *commanding* healing in Jesus' name. I found myself delivering articulate, authoritative commands. I cursed the disease, rebuked the spirit of infirmity and commanded the child's immune system to rise up and fight. I felt so "anointed" and was self-impressed at using all the "right" words. My chest swelled with what I imagined was "authority." Nothing was changing, but I refused to give up. I kept vigil all night, "pressing in" for a miracle.

That night, against the grain of my prayers, I had this "conversation" with Jesus (Remember, I was a charismatic).

Jesus asked, "Did you feel that authority rising up inside you?"

"Yes, Lord," I answered, quite proud of myself.

"That wasn't authority," he said. "That's self-will. Self-will is rooted in the flesh. And the flesh profits nothing."

The authority I felt was nothing but the adrenaline of my own will-power—completely useless. Spiritual haughtiness is not faith. I objected,

"But Lord, you issued words of command to bodies, to diseases and to unclean spirits."

"Yes," he said, "but there were preconditions."

"Preconditions?" I asked, surprised.

What follows is what I discerned then and what I believe today:

Faith goes deeper than mimicking Jesus' words. The power behind Jesus' words of command—what made his prayers effective—were preconditions my self-will was sabotaging. Three words describe the precondition of Christ's authoritative prayers: *kenosis (self-emptying), willingness and surrender.*

### a. Kenosis (self-emptying)

Christ completely emptied himself of self-will so he could be filled with God's supernatural love. The active ingredient behind Christ's authority was self-emptying love, not forceful words or tones, nor magic formulas—not even my precious Jesus Prayer!

**b. Willingness**

Christ's authority in prayer—his faith—came through his complete willingness to be a vessel of divine love. He was filled, moved and empowered by God's supernatural love. *Abba* worked through Jesus' prayers, unobstructed by self-will.

**c. Surrender**

Christ didn't surrender anyone to sickness or death—not even those he left unhealed and dying around the globe when he ascended. Rather, he surrendered all those in his care to *Abba*, whether healthy or sick. We don't surrender to sickness and death. We surrender our lives and our loved ones to the care of triune Love, every day of our lives.

I'm still processing how this "works," because I cannot *make* myself empty, willing or surrendered through self-effort. "Trying" is still fleshly. So, in my weakness, I let go of striving, open my hands and pray, "Lord, have mercy" or "*Abba*, help me!" or just imagine I'm breathing his Love.

In the aftermath of that experience, I no longer commanded or demanded healing. But I could sincerely surrender my little friend into *Abba's* caring hands, believing with all my heart that mercy would come, however God so chose. *Abba's* mercy came the next day. The child requested communion with his parents, said "I love you," and with a final sigh, peacefully surrendered his spirit.

## SURRENDERED FAITH

"Surrender" is also a kind of faith. Surrender *entrusts* God with our needs and our loved ones. We hand over, release, let go of our lives and our will to our loving heavenly *Abba*. In return, we can fully expect *Abba* to deliver mercy (every single time!) without dictating how that must look. I resigned as *Abba's* dictator.

Essentially, contemplative prayer differs from charismatic prayer when, rather than asking for something *from* God, it gives something over *to* God. It's the *kenosis* of letting go. We still heed the words of Jesus, "ask, seek, knock." But any *receiving from* begins by *giving to.* We cast our cares on him, believing he cares for us and delivers mercy (1 Pet. 5:7).

The upside of contemplative prayer is that we never need to slip into groveling, begging, manipulating or demanding. Yes, Jesus affirms "nagging prayer" in the parable of the importunate widow (Luke 18:1-8). That parable encourages persistence, but it does *not* describe the nature of God. It's a parable on prayer that contrasts the unjust and reluctant judge who needs cajoling with our heavenly *Abba* who is just the opposite: he's both just and generous. We are children in his arms, not beggars at his door. Our prayers need only welcome what is already ours to receive: the provision of daily bread (*Grace* sufficient for all our needs) from a resourceful Father.

## CONTEMPLATIVE OVER-STEERING

A word of caution: in pursuing contemplative prayer, I found it tempting to over-correct charismatic control, veering into the opposite ditch. One contemplative bragged to me that he was composing prayers that never disappoint. He found comfort in prayers that require no faith and involve no asking. In reality, he had become as fatalistic and faithless as I was in my camp story, when rather than surrendering to God's care, I just resigned myself and the child to fate.

"God knows anyways. My prayers change nothing—they only change me." This gave my contemplative friend peace, probably because like me, he'd worn himself out with striving prayer. But the cost was high. He had negated Jesus' instructions on prayer and rejected Jesus' clear call to expectant faith. We are meant to bring our requests to the throne of *Grace,* and that risks disappointment. We are meant to seek, which involves grieving what is lost. We are meant to knock, because some doors don't open until we do.

Why the need to ask? Why "the Lord's Prayer" if answering is already *Abba's* intent? Apparently, *Trinity* has chosen to work in this world through willing human partners who welcome divine care into our world through prayer.

Why is that?

- Because our willing "yes" matters to *Abba. Love* doesn't impose on or circumvent the human will.
- Because our conversations with *Abba* nurture relationship with him.
- Because partnership with *Abba* forms us into Christlike disciples. We are the image of *Abba's* love to the world—just as Jesus, the perfect Image of *Love,* was a willing channel for his *Abba's* love to us.
- Because *Grace* recruits us as her willing opposition to our willing resistance. *Love* may only overcome evil with good by *love,* and we're *Love's* willing agents in the battle. Prayer is one means to that end.

Today, I embrace the best of charismatic prayer and am willing to make bold requests, but without trying to manage or bully God. And I continue to practice contemplative prayer through willing surrender, but without failing to present my requests to God (Phil. 4:6).

## THE JESUS PRAYER

Earlier I mentioned how I "lost prayer." When my prayers were drained of expectancy and faithless contemplation felt like a cop-out, I had to detox from prayer altogether. You could say I learned to sit in wordless, imageless prayers—the prayer of silence. That's being kind, but *Abba* IS kind—so there I sat. Eventually, I was reintroduced to the magnificent three-word prayer, "Lord, have mercy" *(from the Greek: kyrie eleison—* remember the Mr. Mister hit of 1989?*).*

I love this prayer on so many levels. Here are just a few:

*The prayer identifies God's primary disposition toward us: loving mercy.* When we pray it, we're approaching *Trinity* in their essential nature and untarnished image. We're relating to the true God of triune mercy.

*The Jesus prayer does not unleash Abba's mercy, it orients us to it. Abba's* mercy is an infinite waterfall that never ceases. We don't turn the tap on. Rather, the Jesus Prayer is just one way I position my heart beneath that flow and willingly receive *Abba's* kindness with open hands and hearts.

*The prayer treats mercy as every gift Abba has for us.* Legalist lenses reduce mercy to withholding judgment. Biblical mercy refers to all the ways we experience *Abba's* goodness. There's a Greek pun at play between the mercies (*eleos*) of *Abba* and the superabundant generosity of the olive tree (*elaia*), providing enormous stores of olives (*elaia*), olive oil (*elaion*) and lamp oil (*elaion*). The *polyeleos* (lit. much oil/many mercies) of *Abba* include every gift he provides—good weather and abundant crops, food and clothing, health and strength, safe travel, spiritual and civic leaders, etc. Again, the prayer doesn't activate *Abba's mercy*—rather, it leads me beneath the ever-flowing spring to receive Mercy's continuous downpour.

*The prayer is expectant without expectations.* That is, we can know for sure that *Abba's* answer to this prayer will always be YES. In fact, because God IS mercy, his YES is an already-flowing spring of divine life and the prayer is our expectant and receptive orientation to *Grace.*

There's no need to ever grovel before God, begging for mercy, as if God were reluctant to turn on the tap or that our prayers are what generates God's generosity. Not at all. *Lord, have mercy* is a grateful acknowledgement of our *Abba's* superabundant *Grace. Lord, have mercy* simply opens my hands to *Abba's* care. The Jesus Prayer combines our grateful, "Thank you for your mercy!" to our willing "Yes, please!"

On the other hand, *Lord, have mercy* imposes no expectations as to what form God's mercy must take—it makes no demands on the when or how or where of God's answer. Rather, we become attentive to the creative genius of the Holy Spirit in delivering God's many mercies beyond the tiny box of our expectations.

*The prayer never becomes vain repetition.* As a young Evangelical, we were warned against reciting and repeating prayers. Jesus tells us to avoid "vain" or "meaningless repetition."

In our prejudice against the liturgists, we failed to see that not all repetition is meaningless and not all spontaneity is meaningful. What does Jesus say?

> "When you pray, don't pile up a jumbled heap of words! That's what the Gentiles do. They reckon that the more they say, the more likely they are to be heard. So don't be like them. You see, your father knows what you need before you ask him."
>
> —Matthew 6:7

Jesus immediately follows up his injunction with his carefully crafted alternative. He says, "So this is how you should pray" and he gives us the dense and meaningful prayer to repeat: the "Our Father."

Similarly, *"Lord, have mercy" is neither vain nor meaningless.* Indeed, it's an inspired and effective prayer used throughout Scripture, found in the regular Jewish hymnody (Ps. 57, 86, 123). Most importantly, Christ himself puts a prayer for mercy in the mouth of his penitent tax-collector: *"God, be merciful to me, sinner that I am"* (Lk. 18:13). Since Jesus commends these words as the prayer that justifies, repeating them from the heart can be powerful and effective.

*The prayer is a shield, guarding the heart and mind.* I have found that *Lord, have mercy* functions as a spiritual shield in the face of temptation, obsession, anxiety and despair. It wards off panic and addictive cravings. When utilizing it as spiritual, emotional and mental armor, I picture Christ at my right hand (so "I will not be shaken") as we face the onslaught shoulder-to-shoulder. The prayer reminds me that I'm not alone in the struggle. I have an ever-present, merciful Lord at my side and on my side.

*My heart can pray Lord, have mercy while my mind goes about its business.* Happily, I've repeated the prayer long enough that, on occasion, my heart spontaneously begins to pray *the Jesus Prayer* in the background without my mind consciously deciding to do so. It's like my mind hears *Lord, have mercy* being prayed from deep within rather than having to actively pray the words. I've met veterans of spirituality for whom this has become their constant experience, day and night—just one example of Paul's call to "pray without ceasing."

*The long form of the prayer, "Lord Jesus Christ, Son of God, have mercy on me a sinner,"* is the perfect length and rhythm for what some call "centering prayer" meditation. I retreat into my heart and quietly sit in an awareness that God loves me. Then, I begin to mindfully breathe the prayer, inhaling Christ's mercy through *"Lord Jesus Christ, Son of God"* and exhaling whatever I need to release with every *"have mercy on me, a sinner."*

### A "SINNER"?

When I say the long form of the *Jesus Prayer,* including the phrase "on me, a sinner," those unfamiliar with how and why the prayer functions may balk that I would self-identify as a "sinner." They imagine I'm indulging in "worm theology" and repudiating my new identity in Christ. The question of how I can speak as both a *beloved son* and a *sinner* is incredibly important, not only theologically, but in the practice of daily surrender to Christ's loving mercy.

First, I've noted above that Jesus composed and affirmed the tax-collector's prayer for mercy. Jesus' attitude toward the self-congratulating, triumphalist prayers of the Pharisee was entirely derogatory. The prayer *Abba* heard and accepted was the self-deprecating confession of the one who described himself as a sinner. That's according to Jesus.

Second, I do not "identify" as a sinner—I identify as a "child." The "sinner" label is not an *identity*—it is a *description.* It *describes* the reality of my daily spiritual struggle to surrender. "Sinner" is not a self-loathing indictment. It is an acknowledgement of the human condition, an honest admission that I wrestle with "the passions," a disavowal of self-sufficiency and a confession of my grateful dependence on the glorious resources of God's mercies—"new every morning."

Third, I know what it is to feel triggered into self-loathing by the word "sin" or "sinner." But the *Jesus Prayer* is not the *cause* of our shame—it's a diagnostic tool that exposes it. Shame and self-loathing may linger from bad teaching or bad experiences. If the *Jesus Prayer* exposes residual shame, it's also one tool *Abba* uses to cleanse us from it. When the "grace teachers" start twitching over the description "sinner," it may indicate that their "freedom in Christ" is more of a denial of sin/shame than the cleansing effects of *Grace.* It feels to me like pride, or more likely, scrunching shut our eyes to our own deep-seated suffering. "I'm fine. I'm a saint." Would your spouse, partner and children agree? What did the apostle John say?

> . . . if we walk in the light, just as he is in the light, we have fellowship with one another, and the blood of Jesus his son makes us pure and clean from all sin. *If we say that we have no sin,* we deceive ourselves and the truth is not in us. *If we confess our sins,* he is faithful and just, and will forgive us our sins and cleanse us from all unrighteousness. *If we say that we have not sinned,* we make him out to be a liar, and his word is not in us. —1 John 1:7-10

Yes, I know the standard work-arounds used to evade John's words here. No, they don't work. Not exegetically and not in practice. The solution to our shame is not hiding our struggles in a sin-denying theological system or dissociating from our brokenness. It's so much easier and powerful to say, *Lord Jesus Christ, Son of God, have mercy on me, a sinner,* then arise and move forward in *Grace.* As my friend Paul E. Ralph says, "Christ came to make us fully human, not superhuman." That includes embracing the fullness of our humanity (as Christ did) without self-hatred or denial. We face the reality of life in this world in our not-yet glorified humanity.

We see ourselves in the prodigal (Lk. 15:11-32), the publican (Luke 18:9-14) and the thief on the cross (Lk. 23:39-43), awake to our need for mercy and gratefully receiving that mercy from Christ the all-merciful. Their prayers are worth recounting:

- "Father, I have sinned against heaven and before you, and I am no longer worthy to be called your son."
- "God, be merciful to me a sinner!"
- "Jesus, remember me when you come into your kingdom."

These prayers should not be scorned for their supposed "worm theology." They are not theological statements to be corrected. They are expressions of the human condition, cries of the stricken conscience, and appeals to the goodness and generosity of *Abba's superabundant Grace.*

Christ not only commended these prayers—he composed two of them and answered all three of them—*even before they asked* (Matt. 6:8)!

Finally, all talk of sin aside, again the mercy of God is *not* defined so narrowly and negatively as "withholding wrath" from some punishment-deserving sin. *Mercy* is every manifestation of divine goodness that we need and experience. The many mercies of God include health and healing, provision and providential care, patience and endurance, guidance and counsel, intimacy with God and fellowship with others . . . I could go on for pages. To summarize, God's mercy is "every good, every perfect gift, [that] comes down from above, from the *Abba* of lights" (Jas. 1:17).

## REMEMBER

- Remember that the Trinity meets you every time you pray, even if all you have is wordless groans (cf. Rom. 8:26-27).

- Remember, Jesus is your advocate, praying with and for you (1 Jn. 1:2).
- Remember, the Father of mercies is the God of all comfort in our afflictions (2 Cor. 1:3-4).
- Remember, the Holy Spirit is our ever-present comforter, helper and guide (Jn. 14:16, 26).
- All three rush to the place where we honestly cry out for help, regardless of what we believe or how poorly we pray.

## SURRENDER AND FREEDOM

I've invested these pages on the *Jesus Prayer* because for me, that little prayer became my gateway to surrender. And only through *radical surrender* was I able to let Jesus into my darkest closets of the hurt, grief and anger behind my inner swirl of repressed violence, hatred and addiction.

What makes hatred so horrid is that it reshapes its victims, fashioning them into the mirror image of the object of their hate. The fists of hatred compress the finest people like putty, kneading into our righteous anger its own malignant toxins—fear and malice—deeply internalizing what we most despise.

No matter how cruel offenders can be, their most pernicious evil is the change they cause in their victims, with or without their consent.

The call to forgive—literally "let go"—whatever it means for the offender, is Christ's plea that we would unchain ourselves from our offender's ongoing negative influence. And Christ delivered us the key. "*Abba,* forgive them" becomes Christ's mandate to us: loose yourselves from the bonds of infectious resentment that unite you to what you hate.

"But what they did . . ."

Yes, what they did.

Forgiveness isn't justifying what they did.

It is unhooking ourselves from the ways what was done continues to torment, twist and diminish us.

"Loose yourself."

"But I can't."

No. You can't.

Christ can, but only when you're finally willing.

When at last you see that the fists of hatred crushing you are your own and you open them up and surrender to *Abba's* embrace.

We'll cover this further under *radical forgiveness*. But for now, let's examine the facet of *radical surrender*.

## REST FROM EXHAUSTING GRIEF AND FURY

I don't write this to chide others into guilt-driven pseudo-forgiveness. I am dealing with my own heart and hoping that others who overhear might also benefit.

You see, in 2018 (ten years after my big crash), I again experienced a long year of chronic grief with a side of seething fury. I managed it as best I could with a bad blend of repression, insomnia and praying angry psalms. Eden tells me that being real is generally better for me than being good. But, then when she takes the brunt of my misery, I eventually opt for a long walk.

On one of these walks, I figured I'd better just sputter the *Jesus Prayer* until the obsessive anger lifted. I strode up the sidewalk, repeating the prayer about three hundred times: *"Lord Jesus Christ, Son of God, have mercy on me a sinner."*

Once that was off my chest and my mind was finally quiet enough for contemplative silence, Jesus' invitation wafted in gently, like a down feather drifting through the aftermath of a flailing pillow fight. He said,

> "Come to Me, all who are weary and heavy-laden, and I will give you rest. Take My yoke upon you and learn from Me, for I am gentle and humble in heart, and you will find rest for your souls."
> —Matthew 11:28-29 (NASB)

Christ skipped past my need for invasive surgery on my emotional tumors or incisions into my vengeful imaginings. This was an offer of simple reprieve: just breathe and give it a rest. Who knew that taking a break from intense feelings isn't always denial? Hmm. I surrendered and in my spirit, leaned back into his arms, let out long sighs and inhaled his solace.

## CONFESSIONS

The next morning, I went to the monastery where I often sing Psalms and prayers or give the eight-minute homily. I know the liturgical format is foreign to most of my readers. Don't worry, I'm not recruiting. But if you'd like to hear my story, carry on.

James 5 says, "Confess your sins to one another, and pray for one another, that you may be healed." Prior to discovering a healthy practice of confession, I struggled with either repressing my secrets, sharing them with unsafe ears (whether condemners or gossips) or the painful ineffective "accountability partner" model. Still, I'm grateful for those friends and mentors who informally provided a shoulder to cry on. Even so, I wanted to develop a regular pattern of therapeutic confession with someone seasoned in Christ-centered wisdom. I began to visit a kindly old confessor, Bishop Varlaam, who understood confession as a place where we embody compassion and *Grace* to those who are struggling.

Confession in my tradition is not about guilt for sin or doing penance. It is a time for him to hear my anxieties and speak the good news of Jesus' love and forgiveness to my accusing conscience. He always, always lightens the load, reminding me to return to the *Abba's* house ASAP, without fear or self-loathing.

"What's troubling you?" he asks as usual.

I say, "I'm furious," picking up my grief and anger once again.

He replies gently, thoughtfully, "Of course, we all experience times of hurt and anger. That comes with the human condition. The problem is that grief and anger make us so weary. And you are exhausted. Perhaps today you could hear these words of Jesus:

> 'Come to Me, all who are weary and heavy-laden, and I will give you rest. Take My yoke upon you and learn from Me, for I am gentle and humble in heart, and you will find rest for your souls.'"

Ah, those words again. A fine confirmation!

As I rose to leave Bishop Varlaam, I noticed a new-to-me antique icon of Christ sitting on a stand beside him. I asked about it and he explained it was a recent gift, more than three centuries years old. The icon depicted Jesus holding an open Bible—the Gospels, actually. A verse was written on the page, but I couldn't read it because it was in Slavonic—old Russian.

"Which verse is that?" I asked. "What does it say?"

Varlaam struggled through hip pain to stand up, then leaned close to the icon and, running his finger over the painted wood, began translating:

*"Come to Me,*
*all who are weary and heavy-laden,*
*and I will give you rest."*

A bit stunned, I shuffled back to the readers' stand, where three of my fellow readers were taking turns praying aloud the ancient prayers used to prepare for the Lord's Supper. Dmitri was waiting for me, already holding a blue prayer book open to "The First Prayer of St. Basil the Great." I began to pray it aloud for the congregation, using the fourth century church father's ancient words to express my own heartfelt confession:

> . . . I have wholly subjected myself to sin and am a slave to pleasures and have defaced your image. Yet being your work and creation, I do not despair of my salvation; but emboldened by your immeasurable compassion, I draw near. Receive even me, O Christ, friend of man, as you did the harlot, the thief, the publican, and the prodigal; and take away the heavy burden of my sins, you who takes away the sin of the world, who heals our infirmities, *who calls to yourself those who labor and are heavy laden and gives them rest,* who came not to call the righteous, but sinners to repentance . . .

By God's *Grace,* I had discovered one of Jesus' approaches to therapy.

He's a "wonderful counselor"! You see, the "rest" Christ gives is not merely a diversion or reprieve from our weariness. It is medicine for it. As I rested from my drama in the arms of Christ, his gentle embrace applied balm to my wounds and soothed my raging heart. His meek touch is no mere "there, there" platitude, but a powerful and effective ministry of detox and rehab for the passions and impulses that would morph me into the monsters I hate.

He wasn't just granting me a rest. His rest was healing my hurt and grief, purifying my anger of malice and renewing my heart with the uncreated energies of divine *Grace.*

## THE ENERGIES OF ANGRY LOVE

Have you heard of Paul's "love chapter"? I like how N.T. Wright renders 1 Corinthians 13:4-8 as poetry in his translation:

*Love's great-hearted; love is kind,*
*Knows no envy, makes no fuss,*
*Is not puffed up, no shameless ways,*
*Doesn't force its rightful claim,*
*Doesn't rage or bear a grudge,*
*Doesn't cheer at other's harm,*
*Rejoices, rather, in the truth.*
*Love bears all things, believes all things;*
*Love hopes all things, endures all things.*
*Love never fails.*

If God is Love, revealed in Christ, then it's fair to plant *Abba's* name or Jesus' name all the way through that same song.

But what about anger? Doesn't *Abba's* pure anger burn against all that harms his children? Doesn't *Love* look like anger in the face of injustice? Think about the innocents—the children who've been tormented in so many ways. Right now, today, over sixty-eight million people around the world have been forcibly displaced by war, violence and persecution. Half of those are children. Thirty-four million children, driven from home as the direct result of purposeful human decision-making. Even supposedly freedom-loving Western democracies sponsor brutal tyrants and their oppressive regimes. Our governments—elected by us, funded by us, serving us—are often directly responsible for policies that leave children around the globe hungry, cold and terrified.

Are you okay with that? Is *Love* okay with that?

Is *Abba* okay with that?

Should we feel guilty? Well, it's not a guilt-trip if we're actually guilty, even if by our silence and inaction.

Should we feel sad? Depressed? Should we despair?

Should we feel anger? Is anger a sin?

When is *not* being angry a greater sin?

Anger is a natural human emotion.

In fact, it's a necessary emotion. If seeing children crying under the cruelties of human violence doesn't raise the voice of lament and outrage, we're likely guilty of smothering our complicity in denial.

For most mentally healthy humans, as it is with Christ, anger is a facet of deep loving concern. Love can be angry—*must* get angry.

But anger is dangerous too. It morphs into malice, rage, vengeance and violence. Those same displaced children lost their homes, their beds and their peace because someone's anger grew to the point of war. And perhaps that someone grew up on the anger of being displaced, losing family to war, experiencing terrible loss to foreign occupiers or local terrorists. The cycles of anger-turned-violent can perpetuate for generations and centuries. Vengeance has a long memory.

So Paul says, "Be angry, but don't sin; don't let the sun go down on you while you're angry."

How about this, then:

### THE "ANGER CHAPTER"

*Love is angry.*
*Loving anger is righteous.*

*Angry Love is not self-righteous or proud,*
*it is not hateful or malicious,*
*never cruel nor mean.*

*The anger of love never vilifies or dehumanizes;*
*its outrage energizes advocacy and does justice.*

*Righteous anger gives way to mercy,*
*because it needs mercy and has received mercy.*

*Love is angry, but only until sundown*
*and only as far as the Cross.*

My issue is that I had been *very* angry. All year.

I monitored my sleep with a phone app and realized sleep deprivation was draining me. And then so much sh*t hit the fan that week: the effects of long-term estrangement from my granddaughter and a fresh wave of online meanness against my friends and me. I was bitter about that. Bruised and weary and "ragey."

I was not patient with those I love. I'm sorry.

But something is different now, I think. I had this moment where my anger was cleansed in the arms of Christ and somehow purified and energized into angry love, free of malice or resentment. Quite suddenly, I just stopped feeling powerless or afraid. Maybe my fear was the root problem and with that gone, I could just love again. I sort of don't care. I found myself spontaneously captioning an Instagram selfie:

*"Do I look afraid? I know the Son of God."*

And it's true. I'm not afraid. And I wrote this poem, too:

*I'm coming around*
*(again, thru the Psalms)*
*from bitterness to a cleaner anger*
*that has energized me*
*beyond powerlessness*
*fear is dissolving and*
*the possibility of forgiveness*
*is emerging.*

Anger is like electricity, someone said.

Well, *Grace* is cleansing my anger from powerlessness to fearless clean energy. Through surrender.

## THOUGHTS

For this chapter, rather than my standard thoughts format, I offer this prayer exercise for *radical surrender.*

### A Contemplative Exercise in Waiting

"God sees the truth and waits."
—Leo Tolstoy

"For there is yet a vision for the appointed time
and a witness for the end who is not false.
Though it tarries, wait for it,
for it shall surely come, it shall not delay."
—Habakkuk 2:3

In a broken world, permeated with every injustice, why does God wait? Or is God waiting for me? How am I to wait when God seems to wait? When am I to be God's hands, mediating God's peace and justice in this world? And how am I to know the difference? Said another way, *How do I wait for God's Grace when I am an agent of God's Grace?*

This is a very difficult question, because rather than directing us to a formula or 'right' answer, the question itself deposits us at the foot of the Cross and requires a posture of humble waiting . . . potentially awkward or even painful waiting. There we are left, often perplexed, with the *Jesus Prayer:* "Lord Jesus Christ, have mercy on me, a sinner"—or the *Serenity Prayer:* "God, grant me the serenity to accept what I cannot change, the courage to change what I can, and the wisdom to know the difference."

*To know the difference:* there's the rub. But, I'm told, the active ingredient in this journey is *surrender.* Easier said than done, because surrender is not just something we *do,* but a way in which we *undergo* waiting. And yet, somehow, surrender involves willing participation. We "yield."

### Step 1 – The Clenched Fist

With your right hand, make a tight fist and just look at it. This fist represents our impulse to act independently of *Abba.* The delusion of autonomy (aka 'the fall'). When we don't see *Abba* acting as we had expected or hoped, we are tempted to take matters into our own hands. Or we may try to force *Abba's* hand, triggering a chaotic series of events ourselves. It's the raised fist of *revolution—of force.*

Some words that I see in this fist are grasping, clinging, scheming, manipulating, mastering, making, taking. It's not a waiting hand. It's not a serving hand. It's the impatient fist of pride and self-will that says, "If God won't do something, I will."

Willfulness can masquerade as initiative, boldness and courage . . . as we make a suicide-charge out of the foxhole into the minefield of life. But there's an old saying, "Discretion is the better part of valor." Or in Jesus' words, "The Son can do nothing on his own initiative, but only what he sees the Father doing" (Jn. 5:19). Some of us learn this the hard way. As one of my mentors once said in his southern drawl, "I've been bit by that dawg."

### Step 2 – The Limp Wrist

Once bitten, twice shy. When acting independently of God goes very badly, the resulting crash leaves us jaded, lethargic with compassion fatigue and finally, paralyzed. Hold out your left hand in front of you, palm down and let your wrist go as limp as possible—like Adam in Michelangelo's painting, "The Creation of Adam."

The limp hand represents *resignation.* We may refuse to participate in the kingdom life, expecting God to act independently of us. When we don't see *Abba* acting as we had expected, hoped (or demanded), we are tempted to sit on the sidelines as depressed observers or cynical critics.

Words I see on this lethargic or wounded hand are fatigue, despair, passivity, abdication and acquiescence. It's the hand that says, "If God won't do something, why should I?" It can masquerade as patience and reflection . . . as we numb out to the suffering of broken people and the darkness of our deteriorating cities. We've heard it said, "The only thing necessary for the triumph of evil is for good men to do nothing" (E. Burke). But of course, that proverb has been used all too often to rally the masses back to the clenched fist of self-will.

Is the dilemma obvious now? *How do I wait for Abba's Grace when I am also made to be an agent of Abba's Grace?*

For those who'd like to think more deeply about this, the underlying problem is, *How is Abba present and immanent in the world when Abba doesn't seem to intervene in the world?* The answer is found in the mystery of the Cross. Slovenian philosopher Slavoj Zizek says,

> God's suffering means that human history is not just a theatre of shadows, but the place of real struggle, the struggle in which the Absolute itself is involved and its fate decided. This is the background of Dietrich Bonhoeffer's deep insight that, after *shoah* [the holocaust], "only a suffering God can save us now."

## Step 3 – Open Hands

Finally, take both hands and open them in front of you, palms up like an expectant child. These are the hands of *receptivity,* willing and waiting for *Grace* in the person of Christ.

Open the eyes of your heart to see how Christ would come to you. Expect the mercy of Christ, but don't project what God must do. On any given day, in any given circumstance, Christ may (i) hold your hands in his wounded hands as you wait together; (ii) Christ may place a gift in your hands that represent *Grace* being offered (e.g. peace, patience, endurance, etc.); or (iii) Christ may anoint and use your hands for some kingdom purpose (giving, serving, loving, healing, comforting, etc.). We may even become highly active and effective, but by waiting and listening first, our actions will be rooted in the Spirit rather than in the ego-self, and thus empowered *by Grace* to *be* grace in the world (as seen in the Sermon on the Mount).

So, how does Christ come to you today? What does he do with these open hands? God's *Grace* to you.

## PRAYERS

*Dear God,*

*I'm so afraid to open my clenched fists. Who will I be when I have nothing left to hold on to? Who will I be when I stand before you with empty hands? Please help me to gradually open my hands and to discover that I am not what I own, but what you want to give me.* –Henri Nouwen

# Facet 7

## "You love the poor? Name them." RADICAL COMPASSION, RADICAL JUSTICE

"For you know the grace of our Lord, King Jesus: he was rich, but because of you he became poor, so that by his poverty you might become rich."

—2 Corinthians 8:9

"So you say you love the poor? Name them."
—Gustavo Gutierrez

The final facet of the *Jesus Way* we'll look at before our grand finale is Christ's *radical identification* with humanity as illustrated in his good news for the poor. From beginning (Jesus' personal commission) to end (his vision of the final judgment), Christ and his apostles' gospel is about God's solidarity with people in the union of divinity and humanity in the Incarnation. In Christ's humbling condescension, God truly becomes one with us and one of us. He fulfills all love by the supreme act of empathy—becoming flesh and taking on the likeness of the fallen human race in order to heal the human race. The author of Hebrews describes this *radical identification:*

> Since the children have flesh and blood, he too shared in their humanity so that by his death he might break the power of him who holds the power of death—that is, the devil—and free those who all their lives were held in slavery by their fear of death. For surely it is not angels he helps, but Abraham's descendants. For this reason he had to be made like them, fully human in every way, in order that he might become a merciful and faithful high priest in service to God, and that he might make atonement for the sins of the people. Because he himself suffered when he was

> tempted, he is able to help those who are being tempted.
> —Hebrews 2:14-18

This identification extends to *all*, including those we might consider "the least"—least healthy, least wealthy, least moral, least innocent, etc. God's heart for the poorest in every category is not an *application* of the gospel. It's *intrinsic* to it. We don't see Christ in the "least of these" because they've chosen to follow him, but because in his Incarnation, Christ identified with the plight of every man, woman and child on the planet.

## GOOD NEWS FOR THE POOR

Two key passages demonstrate that care for the poor (of every type) is inherent and indispensable to our "gospeling." First, from Christ's self-understanding of his own mission (drawn from the prophet Isaiah) at the outset of his ministry:

> The spirit of the Lord is upon me
> because he has anointed me
> to tell the poor the good news.
> He has sent me to announce release to the prisoners
> and sight to the blind,
> to set the wounded victims free,
> to announce the year of God's special favor.
> —Luke 4:18-19

For Christ, the gospel announcement is first of all good news for the poor, which is to say for those experiencing literal poverty, for prisoners, for the disabled, for wounded victims, for the indebted and the enslaved. The stated target group of his mission and invitation was the marginalized. It was those very people who formed his inner audience. We mustn't forget that. And in fact, the central chapterhouse of Christianity in Jerusalem ensured that outbound evangelists didn't forget it either. This was Paul's experience:

> For God, who was at work in Peter as an apostle to the circumcised, was also at work in me as an apostle to the Gentiles. James, Cephas and John, those esteemed as pillars, gave me and Barnabas the right hand of fellowship when they recognized the

> grace given to me. They agreed that we should go to the Gentiles, and they to the circumcised. *All they asked was that we should continue to remember the poor, the very thing I had been eager to do all along.* —Galatians 2:8-10

As the paragraph indicates, remembering the poor is not an optional rider to the gospel. When Paul and Barnabas brought the gospel they preached before Peter, James and John in Jerusalem for quality control, the three pillars approved their message, but with this reminder: *don't forget the poor.* Paul rejoiced, "Just what I was hoping they'd say!"

For all five of these evangelists, compassion ministry for the lowly was central to the message of the gospel (as it had been in the prophets). More than a rider or appendix, good news for the poor reflected the good news that in Christ, divine *Love* had radically and irreversibly thrown in their lot with us. From the very first announcement at Christ's inaugural sermon in Luke 4. "The Spirit of the Sovereign Lord is upon me to preach good news to the poor!"

## WHAT'S THE GOOD NEWS?

What is this good news for those on the margins? That you will all win the lottery or discover a money tree? No. Is it that each of them will find their dream job and fill their bank accounts? No, of course not. Then what?

One of my early pastoral mentors, Peter Bartel, suggested that Christ's gospel to the poor is first that their poverty is not a sign of *Abba's* rejection of them. It is not, as some both then and now suppose, proof that *Abba* has abandoned, cursed them or is punishing them.

Further, the *beautiful gospel* says that *Abba's* care includes actual care-giving. How might the poor experience reprieve from their misery? One answer is through the alternative society Christ was founding, a people for whom the Great Commandment—loving God and neighbor—looks like compassionate care for each other. More than an over-the-counter food bank, Christ's church would become a family who shared meals and more with each other. At least in the early years, Jesus-followers were "selling their possessions and goods, they shared with anyone who was in need" (Acts 2:45). And "there were no needy ones among them, because those who owned lands or houses would sell their property, bring the proceeds from the sales, and lay them at the apostles' feet for distribution to anyone as he need" (Acts 4:34).

Such *radical generosity* occurred for two reasons: First, "abundant grace was upon them all" (Acts 2:33). You just can't be that generous "in the flesh." You can only sell so much stuff to massage your ego before trendy giving runs its course. No, this kind of sharing was a naturally supernatural *Grace* phenomenon! Actual "charity," when charity used to literally mean self-giving love.

The second impetus for this outflow was a *radical faith* in the message of Jesus—particularly his specific directions concerning one's wealth in relation to compassionate giving:

> "If you want to complete the set [be perfected]," Jesus replied, "go and sell everything you own and give it to the poor. That way you'll have treasure in heaven. Then come and follow me."
>
> —Matthew 19:21

What if these words weren't empty rhetoric? What if he was truly intent on meddling with our budgets? I suspect the early disciples who took him seriously were responding, not just from obedience, but by *Grace* from enthusiastic faith in *Abba*, the faithful Father whom Christ had revealed in his sermons and parables. They could give generously because they could trust wholeheartedly.

Note too, the radical compassion of the *beautiful gospel* is not restricted to giving alms to the poor. It's about all kinds of caregiving for every kind of need. In Christ's day, it included all those who suffer and all the ways we might be Christ's hands, feet and heart. Among these, the New Testament includes the poor, naked and hungry; the sick, diseased and demonized, the "sinner," the criminal and the outcast. Good news for all! A *beautiful gospel* of Christ's radical compassion expressed through those who dare emulate him.

Let's review three Gospel parables to reinforce this notion as central to Jesus' gospel. It's easy to skim these because we think we already know (and evade) them well. Bottom line, Jesus is saying take care of people as he has taken care of us. Thanks, we know that. But please, let's plant these seeds a little deeper in our hearts to see what fresh fruit they might bear:

## THE GOOD SAMARITAN

You know the story. A lawyer asks Jesus what he must do to inherit eternal life. Jesus answers the question with a question, "What does the law say?"

The lawyer replies with the great commandment: "to love God with all that you are and love your neighbor as yourself."

Jesus nods, "You've nailed it. Do that and you'll live."

But the lawyer wants to "justify himself." Maybe that means he wants to be sure that he's been loving the right neighbor in the right way. He asks, "Who is my neighbor?"

So, Jesus shares his famous parable: a traveler on the road to Jericho is mugged and beaten half to death. The priest and Levite pass by with their excuses but only the unlikely Samaritan stops to help. He binds the victim's wounds, applies oil and wine, then delivers him on his own beast to an inn. He pays the innkeeper two denarii and promises to repay any over-charges later.

Jesus adds a little twist at the end: it isn't about who your neighbor is, but rather, who is the one being the neighbor to the guy in the ditch.

The story is so profound that it becomes part of our broader culture. Secular law in multiple nations incorporates "Good Samaritan laws" to make "passing by" a criminal act. In some places, it is forbidden to drive by a car accident without stopping. Where I live, it is to remain silent when you know about child abuse. To be a Good Samaritan is to stop and help those in need, whatever their suffering.

I think we ought to embrace all this as an obvious facet of the *beautiful gospel*, the *Christlike Way* forged by Jesus (and the prophets before him). But let's also read it through more Christ-centered and community-based eyes. It's not merely about individuals being prompted to help change a tire (but sure, do that).

Augustine, among others, suggested that the Samaritan in the parable represents Jesus. In John 8:48, his Judaean opponents accused Jesus, saying, "Are we not right in saying that you are a Samaritan and have a demon?"

Jesus replies, "I don't have a demon."

Christ didn't seem troubled about being labeled a Samaritan—he doesn't recoil at their *radical identification* with the enemy other. He had some pretty good friends in Samaria—more hospitable than his haters for sure, especially those priests and Levites who were plotting his death.

Some commentators start there, noting that Jesus the Samaritan was an outsider, rejected by his own, but nevertheless continually pauses to save, deliver and heal those who have been oppressed by poverty, sickness, demons and even death.

I see in the wine and the oil the medicine that Christ, our great Physician, has conferred upon the church: the wine of his blood, shared in the Eucharist, and the oil of the Spirit, with which we anoint the sick. And then Christ transports the broken man on his own beast—perhaps a reference to the spiritual ambulance service provided by frontline evangelists and outreach workers. In this model, the inn represents the faith community where the beaten and downtrodden find their healing. In this way, Christ transforms the hostel into his hospital.

How tragic when the venue meant to be a hospital so often becomes the very place where the most vulnerable are oppressed and excluded. How sad when big business religion imagines it has no surplus for the poor. How damning when the spiritually impoverished come for the Bread of Life, only to find it in short supply of an ugly gospel. Or worse, when anyone is dismissed as undeserving of our material or spiritual help.

Instead, the parable shows us that Christ has given the innkeeper all the resources—the wine, oil and denarii—to nurture the broken man back to health. "And," he says, "if you manage to give him more than I give you, when I return, I will pay you back in full."

The early church trusted Jesus' word on this. As the living Word of God, he was also the living Promise of God. And occasionally, they lived this way. At least for a time.

## THE RICH MAN AND LAZARUS

The next two parables are a little scary, because they both make sins of *omission* concerning the poor as a criterion for final judgment. We are used to squirming free of such indictments with spiritual loopholes and our understanding of God's abundant *Grace.* Fantastic. But that puts the cart before the horse. I don't believe it's legitimate to skip the important task of undergoing the gravity of these cautionary tales, lest we negate the actual words of Jesus and in so doing, exit the *Jesus Way* or trample *Grace* underfoot.

Lest you're tempted to hit the off-ramp prematurely, I will say that Jesus' judgment parables are not primarily about the Day of the Lord or the nature of the afterlife. They are designed as weighty indications of the importance of *radical compassion* to the *Jesus Way* ethic.

The parable of the rich man and Lazarus is straightforward. It stands as a dire warning of a coming inversion—a revolution where the proud and powerful fall as far as they can go and the poor and powerless are raised up into the caring arms of Abraham.

This great reversal was already announced while Christ was still in the womb through the words of his mother in her famous *Magnificat*:

> Mary said,
> "My soul declares that the Lord is great,
> my spirit exults in my savior, my God.
>
> He saw his servant-girl in her humility;
> from now, I'll be blessed by all peoples to come.
> The Powerful One, whose name is Holy,
> has done great things for me, for me.
>
> His mercy extends from father to son,
> from mother to daughter for those who fear him.
> Powerful things he has done with his arm:
> he routed the arrogant through their own cunning.
>
> *Down from their thrones he hurled the rulers,*
> *up from the earth he raised the humble.*
> *The hungry he filled with the fat of the land,*
> *but the rich he sent off with nothing to eat.*
>
> He has rescued his servant, Israel his child,
> because he remembered his mercy of old,
> just as he said to our long-ago ancestors—
> Abraham and his descendants for ever."
>
> —Luke 1:46-55

An ominous tune from a pregnant young virgin, to be sure—especially verses 52-53. And if Christ had been nursed, weaned and raised on that hymn, then his parable might be how he imagined the lyrics in story form.

The lesson is simple enough: be merciful. But let's dig deeper . . .

## BAD ASSUMPTIONS

Let's begin by clearing away four prevalent but mistaken assumptions about the Lazarus parable that permeated ancient worldviews and still linger today:

**Assumption 1: "The rich are righteous and the poor deserve what they get."**

In both the ancient worldview and in the heart of modern capitalism, wealth was seen as a sign of God's blessing and poverty was regarded as a curse. You would know who the righteous were by the health of their crops, flocks and families and the size of their barns, herds and lands. They excelled and prospered because God was rewarding them. Meanwhile, the unrighteous were easily identified because of their poverty, their illness or disability, and by the tragedies they endured.

While the covenant says all this explicitly in Deuteronomy 28-32 (and its parallels), already in the Psalms and Prophets, God's people are asking, "Then why do the wicked prosper?" (Ps. 73, Jer. 12). An entire book, the story of Job, debunks the reality of this worldview. And Jesus lays it to rest in Luke 13 and John 9, effectively saying, "It doesn't work that way. Don't assume the rich are righteous or the poor are cursed."

**Assumption 2: "The rich are corrupt and the poor are virtuous."**

This mirror assumption is also not always true. Yes, the love of money is dangerous—covetousness, greed and hoarding are surely condemned. But the assumption that every wealthy person has a boot on the neck of the poor or that every poor person is up for sainthood is demonstrably false. You may know well-to-do people who use their assets wisely and generously. I do. And you may know those clinging to survival whose sense of entitlement drives conniving, manipulative and dishonest patterns. I do. In short, we ought not presume—it's above our paygrade.

**Assumption 3: "The rich are rich and the poor are poor."**

A third wrong assumption is that those who are rich are happy and healthy while the poor are miserable and depressed. Is this so? Have we not encountered those of great wealth who testified to being lonely, emotionally oppressed or spiritually destitute? Mental health issues are not divvied out in proportion to bank accounts. The elite may succumb to despair as often as anyone.

In the case of the parable, the rich man may not have felt miserable as he luxuriated in his fancy robes and frivolous linen. But we know he was bankrupt of humility, mercy and compassion—a poverty of grace that forewarned his fall.

So too, have we not met those in poverty, struggling for their next meal, who nevertheless radiate joy and surprise us with beautiful smiles? Their joy comes from their faith, from knowing deep love and belonging and from a hope that doesn't die without a fight.

**Assumption 4: "I am not the rich man."**

Whenever I read Jesus' parables, I like to cast myself as the hero or the victim—never the "bad guy." On those occasions where I do identify as the apathetic priest, the rushing Levite or the inconsiderate rich man, it's typically to feed my self-loathing, self-pitying ego rather than arriving at authentic repentance, which is to say change.

I am indebted to author Scot McKnight for helping me see what I could not see for myself: the hard truth is that Christ is NOT asking, "Are you the rich man or Lazarus?" The message is this: "You *are* the rich man. Who is the poor man at your gate?" And the question is not, "What will life after death look like for you?" Rather, "Will you discover life before death?"

We'll see.

## WHY THESE DESTINIES?

The next parade of questions I have is, "Why these destinies?" Why is Lazarus carried by angels to the safe harbor of Abraham's bosom? And why is the rich man consigned to the other place?

We never hear that Lazarus was worthy of paradise for righteous deeds he had done or for putting his faith in Jesus Christ. We know of nothing that would qualify him as a good Jew or good Christian or good human. All we know is that he begged for crumbs and had sores that the dogs used to lick. Gross.

Listen, whatever evils he may have committed had already been paid for in full through his suffering. From a merciful God's point of view, someone that down and out doesn't require further punishment in the next life. Life had already been hell. God was not about to double down on his torment.

What qualified (if that's the right word) him for paradise was not the righteous deeds he had done, but the great mercies of *Abba* (Col. 1:12). If he had ever said a sinner's prayer, it need not have been more than, "Lord, have mercy," though his whole life surely screamed that prayer every hour of every day!

Why Lazarus? In the ancient cycles of Scripture reading, some brilliant soul saw the wisdom of scheduling Ephesians 2:4-10 alongside this parable. I'll start with verses 4-7, which tell us exactly why Lazarus was spirited away and what "heaven" or "Abraham's bosom" actually signifies—being seated with Christ:

> But because of his great love for us, God, who is rich in mercy, made us alive with Christ even when we were dead in transgressions—it is by grace you have been saved. And God raised us up with Christ and seated us with him in the heavenly realms in Christ Jesus, in order that in the coming ages he might show the incomparable riches of his grace, expressed in his kindness to us in Christ Jesus.

But what about the rich man? Why not him? Why his damnation?

The rich man's problem was not directly because he was wealthy. Rather, the rich man's sin was that he was *buried* and *blind*.

## BURIED?

The text reads this way,

*"The man died and was buried. In hades, where he was in torment . . ."*

So, it seems as if the rich man is first buried in a tomb (in his body) and buried in *hades* (in his soul). But before that, was he not already buried in his worldly goods, hopelessly attached to them by his covetousness (suggested just before the parable in Luke 16:14)? And was he not buried in his own ego, expressed by his extravagant clothes and by the pride of his tongue? Figuratively, if the punishment fits the crime, the rich man's essential torment was the flames that licked his tongue!

In a real way, he had already been dead and buried while he was still lounging—overfed and unconcerned—in this world.

## BLIND!

But he was also blind—totally blind to the poor man. Of course, there are varieties of blindness, aren't there?

Some are so blinded by self-love that they see nothing but their own reflection. In their self-obsession, they are altogether oblivious such that the poor are invisible to them.

Others are blind in that when they do look on the poor, they don't see a person—they see an inconvenience to be avoided, a nuisance to be removed or a problem for someone else to solve. They may witness the plight of the poor but have so dehumanized them, that they dehumanize themselves.

More subtly, we may see the poor as a project, an opportunity to massage our guilt or nurture the ego. "Look at me! Aren't I amazing? I helped them, see!" What seems the height of philanthropy may just be another way to blind ourselves from real people and genuine connection. Christ blew the whistle on this trick immediately in his Sermon on the Mount:

> [But] take care not to perform righteous deeds in order that people may see them; otherwise, you will have no recompense from your heavenly Father.
>
> When you give alms, do not blow a trumpet before you, as the hypocrites do in the synagogues and in the streets to win the praise of others. Amen, I say to you, they have received their reward.
>
> But when you give alms, do not let your left hand know what your right is doing, so that your almsgiving may be secret. And your *Abba* who sees in secret will repay you. —Matthew 6:1-4

This is sounding more and more like a lose-lose predicament. But no, there is a way back to spiritual sight embedded right there in the parable.

This chapter opened with the challenge of liberation theologian,

Gustavo Gutierrez: "So you say you love the poor? *Name them.*"

And Jesus does! In all of Christ's parables, this is the only character he names. Why? Some use this to prove the story is not a parable. Why do they do that? To prove that we must take the imagery of *hades* literally. Talk about missing the point. It's as silly as thinking Jesus asked the Gadarene demoniac for his name so that he could find out the demons' name (Legion). No. Just no. This isn't the fable of Rumpelstiltskin!

In both cases, the name is about humanizing the afflicted. Jesus asks the demoniac's name as the first step in rehumanizing the man. And Jesus names Lazarus to rehumanize the poor.

## LINDA

I have an elderly friend in Portland. *Linda is her name.* She's eighty years old, her husband is ninety-two. She uses a walker . . . slowly. But *Abba* has given her a heart for the poor, especially those who camp in the parking lot of the church she attends. With every excuse to pass them by, she nevertheless felt *Abba's* call to help. What could she do?

It began with the heartbreaking death of her daughter. *Her name is Maryellen.* She was fifty-two when the cancer was diagnosed. She graduated to the "great cloud of witnesses" twenty-two months later, free at last from many months of tremendous suffering.

Maryellen's funeral drew four hundred mourners. The great outpouring of love deeply affected Linda, especially as she realized how many people knew her daughter *by name.* As she left the memorial service, Linda's eyes were opened to the many homeless people in her neighborhood—forgotten people whose poverty seemed to include *namelessness.* Such a contrast to the affection her daughter had known! Her eyes brim with tears when she remembers how Christ first awakened her to her new family.

Linda's strategy is simple. Their greatest human need: *rehumanization.* Their greatest physical need: *rehydration.* Their greatest social need: *belonging.* And their greatest spiritual need: *prayer.* How does that look?

Linda humbly asks, "May I ask your *name?* Would you tell me your story? May I offer you a bottle of water? May I invite you inside? May I pray with you?"

*Do you care for the poor?* Linda does.

*Name them. Naming them is seeing them.* Linda does.

*Juan, Heather, Joshua, . . .*

Linda records their names on strips of royal purple fabric and ties them to the turn indicator on her car's steering wheel. There's a parable there.

*Name them. See them. Remember them.*

*Remembering is turning. Turning to Christ in them.*

*Her name is Jade.* She lurks underground in Southampton, UK. Jade injured her left knee and during surgery, suffered permanent nerve damage. She feels nothing below the knee down the front of her left leg. Jade isn't working, her hands are icicles tonight.

Jade is begging for change because if she doesn't find shelter tonight, she may die of hypothermia. Begging for change. Begging for me to change.

Her hands are open to help. Her hands open to help my hands open. Because God knows the mercy I pray for myself can only be received by open hands. I take her hands in mine for a minute, trying to share a little warmth. Tears come.

I can't save her. But she need not freeze tonight.

*Her name is Jade. Remember her name.*

*His name is Brandon.* He has a developmental disability. He rides his awkward little bicycle by my house on garbage day, scanning the recycling bags I've placed by the road. He's hoping to collect a few refundable drink cans. I know I have five bags full in my garage, each worth about five bucks. I think about the old Levitical laws concerning gleaning and I remember that Ruth, from Jesus' family tree, was a gleaner.

But I'm not bound by those laws, am I? No, I'm bound by *Grace.*

"What did you say your name was?"

*My name is Brandon. I haven't been around for a while. Life's been hard.*

"What's going on?"

*Mom has cancer. I have to take care of her.*

Tears. I can't save her. I'm nobody's hero. But I've just met one.

*And his name is Brandon. Don't forget this time.*

*His name is Lazarus.* That's the place he usually begs. He has open sores. And he's thirsty.

*Lazarus,* may I cool your tongue with water? *Lazarus,* I might need you to cool mine one day.

By naming Lazarus, Christ grounds his story in real life. In those who suffer, in those we know and among those we meet.

Jesus used his name to humanize the poor. He shifts the commands "love your neighbor" and "care for the poor" from abstract, faceless charity services to real names we come across in our own neighborhoods.

To *name* them is to *see* them.

We ought always ask the parables, "How is this story about me? And how does it reveal Christ?"

The parable of the rich Man and Lazarus is about me. I am the rich man. Who is *Lazarus* at my gate? Who is suffering? *Her name is Jade. His name is Brandon. Their names are Juan and Heather and Joshua.*

Where is my compassion? Where is my change?

How does the story reveal Christ? To name them is to *see* them. And to *see* them is to find Christ. I meet Christ in the poor, in Jade and in Brandon. Do I *see* him?

Do these questions threaten us? Haunt us?

Or is that still to miss the point?

I think they're meant to invite us.

## *GRACE*-POWERED COMPASSION

We need to close this chapter with an essential caveat lest charity become the new moralism—as it so often has! We do not buy our way to eternal life through the merits of our charitable acts. Yet neither are they dispensable. So how does that work? Again, to the wisdom of the liturgist who brought Paul's epistle to Ephesus into the formula—the rest of the passage:

> For it is by *Grace* you have been saved, through faith—and this is not from yourselves, it is the gift of God—not by works, so that no one can boast. For we are God's handiwork, created in Christ Jesus *to do good* works, which God prepared in advance for us to do.
> —Ephesians 2:8-10

Paul does *not* say that you have been saved by your good works.

Paul does *not* say that you have been saved by faith so works are optional. What Paul says is that by *Grace*, we have been created and saved *for* good works—works of love—he has prepared for us. Why?

To demonstrate that we are *Love's* workmanship.

To participate in *Love's* work.

To encounter *Love* as he appears between helpers and helped, givers and receivers.

## THOUGHTS

1. Had you previously considered how Christ's *radical identification* with fallen humanity connected his gospel to the poor? I've suggested that one leads to the other. How would you describe the link between his solidarity with us and his mandate of compassion?

2. I once gave my grandmother a plaque that said "faith, hope and love (1 Cor. 13:13)." She tried to show me she was grateful, but I could hear some confusion and disappointment in her voice when she said, "I thought it was faith, hope and charity?" That's how the King James English used to translate the Greek word *agape*. What loss do you think Granny sensed in the modern translations? How is "love" less than "charity"? And how does charity become less than love?

3. The parables of Jesus Christ are not merely Old Covenant teaching or salvation by works of charity. The Gospel writers recount these parables as maps for the *Jesus Way*. How do we avoid reducing them to legalistic laws to obey on threat of punishment? How do we avoid ignoring them out of fear that they're works-based? How does *Grace* relate to, require and empower us to *identify* with the poor as Christ *identified* with us? How might *Grace* rehumanize us and those we meet in acts of compassion?

## PRAYERS

*Lord Jesus, Anointed by Grace to share Abba's love, thank you for paving the Jesus Way of radical identification and compassion. We humbly ask that your transforming Grace would open our eyes to see the Lazarus at our gates, the hidden Jade in our cities. Open our hearts and our hands to give and receive—to find the change we need in ourselves. Amen.*

# Finale:

## A MORE BEAUTIFUL VISION
## *Abba's* "I have a dream" Speech

As I wrap up this book, I invoke the visions and dreams of the prophet Isaiah, playing the part of a campaign surrogate for the Kingdom of God. You see, Isaiah's prophecies were primary source material for Jesus Christ's New Covenant of Peace—paving stones of the *Jesus Way*.

Isaiah is looking to mobilize the grassroots and build the base for *Abba's* intentions. He's on the stump, hoping to capture imaginations for the Dream of God. Sounds political . . . for sure, Isaiah 2 does call *Abba's* dream a "government." Jesus calls it a "kingdom." And the platform for *Abba's* dream does sound like a plan with real world policies. *Abba's* dream includes startlingly clear economic, domestic and foreign policies and *Jesus-care*.

But it also transcends the demonic socio-political spectrum we call right and left, so . . . perhaps it's better to call this, "*Abba's* 'I have a dream' speech."

Mural artist Leo Tanguma made a colorful attempt at transposing *Abba's* dream in Isaiah onto the walls of Denver International Airport. You've got children and people of every nation, tribe and color coming together. They're beating their swords into plowshares and their spears into pruning hooks. They're coming together in peace, and you see the flags of warring nations coming together to wrap up the weapons of death and set them aside and enter the kingdom of God.

Isaiah paints a powerful word picture of this kingdom—of these divine intentions, this dream of *Abba* for his world. From these visions of Isaiah, Jesus launched his kingdom campaign trail.

So I come to Isaiah and ask him to open the eyes of my heart.

"Behold," he says, "*Abba's* dream of a new world."

## ISAIAH DREAMS *ABBA'S* DREAM FOR OUR WORLD

The deserts and parched land shall rejoice,
the wilderness exult and bloom like the rose.
It surely shall bloom and exult,
yes, exult and sing out in gladness.
Lebanon's glory is given to it,
the splendor of Carmel and Sharon.
They shall behold the LORD's glory,
the majesty of our God.
Strengthen the slackened hands,
bolster the tottering knees.
Say to the fearful of heart:
Be strong, do not fear.
Look, your God in vengeance shall come,
God's retribution shall come and rescue you.
Then shall the eyes of the blind be opened,
and the ears of the deaf be unstopped.
Then shall the lame skip like a stag,
and the tongue of the mute sing in gladness.
For water shall break forth in the desert
and brooks in the wilderness.
The heat-scorched ground shall become a lake
and the thirsty soil, springs of water.
Where a jackal's abode was, its lair—
a courtyard for reeds and rushes.
And a highway shall be there,
a holy way it shall be called.
No unclean one shall pass over it,
but it shall be for him who goes on the way,
and fools shall not wander there.
No lion shall be there,
nor wild beasts go up on it.
There the redeemed shall go.

Those ransomed by the LORD shall return
and come to Zion with glad song,
joy everlasting on their heads,
delights and joy they attain,
and sorrow and sighing shall flee.
—Isaiah 35:1-10

I turn to Isaiah, and ask, "What is this, some sort of hippy sunflower festival in the sky?"

"No," he replies, "this is *Abba's* dream for this world. Behold!"

And I fall into his vision, ignited in me thirty years ago by a passage from Tom Sine's *Mustard Seed Conspiracy.*

I see the desert, cracked clay and sunbaked. Nothing can grow here, no one could live here. But from the horizon, I see a silver ribbon snaking my way. What starts as a distant, tiny creek grows into a crystal clear freshwater stream, teeming with sparkling fish. The river grows miraculously—wider and deeper as it flows. On its banks, wildflowers begin to sprout into brush, small trees become great cedars. Their branches harbor a numberless choir of songbirds.

It feels like a mirage but I'm drawn to these signs of life—and not only me. From every direction others are coming—individuals, families, groups of every people group. I recognize those of my own people, but also Haitian villagers, Thai street merchants, black-and-white South Africans, caravans of indigenous people from around the globe. Their converging bodies form a highway, a homecoming—a multi-ethnic company of former enemies, animals and children, predators and victims.

I see a woman carrying her malnourished infant, a lame beggar hobbling on makeshift crutches, a blind man groping his way ahead, a terminally ill pilgrim too weak to walk—but this great company of the least and lost help one another. They're loving each other, sharing nourishment and offering real aid.

With each step, we are energized—a healthy cry comes from the baby, no longer lethargic. The lame man casts aside his walking sticks as his legs are strengthened. The blind, the deaf, the terminally ill are now hopping and leaping and praising God.

This enormous column marches in royal procession, disarming themselves, dismantling their weapons, creating harmony and becoming family. Death and the fear of death are dissolved before my eyes. Our nonviolent march leads us to the foot of a mount where we pick our way through boulders and up into the mountain switchbacks. The strongest among us are removing obstacles, filling potholes and making the path smooth for all. We pick up the pace and begin to chant with anticipation, "Further up and further in."

I see a child boldly leading a Lion, calling us up Mount Zion to the temple of the Lord.

I ask, "What is this? Some sort of bleeding heart vision of a reimagined United Nations?"

Isaiah says, "No! This is *Abba's* dream for our world. Behold!"

> And it shall happen in future days
> that the mount of the LORD's house shall be firm-founded
> at the top of the mountains and lifted over the hills.
> And all the nations shall flow to it
> and many people shall go, and say:
> Come, let us go up to the mount of the LORD,
> to the house of Jacob's God,
> that He may teach us of His ways
> and that we may walk in His paths.
> For from Zion shall teaching come forth
> and the LORD's word from Jerusalem.
> And He shall judge among the nations
> and be arbiter for many peoples.
> And they shall grind their swords into plowshares
> and their spears into pruning hooks.
> Nation shall not raise sword against nation
> nor shall they learn war anymore.
> O house of Jacob,
> come, let us walk in the LORD's light.
> —Isaiah 2:2-5

Isaiah's vision! On the plateau, we see the great city of God, its gates always open, and we hear the Spirit and Bride cry out,

"Come! Follow the River of Life, enter the gates, join the great multitude gathering in the square. Behold, the grand banquet is prepared."

The Host is dressed in fine linen, glowing with hospitality, joyfully welcoming us and proclaiming:

*"All oppression is ended, all sins forgiven.*

Proclaim! Proclaim the feast of the Lord, the banquet of our God!"

Isaiah chimes in, "This is *Abba's* dream for our world."

> And the LORD shall prepare a banquet for all the peoples on this mountain, a banquet of rich food, a banquet of well-aged wines, rich food with marrow, well-aged wines fine strained. And He shall swallow up on this mountain the veil that covers all the peoples and the mantle cast over all nations. He shall swallow up death forever, and the Master LORD shall wipe tears from every face, and His people's disgrace He shall take off from all the earth, for the LORD has spoken. —Isaiah 25:6-9

*Abba's dream* for our world.

No more tears, no more war, no more disease, no more poverty, no more oppression, no more exclusion, no more hatred, no more starving, no more -isms.

No more, no more, no more . . . wipe the tears away!

## MICAH DREAMS *ABBA'S* DREAM FOR OUR WORLD

Isaiah was not alone as the downpour of *Abba's* dreams for our world rained on the prophets. The Hebrew prophetic tradition lamented current conditions but was also privy to a great and blessed hope.

Micah was another of the great Jewish dreamers who foresaw and foretold the coming kingdom:

> And it shall happen in future days
> that the mount of the LORD's house shall be firm-founded
> at the top of the mountains and lifted over the hills.
> And the people shall flow to it,

and many nations shall go and say:
"Come, let us go up to the mount of the LORD,
and to the house of Jacob's God,
that He may teach us His ways
and that we may walk in His paths."
For from Zion shall teaching come forth
and the LORD's word from Jerusalem.
And He shall judge among many peoples
and be arbiter to vast nations far away.
And they shall grind their swords into plowshares
and their spears into pruning hooks.
Nation shall not raise sword against nation,
nor shall they learn war anymore.
And they shall dwell each man beneath his vine
and beneath his fig tree, with none to make him tremble,
for the mouth of the LORD of Armies has spoken.
For all the peoples shall walk
each in the name of his god.
But we shall walk
in the name of the LORD our God
forevermore.

On that day, said the LORD:
I will gather the lame one,
and the outcast I will take in
and to whom I did harm.
And I will make the lame one a remnant
and the flailing one a vast nation,
and the Lord shall reign over them
on Mount Zion, from hence and forever.
—Micah 4:1-7 (NIV)

Won't that be wonderful?
Some day . . .

## JESUS PLANTS *ABBA'S* DREAM IN OUR WORLD

Then Jesus comes, proclaiming *Abba's* dream for our world.

Jesus dreams Isaiah's dream and plants the mustard seed of *Abba's* dream.

He comes preaching, calling the whole content of Isaiah's *Abba*-dream "the kingdom of God."

He does not reduce or defer this kingdom vision to a next world, next life event. When we pray, "Let your kingdom come, let your will be done on earth as it is in heaven," we're not merely praying for Christ to speed up his return. We're volunteering as agents to participate in bringing about *Abba's* new world and the restoration of all things.

Jesus quotes Isaiah 61 in his first sermon in Luke, sits down and announces, *Today, Abba's* dream, *Abba's* intentions, *Abba's* kingdom—*today,* this vision is being fulfilled!

*Today,* here and now—*today,* in your midst. Imagine!

And I ask Jesus, "What is this? And who are you? John Lennon? Where's your Beatles' mini-bus?"

And Jesus turns to me, and says, "No. This is my *Abba's* dream for *this* world."

> "What shall we say God's kingdom is like?" he said. "What picture shall we give of it? It's like a grain of mustard seed. When it's sown on the ground, it's the smallest of all the seeds of the earth. But when it's sown, it springs up and becomes the biggest of all shrubs. It grows large branches, so that the birds of the air make their nests within its shade." —Mark 4:30-32

He continues, "I was the child born, the son given and *Abba's* leadership rests on my shoulders.

> "[My] name is called wondrous counselor,
> divine warrior, eternal father, prince of peace,
> making leadership abound and peace without end
> on the throne of David and over [my] kingdom
> to make it firm-founded and stay it up
> in justice and righteousness, forever more."
> —Isaiah 9:6

*When?* "From *this time* forth and forevermore!"

*When?* Jesus tells us! After quoting Isaiah's vision of God's kingdom in his inaugural sermon in Luke 4, Jesus sits down and announces:

*"Today* this Scripture is fulfilled in your own hearing."

Not someday, somewhere else. *Here! Now! Today!*

And Christ does it. He plants the mustard seed.

One person at a time, one healing at a time, one deliverance at a time, one sermon at a time, one village at a time, one crowd at a time, one city at a time, one region at a time, one island at a time, one nation at a time—and the glory of the Lord begins to be revealed, "and all flesh together see that the LORD's mouth has spoken" (Isa. 40:5).

And not seeing it yet, again I ask, "Someday?"

"No, son, my *Abba's* dream for *this* world has been planted and it has been growing. The violent come and hack it to bits, but it keeps growing,

Some try to take it by force and it gets twisted and ugly, but it keeps growing.

Weeds and fires and calamitous droughts come, but it keeps growing.
It gets pruned way back, down to a stump, but it keeps growing,
it keeps growing, it keeps growing."

And I say, "I want to be part of what you're doing."
And he asks, "You want to be part of what I'm doing?"
And I say, "Yes, Lord, I want to be part of what you're doing."

And Jesus says, "Then seek first *Abba's* dream for this world,
Seek first *Abba's* intentions today,
Seek first *Abba's* kingdom here and now.
But seek it *first.* Before your economic agenda.
Seek it first. Before every political allegiance.
Seek it first. Before your own ambitions and ego-needs.
Seek first this *Abba*-dream. Seek first this kingdom.
Seek it in prayer: let your kingdom come on earth, on earth, on earth."

And I pray, "Our *Abba,* let it come, let it grow and let me seek it."
And now here's the hard word.
Seek first this kingdom.
Or don't.

This isn't John Lennon, the ACLU or the United Nations.

This is not spineless Jesus.

This is *King* Jesus who has *already* saved us by *Grace*, forgiven us completely and reconciled us to God.

Nevertheless, the *Lord* of the dream says,

"Seek first *Abba's* dream of co-suffering love,

Seek first the *Jesus Way* of radical forgiveness, and just peacemaking,

Seek first the *Jesus Walk* or you are not ready to be called my disciple.

Follow *Grace* as I restore all things.

Please, don't go away sad. Know that I love you."

Our focus is to be single-minded and clear-eyed on *Abba's* dream for our world as our first agenda. Our *now* agenda.

It has nothing to do with grandiose claims of outer-galactic revivals or "the next big move of God." It's about watching the mustard seed grow by *Grace* and participating in what *Grace* is up to . . .

One poor person at a time,

One naked person at a time,

One prisoner at a time,

One stranger at a time,

One hospital visit at a time.

## ARE YOU THIRSTY?

My visions didn't end with Isaiah's dream. I found myself in the visions of John the Revelator in the last chapters of the Bible. John, like Isaiah, saw *Abba's* dream and said, "Behold!" And I did.

(Excerpt: Brad Jersak, *Her Gates Will Never Be Shut,* 178-179).

> In night visions, the prophet saw a house on top of a mountain. A spring of water bubbles up from the floorboards and trickles across the floor. By the time it exits the door and crosses the deck, it is two feet deep. Running off the deck and toward the cliff, the stream becomes a powerful river. Then it plummets as a deafening waterfall, increasing in volume as it descends to the lush valley below.
>
> I believe such dreams come from the same Spirit who enlivened John's dreams, recounting spiritual truths in familiar ancient symbols, a foretaste of what is to come.

More than a foretaste—an inviting question: *Are you thirsty?* (cf. Isa. 55:1-5) It's the question that opens the door of the city and leads the way into it as far as the river's source. It's the invitation-question of the Spirit and the Bride to the nations outside. It's the question that Revelation 21-22 asks both then and now. *Are you thirsty?* As I've marinated in those chapters for the past two years, this vision has emerged for me . . .

Lost souls languish outside the gates of the great city, their thirst deepening as they fester in the smoking valley of Gehenna. Time has lost all meaning in this non-life of non-being. Lips and hearts are cracked with hopelessness like baked clay. Their time to choose has passed, their judgment just and certain, death eternal their lot. They cannot even make themselves care.

And then an intrusive question forms in their hearts.

*Are you thirsty?*

Beyond ludicrous—the question reawakens the exiles to their torment and intensifies their thirst. *Are you thirsty?* They recall the pointless supplication, "Have pity on me and send someone to dip a fingertip in water to cool my tongue, because I am in agony in this fire." Hopeless.

But the question has begun its work. Hearts gaze longingly at the city walls. The question has energized a plea. What if we trudged out a pilgrimage to Zion's gates to seek an audience with the King? What if—hope against hope—someone opened the gates? Even without hope or courage, the thirst itself drives them.

*Are you thirsty?* There is no choice now. They must try.

Even as the damned set their hearts upon the journey, while still a good distance away, the heart of God is already turned toward them, for the question originated from his throne, amplified beyond the city walls by the voice of the Bride and the Spirit. The question and its answer gushes out with life-giving rivers of liquid love. Christ, the river of living water, pours out of the open gates and into the valley of death. Streams flow into Gehenna, where green shoots spring up on widening banks and moisture feeds the valley.

Parched for life and love, the outcasts rush to the river, falling on their faces to lap up the sparkling water. Tasting the goodness gives them a thirst for even more. They are drawn, freely yet irresistibly, to follow the river upstream. Its path welcomes them in through the open gates, beckons them up the streets, a clear path to its mountain source—to God himself.

As the rapids of Christ's love flow out of the city, so the nations stream into the city, joining the Bride, exalting the Bride, becoming the Bride, ready for the love of her King.

My vision. Isaiah's vision. John's vision.

*Abba's* vision.

## O HOLY NIGHT

I close with these lyrics from *O Holy Night,* Isaiah's vision of a Virgin-born Messiah birthed into the world as the Word made flesh, the prince of peace, whose "law is love and whose gospel is peace."

It's more than a Christmas carol. The hymn is our *Grace* invitation to the *Jesus Way* of the restored cosmos, experienced *today* by those who hear and surrender to the Voice who says, "Follow me."

We'll let this stand as our final thought and prayer.

O, Holy Night
The stars are brightly shining,
    it is the night of the dear Savior's birth.

Long lay the world in sin and error pining
    til He appeared and the soul felt its worth.
A thrill of hope, the weary world rejoices
    for yonder breaks a new and glorious morn.
Fall on your knees! O, hear the angel voices!
O night divine, O night when Christ was born.

He knows our need, to our weakness no stranger!
    Behold your King! Before Him lowly bend!
    Behold your King! your King! Before him bend!

Truly He taught us to love one another;
    his law is Love and his gospel is Peace;

Chains shall he break, for the slave is our brother,
    and in his name all oppression shall cease,
Sweet hymns of joy in grateful Chorus raise we;
    let all within us praise his Holy name!

Christ is the Lord, then ever! ever praise we!
    His pow'r and glory, evermore proclaim!
    His pow'r and glory, evermore proclaim!

*Fiat Lux*

# Gratitude


> I thank my God every time I think of you! I always pray with joy, whenever I pray for you all, because of your partnership in the gospel from the first day until now. Of this I'm convinced: the one who began a good work in you will thoroughly complete it by the day of King Jesus. —Philippians 1:3-6

Of this I am certain: none of us ventures onto the *Jesus Way* alone. I'm grateful for all my fellow sojourners—those who support me, encourage me, enlighten me, challenge me and create space for who I am.

So many people have participated in my spiritual formation, in the development of my convictions and in the final form of this book, that naming them all is as impossible as it is intimidating. The more I add to the list, the more names I remember, and as the list grows, I imagine losing an all-important name in a mental fog bank. I see that cherished friend wondering why they missed the cut when they have been essential to my journey.

For that reason, I ask for your grace as I speak my thanks in broad categories, with this one exception: my deepest gratitude goes to Eden Jersak, my beloved partner. You must remain neither nameless nor voiceless. I love you.

I offer prayers of thanksgiving today, knowing that when I invoke heaven's goodness and mercy for all those who have helped me, I don't need to convince *Abba* of anything. My prayers orient me and those for whom I pray toward the ever-benevolent sunshine of divine *Grace*. In that spirit, I hope you will receive the warmth of God's affection through my inadequate words of gratitude.

I give thanks for all those who have shown me the *Jesus Way* by their lives—for the generations of my family, the faith communities that nurtured me, for the colleagues with whom I've served, for the teachers, mentors and healers who've tucked me under their wings, for friends, peers and intercessors who strengthen me and for the students, readers and would-be foes who sharpen me. For all these, your beloved children, Lord, please shower them with your goodness.

For those who have participated in co-creating this book—the publisher, editors, proofreaders and endorsers, and for the people who have filled its pages with their insights and wisdom, their stories and lives, including their brokenness—Lord, multiply the good fruit beyond what they could ever anticipate. Surprise them with joy.

To the glory of Triune Love—*Abba,* Christ and *Grace*—now and ever unto ages of ages.

Amen.

# Bradley Jersak

I was born in 1964 in Winnipeg, Canada. I was raised in the faith by loving parents who created an environment where I could flourish in my experience of Christ. My love for Christ, prayer and the scriptures grew naturally in that rich spiritual soil. When I was eight years old, I convinced Rev. Virgil Olsen to baptize me upon confession of faith at Grant Memorial Baptist Church.

We moved to Killarney, MB in 1972, where I grew up by the lake and did a lot of fishing, canoeing and swimming.

After graduating from high school, I attended Briercrest Bible College, where I began to pursue a call to teaching under the tutelage of Dr. Carl Hinderager and Prof. Bob Seale.

More importantly, I met Edith Wiebe (her name is now Eden Jersak), who I married in 1986. Since then, we've sprouted an beautiful family —three sons, their partners and now our first grandchild, who we like to call "Peach."

After finishing an M.A. in Biblical Studies, I served at Eden's home church, Bethel Mennonite (Aldergrove, Canada) for ten years (1988-97), where I was Associate Pastor of youth, young adults and outreach. Peter Bartel was my beloved senior pastor and spiritual guide through most of that era.

In 1998, Eden and I joined Brian and Sue West in planting Fresh Wind Christian Fellowship, a community focused on "doing life" with people on the margins. A full third of our faith family were persons with disabilities in full-time care. In 2008, I stepped down and Eden became the team leader for the next five years. She faithfully led Fresh Wind while I worked at my PhD (Political Theology) through Bangor University (Wales), where I studied under Prof. Ron Dart and Dr. Lucy Huskinson.

2012 was another landmark year for me on three fronts. First, Dr. Lucy Peppiatt graciously invited me to Westminster Theological Centre (Cheltenham, UK), where I served on core faculty for six years.

That same autumn, I joined Greg Albrecht's editorial team at Plain Truth Ministries, where I now write, edit and do art design for *CWR*

*Magazine* and other projects.

I also joined the Eastern Orthodox Church in 2012, where I serve as a reader and preacher under Archbishop Lazar Puhalo at the All Saints of N.A. Monastery.

Most recently, as of September 2019, I became Dean of Ministry Studies at St. Stephen's University (St. Stephen, NB Canada). I also maintain an itinerant teaching schedule, sharing the Beautiful Gospel wherever I'm invited.

Readers are welcome to visit me at www.bradjersak.com, follow me on social media or check out my blog posts at *PTM.org/blog* and *Clarion-Journal.com.*

# Notes

# Notes

# Notes

## *A More Christlike God: A More Beautiful Gospel*

Bradley Jersak's *A More Christlike God* (CWRpress 2016) was the foundational book in this series and provides the backdrop to *A More Christlike Way*. It was awarded the gold medal in the "Enduring Light" category at the Illumination Book Awards. It is available through PTM.org and Amazon in both paperback and audio formats.

This excellent and much-needed book confronts with both open heart and very good mind the major obstacles that we created for people in their journey toward God! So many of us are asking, *Why didn't people teach us this many years ago?*

I am so very grateful that Brad Jersak is re-opening the door that Jesus had already opened 2000 years ago. It is so terribly sad that it was ever closed.

– **Fr. RICHARD ROHR, O.F.M.**
*Center for Action and Contemplation*
Albuquerque, New Mexico

Brad Jersak has given us a gift of greatest value: a fresh vision of God, Christ, the Cross, Scripture and ourselves. He demonstrates the rare ability to take deep theological issues and make them understandable to everyone. He represents a new generation of Christian theologians whose work, I believe, is both desperately needed and wonderfully liberating.

– **BRIAN D. McLAREN**
Author of *The Great Spiritual Migration*

***"I don't think I've ever read a book that made my heart sing louder." –Jonathan Hodges***

Printed in Great Britain
by Amazon